INTRODUCTION TO ALGEBRA

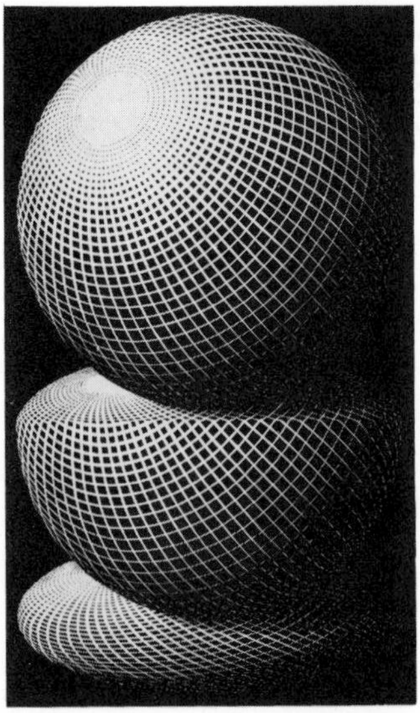

Harper's Series

in Modern Mathematics

I. N. Herstein and Gian-Carlo Rota,

Editors

HARPER & ROW

Publishers, New York

INTRODUCTION TO ALGEBRA

DONALD J. LEWIS

Professor of Mathematics, University of Michigan

The illustrations in this book are reproductions of prints by the Dutch graphic artist, Maurits Escher: title page, THREE SPHERES (*wood engraving*); page 1, RIPPLED SURFACE (*lino-cut*); page 26, THREE WORLDS (*lithograph*); page 77, METAMORPHOSIS (*wood cut*); page 138, RELATIVITY (*lithograph*); page 232, REPTILES (*lithograph*).

INTRODUCTION TO ALGEBRA

 For information address Harper & Row, Publishers, Incorporated, 49 East 33rd Street, New York, N.Y. 10016.

Library of Congress Catalog Card Number: 65–15743

PREFACE

This book is an introduction to algebra for mathematics majors. It has been developed from materials used in an introductory two-semester course in algebra given at the University of Notre Dame during the years 1956–1959. The course was designed for sophomore mathematics majors; however, many first-year graduate students attended, as did a few well-prepared freshmen. It was the students' first truly rigorous course and had a twofold purpose: (1) to make the student conversant with the language and techniques of algebra so that he could handle algebraic arguments in subsequent courses easily; and (2) to develop the student's ability to prove theorems and to train him in the techniques of exposition.

It seemed these two purposes could best be achieved if the student faced the task of proving a wide range of theorems and then had them examined for correctness and for quality of exposition. Since many of the theorems required proofs that involved techniques unfamiliar to young students, it was decided to reduce the more involved proofs to a sequence of more easily verified lemmas. Examples were also needed, for they give reality to discourse, lend familiarity to new ideas, make us aware of the limitations of our theorems, bolster our intuition, and make conjecturing possible. Consequently, examples and theorems were considered of equal importance.

In their original form, these materials consisted only of definitions, examples, and statements of propositions. The instructor discussed about half of the propositions and examples, and the students were responsible for the rest. As the course progressed, the student wrote his own textbook. I prefer such an arrangement, since it imposes few restrictions on the instructor and develops self-reliance in the student. However, it was felt that such a format would not meet with wide approval, and consequently in this book I have included proofs when they entail new ideas or techniques that the ordinary reader would not have encountered. If a proof depends essentially on an idea or technique that has been used several times previously, then the proof is omitted and the reader is expected to supply it. The reader of this text should have paper and pen handy, and if he persists he will become quite fluent in the use of the ideas and techniques of algebra.

The original materials contained some fallacious statements—some intentional, some unintentional. The student was expected to detect such statements, to give counterexamples, and whenever possible to modify the statement in order to obtain a valid theorem. This was an excellent pedagogical tool. The student had always to be on his guard, lest he waste his time attempting to prove false statements. He also learned how to reformulate conjectures in order to obtain a valid result. To have retained this teaching device would have destroyed the reference value of the text, and hence I have endeavoured to delete the fallacious statements. However, such statements have a tendency to escape detection, and, if any remain, I beg the reader's forbearance.

By convention, an introductory course in algebra should include material on groups, rings, fields, and vector spaces. To beginning students these topics often appear unrelated, for although the definitions bear some resemblance, the rationale for the definitions is often missed. Consequently, algebra often seems to be a grab bag of diverse ideas rather than an integrated whole. I have sought to organize the topics in a manner that emphasizes the unity of algebra and so that the various algebraic structures arise in a natural fashion.

Much progress is made in mathematics by noting how one system resembles or reflects another and then testing whether properties of one system carry over to the other. Such analogies are of great value in suggesting conjectures and possible proofs, and they enable one to see various topics in greater perspective. The use of analogy culminates in the formulation of axiomatic or abstract systems. For these reasons I have endeavoured to indicate the existence of analogies in algebra.

In any study of algebra one is eventually forced to make use of the integers. Also, many conjectures in algebra are suggested by analogies with the integers. Therefore, the book begins with a short chapter summarizing those parts of elementary number theory which are algebraic in character.

Many algebraic systems arise as a set of mappings, and most algebraic systems are best analyzed by studying possible maps upon them. Also, it is usually in the discussion of a set of maps that algebra enters other areas of mathematics. Since the concept of a map is intrinsic to algebra and since it is a concept familiar to the student from his study of the calculus, it was decided to organize the course and this book around the concept of a map. Chapter 2 begins with a thorough discussion of maps. In order to develop familiarity with maps, time is spent on several combinatorial topics. Some of these topics are not essential to later work and can be omitted if the instructor so wishes. The first two chapters move at a leisurely rate so that the ordinary sophomore student can follow the discussion easily. More mature students will be acquainted with much of the material in Chapter 1 and the first six sections of Chapter 2, and the instructor may wish to pass over this material quickly. However, most students can benefit from studying these introductory sections, and, as later chapters are based on them, they should not be omitted entirely.

Chapter 2 closes with a detailed study of transformation groups on both finite and infinite domains.

In Chapter 3, abstract groups are studied, and most of the standard results of elementary group theory appear. In addition, automorphism groups of certain groups are examined in detail; the Sylow theorems are developed, using transformations on groups; and decomposition theorems for groups are discussed.

The first three chapters constituted the first semester of the introductory course. These chapters have also been used in teacher-training courses with considerable success.

Chapter 4 opens with a discussion of the ring of endomorphisms of an abelian group. Then abstract rings are examined, as are such refinements as integral domains, skewfields, and fields. The existence of indeterminates over a ring is proved, and the arithmetic of polynomial domains is studied. Criteria for irreducibility, field extensions, algebraic closure, the real field, its construction and its metric properties, and valuation theory are discussed in the remaining sections.

The final chapter (Chapter 5) is concerned with vector spaces. There is a full discussion of linear functionals and linear forms on a vector space. The determinant of a linear transformation is defined, using these concepts. Linear transformations, matrices over rings, various equivalence relations on linear transformations and on matrices, and canonical matrices are examined.

The approach in Chapter 5 is algebraic, and nothing is said concerning the relation between vector spaces and geometry. This topic is of major importance, but in a two-semester course there is not time to cover it in addition to the others discussed in this book. Also, our approach is such that we do not need geometry to motivate the study of vector spaces. A course based on this book should be followed by one in geometry that includes projective geometry, Euclidean geometry, quadratic spaces, and the first elements of algebraic geometry. Since the students will be well versed in algebra, such a course can concentrate on geometry.

The last seven sections of Chapter 4 involve more sophisticated ideas than does Chapter 5, and the instructor may prefer to postpone discussing them until after he has discussed Chapter 5. This can be done provided Chapter 5 is preceded by a short discussion of algebraically closed fields, in particular, the field of complex numbers.

Although the opening chapters begin on an elementary level, the later ones are quite advanced, and some of the material has previously been confined to graduate courses. However, we have found that students, following this arrangement of topics, do not have undue difficulty with any of them. If a student masters all the material discussed, he will be sufficiently well versed in algebra to meet most needs of most mathematicians who are not specializing in algebra. Our experience has indicated that a course based on these materials early in a student's studies accelerates his development as a mathematician and enhances his ability to understand other branches of mathematics.

Over the years one accumulates and absorbs ideas from his teachers, collaborators, colleagues, and students, and it is impossible to look back and recall the origins or the modifying circumstances that have molded his approach to the topic. All one can be certain of is that much of the originality belongs to others, and any error to himself. I have benefited greatly from my associations with R. Brauer, R. M. Thrall, E. Artin, T. H. Hildebrandt, R. Otter, K. Mahler, and H. Davenport, and from the stimulation that I have received from my students.

I wish to thank George Rinehart and James Cohn, who read the manuscript and made many valuable criticisms and suggestions. Various improvements in the exposition arose from their comments. Thanks are also due to Miss Gillian Hodge, who prepared the typescript, and to Carolyn Dana Lewis, who so generously took time from her own writing to assist in the proofreading.

I especially wish to thank M. C. Escher for permitting the inclusion of a number of his prints. For several decades, Mr. Escher's art has fascinated mathematicians the world over. One aspect of this fascination undoubtedly stems from the effect on the eye of the complicated groups of symmetries associated with many of his prints. Except for some elementary cases, groups of symmetries are not discussed in this book. However, after completing Chapter 3, the interested reader will be prepared to examine such questions. For an introduction to these problems he might read H. Weyl, *Symmetry*, Princeton University Press, 1952. Although symmetry plays a dominant role in much of Mr. Escher's art and the eye quickly adjusts to expect certain patterns to continue, one is often surprised and pleased by the discovery that everything is not symmetrical: there can be symmetry in the large and not in the small or vice versa. Similarly, in mathematics one often encounters certain patterns that suggest formalizing a mathematical system, only to discover on further examination that some really striking results are not covered by the system. It is my hope that Mr. Escher's prints will not only please the reader's eye but will also serve to remind him that progress is made in mathematics by recognizing and utilizing the existence of analogies and by careful examination of instances in which analogy breaks down. Like Mr. Escher's prints, the most beautiful results often entail a systematic approach combined with some ingenious ad hoc argument.

Finally, I also wish to thank Harper & Row, and especially Walter E. Sears, who have cooperated so generously in the preparation of this book.

DONALD J. LEWIS

CONTENTS

INTRODUCTION TO ALGEBRA

CHAPTER ONE

THE INTEGERS

1 INTRODUCTION

In algebra we study mathematical systems, attempting to characterize them and their fundamental properties. The systems that we shall study arise in a natural fashion from those which the reader has previously studied. We shall be particularly interested in the interrelation between various systems.

One of our problems is the following: Given a mathematical system, find a small list of basic properties which the system satisfies and from which the other properties possessed by the system may be derived by means of logical argument. Usually, but not always, we seek the smallest possible list, and at all times we wish the list to contain precise but simple statements. Eventually, one faces the question of whether a list of basic properties for an algebraic system characterizes the system, i.e., whether it is the only system possessing these properties. This question is very difficult, and often we shall not be able to give a completely satisfactory answer.

We begin our study by considering the integers, which are in many ways the most fundamental mathematical system. We do not prove there is such a system; rather we assume the reader has had some experience with it, and we seek to give a simple list of basic properties which the set of integers satisfies and from which we are able to derive all the conventional properties of the integers.

Before we begin our study, it will be useful to introduce some language and notations customarily used in mathematics.

2 SETS

A *set* is a collection of objects of some kind, these objects being called *elements* of the set. A set may be given by listing its elements; e.g., pages 3, 4, and 12 of this book form a set, and the polynomials x, $x^2 - 1$, and $x^3 + 1$ form a set. More commonly a set is given by a defining property, e.g., the positive-integer divisors of 24, or the integral multiples of 3, or the polynomials with 1 or -1 as coefficients. The graph of a polynomial equation, $f(x,y) = 0$, is the set of points in the xy plane that satisfy the equation. It is convenient to talk of the set of solutions or the set of roots of an equation.

It is possible to state properties that cannot possibly be satisfied by any object. Thus if we wish to talk glibly concerning sets defined by properties, we need to introduce the concept of the *empty set* or the *vacuous set*. The empty set is a set without elements. The collection of integers x such that $x^2 + 1 = 0$ is the empty set. The set of integers that are both odd and even is the empty set, as is the set of points common to two nonconcurrent parallel lines. When one specifies a set by a defining property, it is not always easy to ascertain whether a particular object belongs to the set or even whether the set is empty. For instance, one does not know if the set of those positive integers $n > 2$ for which there exist positive integers x, y, and z satisfying $x^n + y^n = z^n$ is the empty set.

The elements of a set can be almost anything. They can be numbers, functions, people, animals. They can even be sets themselves, e.g., the collection of pairs of twin primes, i.e., pairs of integers p, $p + 2$, where both are prime. However, when talking about a set of sets one must be careful not to talk of the set of all sets, for to do so leads to certain logical difficulties.

We shall denote sets by capital letters, S, T, etc., and elements of sets by lower-case letters. The fact that x is an element of a set S will be denoted by writing $x \in S$. If x is not in the set S, we shall write $x \notin S$.

The empty set will be denoted by the symbol $\varnothing$. Two sets are said to be equal when they consist of exactly the same elements. Thus

$$S = T$$

means

$$x \in S \qquad \text{if and only if} \qquad x \in T.$$

A set S is said to be a *subset* of a set T, written $S \subset T$, if every element of S is an element of T. Clearly $S \subset S$. If $S \subset T$ and $T \subset S$, then $S = T$. If $S \subset T$ and $T \subset R$, then $S \subset R$. The empty set $\varnothing$ is a subset of every set. A set S is said to be a *proper subset* of a set T if

$$S \subset T \qquad \text{and} \qquad S \text{ is neither } \varnothing \text{ nor } T.$$

The symbol $S \not\subset T$ means S is not a subset of T; i.e., there is an element x of S that is not an element of T.

If π is some defining property, we shall denote those elements in a set T having property π by

$$S = \{x \in T \mid x \text{ has } \pi\};$$

e.g., if $\mathbf{Z}$ is the set of integers, the set E of even integers can be expressed as

$$E = \{x \in \mathbf{Z} \mid 2 \text{ divides } x\},$$

the bisector of the first quadrant can be expressed as

$$\{(x, y) \mid x, y \text{ are real numbers such that } x = y\}.$$

Elements of a set are viewed as being things of a different kind from the set itself; therefore we shall denote the set consisting of the single element x by $\{x\}$. We have $x \in S$ if and only if $\{x\} \subset S$.

If S is a subset of T, we define *the complement of S in T* to be those elements in T not in S. We denote the complement of S in T by $T - S$. Thus

$$T - S = \{x \in T \mid x \notin S\}.$$

One easily shows $T - \varnothing = T$; $T - T = \varnothing$; if $S \subset T$, then $T - (T - S) = S$.

If S and T are subsets of R, we can form two other subsets of R from S and T, namely, the union of S and T and the intersection of S and T. The *union* of S and T, denoted by $S \cup T$, is the subset of R that consists of all elements of R that lie either in S or in T or in both; that is,

$$S \cup T = \{x \in R \mid \text{either } x \in S \text{ or } x \in T\}.$$

For example, the union of the set of odd integers and the set of even integers gives us the set of all integers. The *intersection* of S and T, denoted by $S \cap T$, is the subset of R consisting of all elements of R that lie both in S and in T; that is,

$$S \cap T = \{x \in R \mid x \in S \text{ and } x \in T\}.$$

Thus, the intersection of the set of even integers with the set of integer multiples of 3 is the set of integer multiples of 6. If

$$S \cap T = \varnothing,$$

we say S and T are *disjoint* sets. The set $\varnothing$ is disjoint from all sets, including itself.

Let k be a positive integer. We shall say that a set S is a *finite set of order* k if there is a rule that assigns, or attaches, to each integer of the set $\{1, 2, \ldots, k-1, k\}$ exactly one element of S in such a manner that (1) no element of S is assigned, or attached, to more than one integer and (2) each element of S is assigned, or attached, to some integer. Thus the set of vowels {a, e, i, o, u} is a finite set of order 5, since the rule that assigns

a to 1, e to 2, i to 3, o to 4, and u to 5

satisfies conditions 1 and 2. A rule as prescribed in our definition is often referred to as a 1-1 *correspondence* between the set S and the set $\{1, 2, \ldots, k\}$. The prescribed rule is a procedure for counting the elements in S; the element assigned to 1 being the first element, the element assigned to 2 being the second, ..., the element assigned to k being the kth element. Thus the elements of a finite set S of order k can be arranged in a sequence:

$$x_1, x_2, \ldots, x_k,$$

where x_i is the element in S assigned to the integer i by the prescribed rule. Different rules of assignment of elements of S to the integers in $\{1, 2, \ldots, k\}$ will give different arrangements of the sequence.*

If S is not empty and there is no positive integer k such that S is a finite set of order k, then S is said to be an *infinite set* and to have *infinite order*. Clearly the set of positive integers is an infinite set. The set of even integers and the set of all polynomials with integer coefficients are both infinite sets.

EXERCISES 1 Let S, T be subsets of some set W. Prove the following statements:

A. S is a proper subset of T if and only if $T - S \neq \varnothing$ and $S \neq \varnothing$.

B. $S \cup T \supset S$.

C. $S \cap T \subset T$.

D. $S \cup \varnothing = S$.

E. $S \cap \varnothing = \varnothing$.

F. If $S \cup T = T$, then $S \subset T$; and conversely.

G. If $S \cap T = S$, then $S \subset T$; and conversely.

H. $S \cap (T \cap U) = (S \cap T) \cap U$.

I. If $S \subset T$, then $S \cap (T - S) = \varnothing$ and $S \cup (T - S) = T$.

* It should be noted that we have neither specified nor proved that a finite set cannot have two distinct orders. This needs to be done, and we shall do so in Chap. 2.

2 If S is the set of integer solutions of the equation $f(x) = 0$ and T is the set of integer solutions of the equation $g(x) = 0$, show that $S \cap T$ is the set of integers that are simultaneously solutions of $f(x) = 0$ and of $g(x) = 0$.

3 If R is the xy plane and S is all points above the x axis and T is all points to the right of the y axis, determine $S \cap T$, $S \cup T$, $R - S$, $R - T$, $S \cap (R - T)$, $T \cup (R - S)$, $(S \cap (R - T)) \cap (T \cup (R - S))$, $(S \cup T) - (S \cap T)$, $T - (S \cap T)$, $T \cap (S \cup T)$.

4 Let R, S, T be as in Exercise 3 and let B be all points below the diagonal $x = y$. Determine $(S \cup T) \cap B$, $S \cup (T \cap B)$, $(S \cap B) \cup (T \cap B)$, $(S \cup T) \cap (S \cup B)$, $(S - (S \cap B)) \cap B$.

5 If S, T, B are any subsets of a set R, is it true that $(S \cup T) \cap B = (S \cap B) \cup (T \cap B)$?

3 PROPERTIES OF ADDITION OF THE INTEGERS

We denote the set of all integers by **Z**; i.e.,

$$\mathbf{Z} = \{0, 1, -1, 2, -2, 3, \dots\}.$$

Intuitively **Z** consists of 0, 1, and all finite sums of 1s, and the negatives of these sums.

We have two basic methods* of combining two integers to obtain another integer, namely, addition and multiplication. Given any two integers, a and b, their sum is a unique integer denoted by $a + b$, and their product is a unique integer denoted either by ab or by $a \cdot b$. Thus $2 + 3$ is the integer 5, and $2 \cdot 3$ is the integer 6. If a, b, and c represent integers and if $a = b$ and $b = c$, then a, b, and c all represent the same integer, and so $a = c$. Thus we have: If a, b, and c are integers and if $a = b$, $b = c$, then $a = c$. This statement is called the *transitive law for equality*.

We note that the sum and the product of two integers is uniquely determined by these integers and not by the manner in which the integers are represented. Thus $(2 + 3) + 4 = 5 + 4$, and $(2 + 3) \cdot 7 = 5 \cdot 7$. Thus we have the *rule of substitution:* We may substitute equals for equals in a sum, or product, without changing its value. Some people summarize this rule by the phrase "addition and multiplication are well defined in **Z**."

Relative to addition, the integers satisfy the following properties:

A_1. If a and b are in **Z**, then $a + b = b + a$.

A_2. If a, b, and c are in **Z**, then $(a + b) + c = a + (b + c)$.

* If we deal only with positive integers we can define multiplication in terms of addition. When we consider both positive and negative integers it is best to consider the two operations separately.

A_3. There is a unique integer, 0, such that $a + 0 = a$, for each integer a in **Z**.

A_4. To each integer a in **Z** there is associated a unique integer $(-a)$ such that $a + (-a) = 0$.

The property A_1 tells us that the order in which we add two integers together does not affect their sum. A_1 is called the *commutative law for addition*. The reader will recall that there are other ways of combining two integers together where the order of combining does make a difference, e.g., subtraction and exponentiation.

As defined, addition applies only to addition of two integers at a time; nothing is said about the sum of more integers. However, we often talk of the sum of finitely many integers, and therefore if our list of properties for addition is to be adequate, we must be able to give a meaning to sums of more than two integers using only the listed properties. This we can do. Say we wish to add three integers a, b, and c. We can add a and b to get their sum $a + b$, and then we can add this new integer to c. The resulting sum is $(a + b) + c$. Of course, we could have grouped and combined these three integers in other ways. On so doing, we could obtain

$$a + (b + c), \quad c + (a + b), \quad (a + c) + b, \quad \text{and } a + (c + b),$$

among others. The question immediately arises: Are all these expressions equal? Now A_2 assures us that $(a + b) + c = a + (b + c)$ and $(a + c) + b = a + (c + b)$. Using A_1 and the rule of substitution of equals for equals, we obtain $a + (b + c) = a + (c + b)$. Therefore, we have $(a + c) + b = a + (c + b) = a + (b + c) = (a + b) + c$ and $(a + b) + c = c + (a + b)$. Thus, using the first two listed properties of addition, we have shown that these various ways of adding three integers all give the same integer.

The number of possible ways of expressing the sum of four integers is much greater. To begin with, there are five ways of grouping them into pairs of integers without disturbing their order. These are

$$((a + b) + c) + d, \quad (a + b) + (c + d), \quad a + (b + (c + d)),$$
$$(a + (b + c)) + d, \quad a + ((b + c) + d).$$

The reader should show, using the first two properties of addition, that these five expressions are all equal.

Property A_2 is called the *associative law for addition*. One can prove a *generalized commutative and associative law for addition: Given any finite set of integers, regardless of how we order them or insert parenthesis so as to be able to add two integers at a time, the sum is always the same.* We shall give a proof of this in Sec. 6. Because of the existence of this generalized law, we can drop the use of parenthesis when expressing the sum of finitely many integers. We are unable to give meaning to the sum of infinitely many nonzero integers.

Unique means one and only one. Thus if s is an integer such that for each integer a, $a + s = a$, it necessarily follows from A_3 that $s = 0$, for A_3 states that 0 is the unique integer having this property.

Some people call $(-a)$ the "negative of a" while others call it the "additive inverse of a." The negative of a should not be confused with a negative integer. The integer $(-a)$ is that integer which when added to the integer a gives 0. By A_1, $(-2) + 2 = 0$; hence

$$2 = -(-2).$$

As $0 + 0 = 0$, we have $0 = -0$. Because of the possibility of confusion we shall call $(-a)$ the *additive inverse of a*. In listing the elements of $\mathbf{Z}$, we have indicated the additive inverses of the positive integers. The additive inverses of negative integers are determined by

PROPOSITION 1 *If $a \in \mathbf{Z}$, then $-(-a) = a$.*

PROOF. By A_3, we have $a + (-a) = 0$. Hence by A_1, $(-a) + a = 0$. But by A_3, $-(-a)$ is the unique integer which when added to $(-a)$ gives 0. Hence $a = -(-a)$.

Now assume that a, e, and f are integers and that

$$a + e = a + f,$$

then

$$(-a) + (a + e) = (-a) + (a + f).$$

But $e = (-a) + (a + e)$ and $f = (-a) + (a + f)$ (why?), and hence $e = f$. Thus if $a + e = b$ and $a + f = b$, then we must have $e = f$. Consequently $b + (-a)$ is the unique solution of the equation $a + x = b$. We denote $b + (-a)$ by $(b - a)$. In this way we have defined a new way of combining two integers, b and a, to get another, namely, $(b - a)$. Observe that, given b and a, $(b - a)$ is a unique integer. The operation of associating the integer $(b - a)$ with each pair of integers b and a is customarily called *subtraction*.

We have derived many of the known properties of addition of integers from our listed ones. Can we get all such properties in this way? If not, what other properties are needed? If yes, could we do so with fewer properties? Subsequent exercises and sections will shed light on these important questions.

EXERCISES 1 A. Show that subtraction is not commutative.

B. If $a = -a$ for all integers a, would subtraction be commutative?

2 If a, b, c, and d are in $\mathbf{Z}$, prove $(-a) + (-b) = -(a + b)$, $(b - a) - c = b - (a + c)$, $-(b - a) = (a - b)$, $(a - b) + (c - d) = (a + c) - (b + d)$, $(a - b) - (c - d) = (a + d) - (b + c)$, $(a - b) = (c - d)$ if and only if $a + d = b + c$.

3 Actually one need not assume that 0 and $(-a)$ are unique. Show that we can deduce A_3 and A_4 from A_1, A_2, and the following:

A'_3. 0 is an integer such that $a + 0 = a$ for every integer a.

A'_4. To each a in **Z** there is an integer $(-a)$ such that $a + (-a) = 0$.

4 MULTIPLICATIVE PROPERTIES OF THE INTEGERS

As we noted earlier, given any two integers, their product is a unique integer. The integers satisfy three properties relative to multiplication:

M_1. If a and b are in **Z**, then $ab = ba$ (*commutative law for multiplication*).

M_2. If a, b, and c are in **Z**, then $(ab)c = a(bc)$ (*associative law for multiplication*).

M_3. The integer 1 is unequal to 0 and is such that $a \cdot 1 = a$ for each a in **Z**.

Notice that a system consisting of 0 alone would have a multiplication defined that satisfies M_1 and M_2 but not M_3. Just as for addition, one can prove a generalized commutative and associative law for multiplication. Hence, we can speak of the product of finitely many integers without worrying about how they are arranged.

The integer 1 is unique. For if e were a nonzero integer such that $a \cdot e = a$ for all $a \in \mathbf{Z}$, then $1 \cdot e = 1$. But M_3 tells us that $e \cdot 1 = e$, and hence by M_1 we have $e = e \cdot 1 = 1 \cdot e = 1$; i.e., $e = 1$.

From experience we know that there is no analogy to A_4 for multiplication of integers; e.g., the equation $2x = 1$ has no integer solution. Actually with the preceding properties we are unable to prove that $2x = 1$ has no integer solution, for, as we shall see later, there are systems having all the preceding properties as well as the following analogy to A_4. To each $a \neq 0$ in the system, there is a unique element in the system, denoted by $(1/a)$ such that $a(1/a) = 1$. The set of rational numbers is such a system.

Finally we have one property relating our two basic methods of combining integers.

If a, b, and c are in **Z**, then $a \cdot (b + c) = ab + ac$. This property (D) is called the *distributive law*.

The reader can now prove

PROPOSITION 2 *If a is in* **Z**, *then* $a \cdot 0 = 0 = 0 \cdot a$.

PROPOSITION 3 *If a and b are in* **Z**, *then* $a(-b) = -(ab) = (-a)b$, $(-a)(-b) = ab$, $(-b) = (-1)b$.

In proving the above propositions, one should expect to use the distributive law, since it is the only property relating addition and multiplication, and the symbols 0 and $(-a)$ are defined relative to addition.

The properties listed in these propositions are known as *the algebraic rules of signs*. These rules are concerned with additions and multiplications involving additive inverses and 0 and therefore do not depend on the existence of positive and negative integers but only on the existence of additive inverses.

5 THE POSITIVE CONE AND ORDER

Using only those properties of addition and multiplication of integers listed so far, we are unable to prove that $2x = 1$ has no solution in $\mathbf{Z}$. Nor can we prove that if

$$3x = 3y, \qquad \text{then} \qquad x = y.$$

In fact, we shall later exhibit mathematical systems satisfying all the properties that we have so far listed for $\mathbf{Z}$, for which each of the above statements is false. This should not be surprising, for we have not yet used or stated one of the most important properties of the set of integers, the existence of positive integers. Each of the above unproved statements follows from the existence of the positive integers. We list below properties describing the positive integers.

There is a proper subset of $\mathbf{Z}$ denoted by $\mathbf{Z}^+$, satisfying the following conditions:

P_1. 0 is not in $\mathbf{Z}^+$.

P_2. If a is a nonzero element of $\mathbf{Z}$, then $a \neq -a$, and exactly one of a and $-a$ are in $\mathbf{Z}^+$.

P_3. If a and b are in $\mathbf{Z}^+$, then $a + b$ and ab are in $\mathbf{Z}^+$.

The set $\mathbf{Z}^+$ is called the *positive cone* of $\mathbf{Z}$.

Let

$$\mathbf{Z}^- = \{a \text{ in } \mathbf{Z} \mid -a \text{ is in } \mathbf{Z}^+\}.$$

$\mathbf{Z}^-$ is called the set of negative integers. $\mathbf{Z}$ is the disjoint union of $\mathbf{Z}^+$, $\{0\}$, and $\mathbf{Z}^-$.

We note that P_2 implies that

$$x = -x \qquad \text{only if} \qquad x = 0.$$

Thus, 0 is the only integer that can be its own additive inverse. Earlier we saw that $(-0) = 0$. Later we shall encounter systems where nonzero elements are their own additive inverses.

EXERCISES 1 Prove: 1 is in $\mathbf{Z}^+$. Hence $1 + 1 = 2, 3, 4, \ldots$ are in $\mathbf{Z}^+$, and $-1, -2, \ldots$ are in $\mathbf{Z}^-$.

2 Prove: If a is in $\mathbf{Z}^+$ and b is in $\mathbf{Z}^-$, then ab is in $\mathbf{Z}^-$. If a and b are in $\mathbf{Z}^-$, then ab is in $\mathbf{Z}^+$. For all $a \neq 0$ in $\mathbf{Z}$, a^2 is in $\mathbf{Z}^+$.

PROPOSITION 4 *If $a, b \in \mathbf{Z}$ and $ab = 0$, then at least one of a and b is equal to 0.*

This proposition is often described by saying that $\mathbf{Z}$ has no *proper divisors of* 0. The proof follows directly from P_3 and Exercise 2.

PROPOSITION 5 *If $a, b, c \in \mathbf{Z}$ and $c \neq 0$ and $ac = bc$, then $a = b$.*

This statement is called the *cancellation law*. It is false if $c = 0$. Why?

PROPOSITION 6 *If a is a nonzero integer, then 1 is the unique solution in $\mathbf{Z}$ of the equation $ax = a$.*

Note that in M_3 we had not specified that 1 was unique.

EXERCISES 3 Prove Propositions 4, 5, and 6.

4 As we see from M_3 and Proposition 6, the following statements hold: The integer 1 is such that for every $a \in \mathbf{Z}$ we have $a \cdot 1 = a$. Furthermore if $a \neq 0$, the only solution in $\mathbf{Z}$ of the equation $ax = a$ is 1. Replace M_3 by these two statements, and prove the following results without assuming the existence of a positive cone:

A. If $a \neq 0$, $b \in \mathbf{Z}$ and if $ab = 0$, then $b = 0$.

B. If $a \neq 0$, $b, c \in \mathbf{Z}$ and if $ab = ac$, then $b = c$.

C. If $a \in \mathbf{Z}$, then $a = -a$ if and only if $a = 0$.

5 Prove: $\mathbf{Z}^-$ is closed under addition.

We are now in a position to define the relationship of inequality. If a and b are in $\mathbf{Z}$, we say that a is *less than* b, written $a < b$, whenever $b - a$ is in $\mathbf{Z}^+$. In this case we also say that b is *greater than* a and write $b > a$. We indicate not less than by $\not<$.

EXERCISES 6 Prove: If $a \in \mathbf{Z}^+$, then $a > 0$. If $a \in \mathbf{Z}^-$, then $a < 0$.

7 Prove:

A. If $a, b \in \mathbf{Z}$, then one and only one of the following is true: $a < b$, $a = b$, $a > b$.

B. For every $a \in \mathbf{Z}$ we have $a \not< a$.

8 Let a, b, c, and d be elements of $\mathbf{Z}$, and prove:

A. If $a < b$ and $b < c$, then $a < c$ (*transitive law for inequality*).

B. If $a < b$, then $a + c < b + c$ and $a - c < b - c$.

C. If $a < b$ and $c > 0$, then $ac < bc$.

D. If $a < b$ and $c < 0$, then $ac > bc$.

E. If $a < b$ and $c < d$, then $a + c < b + d$.

9 Prove: There is no integer x such that $x^2 + 1 = 0$. More generally, if $a > 0$, then there is no integer x such that $x^2 + a = 0$.

If the integer a is not greater than the integer b, then either $a < b$ or $a = b$. We indicate this by writing $a \not> b$ or $a \leq b$.

EXERCISES 10 Prove: If $b > 1$, then the equation $bx = 1$ has no solution in **Z**; in particular $2x = 1$ has no integer solution.

11 Show that the properties of $<$ listed in Exercise 8 are also properties of $\leq$.

12 Prove: If a and b are in **Z** and if $a \leq b$ and $b \leq a$, then $a = b$.

13 Prove: There is no integer x such that $x^2 + x + 1 = 0$.

14 Prove: There is no integer that exceeds all other integers.

If a is an integer, its *absolute value* is denoted by $|a|$ and is defined as follows:

$$|a| = \begin{cases} a \text{ if } a \geq 0, \\ -a \text{ if } a < 0. \end{cases}$$

EXERCISES 15 Prove: For every integer a, $|a| \geq 0$, $|a| = |-a|$, $a \leq |a|$.

16 Prove: If a and b are in **Z**, then $|ab| = |a| \cdot |b|$ and $|a + b| \leq |a| + |b|$. (This last result is often called the *triangle inequality*.)

17 Prove: If a and b are in **Z**, then $||a| - |b|| \leq |a + b| \leq |a| + |b|$.

We could have defined $|a|$ as the larger of a and $-a$. We now extend this idea to arbitrary subsets of **Z**. If S is a subset of **Z**, we say that w is the *maximum element* of S, written

$$w = \max S,$$

if w is in S and $w \geq s$ for every s in S. Similarly we say that m is the *minimum element* of S (or the least element of S), written

$$m = \min S,$$

if m is in S and $m \leq s$ for every s in S. Thus

$$|a| = \max \{a, -a\}.$$

Of course not every set of integers need have a minimum or a maximum element. For example, the set **Z** itself has neither a maximum nor a minimum. On the other hand the set $\mathbf{Z}^+$ has no maximum but has a minimum, but the set

$$S = \{1, 2, 4, 8, 16\}$$

has both a maximum and a minimum.

If a set has a least element, that element is unique. For if m and n are both least elements of a set S, they would both be in S, and we would have $m \leq n$ and $n \leq m$ and hence $n = m$. Similarly a set can have at most one maximum.

A subset S of **Z** will be said to be *bounded from above* if there is an integer u such that $s \leq u$ for every $s \in S$. The u need not lie in S. The integer u is said to be an *upper bound* for the set S. Similarly a subset S of $\mathbf{Z}$ is said to be *bounded from below* if there is an integer m such that $m \le s$ for every $s \in S$. The integer m is said to be a *lower bound* for S. A subset of $\mathbf{Z}$ is said to be *bounded* if it is bounded both from above and from below.

EXERCISES 18 Prove: Let S be a subset of $\mathbf{Z}$; the max S and the min S exist and are equal if and only if the set S consists of a single element.

19 Show that, if a set of integers has an upper bound, it has infinitely many upper bounds.

20 Given a subset S of $\mathbf{Z}$ having an upper bound, let $U(S) = \{u \in \mathbf{Z} \mid u$ is an upper bound of $S\}$. Show that $U(S)$ is bounded below. Show that $S \cap U(S)$ contains at most one element.

21 Prove: If S and T are subsets of $\mathbf{Z}$ bounded from above, then $S \cap T$ and $S \cup T$ are subsets of $\mathbf{Z}$ bounded from above.

22 Suppose S and T are subsets of $\mathbf{Z}$ with maximum elements; prove that $\max (S \cup T) = \max (\max S, \max T)$.

23 Prove: If S, T, $S \cap T$ are subsets of $\mathbf{Z}$ having maximums, the $\max (S \cap T) \le \min (\max S, \max T)$.

24 State and prove results analogous to those in Exercises 19 to 23 for sets of integers bounded from below and for sets with a minimum.

Let S and T be subsets of $\mathbf{Z}$, and define the following sets:

$$S + T = \{w \text{ in } \mathbf{Z} \mid w = s + t, \text{ for some } s \text{ in } S \text{ and some } t \text{ in } T\}.$$

$$ST = \{w \text{ in } \mathbf{Z} \mid w = st, \quad \text{for some } s \text{ in } S \text{ and some } t \text{ in } T\}.$$

A set S of integers is said to be *closed under addition* if $S + S \subset S$. S is said to be *closed under multiplication* if $SS \subset S$. S is said to be *closed under subtraction* if $S + (-1)S \subset S$.

EXERCISES 25 Let $S = \{1, 3, 5\}$ and let $T = \{-2, 0, 4, 5\}$; determine $S + T$, ST, $S + S$, SS.

26 Show that the set $\{2\}\mathbf{Z}$ is the set of even integers, say E, and the set $\{5\} + E$ is the set of odd integers.

27 Prove: If S and T are subsets of $\mathbf{Z}$ and $0 \in S$, then $T \subset S + T$.

28 Find subsets S of $\mathbf{Z}$ such that $S + S = \{2\}S$.

29 If S and T are subsets of $\mathbf{Z}$ with maximum elements, determine the maximum element of $S + T$.

30 If S and T are subsets of $\mathbf{Z}^+$ and have maximum elements, determine the maximum element of ST. Discuss the existence of the max ST if S and T are arbitrary subsets of $\mathbf{Z}$ with maximum elements.

31 A. Show that the set of even integers is closed under addition, multiplication, and subtraction, but that this is not so for the set of odd integers.

B. Show that the set S of integers of the form $4m + 1$ is closed under multiplication but not under addition.

C. Exhibit sets of integers that are closed under addition but not under multiplication.

We remark that, if S is the set of all integer squares, then $\mathbf{Z}^+ \subset S + S + S + S$.* It is a classic problem to determine the least integer $n = n(k)$, such that $\mathbf{Z}^+ \subset S_1 + \cdots + S_n$, where $S_1 = \cdots = S_n$ = the set of kth powers of nonnegative integers.

6 INDUCTION AXIOM, WELL-ORDERING PRINCIPLE

From the properties of $\mathbf{Z}^+$ it follows that, if $S = \{1, 2, 3, 4, \ldots\}$, then S is a subset of $\mathbf{Z}^+$. Now we want S to be exactly $\mathbf{Z}^+$. We cannot derive this from the list of properties of $\mathbf{Z}$ that we have accumulated so far, for the set of rational numbers satisfies all the properties but its positive cone is much larger than the set S. Thus we need to add at least one more basic property of integers to our list. We add the *induction axiom:*

INDUCTION AXIOM *If S is a subset of $\mathbf{Z}^+$ such that* (A) *1 is in S and* (B) *$x + 1 \in S$ whenever $x \in S$, then S is exactly $\mathbf{Z}^+$.*†

The induction axiom is a precise statement implying $\mathbf{Z}^+ = \{1, 2, 3, \ldots\}$. It follows from the induction axiom that 1 is the least positive integer, i.e.,

$$1 = \min \mathbf{Z}^+.$$

This completes our list of basic properties of the integers. From our list it is possible to derive all the facts about integers that one is accustomed to using. Our list of basic properties is sufficient to characterize the integers, in the sense that no other system possesses all these properties. The proof of this is involved, and we shall not give it here. We note, but also do not prove, that our list is not minimal.

EXERCISES 1 Prove: If a and b are in $\mathbf{Z}$ and $a < b$, then $a + 1 \leq b$.

2 Prove: If a is in $\mathbf{Z}$, then there is no integer x such that $a < x < a + 1$.

* For a proof see W. J. LeVeque, *Topics in Number Theory*, Addison-Wesley Publishing Company, Inc., Reading, Mass., 1956, vol. I, pp. 133–136.

† There are systems satisfying all the properties of integers and possessing proper subsets S such that (A) $1 \in S$ and (B) $x + 1 \in S$ whenever $x \in S$. The important operational word in the statement of the induction axiom is "exactly."

3 Prove: If a and b are in $\mathbf{Z}$ and if $a^2 < b < (a + 1)^2$, then there is no integer x such that $x^2 = b$. (In particular $x^2 = 2$ has no integer solution.)

4 Let S, $U(S)$ be as in Exercise 20, Sec. 5. Prove: $S \cap U(S) = \max S = \min U(S)$.

In place of the induction axiom we can use the *well-ordering principle*: *Every nonempty subset of* $\mathbf{Z}^+$ *has a least element.* For we have

THEOREM 1 *The induction axiom implies the well-ordering principle.*

PROOF. Let T be a given nonempty subset of $\mathbf{Z}^+$. Define a new set S of $\mathbf{Z}^+$ as follows:

$$S = \{x \in \mathbf{Z}^+ \mid x \leq t, \text{ for every } t \in T\}.$$

Since 1 is the least element of $\mathbf{Z}^+$, it is clearly less than or equal to every element in T, and hence 1 is in S. If S and T have an element in common, it will necessarily be the least element in T and hence will be unique.

Now suppose $S \cap T = \varnothing$. If s is in S and t is any element in T, then $s < t$, and hence $s + 1 \leq t$. It follows that, if s is in S, so is $s + 1$. Hence if $S \cap T = \varnothing$, then S satisfies the hypothesis of the induction axiom, and consequently $S = \mathbf{Z}^+$. But then T is empty, contrary to the original assumption.

PROPOSITION 7 *The well-ordering principle implies that* 1 *is the least element in* $\mathbf{Z}^+$.

PROOF. Suppose that there is an integer x such that $0 < x < 1$. By the well-ordering principle $\mathbf{Z}^+$ has a minimum, say $m = \min \mathbf{Z}^+$. Since m and x are in $\mathbf{Z}^+$, mx must be in $\mathbf{Z}^+$. By Exercise 8C, Sec. 5, $mx < m$, contrary to m being the min $\mathbf{Z}^+$.

We can now show

THEOREM 2 *The well-ordering principle implies the induction axiom.*

PROOF. Let S be a subset of $\mathbf{Z}^+$ having the properties (A) 1 is in S and (B) if s is in S, then $s + 1$ is in S. Let $W = \mathbf{Z}^+ - S$; i.e., W is the set of positive integers not in S. Clearly $W \cap S = \varnothing$. Suppose W is a nonempty subset of $\mathbf{Z}^+$. By the well-ordering principle there is a least element in W, say m. It follows from Proposition 7 that $m \geq 1$; but 1 is in S, and hence $m > 1$. Since $m = \min W$, $m - 1$ is in S. But then by property B of S, we must have m in S, an impossibility. It follows that W is empty, and hence $S = \mathbf{Z}^+$.

Thus the induction axiom and the well-ordering principle are equivalent properties, and when using them to prove theorems, we may use whichever suits our convenience. These two properties are the most characteristic properties of the integers.

The induction axiom and the well-ordering principle are extremely useful tools for proving results about the set of all integers. As a simple example we prove: *The sum of the first n even positive integers is* $n(n+1)$.

Let

$$U = \{k \in \mathbf{Z}^+ \mid 2 + 4 + \cdots + 2k = k(k+1)\};$$

i.e., U consists of those positive integers k which satisfy the equation $2 + 4 + \cdots + 2k = k(k+1)$. Clearly $1 \in U$. If $n \in U$, then $2 + 4 + \cdots + 2n = n(n+1)$, whence

$$2 + 4 + \cdots + 2n + 2(n+1) = n(n+1) + 2(n+1) = (n+1)(n+2).$$

Hence if $n \in U$, then $n + 1 \in U$. It follows from the induction axiom that $U = \mathbf{Z}^+$, thus proving: For every positive integer n, the sum of the first n even positive integers is $n(n+1)$.

The above result could also be proved using the well-ordering principle. In such a proof, one would let

$$T = \{k \in \mathbf{Z}^+ \mid 2 + 4 + \cdots + 2k \neq k(k+1)\}.$$

If $T \neq \varnothing$, let $m = \min T$, which exists by the well-ordering principle. Clearly $1 \notin T$, and so $m \geq 2$. Also $m - 1 \notin T$, but then $2 + 4 + \cdots + 2(m-1) = (m-1)m$; and so $2 + 4 + \cdots + 2m = (m-1)m + 2m = m(m+1)$, contrary to the fact that $m \in T$. Hence T is empty, and the property holds for all positive integers.

Proofs using the axiom of induction are often called *proofs by induction*. Often, when giving such proofs, we omit defining U and proceed to show the result is true for the integer 1 and if true for the integer n then true for $n + 1$. Some properties hold true for the set of integers greater than some given integer X. In proving such results, we either proceed inductively, showing the property is true for $X + 1$ and then, in turn, is true for the integers greater than X, or we consider the set U consisting of $1, 2, \ldots, X$, and those integers $> X$ which have the desired property, and show $U = \mathbf{Z}^+$.

EXERCISE 5 Prove:

A. The sum of the first n odd integers is n^2.

B. The sum of the first n positive cubes is equal to the square of the sum of the first n positive integers.

Let

$$U = \left\{k \in \mathbf{Z}^+ \,\middle|\, \begin{array}{l}\text{every finite set of positive integers}\\ \text{of order } k \text{ has a minimum}\end{array}\right\}.$$

Since a one-element set always has a minimum, U contains 1. Suppose $1 < n \in U$, and let $S = \{x_1, x_2, \ldots, x_{n+1}\} \subset \mathbf{Z}$; then the set $\{x_1, \ldots, x_n\}$ has a minimum, say m, and in this case $\min(m, x_{n+1}) = \min S$. We have shown that $n + 1 \in U$ whenever $n \in U$. It follows from the induction axiom that $U = \mathbf{Z}^+$, and hence every finite set of integers has a minimum. The reader should show in a similar fashion that every finite set of integers has a maximum. We will then have proved

PROPOSITION 8 *Every finite subset of integers has a minimum and a maximum.*

The reader should prove

PROPOSITION 9 *Every subset of* $\mathbf{Z}$ *bounded from below has a minimum. Every subset of* $\mathbf{Z}$ *bounded from above has a maximum.*

We are now in a position to prove the generalized commutative and associative law. Since the proof is essentially the same for addition as for multiplication, we give only the latter. We first prove

THEOREM 3 *Generalized associative law: Let* $a_1, a_2, \ldots, a_n$ *be any* n $(n \geq 3)$ *integers, and let*

$$\rho(a_1, a_2, \ldots, a_n)$$

be the product of these integers obtained by inserting parenthesis in some manner in the ordered sequence $a_1, a_2, \ldots, a_n$. *Then*

$$\rho(a_1, a_2, \ldots, a_n) = (\cdots((a_1a_2)a_3)\cdots)a_n.$$

PROOF. We want to prove that for any finite set the product is independent of the manner of grouping, and so we prove the theorem by induction on n. Let T be those integers n exceeding 2 for which there is a set of n integers $a_1, a_2, \ldots, a_n$ and a grouping such that

$$\rho(a_1, a_2, \ldots, a_n) \neq (\cdots((a_1a_2)a_3\cdots)a_n.$$

Suppose T is not empty; then by the well-ordering principle T has a minimum, say $m = \min T$. The integer m must exceed 3, since M_2 implies the conclusion of the theorem for $n = 3$. Given the product $\rho(a_1, a_2, \ldots, a_m)$, there is an integer r such that

$$\rho(a_1, a_2, \ldots, a_m) = \rho_1(a_1, a_2, \ldots, a_r)\rho_2(a_{r+1}, a_{r+2}, \ldots, a_m),$$

where $1 \leq r < m$. (Why?) Now $m - r$ is not in T, and consequently either

$$\rho_2(a_{r+1}, \ldots, a_m) = a_m$$

or

$$\rho_2(a_{r+1}, \ldots, a_m) = (\cdots(a_{r+1}a_{r+2})\cdots)a_m.$$

In either case, using M_2 in the latter instance, we get

$$\rho(a_1, a_2, \ldots, a_m) = \rho_3(a_1, a_2, \ldots, a_{m-1})a_m,$$

where ρ_3 is some product of $a_1, a_2, \ldots, a_{m-1}$. As $m - 1$ is not in T,

we have

$$\rho_3(a_1, a_2, \ldots, a_{m-1}) = (\cdots((a_1a_2)a_3)\cdots)a_{m-1}$$

and so $$\rho(a_1, a_2, \ldots, a_m) = (\cdots((a_1a_2)a_3)\cdots)a_{m-1})a_m,$$

which contradicts m being in T. Hence T is empty, and we have proved our theorem.

THEOREM 4 *Generalized commutative law: Let $a_1, a_2, \ldots, a_n$ be any set of integers, and let $a_{i_1}, a_{i_2}, \ldots, a_{i_n}$ be any rearrangement of this set. Then*

$$(\cdots((a_{i_1}a_{i_2})a_{i_3})\cdots)a_{i_n} = (\cdots((a_1a_2)a_3)\cdots)a_n.$$

The proof is left to the reader.

We now define *exponentiation* as follows: For any a in $\mathbf{Z}$,

$$a^1 = a,\ a^{n+1} = a^n \cdot a \text{ for any integer } n \geq 1.$$

This is a recursive definition that makes it possible to compute any positive integral power of a in terms of already computed lower powers of a. By induction we see that our definition defines a^m for any positive integer m. We also define

$$a^0 = 1, \qquad \text{for all } a \neq 0 \text{ in } \mathbf{Z}.$$

Note that this definition of a^0 is consistent with our recursive definition of exponentiation.

We wish to show

OPOSITION 10 *If $a \in \mathbf{Z}$ and $m, n \in \mathbf{Z}^+$, then*

$$a^{m+n} = a^m a^n, \tag{1}$$

$$(a^m)^n = a^{mn}. \tag{2}$$

PROOF. Let

$$T = \{1, k \in \mathbf{Z}^+ \mid \text{if } k = x + y, \quad x, y \in \mathbf{Z}^+, \text{ then } a^{x+y} = a^x a^y\}.$$

We can prove the first part of the proposition by showing that $T = \mathbf{Z}^+$. For if $T = \mathbf{Z}^+$ and $m, n \in \mathbf{Z}^+$, then $m + n = k \in \mathbf{Z}^+ \subset T$, and hence $a^{m+n} = a^m a^n$. Clearly $1, 2 \in T$. Suppose that $2 \leq u \in T$ and that $u + 1 = m + n$, where $m, n \in \mathbf{Z}^+$. Then one of m and n exceeds 2, say $n \geq 2$. As $m + (n - 1) = u \in T$, we have $a^u = a^m a^{n-1} = a^{m+n-1}$. But then

$$a^{u+1} = a^u a = (a^m a^{n-1})a = a^m(a^{n-1}a) = a^m a^n.$$

Thus $2 \leq u \in T$ implies $u + 1 \in T$. It follows from the induction axiom that $T = \mathbf{Z}^+$.

To prove the second part of the proposition, we let

$$S = \left\{1, k \in \mathbf{Z}^+ \;\middle|\; \begin{array}{ll} \text{whenever } k = m + n, \text{ with } m, n \in \mathbf{Z}^+ \\ \text{then} \qquad (a^m)^n = a^{mn} \text{ for all } a \in \mathbf{Z} \end{array} \right\}$$

and prove that $S = \mathbf{Z}^+$. We know that $1, 2 \in S$. Suppose $2 \leq u \in S$, and suppose $m + n = u + 1$. If $n = 1$, then $(a^m)^n = (a^m)^1 = a^m = m^{mn}$. If $n > 1$, then $n = r + 1$, with $r \geq 1$; consequently $m + r = u$, with $m, r, u \in \mathbf{Z}^+$. As $u \in S$, we have $(a^m)^r = a^{mr}$, whence

$$(a^m)^n = (a^m)^{r+1} = (a^m)^r(a^m) = (a^{mr})(a^m).$$

By Eq. 1, $(a^{mr})a^m = a^{mr+m}$. But $mr + m = m(r + 1) = mn$, and therefore

$$a^{mr+m} = a^{mn} = (a^m)^n.$$

Thus we have shown $1 \in S$ and $u + 1 \in S$ whenever $u \in S$. It follows from the induction axiom that $S = \mathbf{Z}^+$. This completes the proof of the proposition.

EXERCISE 6 Prove that Proposition 10 is valid for all pairs of nonnegative integers m and n and nonzero integer a.

7 DIVISIBILITY

If a and b are integers, we have seen that the equation $ax = b$ need not have an integral solution. If this equation has an integral solution, we say that *a divides b* and write $a \mid b$. If a does not divide b, we write $a \nmid b$. The cancellation law (Proposition 5) tells us that, if $a \neq 0$, then the equation $ax = b$ has at most one integer solution. If the equation $ax = b$ has a solution, we call that unique solution the *quotient* of b by a.

In the following exercises let a, b, c, d, and e be elements of $\mathbf{Z}$.

EXERCISES 1 Prove: 1 divides every integer. Every integer divides itself. Every integer divides 0. If 0 divides a, then $a = 0$. If $a \mid b$, then $(-a) \mid b$ and $a \mid (-b)$.

2 Prove: If $d \mid a$ and $d \mid b$, then $d \mid (a + b)$, $d \mid (a - b)$, and $d \mid ac$. More generally if $d \mid a$ and $d \mid b$, then $d \mid (ac + be)$.

3 Prove: If $a \mid b$ and $b \mid c$, then $a \mid c$ (transitive law for divisibility).

4 Prove: If $a \neq 0$ and $d \mid a$, then $|d| \leq |a|$.

5 Prove: If $a \mid b$ and $b \mid a$, then $a = \pm b$.

We can deduce from the preceding exercises that 1 and -1 divide every integer and that they are the only divisors of 1. All other integers have at least four distinct divisors, namely,

$$1, -1, a, -a.$$

Thus relative to divisibility 1 and -1 play a special role, and it is useful to give them a special name. We say that 1 and -1 are the *units* of $\mathbf{Z}$.

Exercise 4 assures us that 2 has only four divisors. Since $3 = 2 + 1$ and $2 \nmid 1$, it follows that $2 \nmid 3$ (why?), and so by Exercise 4 the integer 3 has only four divisors. However 4 has six distinct divisors. The reader should prove that 5 and 7 have only four distinct divisors but 6, 8, 9, and 10 have more than four different divisors. A positive integer p that has exactly four distinct integral divisors is called a *prime*. Integers greater than 1 that are not primes are called *composite numbers*.

THEOREM 5 *Every integer greater than* 1 *has a prime as a divisor.*

PROOF. Let T be the set consisting of those integers which exceed 1 and which do not have a prime divisor. Either T is empty, in which case the theorem is true, or by the well-ordering principle T has a minimum, say $m = \min T$. Clearly m cannot be a prime, and hence there is an integer a such that

$$1 < a < m \qquad \text{and} \qquad a \mid m.$$

But then a is not in T and hence has a prime divisor. It follows from Exercise 3 that m has a prime divisor, contrary to m being in T. Therefore T must be empty.

THEOREM 6 *Every integer greater than* 1 *is either a prime or the product of primes.*

The proof is left to the reader.

Let a and b be integers. Let S be the set of integer divisors of a, and let T be the set of integer divisors of b. If at least one of a and b is not in 0, then $U = S \cap T$ is bounded above and below, and hence, by Proposition 9, U has a maximum and a minimum element. Since 1 lies in U, the max U is positive. The maximum element of U is the *greatest common divisor* of a and b. We write

$$\max U = (a, b).$$

It follows that $\min U = -(a, b)$. We say that two integers are *relatively prime* if 1 is their greatest common divisor. Note that we do not define $(0, 0)$.

EXERCISES 6 Prove:

A. If a and b are both integers, not both 0, then $(a, b) = (b, a) = (a, -b)$.
B. If a is an integer, then $(a, 1) = 1$.
C. If a is a nonzero integer, then $(a, 0) = |a|$ and $(a, a) = |a|$.
D. If a and b are both nonzero integers, then $1 \le (a, b) \le \min(|a|, |b|)$.
E. If $a \neq 0$ and b are in **Z** and $a \mid b$, then $(a, b) = |a|$.

7 Prove: If p is a prime, then $(a, p) = \begin{cases} 1 \text{ if } p \nmid a, \\ p \text{ if } p \mid a. \end{cases}$

8 Prove: If $a \neq 0$, b, and n are integers, then $(a, b) = (a, b + na)$.

9 Prove: A finite set of nonzero integers $a_1, a_2, \ldots, a_r$ has a greatest

common divisor. Denote the greatest common divisor by $(a_1, a_2, \ldots, a_r)$. Prove: $(a_1, a_2, \ldots, a_r) = ((a_1, a_2, \ldots, a_{r-1}), a_r)$.

PROPOSITION 11 *If $a \neq 0$ and b are integers, then there is an integer m such that $am > b$.*

PROOF. Since $a \neq 0$, we have $|a| \geq 1$ and

$$(|b| + 1)\cdot|a| > |b| \geq b.$$

If $a > 0$, choose m to be $|b| + 1$; if $a < 0$, choose m to be $-(|b| + 1)$.

Let $a \neq 0$ and b be integers, and let

$$S = \{m \in Z \mid |a|\cdot m > b\}.$$

By Proposition 11, S is not empty. Furthermore S is bounded below by $-|b|$. It follows from Proposition 9 that S has a least element, say $m' = \min S$. Then $|a|m' > b \geq |a|(m' - 1)$. Let q be the integer such that $aq = |a|(m' - 1)$; then

$$b = aq + r, \qquad \text{where } 0 \leq r < |a|.$$

We next show that the q and r in this equation are unique. Suppose

$$aq + r = ag + s,$$

where $\quad a \neq 0, \quad 0 \leq r < |a|, \quad$ and $\quad 0 \leq s < |a|.$

Then $\quad -|a| < r - s < |a| \quad$ and $\quad a(g - q) = r - s.$

Since $a \mid (r - s)$, we have either $|a| \leq |r - s|$ or $r - s = 0$. Since the first cannot occur, it follows that

$$r = s$$

and

$$aq = ag,$$

whence

$$q = g.$$

(Why?) We have proved

THEOREM 7 *Division algorithm: If $a \neq 0$ and b are integers, then there exist unique integers q and r such that*

$$b = aq + r, \qquad \text{where } 0 \leq r < |a|.$$

8 EUCLID'S ALGORITHM

We are now in a position to be able to give a systematic procedure for the calculation of the greatest common divisor of any two nonzero integers. The procedure is known as *Euclid's algorithm*. Since

$$(a, b) = (|a|, |b|),$$

there is no loss in generality in assuming $0 < a \leq b$. By the division algorithm there exist q and r such that $b = aq + r$, where $0 \leq r < a$. Now the greatest common divisor of a and b is exactly the greatest common divisor of a and $b - aq$ (see Exercise 8, Sec. 7), and hence

$$(a, b) = (a, b - aq) = (a, r).$$

In case $r = 0$, we know that $(a, r) = (a, 0) = a$, and we would have the greatest common divisor of a and b. If $r \neq 0$, we have $0 < r < a$, and we may repeat the process, i.e., divide the larger, a, by the smaller, r, and replace a by the remainder so obtained. After at most a such replacements we must get a remainder that is 0, in which case we know the greatest common divisor. We give an illustration:

$$(1197, 2221) = (221, 92) = (92, 37) = (37, 18) = (18, 1) = (1, 0) = 1$$

EXERCISES 1 Compute: $(-3198, 345)$, $(-9876, -5432)$, $(682, 546)$.

2 If a and b are integers, determine $(a + 1, a)$ and $(a, ab + 1)$.

3 Prove: If a, b, and c are integers such that $c \mid a$ and $c \mid b$, then $c \mid (a, b)$.

4 Prove: If a, b, and c are integers and $c \neq 0$, then $(ac, bc) = |c| \cdot (a, b)$.

5 Prove: If $(a, b) = d$, then $a = dA$, $b = dB$, where A, B are relatively prime integers.

THEOREM 8 *The set of all prime integers is infinite.*

(*Hint:* Suppose finite and obtain a contradiction.)

THEOREM 9 *If p is a prime and $p \mid ab$, then p must divide at least one of a and b.*

PROOF. Suppose $p \nmid a$, then $(a, p) = 1$. By Exercise 4 we have

$$(pb, ab) = |b|(p, a) = |b|.$$

But $p \mid pb$ and by assumption $p \mid ab$; hence (Exercise 3) $p \mid (pb, ab)$, i.e., $p \mid b$.

EXERCISES 6 Prove: If $(a, c) = 1$ and $c \mid ab$, then $c \mid b$.

7 Prove: If $(a, c) = 1$ and $(b, c) = 1$, then $(ab, c) = 1$.

8 Prove: If c is an integer and $a_1, a_2, \ldots, a_r$ is a finite set of integers such that $(a_i, c) = 1$ for $i = 1, 2, \ldots, r$, then $(a_1 a_2 \ldots a_r, c) = 1$.

The reader can now prove the following theorems and corollary:

THEOREM 10 *If a positive integer a is expressed as a product of finitely many primes and if p is a prime that divides a, then p must appear among the primes appearing in the product.*

THEOREM 11 *Unique factorization theorem: The expression of a composite integer as a product of finitely many primes is unique except for the order of the factors.*

Compare this result with Theorem 6.

COROLLARY *Every nonzero integer a can be expressed uniquely as* $a = (-1)^v \prod_{i=1}^{r} p_i^{v_i}$, *where* $p_1, p_2, \ldots, p_r$ *is some finite set of distinct primes and where* $v_1, v_2, \ldots, v_r$ *are nonnegative integers and* v *is* 0 *or* 1.

Note that $p_i \mid a$ if and only if $v_i > 0$.

EXERCISES 9 Suppose $m = p^k q$, where p is a prime, $(p, q) = 1$, and $n \nmid k$. Prove that it is impossible to find integers x and y, $y \neq 0$, such that $x^n = my^n$.

10 Prove: If y, x, and m are integers such that $(x, y) = 1$ and $xy = m^2$, then x and y are squares of integers.

11 Prove: If x, y, z, $w > 0$, and $k > 0$ are integers such that x, y, and z are relatively prime in pairs and such that $xyz = w^k$, then x, y, and z are each kth powers.

12 If x, y, z, $w \neq 0$, and $k > 0$ are integers such that $(x, y, z) = 1$ and such that $xyz = w^k$, does it follow that x, y, and z are kth powers?

13 Let S be the set of all positive integers s such that $4 \mid (s - 1)$; i.e., if s is in S, then $s = 4m + 1$ for some integer m. Prove that S is closed under multiplication and satisfies all the multiplicative properties of **Z**. An element of s in S is called a *pseudoprime* if s cannot be expressed as the product of two elements of S each exceeding 1. Prove that every element $s > 1$ of S is either a pseudoprime or can be expressed as the product of finitely many pseudoprimes but that this product need not be unique. Compare this result with what we have for the set of all positive integers. Note that S is not closed under addition and that we do not have a division algorithm for the set S.

14 Prove: If a, b, x, and y are integers such that $(a, b) = 1$ and $ax + by = 0$, then there exists an integer t such that $x = -bt$ and $y = at$. What can be said concerning x and y if $(a, b) = d > 1$ and $ax + by = 0$?

9 LINEAR DIOPHANTINE EQUATIONS

Given nonzero integers a, b, and c, we should like to know when there exist integers x and y such that $ax + by = c$. In answering this question we shall investigate a number of related and interesting questions.

Let S be a nonempty set of integers with the property that, whenever s and t are in S, so is $(s - t)$. If $s \in S$, then $s - s = 0 \in S$, and consequently $0 - s = (-s) \in S$. Thus, if $s, t \in S$, then $t - (-s) = t + s \in S$. Furthermore, if s is in S, then $2s = s - (-s)$, $3s = 2s - (-s)$, $4s$, $5s$, ...

belong to S, but then so do $(-2)s$, $(-3)s$, ...; i.e., if s is in S and n is any integer, then ns is in S. We have proved

ɔPOSITION 12 *If S is a nonempty subset of $\mathbf{Z}$ with the property that $s - t \in S$ whenever $s, t \in S$, then S is closed under addition, and if $s \in S$ and $n \in \mathbf{Z}$, then $ns \in S$.*

A nonempty subset S of $\mathbf{Z}$ that is closed under addition and has the property that $s \in S$, $n \in \mathbf{Z}$ implies $ns \in S$, is called an *ideal* of $\mathbf{Z}$. The set consisting of 0 alone is an ideal, as is the entire set $\mathbf{Z}$. These two ideals are said to be the *trivial ideals* of $\mathbf{Z}$. We can rephrase Proposition 12 as follows: *A nonempty subset of $\mathbf{Z}$ closed under subtraction is an ideal of $\mathbf{Z}$.*

EXERCISES 1 Which of the following subsets of $\mathbf{Z}$ are ideals of $\mathbf{Z}$?

A. The set of all multiples of an integer m.
B. The set of all divisors of 24.
C. The set of all integers relatively prime to 11.
D. The set of all integers x such that 64 is a divisor of some positive power of x.
E. The set of all numbers expressible in the form $\pm 2^n 3^m$, where n and m are nonnegative integers.
F. The set of all numbers expressible in the form $16x + 234y$, where x and y are integers.

2 Prove: Every ideal of $\mathbf{Z}$ is a set closed under subtraction.

Let S be an ideal of $\mathbf{Z}$ other than the 0 ideal. Then S must contain a positive integer. Hence $S^+ = S \cap \mathbf{Z}^+$ is a nonempty subset of the positive integers, and by the well-ordering principle S^+ contains a least element. Denote this least positive element by d. We contend that every element of S is a multiple of d. For if s is in S and is not a multiple of d, then $s = dq + r$, where $0 < r < d$. Since d is in S, so is qd, and hence $r = s - qd$ is in S; but then S^+ contains a smaller positive element than d, namely r, contrary to the definition of d.

THEOREM 12 *An ideal of $\mathbf{Z}$ other than the* 0 *ideal is exactly the set of all multiples of the least positive integer in the ideal.*

EXERCISE 3 Determine the least positive element in those sets in Exercise 1 which are ideals different from $\{0\}$.

Let a and b be nonzero integers, and let S be the set of all integers expressible in the form $ax + by$, where x and y are integers. S contains at least two distinct elements, $\pm a$, and is closed under subtraction for

$$(ax + by) - (as + bt) = a(x - s) + b(y - t).$$

Hence S is a nonzero ideal of $\mathbf{Z}$. Consequently there is a positive integer d in S that is a divisor of every element of S. In particular d divides a and b, and hence $d \mid (a, b)$. But d is of the form $ax + by$, and since $(a, b) \mid ax$ and $(a, b) \mid by$, we have $(a, b) \mid d$. Since (a, b) and d are positive, they must be equal. Thus we have

THEOREM 13 *If a and b are nonzero integers, there exist integers x and y such that $ax + by = (a, b)$.*

The reader should prove

COROLLARY *If a, b, and c are nonzero integers such that $(a, b) \mid c$, then there exist integers x and y such that $ax + by = c$.*

Naturally we should ask whether the x and y of the preceding theorem are unique. Suppose $ax + by = (a, b) = d = as + bt$. Then $a = dA$, $b = dB$, where A and B are integers for which $(A, B) = 1$. Also, $a(x - s) + b(y - t) = 0$, and hence $A(x - s) + B(y - t) = 0$. It follows from Exercise 14, Sec. 8, that there is an integer T such that $x - s = -BT$ and $y - t = AT$. Conversely if $as + bt = d$ and if

$$x = s - BT \qquad \text{and} \qquad y = t + AT, \tag{1}$$

where T is an integer, then $ax + by = d$. Thus the equation $ax + by = d$ has infinitely many solutions. Also, if we know one solution, we can immediately find all other solutions by Eq. 1. Our argument does not give a very constructive process of finding one such solution. If you cannot find a solution quickly by trial and error, one can be obtained by working backwards through Euclid's algorithm.

EXERCISES

4 If a, b, and c are nonzero integers such that (a, b) divides c, exhibit a formula that will give all solutions of the equation $ax + by = c$ in terms of one such solution.

5 Determine all solutions to each of the following equations:
$3x + 7y = 1, \qquad 3x + 7y = 13, \qquad 1{,}197x - 221y = 5.$

6 Prove: If a, b, and c are nonzero integers, then there exist integers x, y, and z such that $ax + by + cz = (a, b, c)$. How are two solutions of this equation related?

7 Given positive integers a, b, and c with $(a, b) = 1$, the equation $ax + by = c$ will have integral solutions, but it is possible that none of these solutions has both x and y nonnegative, e.g., $3x + 5y = 1$. Prove: Given two positive relatively prime integers a and b, the equation $ax + by = c$ has integer solutions with x and y both positive, provided $c > ab$.

8 Prove or disprove the following generalization of Exercise 7. Given positive integers a, b, and c such that $(a, b, c) = 1$, the equation $ax + by + cz = d$ has integer solutions with x, y, and z all positive, provided $d > abc$.

9 If a is a nonnegative integer, let S_a be the set of all positive integers divisible by a. If a and b are nonnegative integers, show that the set $S_a \cap S_b$ contains a least element m. The integer m is called the *least common multiple* of a and b, and we write $m = [a, b]$. Prove:

A. $a \mid [a, b]$.

B. If $a \mid c$ and $b \mid c$, then $[a, b] \mid c$.

C. $ab = (a, b) \cdot [a, b]$.

D. If $a = \prod_{i=1}^{r} p_i^{\nu_i}$ with $\nu_i \geq 0$, and if $b = \prod_{i=1}^{r} p_i^{\mu_i}$ with $\mu_i \geq 0$, where $p_1, p_2, \ldots, p_r$ are distinct primes, then

$$[a, b] = \prod_{i=1}^{r} p_i^{\max(\nu_i, \mu_i)}, \qquad (a, b) = \prod_{i=1}^{r} p_i^{\min(\nu_i, \mu_i)}.$$

In this chapter we have discussed the basic properties of the set of integers, and we have obtained a few facts concerning the integers. In later chapters we shall determine additional facts. However, the goal of this book is not the study of the integers, fascinating as this may be. Readers interested in pursuing such theory further are advised to study books specializing in the theory of numbers. Some interesting books on number theory are H. Davenport, *The Higher Arithmetic*, Hutchinson, London, 1952; G. H. Hardy and E. M. Wright. *Introduction to the Theory of Numbers*, 4th ed., Oxford, Fair Lawn, N.J., 1962; W. J. LeVeque, *Topics in the Theory of Numbers*, Addison-Wesley, Reading, Mass., 1956, 2 vols.

CHAPTER TWO

MAPPINGS

1 INTRODUCTION

Let M and N be two given nonempty sets. These two sets can consist of quite different objects. For example, M could be the set of mathematicians living in the United States, and N could be the set of integers. A rule or procedure that assigns to each element of the set M exactly one element of the set N is said to be a *mapping of M into N*. Thus, the rule that assigns to each mathematician his age is a mapping of the set of mathematicians into the set of integers. Similarly, the rule that assigns to each mathematician his weight, to the nearest pound, is another mapping of the set of mathematicians into the set of integers. When we count the number of elements in a set, we introduce a mapping of the set into $\mathbf{Z}^+$, the first element being assigned to 1, the second to 2, etc. In case M is a finite set, a mapping of M into N can be given by exhibiting a table indicating exactly how the elements are assigned. In case M is an infinite set, we cannot exhibit a table; rather a mapping of M into N is given by some well-defined rule or process whereby one can determine what element of N is assigned to any particular element of M. Functions are mappings; and thus $\sin x$ is a map of the real line into the interval $-1 \leq y \leq 1$.

We shall usually denote mappings by small Greek letters. If φ is a mapping of M into N, we shall indicate this fact by the symbolism

$$M \xrightarrow{\varphi} N.$$

If φ assigns the element y of N to the element x of M, we indicate this by

$$x \xrightarrow{\varphi} y$$

and say that y is the *image of* x *under* φ. In calculus courses one usually denotes the image of x under φ by $\varphi(x)$. In that case we would write

$$x \xrightarrow{\varphi} \varphi(x).$$

When we use this convention, we shall say we are using the *functional notation* for a mapping. There are other notations in common usage. In particular there is the *exponential notation*, where the image of x under φ is denoted by x^φ. In the exponential notation, we would write

$$x \xrightarrow{\varphi} x^\varphi.$$

Somewhat related is the notation

$$x \xrightarrow{\varphi} x\varphi.$$

We can view this notation as being a form of exponential notation where the exponent has been allowed to slide a bit. In the course of our studies we shall need to make use of all these notations. We assume the reader is familiar with the functional notation from his course in calculus, and so for a while we shall use the exponential notation in order to develop familiarity with it.

It is possible that different rules of assignment of elements of N into elements of M produce the same assignment. For example, if $M = N = \mathbf{Z}$, then

$$x \to 2x^2 + 2$$

and

$$x \to (x + 1)^2 + (x - 1)^2$$

are exactly the same mapping, even though the rules of assignment might appear to be quite different. Similarly, the two commands

"Move the stone one unit forward and then one unit to the right" and "Move the stone one unit to the right and then one unit forward" produce different actions, but both lead to the same end result. In dealing with mappings, we are only concerned with the end result of the assignment of elements and not with the process that we went through in making the assignment. Two maps φ and ψ of M into N are unequal or different provided there exists at least one x in M for which $x^\varphi \neq x^\psi$.

We now give several examples of mappings. The reader should examine these examples and assure himself that they are indeed mappings.

EXAMPLE 1 Let $M = N = \mathbf{Z}$:

A. $x^\varphi = 0$, for all $x \in M$.

B. $x^\sigma = x^2$, for all $x \in M$.

C. $x^\iota = x$, for all $x \in M$.

D. $x^\tau = x + 1$, for all $x \in M$.

E. $x^\rho = \begin{cases} 0 & \text{if } x = 0, \\ x/|x| & \text{if } x \neq 0. \end{cases}$

F. $x^\zeta = \begin{cases} 0 & \text{if } |x| \leq 1, \\ (-1)^r & \text{if } |x| > 1 \text{ and } r \text{ is the number of distinct primes dividing } x. \end{cases}$

G. $x^\lambda = \begin{cases} 0 \text{ if } |x| \leq 1, \\ \min \{p \text{ a prime} \mid p|x\}, \text{ if } |x| > 1. \end{cases}$

H. $x^\omega = \begin{cases} -1 & \text{if } x < 0, \\ 0 & \text{if } x = 0, \\ 1 & \text{if } x > 0. \end{cases}$

EXAMPLE 2 Let $M = \mathbf{Z}$, and let N be the collection of all subsets of $\mathbf{Z}$:

A. $x^\varphi = \{x\}$, for all $x \in M$.

B. $x^\sigma = \{d \in \mathbf{Z} \mid d|x\}$, for all $x \in M$.

C. $x^\tau = \{y \in \mathbf{Z} \mid y > x\}$, for all $x \in M$.

D. $x^\rho = \{y \in \mathbf{Z} \mid 3|(x - y)\}$, for all $x \in M$.

E. $x^\mu = \{y \in \mathbf{Z} \mid x \leq y \leq x^2\}$, for all $x \in M$.

F. $x^\lambda = \{y \in \mathbf{Z} \mid \text{if there is an } m \in \mathbf{Z} \text{ such that } x = y + 3m\}$, for all $x \in M$.

These are but a few simple examples of mappings. As the reader continues his study, he will encounter more complicated mappings and will study the algebraic structure of certain sets of mappings. We should point out that mappings appear throughout mathematics. The functions that one studies in calculus are mappings of the set of real numbers into itself. Differentiation is a mapping of the set of polynomials into itself. The study of congruency in geometry is the study of mappings of a plane upon a plane that preserves distance between points. Trigonometric identities are instances in which various rules produce the same mapping. It is not an exaggeration to say that the most fundamental concepts in mathematics are sets, mappings, and integers.

Let φ be a mapping of M into N, and let A be a subset of M. The set

$$\{y \in N \mid \text{there is an } x \in A \text{ for which } x^{\varphi} = y\}$$

is called the *image of A under φ*. If we use the functional notation, we denote the image of A under φ by $\varphi(A)$. If we use the exponential notation we denote this image by A^{φ}. And if we use the notation $x \to x\varphi$, we denote this image by $A\varphi$.

A mapping φ of M into N can always be considered as a mapping of M into M^{φ}.

EXERCISES

1 Determine the image set of M under each of the maps in Example 1.

2 Let A be the set of even integers. Determine the image of A under each mapping in Example 1.

3 Show that the mappings ρ and ω in Example 1 are the same mapping. Are these the only mappings in Example 1 that are the same? Are there mappings in Example 2 that are the same?

A mapping φ of M into N is said to be an *onto mapping* if each y of N is the image under φ of some x in M. Thus, under an onto mapping, each element of N is the image of at least one element of M. Or phrasing it in still one more way, φ is a mapping of M onto N if $M^{\varphi} = N$. An onto mapping is often called a *surjective mapping* or a *surjection*. The mapping $x \to |x| + 1$ is a surjective mapping of $\mathbf{Z}$ onto $\mathbf{Z}^+$.

A mapping φ of M into N is said to be a *one-to-one (1-1) mapping* if distinct elements of M have distinct images under φ. Under a 1-1 mapping of M into N, each element of N is the image of at most one element of M. A one-to-one mapping is also called an *injective mapping* or an *injection*. The mapping $x \to x$ is a simple example of an injective map of $\mathbf{Z}^+$ into $\mathbf{Z}$.

We can, of course, have mappings that are both one-to-one and onto. Such maps are said to be *bijective*. If there is a bijective map of M onto N, we often say there is a *one-to-one correspondence* between the sets.

Given a nonempty set M, the map $x \to x$ that sends each element x of M into itself is a bijective map of M onto M. This map is usually denoted by ι_M and is called the *identity map* of M onto M.

EXERCISES

4 Determine which of the mappings in Examples 1 and 2 are onto, which are one-to-one, and which are both one-to-one and onto.

5 Prove:

A. A map φ is always a mapping of M onto M.

B. If φ is a one-to-one mapping of M into N, then φ is bijective map of M onto M^{φ}.

If L is a nonempty subset of M and if φ is a mapping of M into N, then the mapping $x \to x^\varphi$ (for $x \in L$) is a mapping of L into N. Often we need to emphasize that this new mapping arose from φ but operates only on L, in which case we call this new mapping the *restriction of φ to L* and denote it by $\operatorname{res}_L \varphi$. Thus

$$x^{\operatorname{res}_L \varphi} = x^\varphi, \qquad \text{for all } x \text{ in } L.$$

The notation $\varphi|_L$ is used in place of $\operatorname{res}_L \varphi$ when using the notation $x \to x\varphi$.

If N is a subset of P and φ is a map of M into N, then φ can always be considered to be a map of M into the larger set P.

EXERCISES 6 Assume that L is a proper subset of M and that φ is a mapping of M into N. Prove:

A. If φ is injective, so is $\operatorname{res}_L \varphi$.

B. If $\operatorname{res}_L \varphi$ is onto, so is φ.

7 Let the notation be as in Exercise 6, and give examples justifying the following:

A. If φ is onto, then $\operatorname{res}_L \varphi$ could be, but need not be, onto.

B. If $\operatorname{res}_L \varphi$ is injective, then φ could be, but need not be, injective.

C. There exist φ and ψ such that $\varphi \neq \psi$ and $\operatorname{res}_L \varphi = \operatorname{res}_L \psi$.

2 THE PRODUCTS OF MAPPINGS

Let M, N, and P be arbitrary nonempty sets. Suppose φ is a map of M into N and that ψ is a map of N into P. The rule that assigns each $x \in M$ to $(x^\varphi)^\psi$ is a map of M into P, since x^φ is in N and hence $(x^\varphi)^\psi$ is an element of P. The mapping

$$x \to (x^\varphi)^\psi$$

is called the *product of φ by ψ*, and we denote it by the symbol $\varphi\psi$. Thus

$$x \to x^{\varphi\psi} = (x^\varphi)^\psi.$$

It should be noted that two arbitrary maps may not have a product. For a product $\varphi\psi$ to exist, ψ must be defined on a set that contains the image of φ. For example, if $\mathbf{Z} \xrightarrow{\varphi} \mathbf{Z}^+$ and $\mathbf{Z}^- \xrightarrow{\psi} \mathbf{Z}$, then $\varphi\psi$ is not defined. It should also be noted that in the definition of the product of two maps the order in which the two maps are written is significant. The maps $x \xrightarrow{\varphi} 2x$ and $x \xrightarrow{\psi} x^2$ are maps of $\mathbf{Z}$ into $\mathbf{Z}$ for which $\varphi\psi$ and $\psi\varphi$ are defined, but $\varphi\psi \neq \psi\varphi$. When using the notation $x \to x\varphi$, the product is denoted by $\varphi\psi$ also.

When the functional notation is used to indicate the image of a map, the image of x under the product would be $\psi(\varphi(x))$. It would therefore be natural to denote this product by $\psi\varphi$, which is just the reverse of the notation that we adopted when using the exponential notation. To avoid confusion, when using the functional notation we shall let $\psi \circ \varphi$ denote the product of φ by ψ. Thus

$$(\psi \circ \varphi)(x) = \psi(\varphi(x)).$$

We usually read $\psi \circ \varphi$ as "ψ of φ."

We now state a proposition whose proof is easy and is left to the reader.

PROPOSITION 1 *Let φ be a map of M into N, and let ψ be a map of N into P:*

A. *If φ and ψ are each injective, then $\varphi\psi$ is injective.*
B. *If φ and ψ are each onto maps, then $\varphi\psi$ is an onto map.*
C. *If φ and ψ are each bijective, then $\varphi\psi$ is bijective.*
D. *If $\varphi\psi$ is injective, then φ is injective.*
E. *If $\varphi\psi$ is surjective, then ψ is surjective.*

EXERCISES 1 Let ι_M and ι_N be the identity maps of M into M and N into N, respectively. Prove: If φ is a map of M into N, then $\iota_M\varphi = \varphi = \varphi\iota_N$.

2 Consider the maps in Example 1 and show $\rho\lambda = \varphi$, $\sigma\zeta = \zeta$, $\sigma\lambda = \lambda$.

3 Let φ be a map of M into N, and let ψ be a map of N into P:
A. If φ is onto but ψ is not, what can be said about $\varphi\psi$?
B. If φ is not onto but ψ is, what can be said about $\varphi\psi$?
C. If φ is injective but ψ is not, what can be said about $\varphi\psi$?

4 A. Prove: If φ and ψ are maps of M into M, then $\varphi\psi$ and $\psi\varphi$ are both defined.
B. Show that, if M contains at least two elements, then there are maps φ and ψ of M into M such that $\varphi\psi \neq \psi\varphi$.

Now let M, N, P, and Q be nonempty sets, and suppose φ is a map of M into N, ψ is a map of N into P, and λ is a map of P into Q. Then

$$x \to ((x^{\varphi})^{\psi})^{\lambda}$$

is a map of M into Q that we shall denote by $\varphi\psi\lambda$. The reader can easily verify

PROPOSITION 2 *If φ, ψ, and λ are as above, then*

$$(\varphi\psi)\lambda = \varphi(\psi\lambda) = \varphi\psi\lambda.$$

Thus we have an *associative law* for the products of maps.

In view of the preceding discussion and exercises we have

ROPOSITION 3 *The sets of all maps of a set M into itself is closed under multiplication, satisfies the associative law for multiplication, and has a multiplicative identity.*

Now suppose that φ is a one-to-one map of a set M onto a set N. Then there is a map of N onto M given by mapping each element y of N onto that unique element x of M for which $x^\varphi = y$. If we denote this map by φ^*, then

$$y^{\varphi^*} = x \qquad \text{if} \qquad x^\varphi = y.$$

We should check that this is indeed a map. Since φ is injective, for each $y \in M^\varphi$ there is exactly one $x \in M$ for which $x^\varphi = y$. Thus φ^* is a map of M^φ into M. But $M^\varphi = N$, since φ is an onto map. Therefore φ^* is a map of N into M and

$$\varphi\varphi^* = \iota_M.$$

Since ι_M is surjective, we have by Proposition 1 that φ^* is surjective. Now, for each $y \in N$ we have

$$y^{\varphi^*\varphi} = (x^\varphi)^{\varphi^*\varphi} = (x^{\varphi\varphi^*})^\varphi = x^{\iota_M\varphi} = x^\varphi = y = y^{\iota_N}.$$

Thus, $\varphi^*\varphi = \iota_N$. By Proposition 1, φ^* is injective. Consequently, φ^* is bijective. We have proved

THEOREM 1 *To each one-to-one map φ of M onto N there is a one-to-one map φ^* of N onto M so that*

$$\varphi\varphi^* = \iota_M \qquad \text{and} \qquad \varphi^*\varphi = \iota_N.$$

EXERCISES 5 Given a bijective map φ, prove $(\varphi^*)^* = \varphi$.

6 Prove: If π is a bijective map and if φ and ψ are maps such that $\varphi\pi = \psi\pi$, then $\varphi = \psi$. Similarly, if π is a bijective map and if φ and ψ are maps such that $\pi\varphi = \pi\psi$, then $\varphi = \psi$. Are these results true if π is surjective but not injective?

7 Prove: If φ is a one-to-one map of M onto N and if ψ is a map of N into M such that $\varphi\psi = \iota_M$, then $\psi = \varphi^*$. Similarly, if $\psi\varphi = \iota_N$, then $\psi = \varphi^*$.

8 If φ and ψ are maps such that $\varphi\psi = \varphi$, then ψ must map the set N into itself. If φ is also bijective, then $\psi = \iota_N$.

For the purpose of shorthand, we shall let $\Pi(M, N)$ denote the set of all one-to-one maps of M onto N. Of course, $\Pi(M, N)$ may be the empty set. We let $\Pi(M) = \Pi(M, M)$. If $M \neq \varnothing$, then $\Pi(M) \neq \varnothing$, since it always contains ι_M.

THEOREM 2 *Given a nonempty set M, the set $\Pi(M)$ is a nonempty set of maps closed under multiplication, satisfying the associative law, having a unique* *element ι_M such that $\varphi\iota_M = \iota_M\varphi$ for all $\varphi \in \Pi(M)$, and to each element $\varphi \in \Pi(M)$ there is a unique element $\varphi^* \in \Pi(M)$ such that $\varphi\varphi^* = \iota_M = \varphi^*\varphi$.*

The proof of this theorem follows from Proposition 3, Theorem 1, and Exercises 7 and 8 above.

3 FINITE SETS

In Chap. 1 we defined what we meant by a finite set of order m. In terms of the language we have introduced in this chapter, this definition could be rephrased as follows: A set M is finite if there exists a positive integer m and a bijective map of M onto the segment of integers $\{1, 2, \ldots, m\}$. In that case m is said to be the *order of the set M*. An infinite set is a nonempty set that is not finite. It should be noted that in our definition of a finite set we have not ruled out the possibility of a set M having two different orders. This we shall now do.

If φ is a bijective map of M onto $\{1, 2, \ldots, m\}$, there is a bijective map φ^* of $\{1, 2, \ldots, m\}$ onto M. We can indicate the image of j under φ^* by x_j. If $i \neq j$, then $x_i \neq x_j$, since φ^* is injective. Also $x \in M$ is the image of some j since φ^* is surjective. Thus

$$M = \{x_1, x_2, \ldots, x_m\},$$

where the x_i are distinct elements.

We now prove

PROPOSITION 4 *Suppose M is a finite set of order m and N is a finite set of order n. Then there exists an injective map of M into N if and only if $m \leq n$.*

PROOF. We are given that $M = \{x_1, x_2, \ldots, x_m\}$, where the x_i are distinct elements. Also $N = \{y_1, y_2, \ldots, y_n\}$, where the y_i are distinct. If $m \leq n$, we can define the map

$$M \xrightarrow{\lambda} N \quad \text{by} \quad x_j^\lambda = y_j, \qquad j = 1, 2, \ldots, m.$$

This map is injective.

We next suppose that there is an injective map φ of M into N and prove $m \leq n$. Our proof will be by induction. Let S be the set of positive integers k with the property that the existence of an injective map of a set of order k into a set of order n implies $k \leq n$. We wish to prove $S = \mathbf{Z}^+$. Clearly $1 \in S$, since n being a positive integer satisfies $1 \leq n$. Now suppose that $m - 1$ is in S, and let φ be the assumed injective map of M into N. Define

$$\{x_1, x_2, \ldots, x_{m-1}\} \xrightarrow{\mu} \{y_1, y_2, \ldots, y_{n-1}\}$$

by

$$x_i^\mu = \begin{cases} x_i^\varphi \text{ if } x_i^\varphi \neq y_n, \\ x_m^\varphi \text{ if } x_i^\varphi = y_n. \end{cases}$$

If $$i, j < m \quad \text{and} \quad x_i^\mu = x_j^\mu,$$

then we must have one of the following holding:

$$x_i^\varphi = x_i^\varphi, \qquad x_i^\varphi = x_m^\varphi, \qquad \text{or} \qquad x_m^\varphi = x_j^\varphi.$$

But if i and j are unequal integers less than m, then none of these relations can occur, since φ is injective. Hence μ is injective. But then, since $m - 1$ is in S, we must have $m - 1 \leq n - 1$. Whence $m \leq n$, and hence $m \in S$. It follows by the induction axiom that $S = \mathbf{Z}^+$.

COROLLARY 1 *The order of a finite set is uniquely defined.*

PROOF. Suppose a set has two orders m and n. Then the identity map is an injection of a set of order m into a set of order n, whence $m \leq n$. But this same map is also an injective map of a set of order n into a set of order m, whence $n \leq m$. Therefore $m = n$.

Henceforth, we shall use the phrases "M is a finite set of order m" and "M is a set of m elements" interchangeably. We shall denote the order of a set M by $|M|$. If M is an infinite set, we write $|M| = \infty$.

We can now prove

COROLLARY 2 *The set $\mathbf{Z}^+$ is an infinite set.*

PROOF. Suppose $\mathbf{Z}^+$ is a finite set; then there is a positive integer m and 1-1 map φ of $\mathbf{Z}^+$ onto $\{1, 2, \ldots, m\}$. Let $W = \{1, 2, \ldots, m, m + 1\}$; then $\text{res}_W\, \varphi$ would be an injection of W into $\{1, 2, \ldots, m\}$, contrary to Proposition 4.

COROLLARY 3 *There is a bijective map of a finite set M onto a finite set N if and only if the two sets have the same order.*

The proofs of this corollary and the next are left to the reader.

COROLLARY 4 *If M is a finite subset* of a finite set N, then the order of M does not exceed the order of N.*

COROLLARY 5 *If $m > n$, then no map of m objects into n objects is injective.*

This corollary is merely the rephrasing of part of Proposition 4. This corollary can be rephrased in other ways. One way, which is often referred to as *Dirichlet's box principle* or the *Schubfach prinzip*, is the following:

DIRICHLET'S BOX PRINCIPLE *If m objects are placed in n boxes, where $m > n$, then some box must contain at least two of the objects.*

* It should be noted that so far we have not proved that a subset of a finite set is necessarily finite. Thus, at this juncture, we do need the hypothesis that M is a finite subset.

EXERCISES 1 Show that Dirichlet's box principle and Corollary 5 are equivalent.

2 Show that, if $\{x_0, x_1, \ldots, x_n\}$ is a finite set of integers, then two of them must have the same remainder on division by n.

3 Show that the equation $12x + 23y + 7z = 0$ has an integer solution in x, y, z, not all zero, such that $\max\{|x|, |y|, |z|\} \leq 5$. (*Hint:* Consider the 6^3 integers $12x + 23y + 7z$, obtained by considering $0 \leq x \leq 5$, $0 \leq y \leq 5, 0 \leq z \leq 5$. They are all nonnegative and do not exceed 210.)

4 Show that there exist x and y, not both 0, such that $13x + 28y$ is divisible by 100 and $\max\{|x|, |y|\} \leq 10$.

5 Show that the equation $ax + by + cz = 0$, where a, b, and c are positive integers, has a solution in integers x, y, z, not all 0, such that $|x| \leq A$, $|y| \leq B$, $|z| \leq C$, when $(A + 1)(B + 1)(C + 1) \geqslant Aa + Bb + Cc + 1$.

6 Show that, if 17 points lie in a square whose sides are of length 4, then at least two of them are within a distance of $2^{1/2}$ of each other.

7 Let $(a_1, b_1), (a_2, b_2), \ldots, (a_n, b_n)$ be n pairs of integers chosen from the set $M = \{1, 2, \ldots, 2n - 1\}$ such that for each i, $a_i \neq b_i$. Show that at least one integer from the set M occurs in at least two pairs.

We next prove

PROPOSITION 5 *If W is the disjoint union of two finite sets M and N of orders m and n respectively, then $|W| = m + n$.*

PROOF. By the hypothesis there is an injective map φ of M onto $\{1, 2, \cdots, m\}$ and an injective map ψ of N onto $\{1, 2, \cdots, n\}$. Define a map σ of W onto $\{1, 2, \cdots, m + n\}$ as follows:

$$x^\sigma = \begin{cases} x^\varphi & \text{if } x \in M, \\ m + x^\psi & \text{if } x \in N. \end{cases}$$

Clearly this map is bijective.

By induction on the number of subsets one can prove the following generalization of Proposition 5:

COROLLARY *If W is the disjoint union of sets $U_1, U_2, \cdots, U_k$ then*

$$|W| = |U_1| + \cdots + |U_k|.$$

Next, we prove

PROPOSITION 6 *The number $A(m, n)$ of distinct injections of a set of m objects into a set of n objects is $n(n - 1) \cdots (n - m + 1)$.*

PROOF. By Corollary 3 there are no injections if $n < m$. But $n(n - 1) \cdots (n - m + 1) = 0$ when $n < m$, and therefore the proposition is valid if $n < m$. Clearly $A(1, n) = n$. We now suppose the proposition holds for all pairs (k, t) with $k \leq m$ and $t \leq n$ and prove it holds for all pairs (k, t) with $k \leq m + 1$ and $t \leq n + 1$.

Consider the case $(m+1, t)$, where $t \leq n+1$ and $m \geq 1$. Let $M = \{x_1, x_2, \ldots, x_{m+1}\}$ and $N = \{y_1, y_2, \ldots, y_t\}$. There is a one-to-one correspondence between those injective maps of M into N with $x_{m+1} \to y_j$ and the injective maps of $\{x_1, x_2, \ldots, x_m\}$ into $N_j = N - \{y_j\}$. By hypothesis, for each j there are $(t-1)(t-2) \cdots (t-m) = A(m, t-1)$ such maps. Since this is true for each j, we have, by the corollary above, that

$$A(m+1, t) = tA(m, t-1) = t(t-1) \cdots (t-m).$$

Next consider the case $(k, n+1)$, where $k \leq m$. Let $M = \{x_1, x_2, \ldots, x_k\}$ and $N = \{y_1, y_2, \ldots, y_{n+1}\}$. First of all there are the injective maps σ of M into N for which $y_{n+1} \notin M^\sigma$. These are injective maps of M into a set of n objects and so are $A(k, n)$ in number. Second, there exists a one-to-one correspondence between the set of injective maps of M into N, which map x_i onto y_{n+1}, and the set of injective maps of $M_i = M - \{x_i\}$ into $\{y_1, y_2, \ldots, y_n\}$. By hypothesis, the latter are $A(k-1, n)$ in number. Hence

$$\begin{aligned} A(k, n+1) &= A(k, n) + kA(k-1, n) \\ &= (n+1)(n) \cdots (n-k+2), \end{aligned}$$

thus proving our proposition.

It is customary to denote the product of the first k positive integers by $k!$, which we read *k factorial.* For simplicity of calculation we also define $0! = 1$. Then $A(m, n) = n!/(n-m)!$.

We now prove a result for surjective maps that is analogous to Proposition 4.

PROPOSITION 7 *Let M and N be finite sets of orders m and n respectively. Then there exists a map of M onto N if and only if $m \geq n$.*

PROOF. Suppose φ is a map of M onto N. Let $N = \{y_1, y_2, \ldots, y_n\}$, and let u_i be the number of x in M for which $x^\varphi = y_i$. Since φ is surjective, each $u_i \geq 1$. As each x has only one image, we have

$$m = \sum_{i=1}^{n} u_i \geq \sum_{i=1}^{n} 1 = n.$$

The proof of the converse is left to the reader.

EXERCISES 8 Prove: Let M be a finite set. φ is a one-to-one map of M into M if and only if φ is surjective.

9 Prove: There are exactly $k!$ bijective maps of a set of k objects onto itself.

ROPOSITION 8 *Let $W = \{(x, y) \mid x \in M, y \in N\}$. If M and N are finite sets of orders m and n respectively, then W is a finite set of mn elements.*

PROOF. We may take $M = \{x_1, x_2, \ldots, x_m\}$ and $N = \{y_1, y_2, \ldots, y_n\}$. Then

$$W = \{(x_i, y_j) \mid x_i \in M, y_j \in N\}.$$

The map

$$(x_i, y_j)^\tau = i + (j-1)m$$

is a one-to-one map of W onto $\{1, 2, \ldots, mn\}$.

The set W is called the *cartesian product* of the sets M and N.

COROLLARY 1 *Let $M_1, M_2, \ldots, M_k$ be a finite number of sets containing $m_1, m_2, \ldots, m_k$ elements, respectively. Let $W = \{(x_1, x_2, \ldots, x_k) \mid x_i \in M_i\ (i = 1, 2, \ldots, k)\}$. Then W contains $m_1 m_2 \cdots m_k$ elements.*

The proof is left to the reader.

A map φ of $\{1, 2, \ldots, k\}$ into a set N is completely described by giving the images $1^\varphi, 2^\varphi, \ldots, k^\varphi$ in order. Such an ordered set is called a sequence of k elements of N. For all intents and purposes a map of $\{1, 2, \ldots, k\}$ into N and a sequence of k elements of N are the same thing. *Note:* It is not necessary that the elements in a sequence be distinct. A sequence of k elements of N is also called an *ordered k-tuple* with coordinates or entries from N. Ordered 2-tuples and ordered 3-tuples are usually called ordered pairs and ordered triples, respectively. An ordered k-tuple with distinct coordinates from a set N defines an injective map of $\{1, 2, \ldots, k\}$ into N.

If, in Corollary 1, we take each of the sets M_i to be the same set N, then W is the set of all ordered k-tuples with entries from N. Hence, we have

COROLLARY 2 *There are n^k distinct ordered k-tuples with entries from a set of n elements.*

PROPOSITION 9 *Let N be a finite set of n elements, and let $0 \leq k \leq n$. There are*

$$\binom{n}{k} = \frac{n!}{k!(n-k)!}$$

distinct subsets of N that contain exactly k elements.

EXERCISES 10 If there are five roads from A to B and seven from B to C, how many different roads are there from A to C?

11 Prove: Let M be a finite set of m elements. There is a one-to-one correspondence between the set of maps of M into a set N and the set of ordered m-tuples with coordinates from N.

12 Prove: Let A be a finite subset of N containing k elements. There are $k!$ different injections φ of A into N so that $A^\varphi = A$.

13 Prove Proposition 9.

4 COUNTABLE SETS

A set M is said to be *countable* if there is an injective map of M into $\mathbf{Z}^+$. Thus every finite set is a countable set. However, the converse is clearly not true, since $\mathbf{Z}^+$ is countable and not finite. A countable infinite set is also said to be *denumerable*. A set that is not countable is said to be *uncountable*.

Just as we identified the injective maps of $\{1, 2, \ldots, k\}$ into a set N with the set of sequences of k elements of N, so we can identify injective maps of $\mathbf{Z}^+$ into N with denumerable sequences of elements from N.

EXERCISES 1 A. Show that $\mathbf{Z}$ and $\mathbf{Z}^-$ are denumerable sets.

B. If d is a nonzero integer, show that the set of all integral multiples of d is denumerable.

2 Prove:

A. A nonempty subset of a countable set is countable.

B. The intersection of two countable sets is countable.

C. The union of two countable sets, not necessarily disjoint, is countable.

D. If $M \subset N$ and M is uncountable, then N is uncountable.

E. If there is an injection of M into N and N is a countable set, then M is a countable set.

From an intuitive approach, our definition of a finite set is very satisfactory. However, it does not make for simple proofs. For example, try proving that the intersection of two finite sets is finite. We now prove a proposition that yields an equivalent definition for finite sets which is analogous to that for countable sets and which is more easily checked.

OPOSITION 10 *If there is an injective map of a nonempty set M into a bounded subset of $\mathbf{Z}^+$, then M is a finite set.*

PROOF. There may be several injections of M into bounded subsets of $\mathbf{Z}^+$. To each such injection φ we associate the integer

$$m_\varphi = \max(M^\varphi)$$

(why does max M^φ exist?). We also note that each φ may be considered as an injection of M into $\{1, 2, \ldots, m_\varphi\}$. Let A be the set of all such m_φ. By hypothesis at least one injection φ exists, and hence A is a nonempty subset of $\mathbf{Z}^+$. By the well-ordering principle A has a minimal element, say m. Let ψ be an injection of M into $\{1, 2, \ldots, m\}$, such that $m = \max M^\psi$. If ψ were not surjective, there would exist an integer k such that

$1 \le k < m$ and $k \notin M^{\psi}$. Then M is the disjoint union of

$$M_1 = \{x \in M \mid x^{\psi} < k\} \qquad \text{and} \qquad M_2 = \{x \in M \mid x^{\psi} > k\}.$$

Define

$$x^{\lambda} = \begin{cases} x^{\psi} & \text{if } x \in M_1, \\ x^{\psi} - 1 & \text{if } x \in M_2; \end{cases}$$

then λ is an injection of M into $\{1, 2, \ldots, m-1\}$ and $(m-1) \in A$, contrary to the assumption that $m = \min A$. Hence ψ is a bijection, and M is a finite set of order m.

COROLLARY 1 *If there is an injection of a set M into $\{1, 2, \ldots, m\}$, then M is a finite set of order $\le m$.*

COROLLARY 2 *A subset of a finite set of m elements is finite and contains at most m elements.*

If N is a proper subset of a set of m elements, there is an injective map of N into $\{1, 2, \ldots, m-1\}$. Why? Hence

COROLLARY 3 *A proper subset of a finite set of m elements is a finite set of order less than m.*

It follows that

COROLLARY 4 *There does not exist a bijective map of a proper subset of a finite set upon itself.*

Proofs of these corollaries are left to the reader.

We note that the map $x \to x - 1$ is a bijective map of $\mathbf{Z}^+ - \{1\}$, onto $\mathbf{Z}^+$. Thus we cannot extend the results of Corollary 4 to infinite sets. Using the axiom of choice, which will be described in Sec. 8, one can prove

PROPOSITION 11 *M is an infinite set if and only if M contains a proper subset N for which there is a bijective map of N onto M.*

The next result is a converse to Proposition 10.

PROPOSITION 12 *If there is a map of a set M onto $\mathbf{Z}^+$, then $|M| = \infty$.*

PROOF. We suppose that M is a finite set, say $|M| = m$, and obtain a contradiction. Let φ be a map of M onto $\mathbf{Z}^+$. Set $W = \{1, 2, \cdots, m+1\}$, and let $V = \{x \in M \mid x^{\varphi} \in W\}$. Since $V \subset M$ and M is a finite set, by Corollary 2, Proposition 10, V is a finite set and $|V| \le m$. On the other hand, $\text{res}_V\, \varphi$ is a map of V onto W. It follows from Proposition 7 that $|V| \ge |W| = m + 1$, and we have a contradiction.

Let S be an unbounded subset of $\mathbf{Z}^+$, and define

$$S_1 = S,\ S_2 = S_1 - \min(S_1), \ldots, S_{t+1} = S_t - \min(S_t), \ldots.$$

Clearly, each $S_t \neq \emptyset$, else S would be a finite, hence bounded subset of $\mathbf{Z}^+$. Furthermore, if $x \in S$, then $x \notin S_{x+1}$. Define

$$x \to x^{\psi} = \max\{j \mid x \in S_j\}, \qquad \text{for each } x \in S.$$

Then ψ is a bijection of S onto $\mathbf{Z}^+$. Now if φ is a bijection of a set M onto S, then $\varphi\psi$ is a bijection of M onto $\mathbf{Z}^+$, thus proving

PROPOSITION 13 *If there is a bijective map of a set M onto an unbounded subset of $\mathbf{Z}^+$, then there is a bijection of M onto $\mathbf{Z}^+$ and M is denumerable.*

If M is a denumerable set, there is an injection of M into $\mathbf{Z}^+$. The image set must be unbounded, else by Proposition 10, M would be finite. Hence there is a bijective map λ of M onto $\mathbf{Z}^+$, but then λ^* is a bijective map of $\mathbf{Z}^+$ onto M, yielding

COROLLARY *A denumerable set may be arranged in an infinite sequence of distinct elements.*

EXERCISES 3 Prove:

A. The intersection of two finite sets is finite.

B. The union of two, not necessarily disjoint, finite sets is finite.

4 Prove:

A. A countable set is infinite if and only if it contains a proper subset that can be put into a one-to-one correspondence with the entire set.

B. If $M \subset N$ and M is infinite, then N is infinite.

5 Let W be the set of all ordered pairs of positive integers:

A. Show that the map $(x, y) \longrightarrow 2^x 3^y$ is an injective map of W into $\mathbf{Z}^+$.

B. Show that the map in part A is not bijective.

C. Find a bijective map of W onto $\mathbf{Z}^+$.

D. Are there other bijective maps of W onto $\mathbf{Z}^+$? Explain.

6 A. Prove: If k is a positive integer, the set of all ordered k-tuples of positive integers is denumerable.

B. Prove that the set of all injections of $\{1, 2, \ldots, k\}$ into a denumerable set is denumerable.

7 A. Prove: The union of two disjoint denumerable sets is denumerable.

B. Prove: The union of a denumerable set of disjoint countable sets is denumerable.

We have seen (Exercise 6 above) that the set of all maps of $\{0, 1\}$ into $\mathbf{Z}^+$ is a denumerable set. We now consider the set M of all maps of $\mathbf{Z}^+$ into $\{0, 1\}$. Clearly M is an infinite set. Suppose M were a denumerable set; then we could arrange M as an infinite sequence, say $M = \{\varphi_1, \varphi_2, \varphi_3, \ldots\}$. Consider the map ψ of $\mathbf{Z}^+$ into $\{0, 1\}$ given by

$$j^{\psi} = 1 - (j)^{\varphi_j}, \qquad \text{for each } j \text{ in } \mathbf{Z}^+.$$

For each j, $\psi \neq \varphi_j$, since $j^{\psi} \neq (j)^{\varphi_j}$. But ψ is in M. It follows that M cannot be a denumerable set. Thus we have

PROPOSITION 14 *The set of all maps of $\mathbf{Z}^+$ into the set $\{0, 1\}$ is an uncountable set.*

The reader should prove

COROLLARY *Let N be any set containing more than one element; then the set of all maps of $\mathbf{Z}^+$ into N is an uncountable set.*

PROPOSITION 15 *Let M be a set containing at least two elements; then there is no bijective map of M onto the set of all maps of M into M.*

EXERCISES 8 A map φ of $\mathbf{Z}^+$ into $\mathbf{Z}$ is said to be "ultimately c" if $n^{\varphi} = c$ for all but finitely many n of $\mathbf{Z}^+$:

A. Show that φ is ultimately c if and only if there exists an integer n_{φ}, which depends on φ, such that $n^{\varphi} = c$ for all $n \geq n_{\varphi}$.

B. Is the set of ultimately zero maps of $\mathbf{Z}^+$ into $\{0, 1\}$ finite, denumerable, or uncountable? Explain.

C. Is the set of ultimately zero maps of $\mathbf{Z}^+$ into $\{0, 1, 2\}$ a finite, denumerable, or uncountable set? Explain.

D. Is the set of ultimately zero maps of $\mathbf{Z}^+$ into $\mathbf{Z}$ denumerable? Explain.

E. Let $c, c' \in M \subset \mathbf{Z}^+$. Show that there is a 1-1 correspondence between the set of maps of $\mathbf{Z}^+$ into M that are ultimately c and the set of maps of $\mathbf{Z}^+$ into M that are ultimately c'.

9 Prove Proposition 15.

5 PARTITIONS, THE INVERSE MAP

A *partition* of a set M is a collection of disjoint subsets of M whose union is M. Given a partition of M, each element of M lies in one and only one of the subsets of the partition. If the collection of subsets of a partion is finite of order k, we say M has been *partitioned into k subsets.* However, a partition may consist of denumerably many or even uncountably many subsets. Our definition of a partition allows some of the subsets to be empty. If none of the subsets of the partition is empty, we say that we have a *proper partition.*

Each subset A of M determines a partition of M into two subsets, namely,

$$M = A \cup (M - A).$$

A is a proper subset of M if and only if the associated partition is proper.

Associated with each subset A of a set M is a map φ_A of M into $\{0, 1\}$,

$$(x)^{\varphi_A} = \begin{cases} 1 \text{ if } x \in A, \\ 0 \text{ if } x \notin A. \end{cases}$$

If A and B are different subsets of M, there is an x in one that is not in the other, and for that x, $(x)^{\varphi_A} \neq (x)^{\varphi_B}$. Finally, we observe that, if ψ is any map of M into $\{0, 1\}$ and if we let

$$C = \{x \in M \mid x^{\psi} = 1\},$$

then ψ is the map associated with the set C; i.e., $\psi = \varphi_C$. Thus we have established

PROPOSITION 16 *There is one-to-one correspondence between the collection of all subsets of M and the set of all maps of M into $\{0, 1\}$.*

This result together with Corollary 2, Proposition 8, gives

COROLLARY 1 *A finite set of order m has 2^m different subsets.*

The reader can now prove

COROLLARY 2 *There are 2^{m-1} different partitions of m objects into two sets, and there are $2^{m-1} - 1$ different proper partitions of m objects into two sets.*

The combination of Corollary 1 and Proposition 9 yields

COROLLARY 3 *If $m \in \mathbf{Z}^+$, then* $\sum_{k=0}^{m} \binom{m}{k} = 2^m$.

The combination of Propositions 14 and 16 yields

COROLLARY 4 *There are uncountably many subsets of a denumerable set.*

COROLLARY 5 *There are uncountably many different partitions of a denumerable set into two proper subsets.*

EXERCISES 1 Prove: If a, b and $m \geq 0$ are integers, then $(a + b)^m = \sum_{k=0}^{m} \binom{m}{k} a^{m-k} b^k$.

2 Let m, n, p, and k be nonnegative integers. Prove:

A. $\binom{m}{k} = \binom{m}{m-k}$ if $0 \leq k \leq m$.

B. $\sum_{k=0}^{m} (-1)^k \binom{m}{k} = 0$.

C. $\sum_{k=0}^{m} \binom{m}{2k} = 2^{m-1}$.

D. If $0 \le p \le \min\{n, m\}$, then $\sum_{k=0}^{p} \binom{n}{k}\binom{m}{p-k} = \binom{n+m}{p}$.

E. $\sum_{k=0}^{m} \binom{m}{k}\binom{m}{m-k} = \sum_{k=0}^{m} \binom{m}{k}^2 = \binom{2m}{m}$.

3 Prove in detail the various corollaries listed above.

We shall now show that each map from M to some set N determines a partition of M. Let $\mathscr{S}(M)$ be the set of all subsets of M, including the empty one. Let

$$n^{\varphi^{-1}} = \{m \in M \mid m^{\varphi} = n\};$$

i.e., $n^{\varphi^{-1}}$ is the set of elements of M whose image under φ is n. Then

$$n \to n^{\varphi^{-1}}$$

is a map of N into $\mathscr{S}(M)$. This map, which we shall denote by φ^{-1}, is called the *inverse of* φ. Notice that the inverse of φ does not map N into M but rather maps N into $\mathscr{S}(M)$. One can check to see that, if φ and ψ are different maps of M into N, then φ^{-1} and ψ^{-1} are different maps of N into $\mathscr{S}(M)$.

It is obvious from the definition of φ^{-1} that

$$M = \bigcup_{n \in N} n^{\varphi^{-1}}$$

and $$n^{\varphi^{-1}} = \varnothing \text{ if and only if } n \notin M^{\varphi}.$$

Also, φ^{-1} is an injection of M^{φ} into $\mathscr{S}(M)$, for if $x \in n_1^{\varphi^{-1}} \cap n_2^{\varphi^{-1}}$, then $x^{\varphi} = n_1$, $x^{\varphi} = n_2$; whence $n_1 = n_2$. Thus we have

PROPOSITION 17 *Each map φ of M into N induces a proper partition of M, namely,*

$$M = \bigcup_{n \in M^{\varphi}} n^{\varphi^{-1}}.$$

To each partition of M into k subsets, say $M = A_1 \cup A_2 \cup \cdots \cup A_k$, we can associate a map φ of M into $\{1, 2, \ldots, k\}$, namely,

$$x^{\varphi} = i \text{ exactly when } x \in A_i.$$

The map φ has the property (P): Elements in the same subset of the partition have the same image under φ, and elements from different subsets of the partition have different images. The map φ is surjective if and only if the partition is proper, and it is injective if and only if each subset of the partition consists of a single element. The map depends not only on the partition but also on how we attached subscripts to the subsets of the partition. If the partition is proper there are $k!$ different maps of M onto $\{1, 2, \ldots, k\}$ satisfying (P). For if φ is as above and $\pi_1 \neq \pi_2$ are maps of $\{1, 2, \ldots, k\}$ onto itself, then $\varphi\pi_1$, $\varphi\pi_2$

satisfy (P) and are unequal maps. Finally, it can be seen that, if φ and ψ are maps of M onto $\{1, 2, ..., k\}$ that satisfy (P), then there is a map π of $\{1, 2, ..., k\}$ onto itself so that $\psi = \varphi\pi$. By Exercise 13, Sec. 3, there are $k!$ different maps of $\{1, 2, ..., k\}$ onto itself. Thus we have

OPOSITION 18 *Given a proper partition of M into k subsets, there are exactly $k!$ different maps of M onto $\{1, 2, ..., k\}$, each inducing the given partition.*

EXERCISES 4 Prove: If φ^{-1} is onto, then φ is not onto and M contains exactly one element.

5 Prove: The map φ^{-1} is injective if $N - M^{\varphi}$ contains at most one element. In particular, if φ is onto, then φ^{-1} is injective.

6 Prove: The map φ^{-1} is bijective if and only if M contains exactly one element and N contains exactly two elements.

7 A. Under what conditions on φ does $n^{\varphi^{-1}}$ contain at most one element for each $n \in N$?

B. Give a necessary condition on φ so that, for each $n \in N$, the set $n^{\varphi^{-1}}$ consists of exactly one element.

8 Prove: The number of partitions of a set of m objects into two sets, one with k objects, the other with $m - k$ objects, is $\binom{m}{k}$ if $2k \neq m$ and $\frac{1}{2}\binom{m}{k}$ if $m = 2k$.

9 Prove, by induction on n: The number of partitions of m objects into n objects, the first containing k_1 objects, the second k_2 objects, etc., is $m!/(k_1!\, k_2! \cdots k_n!)$, provided the k_i's are distinct. Is this formula correct if two of the k_i's are equal? Explain.

10 Determine the number of partitions of 12 objects into 3 proper subsets.

11 Prove: If $x_1, x_2, ..., x_n$ are integers, then

$$(x_1 + \cdots + x_n)^m = \sum_{\substack{k_i \geq 0 \\ k_1 + \cdots + k_n = m}} \frac{n!}{k_i! \cdots k_n!} \; {x_1}^{k_1} {x_2}^{k_2} \cdots {x_n}^{k_n}.$$

6 THE INPUT-OUTPUT FORMULA

By the corollary to Proposition 5 the number of objects in the disjoint union of finitely many finite sets is the sum of the number of objects in each set. Obviously this result does not hold for the union of sets that are not disjoint. We now seek a result that holds in all cases.

We first seek a formula for $|M \cup N|$, where M and N are finite sets and where $M \cap N$ need not be empty. Let

$$M' = M - (M \cap N), \qquad N' = N - (M \cap N).$$

Clearly M is the disjoint union of $M \cap N$ and M', and N is the disjoint union of $M \cap N$ and N'. Now

$$M' \cap N' \subset M \cap N,$$

but M' is disjoint from $M \cap N$, and hence

$$M' \cap N' = \varnothing.$$

Therefore, $M \cup N$ is the disjoint union of M', N' and $M \cap N$. By the corollary to Proposition 5, we have

$$|M \cup N| = |M'| + |N'| + |M \cap N|.$$

By Proposition 5, $|M| = |M'| + |M \cap N|$, and $|N| = |N'| + |M \cap N|$, and so

$$|M \cup N| = |M| + |N| - |M \cap N|.$$

It is this formula which generalizes Proposition 5 and which we now extend to the case of the union of finitely many finite subsets.

PROPOSITION 19 *Input-Output Formula. Let $M_1, M_2, \ldots, M_n$ be finite subsets of some set M. Let $M_{ij\cdots k} = M_i \cap M_j \cap \cdots \cap M_k$. Then*

$$\begin{aligned}|M_1 \cup M_2 \cup \cdots \cup M_n| = \sum_{i=1}^{n} |M_i| - \sum_{1 \le i_1 < i_2 \le n} |M_{i_1 i_2}| \\ + \cdots + (-1)^{t-1} \sum_{1 \le i_1 < \cdots < i_t \le n} |M_{i_1 i_2 \cdots i_t}| \\ + \cdots + (-1)^{n-1} |M_{12\cdots n}|.\end{aligned}$$

PROOF. Suppose x appears in exactly r of the sets, say $M_1, M_2, \ldots, M_r$. Then x is in $M_{i_1 i_2 \cdots i_t}$ only if all the subscripts do not exceed r. But the number of choices of $i_1, \ldots, i_t$ from $\{1, 2, \ldots, r\}$ is $\binom{r}{t}$ (see Proposition 9). Hence x appears in exactly $\binom{r}{t}$ of the sets $M_{i_1 i_2 \cdots i_t}$. Thus the contribution of x to the right-hand side of the formula is

$$\sum_{t=1}^{r} \binom{r}{t} (-1)^{t-1} = 1,$$

which is the contribution of x to the left-hand side of the formula. Since this is true for all x in $M_1 \cup M_2 \cup \cdots \cup M_h$, the conclusion follows.

EXERCISES 1 Let $M_1, M_2, \ldots, M_h$ be finite subsets of some set M. Derive a formula giving the number of elements in one but not more than one of the sets M_i.

2 Let $p_1, p_2, \ldots, p_h$ be the distinct prime divisors of an integer $m > 0$. Let $M_i = \{x \in \mathbf{Z}^+ \mid x \le m \text{ and } p_i | m\}$. Determine $|M_1 \cup M_2 \cup \cdots \cup M_h|$.

Let $M = \{1, 2, \ldots, m\} - \bigcup_{i=1}^{h} M_i$, and show that $|M| = m \prod_{i=1}^{h} (1 - p_i^{-1})$. Note that $|M|$ is the number of positive integers not exceeding m that are relatively prime to m. It is customary to denote $|M|$ by $\varphi(m)$. The map, or function, $m \to \varphi(m)$ is a map of $\mathbf{Z}^+$ into $\mathbf{Z}^+$. $\varphi(m)$ is often referred to as the *Euler phi function*.

The reader should prove

OPOSITION 20 *If* $(m, n) = 1$, *then* $\varphi(mn) = \varphi(m) \cdot \varphi(n)$.

7 BINARY RELATIONS, EQUIVALENCE RELATIONS

If M is a set, we shall let $M^{(k)}$ denote the set of all sequences of k elements from M. In particular $M^{(2)}$ is the set of all ordered pairs of elements of M.

In our study of the integers we encountered several binary relations, e.g., "less than" and "divides." A *binary relation* on a set M is a rule that tells you whether or not any ordered pairs of elements of M have a certain property. Thus a binary relation on M is given by a map of $M^{(2)}$ into the set $\{0, 1\}$ or, if one prefers, into the set {yes, no}. For example, the relation "less than" on $\mathbf{Z}$ is given by the map φ of $\mathbf{Z}^{(2)}$ into $\{0, 1\}$, where

$$(a, b)^{\varphi} = \begin{cases} 0 \text{ if } a < b, \\ 1 \text{ if } a \geq b. \end{cases}$$

The adjective "binary" is used, since we are defining a relation between two elements of M.

Since the typical example of a binary relation is inequality, it makes for more suggestive proofs if we introduce a notation that is analogous to $a < b$. If a binary relation is given by a map φ of $M^{(2)}$ into $\{0, 1\}$, we shall use the following notation:

$$a < \varphi\, b \text{ if and only if } (a, b)^{\varphi} = 0,$$
$$a \nless \varphi\, b \text{ if and only if } (a, b)^{\varphi} = 1.$$

We read $a < \varphi\, b$ as "a stands in the relation φ to b." We shall omit the symbol φ in $<\varphi$ whenever we feel that confusion will not arise.

To each binary relation $<\varphi$ on M, we can associate a set of $M^{(2)}$:

$$A_{\varphi} = \{(a, b) \in M^{(2)} \mid (a, b)^{\varphi} = 0\} = 0^{\varphi^{-1}}.$$

The set A_{φ} is sometimes called the *graph of the relation* $<\varphi$.

If φ and ψ are different maps of $M^{(2)}$ into $\{0, 1\}$, then $<\varphi$ and $<\psi$ are different relations on M, and A_{φ} and A_{ψ} are different subsets of $M^{(2)}$. Also any subset A of $M^{(2)}$ determines a map λ of $M^{(2)}$ into $\{0, 1\}$ with $0^{\lambda^{-1}} = A$. Thus there is a 1-1 correspondence between subsets of

$M^{(2)}$ and binary relations on M. We also note that each binary relation $<\varphi$ on M has a dual $<\varphi'$ where

$$a < \varphi' b \qquad \text{exactly when} \qquad a \nless \varphi b.$$

The dual of "less than" is "does not exceed." Equality is a relation on M, the graph of which is $D = \{(a, b) \in M^{(2)} \mid a = b\}$; D is called the *diagonal of* $M^{(2)}$.

A map σ of M into M determines a binary relation $<$ on M where $a < b$ exactly when $a^\sigma = b$. Such a relation has the property that to each $a \in M$ there is a unique $b \in M$ such that $a < b$. Conversely, any binary relation on M having this property determines a map $a \to b$, where b is the unique element such that $a < b$. Thus the set $\mathcal{T}(M)$ of maps of M into M can be mapped 1-1 into the set of all binary relations on M. We define the *graph of a map* of M into M to be the graph of the related binary relation. The reader should examine how the graph of a map of M into M differs from the graph of a general binary relation on M.

Let $<$ be a binary relation on a set M. If

$$a < a, \qquad \text{for all } a \in M,$$

we say $<$ is a *reflexive relation* on M. We say $<$ is a *symmetric relation* on M if it has the property that

$$b < a \qquad \text{whenever} \qquad a < b.$$

We say $<$ is a *transitive relation* on M if $<$ has the property that

$$a < c \qquad \text{whenever} \qquad a < b \qquad \text{and} \qquad b < c.$$

We say $<$ is a *circular relation* on M if $<$ has the property that

$$c < a \qquad \text{whenever} \qquad a < b \qquad \text{and} \qquad b < c.$$

If $<$ is a reflexive, symmetric, transitive relation, we say that $<$ is an *equivalence relation* on M. Equality is an equivalence relation and is the prototype of all equivalence relations, and for this reason it is common to denote equivalence relations by a "wavy equality symbol" ($\approx$).

EXERCISES

1 Do there exist binary relations $<$ on M such that there are $a \in M$ for which $a < b$ for all b in M?

2 Show that a binary relation is reflexive if and only if the diagonal is a subset of the graph of the relation. Show that a binary relation on the set of points of a line is symmetric if and only if the graph of the relation is symmetric about the diagonal.

3 The following are binary relations on $\mathbf{Z}$: "less than," "does not exceed," "divides," "is a multiple of," "is divisible by exactly the same power of 2 and no higher power of 2," and "their product is less than their sum." Determine which of these relations are reflexive; symmetric; circular; transitive.

4 Find a reflexive binary relation that is not symmetric. Find a symmetric binary relation that is not reflexive. Are there reflexive, symmetric relations that are not transitive? Why?

5 Prove: A reflexive, circular relation is symmetric. Is a symmetric and circular relation always reflexive?

6 Prove: An equivalence relation is circular. Is a reflexive, circular (hence symmetric) relation always an equivalence relation?

A binary relation $<$ on M determines a map of M into $\mathscr{S}(M)$, the set of all subsets of M, namely,

$$a \to \{x \in M \mid x < a\} = S(a, <).$$

EXERCISES 7 Prove:

A. A binary relation $<$ on M is reflexive if and only if $a \in S(a, <)$ for each $a \in M$.

B. A symmetric binary relation $<$ on M has the property that $y \in S(x, <)$ whenever $x \in S(y, <)$. If a binary relation $<$ on M has this property, does it follow that it is symmetric?

C. If $<$ is a transitive relation and $x < y$, then $S(x, <) \subset S(y, <)$.

8 Let $\approx$ be an equivalence relation on M, and let $S(a) = S(a, \approx)$. Prove the following:

A. $x \approx y$ if and only if $S(x) = S(y)$.

B. If x and y are in M, then either $S(x) = S(y)$ or $S(x) \cap S(y) = \varnothing$.

C. M is the disjoint union of the sets $S(x)$, where each set is counted but once.

It follows from Exercise 8 that an equivalence relation on M induces a partition on M, where each subset of the partition consists of all elements of M that are related by the equivalence to any one element in the subset. Each subset of this partition is said to be an *equivalence class* of the equivalence relation $\approx$. The elements of an equivalence class are related by the equivalence to one another and are not related by the equivalence to any other element of M.

Conversely, each partition of M determines an equivalence relation on M, where $x \approx y$ exactly when x and y belong to the same subset of the partition. That this is an equivalence relation is more or less obvious, but the reader should check that this is indeed the case. Now it is also quite clear that different equivalence relations determine different partitions and conversely. Hence

THEOREM 3 *Each equivalence relation on a set M determines a partition of M, and conversely each partition of M determines an equivalence relation on M. There is a 1-1 correspondence between equivalence relations on M and partitions of M.*

EXERCISES 9 Determine the number of distinct equivalence relations on a set of six elements.

10 Show that the number of equivalence relations on $\mathbf{Z}$ is uncountable.

11 Let $J_n = \{x \in \mathbf{Z}^+ \mid 2^{n-1} \le x < 2^n\}$, $(n = 1, 2, \ldots)$. Show that the sets J_n form a partition of $\mathbf{Z}^+$. Is the associated equivalence relation any of the relations discussed in Exercise 3?

Let d be an integer, and consider the following relation on $\mathbf{Z}$: x is equivalent to y exactly when $d \mid (x - y)$. The reader should check that this is indeed an equivalence relation on $\mathbf{Z}$. This relation is usually called a *congruence relation modulo d*, (often the word "relation" is omitted). It is customary to indicate this relation by the symbol

$$x \equiv y \pmod{d},$$

which is read "x is congruent to y modulo d." Thus

$$x \equiv y \pmod{d} \text{ if and only if } d \mid (x - y).$$

The equivalence classes of this relation are called *residue classes modulo d*, and it is customary to denote that residue class modulo d which contains the integer a by $\lfloor a \rfloor_d$, or just $\lfloor a \rfloor$ if no confusion can arise.

EXERCISE 12

A. Determine the residue classes modulo 0.

B. Determine the residue classes modulo 1.

C. Determine the residue classes modulo 2.

D. Prove: If x, y, and d are integers, then $x \equiv y \pmod{d}$ exactly when $x \equiv y \pmod{-d}$. Hence in studying congruences, we can restrict the modulus to be a nonnegative integer without loss of generality.

E. Prove: If x and y have the same minimal nonnegative remainder on division by $d \neq 0$, then $x \equiv y \pmod{d}$. Conversely, if $x \equiv y \pmod{d}$, then x and y have the same minimal nonnegative remainder on division by d.

F. Let $S(x) = \{y \in \mathbf{Z} \mid x \equiv y \pmod{d}\}$. Prove: $S(x)$ is the set of integers of the form $x + kd$.

G. Prove: If $d \neq 0$, then there are exactly $|d|$ distinct residue classes modulo d.

PROPOSITION 21 *If* $a \equiv b \pmod{d}$ *and if* $x \equiv y \pmod{d}$, *then* $a + x \equiv b + y \pmod{d}$, $a - x \equiv b - y \pmod{d}$, $ax \equiv by \pmod{d}$.

EXERCISE 13

A. Prove Proposition 21.

B. Does the equivalence relation defined in Exercise 11 possess the properties attributed in Proposition 21 to congruences?

We now investigate what other equivalence relations on **Z** have the properties attributed by Proposition 21 to congruences. Suppose that $\approx$ is an equivalence relation on **Z** with the property that

$$a - x \approx b - y, \qquad \text{whenever} \qquad a \approx b \qquad \text{and} \qquad x \approx y.$$

Let

$$S(a) = \{x \in \mathbf{Z} \mid x \approx a\}.$$

If x and y are in $S(0)$, then $x - y \in S(0)$ and consequently (by Theorem 12, Chap. 1) $S(0)$ is the set of all multiples of some nonnegative integer d. When $x \approx y$, we have $x - y \approx y - y = 0$, and hence $x - y = kd$, for some $k \in \mathbf{Z}$. Conversely if $x - y = kd$, then $x - y \in S(0)$, and hence $x = (x - y) - (-y) \approx 0 - (-y) = y$. Thus we have shown that

$$S(x) = \{y \in \mathbf{Z} \mid d \mid (x - y)\} = \lfloor x \rfloor_d.$$

Since this is the case for all $x \in \mathbf{Z}$, the equivalence classes defined by $\approx$ are exactly the residue classes modulo d, and hence the relation $\approx$ must be congruence modulo d. We have proved

THEOREM 4 *The congruence relations on* **Z** *are the only equivalence relations* $\approx$ *on* **Z** *with the property that* $a - x \approx b - y$, *whenever* $a \approx b$ *and* $x \approx y$.

XERCISES 14 Let $\approx$ be an equivalence relation on **Z** with the property that, if $a \approx b$ and $x \approx y$, then $a + x \approx b + y$. Prove: Such equivalence relations also have the property that $a - x \approx b - y$, whenever $a \approx b$ and $x \approx y$. State a corollary to Theorem 4.

15 Give an example of an equivalence relation $\approx$ on **Z** which is not a congruence and which has the property that $ax \approx by$ whenever $a \approx b$ and $x \approx y$.

16 Prove the following:

OPOSITION 22 *Let* $<$ *be a reflexive, symmetric relation on* **Z** *with the property that* $a + x < b + y$, *whenever* $a < b$ *and* $x < y$. *The relation* $<$ *is a congruence relation.*

Given integers a, b, and d, we next ask if there is an integer x such that

$$ax \equiv b \pmod{d}.$$

Clearly, there is such an x if and only if there are integers x and y such that $ax + dy = b$. By the corollary to Theorem 13, Chap. 1, such x and y exist if and only if (a, d) is a nonzero divisor of b. Hence we have

OPOSITION 23 *Given integers* a, b, *and* d *such that* a *and* d *are not both* 0*; then there exists an integer* x *such that* $ax = b \pmod{d}$ *if and only if* $(a, d) \mid b$.

The integer x of Proposition 23, if it exists, need not be unique, for if $z \equiv x \pmod{d}$, then $az \equiv ax \equiv b \pmod{d}$. Let

$$S = \{x \in \mathbf{Z} \mid ax \equiv b \pmod{d}\}.$$

If $S \neq \varnothing$, then S contains a complete residue class modulo d, but S need not be a residue class modulo d. For example, 2 and 6 both satisfy $6x \equiv 4 \pmod{8}$, but $2 \not\equiv 6 \pmod{8}$. This phenomena is explained by

PROPOSITION 24 *Let $S = \{x \in \mathbf{Z} \mid ax \equiv b \pmod{d}\}$, and let $d = (a, d)D$. If $S \neq \varnothing$, then there exists an integer x_0 such that $S = \lfloor x_0 \rfloor_D$.*

PROOF. Let $a = (a, d)A$. Since $S \neq \varnothing$, we have $b = (a, d)B$. Then every integer solution of $ax + dy = b$ is a solution of $Ax + Dy = B$, and conversely. If x, y is a solution of the linear equation $Ax + Dy = B$, then $x - Dt, y + At$ $(t \in \mathbf{Z})$ is also a solution. Furthermore, every solution is of this form, whence $S = \lfloor x_0 \rfloor_D$, for some x_0. In particular, we can choose x_0 so that $0 \leq x_0 < D$.

COROLLARY *If $S = \{x \in \mathbf{Z} \mid ax \equiv b \pmod{d}\} \neq \varnothing$, then S is the union of exactly (a, d) distinct residue classes modulo d.*

The proof is straightforward and is left to the reader.

EXERCISE 17 Find all the solutions, if any, of each of the congruences

$$36x \equiv 15 \pmod{21},$$
$$49x \equiv 16 \pmod{21}.$$

The reader should prove the following propositions.

PROPOSITION 25 *Given integers $a_1, a_2, \ldots, a_r, b$ and d, there exist integers $x_1, \ldots, x_r$ such that $a_1x_1 + \cdots + a_rx_r \equiv b \pmod{d}$ if and only if $(a_1, a_2, \ldots, a_r, d) \mid b$.*

PROPOSITION 26 *Given integers b_1, b_2, d_1, d_2, there exists an integer x such that $x \equiv b_1 \pmod{d_1}$ and $x \equiv b_2 \pmod{d_2}$ if and only if $(d_1, d_2) \mid (b_1 - b_2)$.*

This last proposition is often called the *Chinese remainder theorem.*

EXERCISE 18 Generalize Proposition 26 to the case in which you are given s pairs of integers b_i, d_i, $(i = 1, \ldots, s)$.

19 Find an integer x such that

$$x \equiv 1 \pmod{2}, \qquad x \equiv 2 \pmod{3}, \qquad \text{and} \qquad x \equiv 3 \pmod{5}.$$

20 Given integers $a, b, c > 1$, with $(a, b) = 1$, show that there is an integer x such that $(ax + b, c) = 1$. *Hint:* Show that there is an x so that $p \nmid ax + b$, for any prime p that divides c.

8 RIGHT AND LEFT INVERSE MAPS, THE AXIOM OF CHOICE

Let φ be a map of M into N. A map ρ of N into M such that

$$\varphi\rho = \iota_M$$

is said to be a *right inverse of* φ. A map λ of N into M such that

$$\lambda\varphi = \iota_N$$

is said to be a *left inverse of* φ. Notice that left inverses and right inverses of φ are maps of N into M; however φ^{-1}, the inverse of φ (which we studied in Sec. 5), mapped N into $\mathscr{S}(M)$, the collection of subsets of M.

If φ is a bijective map, we saw in Theorem 1 that φ^* was both a left inverse and a right inverse of φ. Also, in the exercises following this theorem, we saw that φ^* was the only left inverse of φ and the only right inverse of φ. We shall now investigate which maps have left or right inverses.

Suppose that $\varphi\psi = \iota_M$. We apply Proposition 1. Since ι_M is a map of M onto M, it follows that ψ is an onto map. Since ι_M is injective, φ must be injective. Hence

POSITION 27 *If a map φ has a right inverse, then φ is a* 1-1 *map, and any right inverse of φ must be an onto map. If a map φ has a left inverse, then φ is an onto map, and any left inverse of φ is a* 1-1 *map.*

Now suppose that φ is an injection of M into N. Then φ is a bijective map of M onto M^φ, and hence φ^* is a bijective map of M^φ onto M such that $\varphi\varphi^* = \iota_M$. If ρ is any map of N into M such that

$$\text{res}_{M^\varphi}(\rho) = \varphi^*,$$

then $\varphi\rho = \iota_M$ and ρ is a right inverse of φ.

Conversely, suppose that ρ is a right inverse of φ. Then φ is a 1-1 map of M into N and

$$(x^\varphi)^\rho = x^{\iota_M} = x, \text{ for } x \in M.$$

But $(x^\varphi)^{\varphi^*} = x$, for all $x \in M^\varphi$. Since φ^* and ρ agree on M^φ, we have

$$\text{res}_{M^\varphi}\, \rho = \varphi^*.$$

We have proved

POSITION 28 *Let φ be an injection of M into N. A map ρ of N into M is a right inverse of φ if and only if $\text{res}_{M^\varphi}\, \rho = \varphi^*$.*

We leave the following corollaries for the reader to prove.

OROLLARY 1 *A map φ of M into N has a right inverse if and only if φ is injective.*

COROLLARY 2 *There are as many right inverses of an injection φ of M into N as there are maps of $N - M^{\varphi}$ into M.*

COROLLARY 3 *If M contains at least two elements, then a map of M into N has a unique right inverse if and only if it is bijective.*

EXERCISES 1 Prove: If M and N are finite sets of m and n elements respectively and if φ is a 1-1 map of M into N, then $m \leq n$ and there are exactly m^{n-m} distinct right inverses of φ.

2 Let j be the natural injection map of $\mathbf{Z}^+$ into $\mathbf{Z}$, i.e., $x^j = x$, for all $x \in \mathbf{Z}^+$. Show that there are uncountably many different right inverses of j.

We saw, in Proposition 27, that a necessary condition for a map to have a left inverse was that the map be surjective. In order to show that this is also a sufficient condition, we need the concept of a choice map.

Given a set M, let $\mathscr{S}' = \mathscr{S}'(M)$ denote the set of all nonempty subsets of M. Any map γ from $\mathscr{S}'$ into M such that $X^{\gamma} \in X$, for each set X in $\mathscr{S}'$, is called a *choice map* of M. A choice map implies that we have a method of selecting an element, X^{γ}, from each nonempty subset X of M. We note that a choice map is onto, since $\mathscr{S}'$ contains all one-element sets; but a choice map is not 1-1 if M contains at least two elements.

We now give two examples of a choice map. (A) Let $M = \mathbf{Z}^+$ and define

$$X^{\gamma} = \min X.$$

Then γ is a choice map for $\mathbf{Z}^+$. (B) If M is a countable set, we have seen (Corollary to Proposition 13) that it is possible to attach positive-integer subscripts to the elements of M. Having done so, define X^{γ} to be that element in X with minimal subscript. This γ is a choice map for the set M. Note that this last definition of γ depended on the assignment of subscripts. Hence, it is possible to have many choice maps on a countable set.

When we come to the case where M is an uncountable set, it is more difficult to define a choice map. Although it seems reasonable to be able to associate with each nonempty subset an element in that subset, we are not able to give such a rule in an explicit fashion, as we did for countable sets. It is customary for mathematicians to postulate that every set M has a choice map. This postulate, or an equivalent of it, is customarily referred to as the *axiom of choice*. We should, however, warn the reader that not all mathematicians accept this postulate; some demand that a choice map must be given explicitly, as we did for countable sets, before one can make use of its existence.* For the remainder

* For a readable discussion of these matters we refer the reader to the excellent book by R. L. Wilder, *Introduction to the Foundations of Mathematics*, John Wiley & Sons, Inc., New York, 1952, pp. 71–74.

of this text, we shall follow the customary practice and assume that each set M has at least one choice map.

Now suppose that φ is a map of M onto N. Then φ^{-1} is a 1-1 map of N into $\mathcal{S}' = \mathcal{S}'(M)$, the collection of nonempty subsets of M. (Why $\mathcal{S}'$ and not the collection of all subsets of M?) Let γ be some choice map of M; then $\gamma:\mathcal{S}' \to M$. The map $\varphi^{-1}\gamma = \lambda$ is a 1-1 map of N into M, and furthermore $\lambda\varphi = \iota_N$. Clearly, if there are several choice maps for M, say γ_1 and γ_2, such that

$$\text{res}_{N\varphi^{-1}}(\gamma_1) \neq \text{res}_{N\varphi^{-1}}(\gamma_2),$$

then there are several possibilities for λ. Summarizing, we have proved

OPOSITION 29 *A map φ of M into N has a left inverse if and only if φ is an onto map.*

Suppose φ is a map of M onto N that is definitely not 1-1, say $x_1{}^\varphi = x_2{}^\varphi = y$. Let γ be a choice map for M, and define new choice maps as follows: $X^{\gamma_1} = X^{\gamma_2} = X^\gamma$, for all X in $\mathcal{S}'$ except $X = y^{\varphi^{-1}}$; and $(y^{\varphi^{-1}})^{\gamma_1} = x_1$, $(y^{\varphi^{-1}})^{\gamma_2} = x_2$. Then

$$\text{res}_{N\varphi^{-1}}(\gamma_1) \neq \text{res}_{N\varphi^{-1}}(\gamma_2),$$

and hence $\varphi^{-1}\gamma_1 \neq \varphi^{-1}\gamma_2$. Thus φ has at least two left inverses. Combining this information with that of Theorem 1 and Exercise 7, Sec. 2, we get

POSITION 30 *A map has a unique left inverse if and only if it is bijective.*

XERCISES 3 If $M = \{a, b, c, d, e, f, g\}$ and $N = \{1, 2, 3\}$ and $a^\varphi = b^\varphi = c^\varphi = d^\varphi = e^\varphi = 1, f^\varphi = 2, g^\varphi = 3$, show that there are five distinct left inverses of the map φ.

4 Let N be the set of all nonnegative integers; show that the map $m^\varphi = |m|$ of **Z** onto N has an uncountable number of left inverses.

5 Discuss the existence and uniqueness of a left inverse for each of the following maps of $\mathbf{Z}^+$ into **Z**. Also, discuss the existence and uniqueness of a right inverse for each map.

A. $n^\varphi = (-1)^n n$.

B. $n^\psi = (-1)^n[n/2]$, where $[a]$ is the largest integer not exceeding a.

C. $n^\delta = (-1)^n m$, where $2^m \leq n < 2^{m+1}$.

6 Prove Proposition 11.

9 TRANSFORMATION GROUPS

The following theorem is a direct consequence of the propositions of the last sections:

THEOREM 5 *Let $\mathcal{T} = \mathcal{T}(M)$ denote the set of all maps of a set M into itself:*

A. *If φ qnd ψ are in $\mathcal{T}$, then $\varphi\psi$ is in $\mathcal{T}$.*

B. *If φ, ψ, and λ are in $\mathscr{T}$, then $(\varphi\psi)\lambda = \varphi(\psi\lambda)$.*

C. *There is a unique map ι in $\mathscr{T}$ such that for each map φ in $\mathscr{T}$ we have $\varphi\iota = \iota\varphi = \varphi$.*

D. *If M contains at least two elements, there exist φ and ψ in $\mathscr{T}$ such that $\varphi\psi \neq \psi\varphi$.*

E. *If φ is in $\mathscr{T}$, the equation $\varphi\chi = \iota$ has no solution χ in $\mathscr{T}$ if φ is not* 1-1, *it has more than one solution in $\mathscr{T}$ if φ is* 1-1 *but not onto, it has exactly one solution in $\mathscr{T}$ if φ is* 1-1 *and onto. The equation $\omega\varphi = \iota$ has no solution ω in $\mathscr{T}$ if φ is not onto, it has more than one solution in $\mathscr{T}$ if φ is onto but not* 1-1, *it has exactly one solution in $\mathscr{T}$ if φ is* 1-1 *and onto.*

If $\varphi \in \mathscr{T}$, we define, as usual, the positive powers of φ by induction, namely,

$$\varphi^0 = \iota_M = \iota, \qquad \varphi^n = \varphi\varphi^{n-1}, \qquad \text{for } n \in \mathbf{Z}^+.$$

EXERCISES 1 Prove: $\varphi^m\varphi^n = \varphi^{m+n}$, $(\varphi^m)^n = \varphi^{mn}$, for all nonnegative integers m and n and all $\varphi \in \mathscr{T}$.

2 To each $\varphi \in \mathscr{T}(M)$ there is associated a binary relation on M defined as follows: $x < y$ whenever there is a nonnegative integer n such that $x^{\varphi^n} = y$. Show that this relation is reflexive and transitive. Exhibit a $\varphi \in \mathscr{T}(\mathbf{Z}^+)$ to show that these relations need not be equivalence relations. Prove: This relation is an equivalence relation on M if and only if to each $x \in M$ there is a positive integer $u(x)$ such that $x^{\varphi^{u(x)}} = x$. Give examples in which the $u(x)$ are unbounded.

3 Given a map $\varphi \in \mathscr{T}(M)$, show that, if the associated binary relation on M is an equivalence relation, then φ is a 1-1 map of M onto M.

A nonempty subset S of M is said to be *invariant relative to the map* $\varphi \in \mathscr{T}(M)$, provided

$$S^\varphi \subset S.$$

Clearly M is invariant for all $\varphi \in \mathscr{T}(M)$, and all nonempty subsets of M are invariant relative to ι_M. The set

$$I(\varphi) = \{x \in M \mid x^\varphi = x\}$$

is the set of *fixed points of* φ and is clearly invariant relative to φ.

PROPOSITION 31 *If φ and ψ are* 1-1 *maps of M into M such that $M = I(\varphi) \cup I(\psi)$, then $\varphi\psi = \psi\varphi$.*

PROPOSITION 32 *If M is the disjoint union of two sets X and Y, each invariant relative to $\varphi \in \mathscr{T}(M)$, then there exists maps α and β in $\mathscr{T}(M)$ such that $\alpha\beta = \varphi = \beta\alpha$, where $I(\alpha) \supset X$ and $I(\beta) \supset Y$.*

EXERCISES 4 Prove:

A. If X and Y are invariant subsets of M relative to $\varphi \in \mathscr{T}(M)$, so are $X \cap Y$ and $X \cup Y$.

B. If X is any subset of M, then $S = \bigcup_{n=0}^{\infty} X^{\varphi^n}$ is invariant relative to φ.

C. If X is an invariant set relative to both φ and ψ, then X is invariant relative to the product $\varphi\psi$.

D. $X \subset I(\varphi)$ if and only if $\text{res}_X\, \varphi = \iota_X$.

E. $I(\varphi) = M$ if and only if $\varphi = \iota_M$.

5 A. Prove Proposition 31. (*Hint:* If φ is 1-1 and $x \notin I(\varphi)$, then $x^{\varphi} \notin I(\varphi)$.)

B. Show that the assumption that φ and ψ are 1-1 maps is necessary for the conclusion of Proposition 31.

C. If φ and ψ are 1-1 and commute, does it follow that $M = I(\varphi) \cup I(\varphi)$?

6 A. Prove Proposition 32.

B. Generalize Proposition 32 to the case where M is the disjoint union of finitely many subsets that are invariant relative to φ.

A bijective map of M onto itself is called a *transformation on M*. Sometimes, and especially if M is a finite set, a transformation on M is called a *permutation on M*. As we saw in Theorem 2, to each transformation φ on M there is a unique transformation φ^* of M that is both a unique left inverse and a unique right inverse of φ. We note that $y^{\varphi^{-1}} = \{y^{\varphi^*}\}$, for all y in M. Now we can tell from the context in which it is used whether the symbol y designates the element y or the one-element set $\{y\}$, and as it is desirable to eliminate excess notation in the case of transformations on a set, we let φ^{-1} designate both φ^* and φ^{-1}. We also note that the product of any two transformations on M is again a transformation on M. We shall denote the set of all transformations on M together with our usual product of transformations by the symbol $\Pi(M)$. We shall call $\Pi(M)$ *the group of transformations on M* (or *the group of permutations on M*).* We can rephrase Theorem 2 as follows:

THEOREM 2′ *Let $\Pi(M)$ be the group of transformations on M; then:*

A. *If φ, ψ, and λ are in $\Pi(M)$, then $(\varphi\psi)\lambda = \varphi(\psi\lambda)$.*

B. *There is a unique element $\iota \in \Pi(M)$ such that $\varphi\iota = \varphi = \iota\varphi$ for all $\varphi \in \Pi(M)$.*

C. *To each $\varphi \in \Pi(M)$ there exists a unique element $\varphi^{-1} \in \Pi(M)$ such that $\varphi\varphi^{-1} = \iota = \varphi^{-1}\varphi$.*

Now, let $\mathscr{G}$ be a subset of $\mathscr{T}(M)$ such that (A) $\mathscr{G}$ is closed under multiplication of maps, (B) $\iota \in \mathscr{G}$, (C) to each $\varphi \in \mathscr{G}$ there is an element $\psi \in \mathscr{G}$ such that $\varphi\psi = \iota = \psi\varphi$. It would follow from property C and Theorem 5 that $\mathscr{G}$ is a subset of $\Pi(M)$ and the ψ of property C is unique.

* Whenever we use the word "group," we shall mean a set together with a binary operation on the set satisfying certain properties. A binary operation is a way of combining two elements of the set to get a third element of the set. A binary operation on the set M may always be viewed as a map of $M^{(2)}$ into M.

Clearly the elements of $\mathcal{G}$ satisfy the associative law. Thus $\mathcal{G}$ is a set with a binary operation satisfying the three properties of Theorem 2′. A subset of $\mathcal{T}(M)$ satisfying properties A, B, and C will be called *a group of transformations on M*. We note that $\Pi(M)$ is the maximal subset of $\mathcal{T}(M)$ satisfying properties A, B, and C.

Since a group of transformations on M is both a group and a subset of $\Pi(M)$, one often refers to a group of transformations on M as a subgroup of $\Pi(M)$.

If M is the set $\{1, 2, \ldots, m\}$, it is customary to use Π_m or $\mathfrak{S}_m$ rather than $\Pi(M)$. When considering Π_m, it is convenient to denote each element $\varphi \in \Pi_m$ by

$$\begin{pmatrix} 1 & 2 & 3 & \cdots & m \\ 1^\varphi & 2^\varphi & 3^\varphi & \cdots & m^\varphi \end{pmatrix}.$$

On the other hand, each such array, where the bottom row is some rearrangement of the symbols of the top row, defines an element of Π_m. We call such an array the *analytic representation of* φ. This representation is especially convenient for computing products of transformations of Π_m. Thus

$$\begin{pmatrix} 1 & 2 & 3 & 4 & 5 \\ \downarrow & & & \downarrow & \\ 2 & 3 & 1 & 5 & 4 \end{pmatrix}\begin{pmatrix} 1 & 2 & 3 & 4 & 5 \\ & \downarrow & & & \downarrow \\ 5 & 4 & 1 & 3 & 2 \end{pmatrix} = \begin{pmatrix} 1 & 2 & 3 & 4 & 5 \\ & & & & \\ 4 & 1 & 5 & 2 & 3 \end{pmatrix}.$$

EXERCISES 7 Compute the products:

$$\begin{pmatrix} 1 & 2 & 3 & 4 & 5 & 6 \\ 6 & 5 & 4 & 1 & 2 & 3 \end{pmatrix}\begin{pmatrix} 1 & 2 & 3 & 4 & 5 & 6 \\ 3 & 1 & 2 & 5 & 4 & 6 \end{pmatrix},$$

$$\begin{pmatrix} 1 & 2 & 3 & 4 & 5 & 6 & 7 \\ 2 & 3 & 4 & 5 & 6 & 7 & 1 \end{pmatrix}\begin{pmatrix} 1 & 2 & 3 & 4 & 5 & 6 & 7 \\ 2 & 3 & 4 & 5 & 6 & 7 & 1 \end{pmatrix},$$

$$\begin{pmatrix} 1 & 2 & 3 & 4 & 5 \\ 5 & 4 & 3 & 2 & 1 \end{pmatrix}\begin{pmatrix} 1 & 2 & 3 & 4 & 5 \\ 3 & 4 & 1 & 5 & 2 \end{pmatrix}\begin{pmatrix} 1 & 2 & 3 & 4 & 5 \\ 1 & 3 & 2 & 5 & 4 \end{pmatrix}.$$

8 Compute the multiplication tables for Π_1, Π_2, Π_3, and Π_4.

9 A. Show that, if M contains at most two elements, then every two elements of $\Pi(M)$ commute with each other.

B. Prove: If M contains at least three elements, then there exist φ and ψ in $\Pi(M)$ such that $\varphi\psi \neq \psi\varphi$.

10 Prove: If M is a finite set of m elements, then $\Pi(M)$ is a finite set of $m!$ elements.

11 Prove: $\Pi(\mathbf{Z}^+)$ is an uncountable set.

12 Prove: If $\varphi, \psi \in \Pi(M)$, then $\psi^{-1}\varphi^{-1}$ is the inverse of $\varphi\psi$ in $\Pi(M)$; i.e., $(\varphi\psi)^{-1} = \psi^{-1}\varphi^{-1}$. Generalize this result by finding the inverse of a transformation that is the product of finitely many transformations.

What is the inverse of $\begin{pmatrix} 1 & 2 & 3 & 4 & 5 \\ 5 & 3 & 2 & 1 & 4 \end{pmatrix}$? Formulate a rule that gives the inverse of an analytic representation of φ.

13 A. Prove: The set $\{\iota\}$ is a group of transformations on a set M.

B. Prove: If x is an element of M, then the set of all transformations on M that leave x fixed is a group of transformations on M.

C. Prove: If N is a subset of M, then $U(M:N) = \{\varphi \in \Pi(M) \mid N \subset I(\varphi)\}$ is a group of transformations on M.

D. If $N \subset M$, is the set $U'(M:N) = \{\varphi \in \Pi(M) \mid N = I(\varphi)\}$ a group of transformations on M?

E. Determine necessary and sufficient conditions on the subset N so that every two elements in $U(M:N)$ commute.

14 A. Let N be a subset of M and let $V(M:N) = \{\varphi \in \Pi(M) \mid N^\varphi = N\}$. Show that $V(M:N)$ is a group of transformations on M.

B. Let N be a subset of M and let $W(M:N) = \{\varphi \in \Pi(M) \mid N^\varphi \subset N\}$. Under what circumstances is $W(M:N)$ a group of transformations on M? (*Hint:* If N is infinite, does $N^\varphi \subset N$ imply $N^\varphi = N$?)

If $\varphi \in \Pi(M)$, let

$$X(\varphi) = \{x \in M \mid x^\varphi \neq x\}.$$

$X(\varphi)$ is the set of elements moved by φ. Clearly M is the disjoint union of $I(\varphi)$ and $X(\varphi)$, and $X(\varphi)$ is the complement of $I(\varphi)$ in M. If $\varphi, \psi \in \Pi(M)$ and $X(\varphi) \cap X(\psi) = \varnothing$, we say φ and ψ are *disjoint transformations.*

EXERCISES 15 A. Prove: If M is a finite set and $\varphi \in \Pi(M)$, then $X(\varphi)$ is invariant relative to φ.

B. Does the conclusion of part A follow if M is infinite?

C. Prove: $X(\iota) = \varnothing$.

D. If $X(\varphi) = \varnothing$, must $\varphi = \iota$?

E. Show that there exists $\varphi, \psi \in \Pi(\mathbf{Z}^+)$ such that $X(\varphi)$ is an infinite set and $X(\psi)$ is a finite set.

16 Let M be a set and let

$\mathscr{F}(M) = \{\varphi \in \Pi(M) \mid X(\varphi)$ is finite or empty$\}$,
$\mathscr{I}(M) = \{\varphi \in \Pi(M) \mid X(\varphi)$ is infinite$\}$,
$\mathscr{C}(M) = \{\varphi \in \Pi(M) \mid X(\varphi)$ is countable or empty$\}$.

A. Show that $\mathscr{F}(M)$ is a group of transformations on M and that neither $\mathscr{I}(M)$ nor $\mathscr{I}(M) \cup \{\iota\}$ is such a group. Decide whether $\mathscr{C}(M)$ is such a group.

B. Show that $\mathscr{F}(\mathbf{Z}^+)$ is a countable set.

17 Prove: Disjoint transformations commute.

10 ORDER OF AN ELEMENT OF $\Pi(M)$

We saw in the paragraph following Theorem 5 that, if $\varphi \in \Pi(M)$ and k is a nonnegative integer, then φ^k was a uniquely defined element of $\Pi(M)$; specifically

$$\varphi^0 = \iota, \qquad \varphi^n = \varphi \cdot \varphi^{n-1}, \qquad \text{for } n \in \mathbf{Z}^+.$$

Since φ^{-1} is uniquely determined by φ, if we define

$$\varphi^{-n} = (\varphi^{-1})^n, \qquad \text{for } n \in \mathbf{Z}^+,$$

then φ^k is a uniquely defined element of $\Pi(M)$ for all $k \in \mathbf{Z}$. The rules

$$\varphi^m\varphi^n = \varphi^{m+n}, \qquad (\varphi^m)^n = \varphi^{mn}$$

hold for all integers m and n.

Let

$$S_\varphi = \{n \in \mathbf{Z} \mid \varphi^n = \iota\}.$$

Clearly S_φ is an ideal of $\mathbf{Z}$. As usual, we let $S_\varphi^+ = S_\varphi \cap \mathbf{Z}^+$. S_φ^+ is nonempty if and only if S_φ contains an element other than 0. If $\varphi \in \Pi(M)$, we define the *order* of φ, denoted by $o(\varphi)$, as follows:

$$o(\varphi) = \begin{cases} \min S_\varphi^+ & \text{if } S_\varphi^+ \text{ is not empty,} \\ \infty & \text{if } S_\varphi^+ \text{ is empty.} \end{cases}$$

The reader should prove

PROPOSITION 33 A. *If $o(\varphi)$ is finite, then S_φ is the set of all integral multiples of $o(\varphi)$.*
B. *$o(\varphi) = 1$ if and only if $\varphi = \iota$.*
C. *$o(\varphi) = o(\varphi^{-1})$, for all $\varphi \in \Pi(M)$.*
D. *$o(\varphi)$ is finite if and only if there exist integers $m \neq n$ such that $\varphi^m = \varphi^n$.*

Let $\varphi \in \Pi_m$. As Π_m contains exactly $m!$ elements, by Dirichlet's box principle, two of $\varphi^0, \varphi^1, \ldots, \varphi^m$ must be equal. Hence

PROPOSITION 34 *Every element of Π_m has finite order not exceeding $m!$*

EXERCISES 1 Prove: If $\varphi \in \Pi(M)$ and $m, n \in \mathbf{Z}$, then $\varphi^m\varphi^n = \varphi^{m+n}$ and $(\varphi^m)^n = \varphi^{mn}$.

2 Prove: If $o(\varphi) = 2$, then $\varphi = \varphi^{-1}$. Is the converse true? Prove: If $o(\varphi) = n$, then $\varphi^{n-1} = \varphi^{-1}$.

3 Determine the order of each element in Π_3 and Π_4.

4 A. Show that the map $n^\varphi = -n$ is a transformation on $\mathbf{Z}$ of order 2.
B. Show that to each $n \in \mathbf{Z}^+$ there is an element of $\Pi(\mathbf{Z})$ of order n. Show that these elements may be chosen so that the fixed set is empty and that they may also be chosen so that the set of moved elements is finite.
C. Show that the map $n^\psi = n + 1$ is an element of $\Pi(\mathbf{Z})$ of infinite order. Determine ψ^k for every integer k.

D. Show that for every integer $n \geq 2$ there are infinitely many different elements in $\Pi(\mathbf{Z})$ of order n.

5 A. Prove: If $o(\varphi) = 2u$, then $o(\varphi^2) = u$.

B. Prove: If $2 \nmid o(\varphi)$, then $o(\varphi^2) = o(\varphi)$.

C. Generalize parts A and B where 2 is replaced by a prime p.

D. If $4 \nmid o(\varphi)$, does it follow that $o(\varphi^4) = o(\varphi)$?

E. Prove or disprove: $o(\varphi^k) = o(\varphi)/(k, o(\varphi))$.

6 Let $\varphi \in \Pi_m$ and for each $s = 1, 2, \ldots, m$ let $k(s) = \min\{k \in \mathbf{Z}^+ \mid s^{\varphi^k} = s\}$. Prove:

A. $k(s) \leq m$ for all s.

B. $o(\varphi) = \text{l.c.m.}\ [k(1), k(2), \ldots, k(m)]$.*

C. $o(\varphi)$ is a divisor of $m!$

D. Show that there exist elements in Π_{10} of orders 10, 12, 21, and 30.

7 A. Prove: If φ and ψ are transformations on M of finite order that commute, then $o(\varphi\psi) = \text{l.c.m.}\ [o(\varphi), o(\psi)]$, provided $(o(\varphi), o(\varphi)) = 1$.

B. Find φ and ψ in $\Pi(\mathbf{Z})$ of finite order whose product is of infinite order.

11 CYCLES

To each $\varphi \in \Pi(M)$ we can associate a binary relation on M as follows: x is related to y provided $x^{\varphi^k} = y$, for some integer k.† This relation is reflexive, since $x^{\varphi^0} = x$. It is symmetric, since $x^{\varphi^k} = y$ if and only if $x = y^{\varphi^{-k}}$. It is transitive, for if $x^{\varphi^k} = y$ and $y^{\varphi^h} = z$, then $x^{\varphi^{k+h}} = x$. Thus this relation is an equivalence relation, which we shall denote by $\sim_\varphi$.

It should be noted that φ and φ^{-1} determine the same equivalence relation on M and the relation $\sim_\iota$ is ordinary equality.

Let X be an equivalence class for $\sim_\varphi$ and suppose $x \in X$. Then $x^{\varphi^k} \in X$ for all $k \in \mathbf{Z}$. Also, if $y \in X$, then y is of the form $y = x^{\varphi^h}$ for some $h \in \mathbf{Z}$. Thus

$$X = \{x^{\varphi^k} \mid k \in \mathbf{Z}\}.$$

Clearly X is an invariant set under φ, and the map $\text{res}_X\ \varphi$ is a transformation on the set X. If M is infinite, then X may be infinite but may also be finite. A one-element set $X = \{x\}$ is an equivalence class for $\sim_\varphi$ if and only if $x^\varphi = x$, i.e., $x \in I(\varphi)$.

Suppose that X is a finite set that is an equivalence class for $\sim_\varphi$. Let $x \in X$. By Dirichlet's box principle there exist integers s and t such that $x^{\varphi^s} = x^{\varphi^t}$, and hence there exists a positive integer r such that

* We denote the least common multiple of a set $\{a, b, \ldots, c\}$ by l.c.m. $[a, b, \ldots, c]$.

† Observe the slight difference in the definition of this relation and the one of Exercise 2, Sec. 9.

$x^{\varphi^r} = x$. Let

$$m = m(X) = \min \{r \in \mathbf{Z}^+ \mid x^{\varphi^r} = x\}.$$

Then the equivalence class X contains exactly m elements. Set $x_j = x^{\varphi^{j-1}}$, $(1 \leq j \leq m)$. Then $X = \{x_1, x_2, \ldots, x_m\}$ and $x_j^{\varphi} = x_k$, where $k \equiv j + 1 \pmod{m}$. Thus, if we arrange the elements of X about the circumference of a circle at equally spaced intervals in the order specified, the effect of applying φ to X is the same as that produced by a rotation of the circle through an angle of $2\pi/m$ radians.

Now suppose that X is an equivalence class for $\sim_{\varphi}$ and that X is an infinite set. The set X is denumerable, since the map $y = x^{\varphi^k} \to k$ is a bijection of X onto $\mathbf{Z}$. In this case, if $x \in X$, there is no nonzero integer r such that $x^{\varphi^r} = x$, for if there were, then x would be equivalent to only finitely many elements of X. Set $x_j = x^{\varphi^j}$; then $x_j^{\varphi} = x_{j+1}$, for all $j \in \mathbf{Z}$. In this case, if we arrange the elements of X along a line at equally spaced intervals in the order just prescribed, the effect of applying φ to X is a translation of the line one interval to the right. If we think of the line as a circle of infinite radius, we can see the analogy between the finite and the infinite cases. In each case φ is said to permute the elements of X cyclicly.

A transformation γ on M is said to be a *cycle* (*on* C) if (A) C is an equivalence class for γ and (B) $I(\gamma) = M - C$. The terminology arises from the effect γ has on the set C. Now $I(\iota) = M$, and so ι might be said to be a cycle on the empty set. We shall refer to the identity map as the trivial cycle. If γ is a cycle on C, then γ^{-1} is also a cycle on C.

Let γ be a cycle on $\{x_1, x_2, \ldots, x_m\}$, where $x_j^{\gamma} = x_h$ with $j + 1 \equiv h \pmod{m}$. It is customary to simplify the analytic representation of a cycle, and to write

$$\gamma = (x_1 \;\; x_2 \;\; \ldots \;\; x_m).$$

It should be noted that

$$(x_1 \;\; x_2 \;\; \ldots \;\; x_m) = (x_i \;\; x_{i+1} \;\; \ldots \;\; x_m \;\; x_1 \;\; \ldots \;\; x_{i-1}),$$

for $1 \leq i \leq m$.

EXERCISES 1 Prove:

A. If γ is a cycle on C, then $o(\gamma) = m(C) = |C|$.

B. If $\gamma = (x_1 \;\; x_2 \;\; \ldots \;\; x_m)$, then $\gamma^{-1} = (x_m \;\; x_{m-1} \;\; \ldots \;\; x_2 \;\; x_1)$.

2 A. Decide which of the following transformations are cycles:

$$\begin{pmatrix} 1 & 2 & 3 & 4 & 5 & 6 & 7 \\ 1 & 2 & 5 & 4 & 6 & 3 & 7 \end{pmatrix}, \quad \begin{pmatrix} 1 & 2 & 3 & 4 & 5 & 6 & 7 \\ 2 & 3 & 6 & 5 & 4 & 1 & 7 \end{pmatrix}, \quad \begin{pmatrix} 1 & 2 & 3 & 4 & 5 & 6 & 7 \\ 2 & 1 & 4 & 3 & 5 & 7 & 6 \end{pmatrix}.$$

B. Exhibit some transformations of $\Pi(\mathbf{Z})$ that are cycles on a finite set; on an infinite set.

3 A. Give an example of a cycle whose square is a cycle and an example of a cycle whose square is not a cycle.

B. If γ and γ^2 are cycles, show that they are cycles on the same set.
C. If γ is a cycle but γ^2 is not a cycle, show that γ^2 is the product of two disjoint cycles γ_1 and γ_2 with $X(\gamma_1) \cup X(\gamma_2) = X(\gamma)$.
D. Prove: If γ is a cycle of order k, then γ^3 is a cycle if and only if $3 \nmid k$.
E. Generalize part D.
F. Generalize part C.

4 Is it possible to define several unequal cycles on the same finite set C? If yes, determine the number of unequal cycles on a finite set C.

5 Prove: If γ is a nontrivial cycle, then $X(\gamma)$ contains at least two elements.

If φ is a transformation on M and X is an equivalence class for $\sim_\varphi$, then $X^\varphi = X$, and hence $Y = M - X$ is invariant for φ, and M is the disjoint union of X and Y. It follows from Proposition 32 that $\varphi = \gamma\psi$, where $I(\gamma) \supset Y$ and $I(\psi) \supset X$. Now, if X is not a one-element set, then $X \cap I(\varphi) = \varnothing$. But $I(\varphi) \supset I(\gamma) \cap I(\psi)$, and hence

$$\varnothing = X \cap I(\varphi) \supset X \cap I(\gamma) \cap I(\psi) \supset X \cap I(\gamma),$$

whence $X \cap I(\gamma) = \varnothing$, and consequently $I(\gamma) = Y$. Since $I(\psi) \supset X$, we have $\operatorname{res}_X \gamma = \operatorname{res}_X \varphi$. It follows that X is an equivalence class for γ, and therefore γ is a cycle on X. Thus, if X is not a one-element set, we have proved

OPOSITION 35 *Let $\varphi \in \Pi(M)$, and let X be an equivalence class for $\sim_\varphi$. Then $\varphi = \gamma\psi$, where γ is a cycle on X and $I(\psi) \supset X$.*

Should X be a one-element set, then $X \subset I(\varphi)$, and we obtain the result by taking γ to be ι and ψ to be φ. Thus the proposition holds for all equivalence classes X.

THEOREM 6 *Let $\varphi \in \Pi(M)$, and suppose that there are only finitely many equivalence classes for $\sim_\varphi$ that contain more than one element. Let these classes be $X_1, X_2, \ldots, X_s$. Then $\varphi = \gamma_1\gamma_2 \cdots \gamma_s$, where γ_i is a cycle on $X_i (i = 1, 2, \ldots, s)$. Furthermore, the γ_i commute among themselves.*

PROOF. The proof of this theorem is by induction on s. Should $s = 1$, the transformation φ must be a cycle on this single set and there is nothing more to prove.

Now suppose that the theorem is true for all maps ψ such that $\sim_\psi$ has less than s equivalence classes each containing at least two elements. Let φ be as in the hypothesis of the theorem. By Proposition 35, $\varphi = \gamma\psi$, where γ is a cycle on X_1 and $I(\psi) \supset X_1$. Then $X_2, \ldots, X_s$ are equivalence classes for ψ, and they are the only ones that contain at least two elements. Hence, by the induction hypothesis

$$\psi = \gamma_2\gamma_3 \cdots \gamma_s,$$

where the γ_i are cycles on X_i. The conclusion of the theorem now follows. The cycles commute since they are disjoint in pairs.

The theorem breaks down when there are infinitely many equivalence classes containing at least two elements, since we have no way of speaking of an infinite product of transformations. Thus the transformation $\varphi \in \Pi(\mathbf{Z})$, given by

$$u^{\varphi} = \begin{cases} u + 1 \text{ if } u \not\equiv 3 \pmod 4, \\ u - 3 \text{ if } u \equiv 3 \pmod 4, \end{cases}$$

cannot be expressed as the product of finitely many disjoint cycles. However, there are elements of $\Pi(\mathbf{Z})$ that can be so expressed.

When M is a finite set, there can only be finitely many equivalence classes, and hence we have

COROLLARY 1 *If M is a finite set, every transformation in $\Pi(M)$ is the unique product, to within order of multiplication, of finitely many disjoint cycles.*

The reader should note the analogy between this corollary and the unique factorization theorem for integers.

EXERCISES 6 Express the following as products of disjoint cycles:

$$\begin{pmatrix} 1 & 2 & 3 & 4 & 5 & 6 \\ 2 & 1 & 4 & 6 & 5 & 3 \end{pmatrix}, \begin{pmatrix} a & b & c & d & e \\ c & b & d & e & a \end{pmatrix}, \begin{pmatrix} 1 & 2 & 3 & 4 & 5 & 6 \\ 2 & 4 & 5 & 6 & 3 & 1 \end{pmatrix}, \begin{pmatrix} 1 & 2 & 3 & 4 & 5 & 6 \\ 6 & 5 & 4 & 3 & 2 & 1 \end{pmatrix}.$$

7 Give examples of transformations on $\mathbf{Z}$ of finite order and of infinite order that cannot be expressed as the product of finitely many disjoint cycles.

8 A. Prove: If $\varphi = \gamma_1\gamma_2 \cdots \gamma_s$, where the γ_i are disjoint cycles, then

$$o(\varphi) = \begin{cases} \infty, \text{ if for some } i,\ o(\gamma_i) = \infty, \\ \text{l.c.m. } [o(\gamma_1), o(\gamma_2), \ldots, o(\gamma_s)], \text{ if each } o(\gamma_i) < \infty. \end{cases}$$

B. Using part A prove: If $\varphi \in \Pi_m$, then $o(\varphi) \leq m!$.

C. Determine the order of each transformation in Exercise 6.

9 Let $e(\Pi_m) = \max \{o(\varphi) \mid \varphi \in \Pi_m\}$. Determine $e(\Pi_2)$, $e(\Pi_3)$, $e(\Pi_4)$. Show that $e(\Pi_m) \leq \prod_{p \leq m} p^u$, where p is a prime and $p^u \leq m < p^{u+1}$. Is it true that $e(\Pi_m) < m!$ for all large m?

10 A. If γ is a cycle of infinite order, can γ^k, $k \in \mathbf{Z}$ always be expressed as a finite product of disjoint cycles.?

B. Prove or disprove: If φ is a transformation on M and φ can be expressed as the product of finitely many disjoint cycles, then each power of φ can be so expressed.

11 Let $\mathscr{F}(M)$ be defined as in Exercise 16, Sec. 9. Prove:

COROLLARY 2 *If $\varphi \in \mathscr{F}(M)$, then φ is expressible as a finite product of disjoint cycles, uniquely to within order of multiplication.*

EXERCISE 12 Let φ, ψ be cycles of $\Pi(\mathbf{Z})$, where

$$\begin{aligned} \varphi &= (\ldots 8k+1 \quad 8k+3 \quad 8k+5 \quad 8(k+1)+1 \ldots), \\ \psi &= (\ldots 8k+5 \quad 8k+4 \quad 8k+1 \quad 8(k+1)+1 \ldots). \end{aligned}$$

Show that $\varphi\psi$ is not expressible as a finite product of disjoint cycles. It follows that the set of transformations on $\mathbf{Z}$ that are expressible as finite products of disjoint cycles is not a group of transformations on $\mathbf{Z}$.

12 INTERSECTIONS, GENERATING SETS

ROPOSITION 36 *If $\mathscr{G}$ and $\mathscr{H}$ are groups of transformations on M, then $\mathscr{G} \cap \mathscr{H}$ is a group of transformations on M.*

PROOF. Clearly $\iota \in \mathscr{G} \cap \mathscr{H}$. If φ and ψ are in $\mathscr{G} \cap \mathscr{H}$, then φ and ψ are in $\mathscr{G}$. But $\mathscr{G}$ is a group of tranformations, and hence $\varphi\psi \in \mathscr{G}$. Similarly $\varphi\psi \in \mathscr{H}$. Thus we have $\varphi\psi \in \mathscr{G} \cap \mathscr{H}$. Furthermore, if $\varphi \in \mathscr{G} \cap \mathscr{H}$, then φ^{-1} is in $\mathscr{G}$ and in $\mathscr{H}$, and hence $\varphi^{-1} \in \mathscr{G} \cap \mathscr{H}$. Proposition 36 now follows from the definition of a group of transformations.

More generally, as the reader should prove, we have

OPOSITION 37 *If $\mathscr{A}$ is any set and if to each $\alpha \in \mathscr{A}$ there is a group of transformations $\mathscr{G}_\alpha$ on M, then $\bigcap_{\alpha \in \mathscr{A}} \mathscr{G}_\alpha$ is a group of transformations on M.*

Let $\mathscr{S}$ be any set of transformations on M. There are groups of transformation on M that contain the set $\mathscr{S}$, e.g., $\Pi(M)$. Denote the intersection of all these groups by $\langle \mathscr{S} \rangle$. By Proposition 37 $\langle \mathscr{S} \rangle$ is a group of transformations on M. Clearly $\langle \mathscr{S} \rangle \supset \mathscr{S}$. Furthermore, if $\mathscr{H}$ is a group of transformations on M such that $\mathscr{H} \supset \mathscr{S}$, then $\mathscr{H} \supset \langle \mathscr{S} \rangle$. (Why?) Hence $\langle \mathscr{S} \rangle$ is the smallest group of transformations on M that contains the set $\mathscr{S}$. We say that $\langle \mathscr{S} \rangle$ is the group *generated by the set* $\mathscr{S}$. For example, if $\mathscr{S} = \{\varphi\}$, then $\langle \mathscr{S} \rangle = \{\varphi^k \mid k \in \mathbf{Z}\} = \langle \varphi \rangle$. There are exactly $o(\varphi)$ elements in the group $\langle \varphi \rangle$.

The following proposition gives us additional insight into the group $\langle \mathscr{S} \rangle$.

OPOSITION 38 *Let $\mathscr{S} \subset \Pi(M)$, and let $\mathscr{S}^{(-1)} = \{\psi \in \Pi(M) \mid \psi^{-1} \in \mathscr{S}\}$. Then $\varphi \in \langle \mathscr{S} \rangle$ if and only if φ can be expressed as a finite product, repetitions being permitted, of elements from the set $\mathscr{S} \cup \mathscr{S}^{(-1)}$.*

COROLLARY *If all the elements of $\mathscr{S}$ have finite order, then $\varphi \in \langle \mathscr{S} \rangle$ if and only if φ can be expressed as a finite product, repetitions permitted, of elements from $\mathscr{S}$.*

EXERCISES 1 Prove Proposition 38 and its corollary.

2 A. If $\mathscr{S} = \{(1\ 2), (3\ 4\ 5)\} \subset \Pi_7$, determine $\langle \mathscr{S} \rangle$.

B. If $\mathscr{S} = \{(1\ 2), (1\ 2\ 3\ 4)\} \subset \Pi_7$, determine $\langle \mathscr{S} \rangle$.

3 Given an example to show that, if $\mathscr{G}$ and $\mathscr{H}$ are groups of transformations on M, then $\mathscr{G} \cup \mathscr{H}$ need not be such a group. Show that $\langle \mathscr{G} \cup \mathscr{H} \rangle$ is the smallest group which contains both $\mathscr{G}$ and $\mathscr{H}$.

4 Prove:

A. If $\mathfrak{Z}(\varphi) = \{\psi \in \Pi(M) \mid \varphi\psi = \psi\varphi\}$, then $\mathfrak{Z}(\varphi)$ is a subgroup of $\Pi(M)$.

B. Let R be a subset of $\Pi(M)$, and let $\mathfrak{Z}(R) = \{\psi \in \Pi(M) \,|\, \psi$ commutes with each $\sigma \in R\}$; then $\mathfrak{Z}(R)$ is a subgroup of $\Pi(M)$. Furthermore $\mathfrak{Z}(R) = \bigcap_{\sigma \in R} \mathfrak{Z}(\sigma)$.

13 TRANSPOSITIONS, THE ALTERNATING GROUP

A transposition is a cycle of order 2. A transposition is its own inverse. We observe that

$$\begin{aligned}(1\ 3\ 5\ 4\ 6) &= (1\ 3)(1\ 5)(1\ 4)(1\ 6) = (1\ 3)(1\ 5)(1\ 2)(1\ 2)(1\ 4)(1\ 6)\\ &= (2\ 1)(2\ 3)(2\ 5)(2\ 4)(2\ 6)(2\ 1).\end{aligned}$$

Using the ideas exemplified in the above equations, one can prove

PROPOSITION 39 *Every cycle of finite order is expressible as the product of finitely many transpositions. Such expressions are not unique.*

Combining this result with that of Corollary 2, Theorem 6, we obtain

COROLLARY 1 *If $\varphi \in \mathscr{F}(M)$, then φ is expressible as a product of finitely many transpositions.*

On the other hand, since each transposition is an element of $\mathscr{F}(M)$, a product of finitely many transpositions is an element of $\mathscr{F}(M)$. Thus we have

COROLLARY 2 *Let M be a nonempty set. The group $\mathscr{F}(M)$ is generated by the set of all transpositions definable on M.*

EXERCISES 1 Give detailed proofs of the above proposition and its corollaries.

2 Prove: $\Pi_m = \langle (1\ 2), (1\ 3), \ldots, (1\ m) \rangle$. More generally, for any j, $1 \leq j \leq m$ we have $\Pi_m = \langle (j\ 1), (j\ 2), \ldots, (j\ m) \rangle$.

3 Is it true that the set of transpositions of the form $(1\ k)$ generates the group $\Pi(\mathbf{Z})$?

4 Prove: $\Pi_m = \langle (1\ 2), (1\ 2\ 3\ \ldots\ m) \rangle$.

5 Verify: $(x_1\ x_2)(x_2\ x_3) \cdots (x_{h-1}\ x_h)(x_h\ x_1) = (x_2\ x_h)(x_2\ x_{h-1}) \cdots (x_2\ x_3)$.

A transposition is never the identity map; hence if we express ι as the product of u transpositions, then $u \geq 2$. Furthermore if ι is the product of two transpositions, they must be equal. We now prove

LEMMA 1 *If ι can be expressed as the product of $u \geq 3$ transpositions, then ι can be expressed as the product of u - 2 transpositions.*

PROOF. Suppose $\iota = \tau_1\tau_2 \cdots \tau_u$, where the τ_i are transpositions. Suppose that $\tau_j = (x \ \ y)$ and that y does not appear in any of the τ_h with $h < j$. Then y must appear in some τ_k with $k > j$. (Why?) Consider all expressions of ι as the product of u transpositions where the first j transpositions are $\tau_1, \tau_2, \ldots, \tau_j$. To each such expression we can associate the integer

$$m = \min \{k \in \mathbf{Z} \,|\, k > j \text{ and } y \text{ in } \tau_k\}.$$

Among all such expressions of ι, choose one with m minimal. Let this expression be

$$\iota = \tau_1\tau_2 \cdots \tau_j \cdots \tau_u.$$

We claim that $m = j + 1$. For suppose $m > j + 1$, and let $\tau_m = (y \ \ z)$. By the definition of m, y does not appear in τ_{m-1}. If z does not appear in τ_{m-1}, then τ_m and τ_{m-1} commute, and hence

$$\iota = \tau_1\tau_2 \cdots \tau_j \cdots \tau_{m-2}\tau_m\tau_{m-1}\tau_{m+1} \cdots \tau_u,$$

contradicting the choice of m. If z does appear in τ_{m-1}, say $\tau_{m-1} = (z \ \ w)$, we have

$$\tau_{m-1}\tau_m = (z \ \ w)(y \ \ z) = (y \ \ z)(y \ \ w),$$

and hence

$$\iota = \tau_1\tau_2 \cdots \tau_{m-2}(y \ \ z)(y \ \ w)\tau_{m+1} \cdots \tau_u,$$

again contradicting the choice of m.

Now suppose that $\tau_1 = (x_1 \ \ x_2)$. Then, using repeatedly the technique just enunciated in the paragraph above, we can find an integer s such that $2 \leq s \leq u$ and an expression

$$\iota = (x_1 \ \ x_2)(x_2 \ \ x_3) \cdots (x_{s-1} \ \ x_s)(x_s \ \ x_1)\tau_{s+1} \cdots \tau_u.$$

But then

$$\iota = (x_2 \ \ x_s)(x_2 \ \ x_{s-1}) \cdots (x_2 \ \ x_3)\tau_{s+1} \cdots \tau_u,$$

and we have proved the lemma.

The following is immediately deduced from Lemma 1:

LEMMA 2 *The identity map can never be the product of an odd number of transpositions.*

THEOREM 7 *If $\varphi \in \Pi(M)$ and if $\varphi = \prod_{i=1}^{s} \tau_i = \prod_{i=1}^{t} \tau_i'$, where τ_i and τ_i' are transpositions, then $s = t$ (mod 2).*

PROOF. If φ is as stated in the hypothesis, then $\iota = \tau_1 \cdots \tau_s(\tau_t')^{-1} \cdots (\tau_1')^{-1} = \tau_1 \cdots \tau_s\tau_t' \cdots \tau_1'$. By Lemma 2, $s + t \equiv 0$ (mod 2), and hence $s \equiv t$ (mod 2).

We shall say that a transformation φ is an *odd* transformation if φ can be expressed as the product of an odd number of transpositions, and we shall say that φ is an *even* transformation if φ can be expressed as a product of an even number of transformations. Because of Theorem 7, it is impossible for a transformation to be both odd and even. However, if M is an infinite set, it can occur that a transformation on M is neither odd nor even, since it may not be expressible as a product of finitely many transpositions. Our definitions lead to a partition of $\mathscr{F}(M)$ into two sets, the set $\mathfrak{A}(M)$ of even transformations in $\mathscr{F}(M)$ and the set $\mathfrak{O}(M)$ of odd transformations in $\mathscr{F}(M)$. It is an easy exercise to prove.

PROPOSITION 40 *The set $\mathfrak{A}(M)$ is a subgroup of $\mathscr{F}(M)$.*

The group $\mathfrak{A}(M)$ is called the *alternating group on M*. We let $\mathfrak{A}_m$ denote the alternating subgroup of Π_m. The set $\mathfrak{O}(M)$ does not form a group, since it does not contain ι, and the product of any two elements in $\mathfrak{O}(M)$ is not in $\mathfrak{O}(M)$.

EXERCISES 6 A. Prove: If $\psi \in \mathscr{F}(M)$, then the map $\varphi \xrightarrow{\Psi} \varphi\psi$ is a 1-1 map of $\mathscr{F}(M)$ onto $\mathscr{F}(M)$.

B. When is $\mathfrak{A}(M)$ invariant under Ψ?

C. Exhibit a 1-1 map of $\mathfrak{A}(M)$ onto $\mathfrak{O}(M)$.

D. Determine the number of elements in $\mathfrak{A}_m$.

7 A. Prove: $\mathfrak{A}_m$ is generated by the set of all cycles of order 3.

B. If M is an infinite set, is it true that $\mathfrak{A}(M)$ is generated by the set of all three cycles on M?

8 Is $\mathfrak{A}_m = \langle(1\ 2\ 3), (1\ 2\ 4), \ldots, (1\ 2\ m)\rangle$?

14 CONJUGATION, CENTRALIZERS

Let σ be a 1-1 map of a set M onto a set N. By Theorem 1, there is a 1-1 map σ^* of N onto M such that $\sigma\sigma^* = \iota_M$, $\sigma^*\sigma = \iota_N$. If $\varphi \in \Pi(M)$, then $\sigma^*\varphi\sigma \in \Pi(N)$. Furthermore, if $\varphi \neq \psi$ are elements in $\Pi(M)$, then $\sigma^*\varphi\sigma \neq \sigma^*\psi\sigma$. Thus the mapping Σ of $\Pi(M)$ into $\Pi(N)$ given by

$$\varphi \to \varphi^\Sigma = \sigma^*\varphi\sigma$$

is injective. The map Σ is also onto, for if $\lambda \in \Pi(N)$, then $\sigma\lambda\sigma^* \in \Pi(M)$ and $(\sigma\lambda\sigma^*)^\Sigma = \lambda$. Finally, we observe

$$(\varphi\psi)^\Sigma = \varphi^\Sigma\psi^\Sigma, \qquad \text{for all } \varphi, \psi \in \Pi(M).$$

Thus we have proved

PROPOSITION 41 *Let σ be a 1-1 map of M onto N and let Σ be the map $\varphi^\Sigma = \sigma^*\varphi\sigma$ of $\Pi(M)$ onto $\Pi(N)$. Then Σ is a bijective map and*

$$(\varphi\psi)^\Sigma = \varphi^\Sigma\psi^\Sigma, \qquad \textit{for all } \varphi, \psi \in \Pi(M). \tag{1}$$

COROLLARY *Assume the hypothesis of Propositions* 41. *Then:*

A. $\iota_M{}^\Sigma = \iota_N$

B. *If* $\varphi \in \Pi(M)$, *then* $o(\varphi) = o(\varphi^\Sigma)$.

C. *If* φ *and* ψ *are elements of* $\Pi(M)$ *that commute, then* φ^Σ *and* ψ^Σ *commute.*

PROOF. This corollary is an immediate consequence of Eq. 1. We have

$$\varphi^\Sigma = (\varphi\iota_M)^\Sigma = \varphi^\Sigma(\iota_M)^\Sigma, \qquad \text{for all } \varphi \in \Pi(M).$$

Since Σ is surjective, this becomes

$$\lambda = \lambda(\iota_M)^\Sigma, \qquad \text{for all } \lambda \in \Pi(N).$$

Since ι_N is that unique element of $\Pi(N)$ such that

$$\lambda = \lambda\iota_N, \qquad \text{for all } \lambda \in \Pi(N),$$

it follows that $(\iota_M)^\Sigma = \iota_N$.

Now Eq. 1 implies that $(\varphi^m)^\Sigma = (\varphi^\Sigma)^m$ for all $\varphi \in \Pi(M)$ and all $m \in \mathbf{Z}^+$. Since Σ is bijective, $\varphi^m = \iota_M$ if and only if $(\varphi^\Sigma)^m = \iota_N$. Thus φ and φ^Σ must have the same order. Property C is also a direct consequence of Eq. 1.

OPOSITION 42 *Assume the hypothesis of Proposition* 41. *Then*

$$I(\varphi)^\sigma = I(\varphi^\Sigma), \quad X(\varphi)^\sigma = X(\varphi^\Sigma).$$

PROOF. If $x \in I(\varphi)$, then

$$(x^\sigma)^{\varphi^\Sigma} = (x^\sigma)^{\sigma^*\varphi\sigma} = (x^{\sigma\sigma^*})^{\varphi\sigma} = x^{\varphi\sigma} = x^\sigma.$$

Hence $I(\varphi)^\sigma \subset I(\varphi^\Sigma)$. On the other hand, if $y \in I(\varphi^\Sigma)$, then $y^{\sigma^*} \in M$ and

$$y^{\sigma^*} = (y^{\varphi^\Sigma})^{\sigma^*} = (y^{\sigma^*\varphi\sigma})^{\sigma^*} = y^{\sigma^*\varphi} = (y^{\sigma^*})^\varphi.$$

Hence $I(\varphi^\Sigma)^{\sigma^*} \subset I(\varphi)$. It follows that $I(\varphi^\Sigma) = I(\varphi^\Sigma)^{\sigma^*\sigma} \subset I(\varphi)^\sigma$, and therefore $I(\varphi)^\sigma = I(\varphi^\Sigma)$.

We can prove the property for the set of nonfixed elements in the same way as we treated the set of fixed elements, or we can deduce it in the following manner: M is the disjoint union of $I(\varphi)$ and $X(\varphi)$. Also, N is the disjoint union of $I(\varphi^\Sigma)$ and $X(\varphi^\Sigma)$. Now σ is a bijective map of M onto N that is also a bijective map of $I(\varphi)$ onto $I(\varphi^\Sigma)$. It therefore follows that σ is a bijective map of $X(\varphi)$ onto $X(\varphi^\Sigma)$.

COROLLARY 1 *Assume the hypothesis of Proposition* 41*:*

A. *If* $\gamma \in \Pi(M)$ *is a cycle on* C, *then* γ^Σ *is a cycle on* C^σ.

B. *If* $\varphi \in \Pi(M)$ *is expressible as the product of* r *disjoint cycles, then* φ^Σ *is the product of* r *disjoint cycles.*

Thus we see that properties of elements of $\Pi(M)$ carry over to their images in $\Pi(N)$. Consequently, it is sufficient to study but one of the groups $\Pi(M)$ and $\Pi(N)$ to learn everything about both groups. In particular, for countable sets M, it is sufficient to study $\Pi(\mathbf{Z})$ and Π_m (where $m \in \mathbf{Z}^+$).

COROLLARY 2 *Assume the hypothesis of Proposition 41. Then:*

A. *The map* res $_{\mathscr{F}(M)}\, \Sigma$ *is a* 1-1 *map of* $\mathscr{F}(M)$ *onto* $\mathscr{F}(N)$.

B. *The map* res $_{\mathfrak{A}(M)}\, \Sigma$ *is a* 1-1 *map of* $\mathfrak{A}(M)$ *onto* $\mathfrak{A}(N)$.

EXERCISES 1 Prove Corollaries 1 and 2 above.

2 A. Let σ be a 1-1 map of M onto N. Show that the map $\varphi^\Sigma = \sigma^* \varphi \sigma$ is a 1-1 map of $\mathscr{T}(M)$ onto $\mathscr{T}(N)$ such that $(\varphi\psi)^\Sigma = \varphi^\Sigma \psi^\Sigma$, for all $\varphi, \psi \in \mathscr{T}(M)$. Furthermore, $\iota_M{}^\Sigma = \iota_N$ and $(\varphi^{-1})^\Sigma = (\varphi^\Sigma)^{-1}$ for all $\varphi \in \Pi(M)$.

B. Prove: A subset $S \subset M$ is invariant under $\varphi \in \mathscr{T}(M)$ if and only if the subset $S^\sigma \subset N$ is invariant under φ^Σ.

3 A. Let σ be a map of M onto N. Let λ be a left inverse of σ. Show that the mapping $\mathscr{T}(M) \xrightarrow{\Lambda} \mathscr{T}(N)$ given by $\varphi^\Lambda = \lambda\varphi\sigma$ is a map of $\mathscr{T}(M)$ onto $\mathscr{T}(N)$. Under what conditions on σ is Λ bijective? Is it true that $(\varphi_1\varphi_2)^\Lambda = \varphi_1{}^\Lambda\varphi_2{}^\Lambda$? Explain. If λ_1 and λ_2 are two different left inverses of σ, is it possible that the corresponding maps Λ_1 and Λ_2 are equal?

B. Let A be the mapping of $\mathscr{T}(N)$ into $\mathscr{T}(M)$ given by $\delta^A = \sigma\delta\lambda$. Show that $(\delta_1\delta_2)^A = \delta_1{}^A\delta_2{}^A$. Prove that A is an injection of $\mathscr{T}(N)$ into $\mathscr{T}(M)$. Is A also an injection of $\Pi(N)$ into $\Pi(M)$?

C. Analyze the case in which σ is an injection of M into N, ρ is a right inverse of σ, and $\varphi^R = \rho\varphi\sigma$ is the mapping of $\mathscr{T}(M)$ into $\mathscr{T}(N)$.

We can now specialize and let $M = N$. Then $\sigma \in \Pi(M)$, $\sigma^* = \sigma^{-1}$, and $\varphi^\Sigma = \sigma^{-1}\varphi\sigma \in \Pi(M)$, for all $\varphi \in \Pi(M)$; i.e., Σ is a mapping of $\Pi(M)$ onto $\Pi(M)$. It follows from the propositions and corollaries listed above that $o(\sigma^{-1}\varphi\sigma) = o(\varphi)$, $I(\varphi)^\sigma = I(\sigma^{-1}\varphi\sigma)$, $X(\varphi)^\sigma = X(\sigma^{-1}\varphi\sigma)$, for all $\sigma, \varphi \in \Pi(M)$. Also, $\gamma \in \Pi(M)$ is a cycle on C if and only if for each $\sigma \in \Pi(M)$, $\sigma^{-1}\gamma\sigma$ is a cycle on C^σ. We also note that $\mathscr{F}(M)$ and $\mathfrak{A}(M)$ are invariant subsets of $\Pi(M)$ under the maps $\varphi \to \sigma^{-1}\varphi\sigma$.

We next define a binary relation on $\Pi(M)$. Given $\varphi, \psi \in \Pi(M)$, we say φ *is conjugate to* ψ if there is a $\sigma \in \Pi(M)$ such that $\sigma^{-1}\varphi\sigma = \psi$. One easily proves

PROPOSITION 43 *The binary relation "is conjugate to" is an equivalence relation on* $\Pi(M)$.

We shall denote the relation "φ is conjugate to ψ" by "$\varphi \sim \psi$." An equivalence class under conjugation is called a *conjugate class.* Elements in the same conjugate class are said to be conjugates.

The set

$$\mathfrak{Z} = \{\varphi \in \Pi(M) \mid \sigma\varphi = \varphi\sigma \text{ for all } \sigma \in \Pi(M)\}$$

is called the *center* of $\Pi(M)$. Obviously, $\varphi \in \mathfrak{Z}$ if and only if φ commutes with each element in $\Pi(M)$. The reader can prove

OPOSITION 44 *A one element subset $\{\varphi\}$ is a conjugate class of $\Pi(M)$ if and only if φ is in the center of $\Pi(M)$.*

Let $\gamma = (y_1 \ y_2 \ \ldots \ y_p)$ be a cycle of Π_m. The map

$$j^\sigma = \begin{cases} y_j & \text{for } j = 1, 2, \ldots, p, \\ \min[\{1, 2, \ldots, m\} - \{1^\sigma, 2^\sigma, \ldots, (j-1)^\sigma\}] & \text{for } j > p, \end{cases}$$

is an element of Π_m such that $\sigma^{-1}(1 \ 2 \ \ldots \ p)\sigma = \gamma$. Hence $(1 \ 2 \ \ldots \ p) \sim \gamma$. Since γ could have been any cycle of order p in Π_m, we have shown that all cycles in Π_m of order p are conjugate to $(1 \ 2 \ \ldots \ p)$ and hence to each other. Summarizing, we have proved

OPOSITION 45 *Any two cycles in Π_m of the same order are conjugate.*

On the other hand, it is not true that cycles in $\Pi(\mathbf{Z})$ of the same order are necessarily conjugate. We show this fact by an example. The cycle $x^\lambda = x + 1$ and the cycle

$$x^\mu = \begin{cases} x + 2 & \text{if } x \text{ is even,} \\ x & \text{if } x \text{ is odd,} \end{cases}$$

are both of infinite order. However, $I(\lambda)$ is empty, and $I(\mu)$ is infinite. Should $\lambda \sim \mu$, then there must exist a 1-1 map of $I(\lambda)$ onto $I(\mu)$. But this is clearly impossible in this case, and so λ and μ are not conjugate. The proper generalization of Proposition 45 for general M is

OPOSITION 46 *Let γ, λ be cycles in $\Pi(M)$. Then $\lambda = \sigma^{-1}\gamma\sigma$, for some $\sigma \in \Pi(M)$, if and only if $I(\gamma)^\sigma = I(\lambda)$ and $X(\gamma)^\sigma = X(\lambda)$.*

The proof is left to the reader.

By an elaboration of the argument given in the proof of Proposition 45, one can prove

ROPOSITION 47 *Let $\gamma_1, \gamma_2, \ldots, \gamma_s$ be disjoint cycles of Π_m of orders $k_1, k_2, \ldots, k_s$ respectively. Let $\lambda_1, \lambda_2, \ldots, \lambda_s$ be another set of disjoint cycles of Π_m of orders $k_1, k_2, \ldots, k_s$ respectively. Then $\gamma_1\gamma_2 \cdots \gamma_s \sim \lambda_1\lambda_2 \cdots \lambda_s$. Conversely, if $\gamma_1\gamma_2 \cdots \gamma_s \sim \delta \in \Pi_m$, then δ can be expressed as the product of disjoint cycles of orders $k_1, k_2, \ldots., k_s$.*

EXERCISES 4 Prove Propositions 43, 44, 46, and 47.

5 Prove: Each cycle $\gamma \in \Pi(\mathbf{Z})$ such that $I(\gamma)$ and $X(\gamma)$ are both infinite is conjugate to the cycle μ defined above.

6 A. Prove: All elements in a conjugate class have the same order.

B. Show that the converse of part A is false.

7 A. Show that the existence of a surjective map of $I(\gamma)$ onto $I(\lambda)$ and a surjective map of $X(\gamma)$ onto $X(\lambda)$ implies that the cycles λ, $\gamma \in \Pi_m$ are conjugate.

B. Decide if the existence of an injection of $I(\gamma)$ into $I(\lambda)$ and an injection of $X(\gamma)$ into $X(\lambda)$ imply that the cycles γ, $\lambda \in \Pi(M)$ are conjugate.

8 Prove the following corollaries to Proposition 46:

COROLLARY 1 *If γ and λ are cycles in $\Pi(\mathbf{Z})$ such that $o(\gamma) = o(\lambda) < \infty$, then $\gamma \sim \lambda$.*

COROLLARY 2 *There are infinitely many distinct conjugate classes of elements of infinite order in $\Pi(\mathbf{Z})$.*

By use of the axiom of choice, prove the following:

COROLLARY 3 *Let M be a set. If γ and λ are cycles in $\Pi(M)$ such that $o(\gamma) = o(\lambda) < \infty$, then $\gamma \sim \lambda$.*

EXERCISES 9 Given $(1\ 2\ 3)$ and $(3\ 4\ 5)$ in Π_7, determine the number of distinct elements $\sigma \in \Pi_7$ such that $\sigma^{-1}(1\ 2\ 3)\sigma = (3\ 4\ 5)$.

10 Determine the number of conjugate classes in Π_m, for $m = 3, 5, 10$. Can you find a formula for the number g_m of conjugate classes in Π_m?

We now investigate the number of elements in a conjugate class of Π_m. If $\varphi \in \Pi_m$, we denote the conjugate class containing φ by $\mathscr{C}(\varphi)$; i.e.,

$$\mathscr{C}(\varphi) = \{\psi \in \Pi_m \mid \varphi \sim \psi\}.$$

Also, if $\varphi \in \Pi_m$, we let

$$\mathscr{H}(\varphi, \psi) = \{\rho \in \Pi_m \mid \rho^{-1}\varphi\rho = \psi\}.$$

Clearly, $\mathscr{H}(\varphi, \psi)$ is empty whenever φ and ψ are not conjugate. Also

$$\mathscr{H}(\varphi, \varphi) = \mathfrak{Z}(\varphi) = \{\sigma \in \Pi_m \mid \sigma\varphi = \varphi\sigma\}.$$

Now suppose that $\mathscr{H}(\varphi, \psi)$ is not empty and that $\rho \in \mathscr{H}(\varphi, \psi)$ and $\sigma \in \mathfrak{Z}(\varphi)$. Then

$$(\sigma\rho)^{-1}\varphi(\sigma\rho) = \rho^{-1}(\sigma^{-1}\varphi\sigma)\rho = \rho^{-1}\varphi\rho = \psi.$$

Thus the set

$$\mathfrak{Z}(\varphi)\cdot\rho = \{\delta \in \Pi_m \mid \delta\rho^{-1} \in \mathfrak{Z}(\varphi)\}$$

lies in $\mathscr{H}(\varphi, \psi)$. On the other hand, if ρ, $\xi \in \mathscr{H}(\varphi, \psi) \neq \varnothing$, then $\rho^{-1}\varphi\rho = \psi = \xi^{-1}\varphi\xi$, and we see that $(\xi\rho^{-1})\varphi = \varphi(\xi\rho^{-1})$. Thus $\xi\rho^{-1} \in \mathfrak{Z}(\varphi)$, and $\xi \in \mathfrak{Z}(\varphi)\cdot\rho$. It follows that

$$\mathscr{H}(\varphi, \psi) = \mathfrak{Z}(\varphi)\cdot\rho.$$

In particular, we see that, if $\mathscr{H}(\varphi, \psi) \neq \varnothing$, then $\mathfrak{Z}(\varphi)$ and $\mathscr{H}(\varphi, \psi)$ contain the same number of elements.

Since $\mathscr{C}(\varphi)$ is a subset of the finite set Π_m, $\mathscr{C}(\varphi)$ is a finite set, say

$$\mathscr{C}(\varphi) = \{\psi_1, \psi_2, \ldots, \psi_r\},$$

where all ψ_i are distinct. Clearly, if $i \neq j$, then $\mathscr{H}(\varphi, \psi_i) \cap \mathscr{H}(\varphi, \psi_j) = \varnothing$. To each $\sigma \in \Pi_m$ there is a ψ_j such that $\sigma^{-1}\varphi\sigma = \psi_j$, and hence $\sigma \in \mathscr{H}(\varphi, \psi_j)$. Thus

$$\mathscr{H}(\varphi, \psi_1) \cup \mathscr{H}(\varphi, \psi_2) \cup \cdots \cup \mathscr{H}(\varphi, \psi_r)$$

is a proper partition of Π_m. As each of these subsets contains exactly $|\mathfrak{Z}(\varphi)|$ elements, we have

POSITION 48 *If* $\varphi \in \Pi_m$, *then* $m! = |\mathfrak{Z}(\varphi)|\,|\mathscr{C}(\varphi)|$.

Thus the determination of the number of elements in a conjugate class $\mathscr{C}(\varphi)$ depends on determining the number of elements in the subgroup $\mathfrak{Z}(\varphi)$. The remainder of this chapter is devoted to the study of such subgroups. The subgroup $\mathfrak{Z}(\varphi)$ is called the *centralizer of* φ *in* Π_m.

We first study the centralizer of a cycle. Let $\gamma = (1\ 2\ \ldots\ k)$ be a cycle of Π_m. (Then $k \leq m$). If $\psi \in \mathfrak{Z}(\gamma)$, then $\gamma = \psi^{-1}\gamma\psi$, and by Proposition 46, letting $N = M = \{1, 2, \ldots, m\}$, we see that $I(\gamma)^\psi = I(\gamma)$. Since ψ is bijective and $I(\gamma) \cup X(\gamma)$ is a partition of M, we also have $X(\gamma)$ invariant under ψ. But then, as in Proposition 32, we can express ψ as the product of commuting transformations λ and μ of Π_m, where $I(\gamma) \subset I(\lambda)$, $X(\gamma) \subset I(\mu)$, $\text{res}_{X(\gamma)}\ \lambda = \text{res}_{X(\gamma)}\ \psi$, and $\text{res}_{I(\gamma)}\ \mu = \text{res}_{I(\gamma)}\ \psi$.

If $x \in I(\gamma)$, then $x^\lambda = x$. If $x \in X(\gamma)$, then $x^{\psi\gamma} = x^{\mu\lambda\gamma} = (x^\mu)^{\lambda\gamma} = x^{\lambda\gamma}$, and $x^{\gamma\psi} = x^{\gamma\mu\lambda} = [(x^\gamma)^\mu]^\lambda = (x^\gamma)^\lambda$. Hence $x^{\lambda\gamma} = x^{\gamma\lambda}$ for all $x \in M$. In particular we have,

$$1^\lambda = k^{\gamma\lambda} = k^{\lambda\gamma} \equiv k^\lambda + 1 \pmod{k},$$
$$u^\lambda = (u-1)^{\gamma\lambda} = (u-1)^{\lambda\gamma} \equiv (u-1)^\lambda + 1 \pmod{k}, \quad \text{for } 1 < u \leq k,$$

and

$$u^\lambda = u, \qquad \text{for all } u > k.$$

Thus we see that $\lambda = \gamma^q$, where $q + 1 = 1^\lambda$. Collecting our results, we see that $\psi = \gamma^q\mu$, where $0 \leq q < k$ and $X(\gamma) \subset I(\mu)$. In particular γ and μ are disjoint. The reader can easily check that such products do indeed belong to $\mathfrak{Z}(\gamma)$, thus completing the proof of

LEMMA 1 *If* $\gamma = (1\ 2\ \ldots\ k) \in \Pi_m$, *then* $\mathfrak{Z}(\gamma) = \{\psi \in \Pi_m \mid \psi = \gamma^q\mu$ *where* $0 \leq q < k$, *and* γ *and* μ *are disjoint*$\}$.

More generally, let $\rho = (x_1\ x_2\ \ldots\ x_k)$ be a cycle in Π_m. Then there is an element $\sigma \in \Pi_m$ such that $x_i^\sigma = i$ for $i = 1\ 2\ \ldots\ k$. If ψ commutes with ρ, then ψ^Σ commutes with ρ^Σ, where $\delta^\Sigma = \sigma^{-1}\delta\sigma$. But $\rho^\Sigma = (1\ 2\ \ldots\ k)$, and hence by the lemma we have

$$\psi^\Sigma = (\rho^\Sigma)^q(\mu^\Sigma) = (\rho^q\mu)^\Sigma,$$

where μ^Σ is disjoint from ρ^Σ. Since Σ is a 1-1 map of Π_m onto itself, we have $\psi = \rho^q\mu$, thus proving

PROPOSITION 49 *If ρ is a cycle of order k in Π_m, then $\mathfrak{Z}(\rho) = \{\psi \in \Pi_m \mid \psi = \rho^q\mu$, where $0 \le q < k$, ρ and μ are disjoint$\}$.*

Now suppose that $\varphi \in \Pi_m$ is the product of finitely many disjoint cycles, say $\varphi = \gamma_1\gamma_2 \dots \gamma_s$, where γ_i is a cycle of order k_i. If $\psi \in \mathfrak{Z}(\varphi)$, then

$$\varphi = \psi^{-1}\varphi\psi = (\psi^{-1}\gamma_1\psi)(\psi^{-1}\gamma_2\psi)\cdots(\psi^{-1}\gamma_s\psi),$$

and by the uniqueness of factorization (Corollary 1, Theorem 6) we have the set of cycles

$$\{(\psi^{-1}\gamma_1\psi), \dots, (\psi^{-1}\gamma_s\psi)\},$$

which is some permutation of the cycles

$$\{\gamma_1, \gamma_2, \dots, \gamma_s\}.$$

If no two of the cycles γ_i have the same order, then $\gamma_i = \psi^{-1}\gamma_i\psi$, for $i = 1, 2, \dots, s$. Hence $\mathfrak{Z}(\psi) = \bigcap_{i=1}^{s} \mathfrak{Z}(\gamma_i)$. It then follows from Corollary 1, Theorem 6, that

$$\psi = \gamma_1^{q_1}\gamma_2^{q_2} \dots \gamma_s^{q_s}\mu,$$

where $I(\mu) \supset X(\gamma_1) \cup X(\gamma_2) \cup \cdots \cup X(\gamma_s)$, i.e., μ and φ are disjoint.

If all the cycles have the same order, say $k = k_i$, then $\psi^{-1}\gamma_i\psi = \gamma_{(i^\tau)}$, where $\tau \in \Pi_s$. Hence if $X(\gamma_i) = \{x_{1i}\, x_{2i} \dots x_{ki}\}$, then

$$\psi = \nu\gamma_1^{q_1} \dots \gamma_s^{q_s}\mu,$$

where μ and φ are disjoint, and

$$(x_{ji})^\nu = x_{ji^\tau}, \qquad 1 \le i \le s,\ 1 \le j \le k,$$

$$x^\nu = x \qquad \text{if} \qquad x \notin X(\gamma_1) \cup \cdots \cup X(\gamma_s).$$

The general situation is a combination of the two special cases just analyzed.

THEOREM 8 *Let $\varphi \in \Pi_m$ be the product of disjoint cycles, say*

$$\varphi = \prod_s \prod_t \gamma_{st},$$

where γ_{st} are disjoint cycles and $o(\gamma_{st}) = o(\gamma_{uv})$ exactly when $s = u$. The element ψ commutes with φ if and only if

$$\psi = \prod_s v_s \prod_t \gamma_{st}^{q_{st}}\mu,$$

where v_s permutes the cycles in φ of order k_s and leaves all other elements fixed, $0 \le q_{st} < k_{st}$, and the transformation μ is disjoint from φ.

ERCISES 11 Find all elements in $\mathfrak{Z}(\varphi)$ in Π_7 if $\varphi = (1\ \ 2)(3\ \ 4)(5\ \ 6\ \ 7)$.

12 Find all elements in Π_7 that commute with both $(1\ \ 2)$ and $(1\ \ 3\ \ 5)$.

13 If $\gamma = (1\ \ 2\ \ \ldots\ \ k) \in \Pi_m$, determine $\mathfrak{Z}(\gamma)$ and $\mathscr{C}(\gamma)$.

14 Let $\varphi \in \Pi_m$ and determine the number of elements in $\mathfrak{Z}(\varphi)$ when φ is the product of s disjoint cycles of order k.

15 Prove the following corollary:

COROLLARY *If $m \geq 3$, then the center of Π_m consists only of the identity transformation.*

16 Determine the center of $\mathfrak{A}_m$ for $m = 3, 4, 5$, and 6.

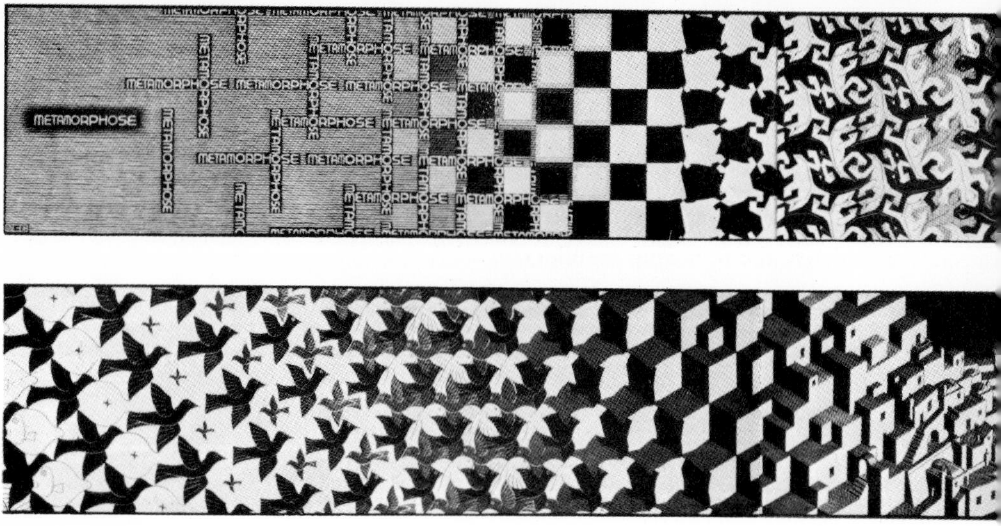

CHAPTER THREE

ABSTRACT GROUPS

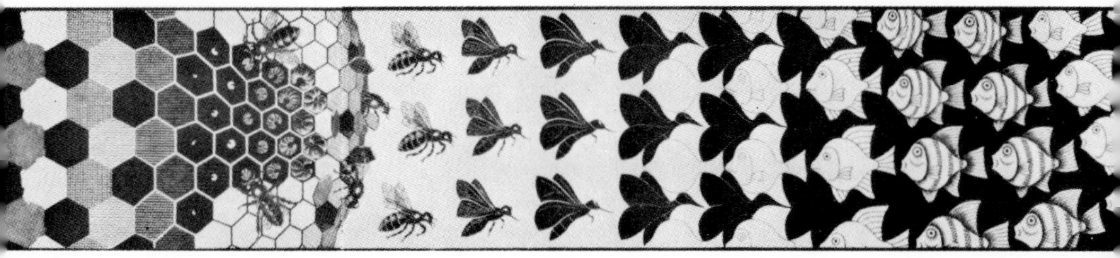

1 INTRODUCTION

We have been studying transformation groups on various sets. These groups consisted of a set of elements, namely, transformations, together with a method or rule for combining two elements in the set to obtain a third element (the product of maps) relative to which certain properties held, e.g., the associative law, the existence of an identity, and the existence of inverses. We saw that certain facts held whenever we were considering transformation groups, regardless of the underlying set of objects. On reflection, it will be noted that the integers under the operation of addition possess these same properties.

These examples of sets with their rules of combination appear to be quite different in nature; yet they possess a number of common properties. This suggests that we should investigate exactly what other properties they have in common. The procedure is somewhat similar to that used in Chap. 1, where we studied the integers and demonstrated how all the properties of the integers could be obtained as logical consequences of a very small set of properties.

In order to be precise, we shall need several definitions. A *binary operation on a set* $\mathscr{G}$ is a mapping of the set $\mathscr{G}^{(2)}$† into $\mathscr{G}$. Thus the product of two maps of $\mathscr{T}(M)$ is the binary operation on $\mathscr{T}(M)$ given by the map

$$(\varphi, \psi) \to \varphi\psi.$$

The addition of two integers is a binary operation on $\mathbf{Z}$, as is multiplication. The mapping

$$(m, n) \to m^n$$

is a binary operation on $\mathbf{Z}^+$.

† $\mathscr{G}^{(2)}$ denotes the set of ordered pairs of elements from $\mathscr{G}$.

A binary operation is a generalization of addition and multiplication. To remind us of this fact it is customary to denote the image of (x, y) under the binary operation α by $x \textcircled{a} y$. Thus

$$(x, y) \xrightarrow{\alpha} x \textcircled{a} y.$$

This notation is especially useful if we wish to study the image of $(x \textcircled{a} y, z)$ under the map α.

One quickly observes that some binary operations on a set $\mathcal{G}$ satisfy

$$x \textcircled{a} y = y \textcircled{a} x, \qquad \text{for all } x, y \in \mathcal{G} \tag{1}$$

but others do not. Binary operations satisfying Eq. 1 are said to be *commutative.*

Associated with each binary operation α on a finite set $\mathcal{G}$ is its table. This table is a square array of elements of $\mathcal{G}$ obtained in the following fashion: The elements of $\mathcal{G}$ are ordered, say $\mathcal{G} = \{g_1, g_2, \ldots, g_m\}$. In the spot where the ith row (of the array) meets the jth column (of the array) the element $g_i \textcircled{a} g_j$ is placed. To each binary operation α there are a number of tables, depending on the different orderings of the elements of $\mathcal{G}$. However, if the ordering of the elements of $\mathcal{G}$ is kept fixed, then there is a 1-1 correspondence between binary operations on $\mathcal{G}$ and the set of all $m \times m$ arrays of elements of $\mathcal{G}$. Hence there are m^{m^2} binary operations on a set of m elements.

Inspection of an operation's tables can yield much information about the operation. For example, a binary operation α is commutative if and only if its tables are each symmetric about the main diagonal.†

EXERCISES

1 If $|\mathcal{G}| = m$, determine the maximum number of commutative binary operations on $\mathcal{G}$.

2 A binary operation α on $\mathcal{G}$ is said to be *associative* provided

$$(x \textcircled{a} y) \textcircled{a} z = x \textcircled{a} (y \textcircled{a} z), \qquad \text{for all } x, y, z \in \mathcal{G}.$$

A. If $|\mathcal{G}| \leq 3$, show that each associative binary operation on $\mathcal{G}$ is also commutative.

B. Give examples of binary operations on a finite set $\mathcal{G}$ that are associative and not commutative.

C. Give examples of binary operations on a finite set $\mathcal{G}$ that are commutative and not associative.

D. Determine the number of commutative and associative binary operations on $\{g_1, g_2, g_3, g_4\}$ if the first row of the table is g_4, g_3, g_1, g_2.

3 A binary operation α on $\mathcal{G}$ is said to satisfy the cancellation laws if

$$\begin{cases} x \textcircled{a} y = x \textcircled{a} z & \text{implies} \quad y = z, \text{ and} \\ y \textcircled{a} x = z \textcircled{a} x & \text{implies} \quad y = z. \end{cases} \tag{2}$$

† The main diagonal is customarily defined to be the diagonal joining the upper left-hand corner with the lower right-hand corner.

A. Give examples, with $|\mathscr{G}| = 4$ and 5, of nonassociative binary operations satisfying Eq. (2).
B. Prove: If $|\mathscr{G}|$ is finite and if α is a binary operation satisfying (2), then the maps $x \xrightarrow{\rho_a} (x \circledast a)$, $x \xrightarrow{\lambda_a} (a \circledast x)$ are transformations on $\mathscr{G}$.
C. Prove: If α is a binary operation on $\mathscr{G}$ satisfying (2), then no element appears twice in any row or column of a table for α.
D. If $|\mathscr{G}| = m$, determine the number of binary operations α on $\mathscr{G}$ that satisfy (2).

4 A binary operation $\circledast$ on $\mathscr{G}$ is said to possess an identity in $\mathscr{G}$ provided there is an $e \in \mathscr{G}$ such that

$$x \circledast e = x = e \circledast x, \qquad \text{for all } x \in \mathscr{G}.$$

When $|\mathscr{G}| = 3$ and 4, determine the number of associative binary operations on $\mathscr{G}$ which have an identity in $\mathscr{G}$ and which satisfy (2).

In case we restrict our attention to a single binary operation $\circledast$ on $\mathscr{G}$, it is customary to omit the α from the circle and to write

$$x \circ y$$

or even

$$x \cdot y$$

for $x \circledast y$. Since the last notation is exactly like that for multiplication, it is quite common, when confusion will not arise, to omit the symbol for the operation altogether and to write

$$xy.$$

In this case, we may abuse the language and speak of the binary operation as the "product."

A *group* $\mathscr{G}$ is a set of elements together with an associative binary operation on $\mathscr{G}$ such that:

A. There is an element $e \in \mathscr{G}$ such that

$$xe = x = ex, \qquad \text{for all } x \in \mathscr{G}.$$

B. To each $a \in \mathscr{G}$ there is at least one element $a' \in \mathscr{G}$ such that

$$aa' = e = a'a.$$

The set $\Pi(M)$ together with the operation of iteration of maps is a group. The set $\mathscr{T}(M)$ with the operation of iteration of maps is not a group, since condition B is not satisfied. The set of integers **Z** with the operation of addition is a group, but **Z** with the operation of multiplication is not. This chapter will be devoted to determining various properties of groups.

We have

PROPOSITION 1 *The operation of a group satisfies the cancellation laws.*

PROOF. Let x' be an element of $\mathcal{G}$ such that $xx' = e$ (see B). Suppose $ax = bx$; then

$$a = ae = a(xx') = (ax)x' = (bx)x' = b(xx') = be = b.$$

Similarly $xa = xb$ implies $a = b$.

COROLLARY *If $\mathcal{G}$ is a group and $a, b \in \mathcal{G}$, then there exists exactly one $x \in \mathcal{G}$ such that $ax = b$ and exactly one $y \in \mathcal{G}$ such that $ya = b$.*

PROOF. Suppose $aa' = e$. Then $a(a'b) = b$, and hence the equation $ax = b$ has at least one solution. If $ax = b$ and $ay = b$, then $ax = ay$ and by Proposition 1 we have $x = y$. Thus there is at most one solution of $ax = b$. The equation $ya = b$ can be handled analogously.

It should be noted that in the definition of a group, conditions A and B only stipulated that the equations $ax = x$ and $ax = e$ have solutions in $\mathcal{G}$. The corollary assures us that these equations each have exactly one solution in $\mathcal{G}$. The unique solution of $ax = e = xa$ is usually denoted by a^{-1}. Hence, if $\mathcal{G}$ is a group, then to each $a \in \mathcal{G}$ there is a unique element $a^{-1} \in \mathcal{G}$ such that $aa^{-1} = e = a^{-1}a$. The element a^{-1} is called the *inverse of a in $\mathcal{G}$*. The unique element e such that $ae = a = ea$ is called the *identity of $\mathcal{G}$*.

EXERCISES 5 A. Prove: In a group we have $e^{-1} = e, (xyz)^{-1} = z^{-1}y^{-1}x^{-1}, (x^{-1})^{-1} = x$.
B. Discuss the inverse of a finite product of elements of a group.

6 Does the generalized associative law hold in groups?

7 Can you prove that the x and y of the corollary are equal?

8 Let $\mathcal{G}$ be a set with an associative binary operation on its elements and suppose:
A. There is an element e' in $\mathcal{G}$ such that $xe' = x$ for all x in $\mathcal{G}$.
B. To each x in $\mathcal{G}$ there is an element x' in $\mathcal{G}$ such that $xx' = e'$.
Prove that $\mathcal{G}$ is a group. (*Hint:* Show that, if $ax = bx$, then $a = b$. Next observe that $e'(aa') = e'e' = e' = aa'$, and hence $e'a = a$, for all a in $\mathcal{G}$. Finally show that $x'x = e'$.)
Compare A and B of the definition of a group with Exercise 8A and B.

Clearly each finite group has a table determined by its operation. Usually, in writing the table for a finite group, we order the elements so that $e = g_1$. Since a group operation satisfies the cancellation law, no element appears twice in any one row or any one column of a group table (Exercise 3B). Also, because of the corollary every element of $\mathcal{G}$ appears in each row and in each column. It follows that no two rows coincide; also no two columns coincide. Each row, also each column, of the group table represents a distinct transformation on the set $\mathcal{G}$. It is natural to ask how many binary operations can be defined on a set $\mathcal{G} = \{e, a_2, a_3, \ldots, a_n\}$ so that $\mathcal{G}$ has the structure of a group. Some information can be obtained from considering the group table. For example, if $\mathcal{G}$ consists of two elements only, say e and a, then the only possible group table is

$$\begin{pmatrix} e & a \\ a & e \end{pmatrix}.$$

Similarly, to within an interchange of subscripts,

$$\begin{pmatrix} e & a_1 & a_2 \\ a_1 & a_2 & e \\ a_2 & e & a_1 \end{pmatrix}$$

is the only possible group table on three elements.

ERCISES 9 Prove the last two statements in the above paragraph.

10 Do any of the following tables describe a group?

$$\begin{pmatrix} e & a & b & c \\ a & b & c & a \\ b & c & e & a \\ c & b & a & e \end{pmatrix}, \quad \begin{pmatrix} e & a & b & c \\ a & b & c & e \\ b & c & e & a \\ c & e & a & b \end{pmatrix}, \quad \begin{pmatrix} e & a & b & c \\ a & e & c & b \\ b & c & e & a \\ c & b & a & e \end{pmatrix}, \quad \begin{pmatrix} e & a & b & c \\ a & b & c & e \\ b & c & e & a \\ c & e & a & b \end{pmatrix}.$$

11 How many different binary operations can be defined on a set $\mathcal{G}$ of five elements so that $\mathcal{G}$ is a group?

12 Suppose that $\mathcal{G}$ is a finite set with an associative binary operation that satisfies the cancellation law. Prove that $\mathcal{G}$ together with this operation is a group. Give an example to show that this theorem does not hold if $\mathcal{G}$ is an infinite set.

2 RESIDUE CLASS GROUPS

Recall the definition of congruence modulo m (Chap. 2, Sec. 7): If a, b, and m are in $\mathbf{Z}$, we say that $a \equiv b \pmod{m}$ if and only if $m \mid (a - b)$. We saw that congruence modulo 0 is the same as ordinary equality. Also congruence modulo m is the same as congruence modulo $-m$. Therefore for the remainder of this section, when we speak of congruence modulo m, we shall assume that m is a positive integer. We saw that $a \equiv b \pmod{m}$ if and only if a and b have the same least non-negative remainder on division by m; i.e., $a \equiv b \pmod{m}$ implies $a = mq + r$, $b = mp + r$, where $p, q, r \in \mathbf{Z}$ and $0 \leq r \leq m$.

Let $\lfloor a \rfloor$ denote the equivalence class modulo m that contains a; i.e.,

$$\begin{aligned} \lfloor a \rfloor &= \{x \in \mathbf{Z} \mid x \equiv a \pmod{m}\} \\ &= \{x \in \mathbf{Z} \mid m \mid (x - a)\}. \end{aligned}$$

The set $\lfloor a \rfloor$ is called a *residue class modulo m*. As sets, we have $\lfloor a \rfloor = \lfloor a + mk \rfloor$, for every k in $\mathbf{Z}$. If $a = qm + r$, then $\lfloor a \rfloor = \lfloor r \rfloor$. If $\lfloor a \rfloor = \lfloor c \rfloor$, then $m \mid (a - c)$. If $\lfloor a \rfloor \cap \lfloor c \rfloor \neq \varnothing$, then $\lfloor a \rfloor = \lfloor c \rfloor$. Finally, we have

$$\mathbf{Z} = \lfloor 0 \rfloor \cup \lfloor 1 \rfloor \cup \lfloor 2 \rfloor \cup \cdots \cup \lfloor m - 1 \rfloor.$$

Let $\mathbf{Z}_m$ be the set of distinct residue classes modulo m; then $\mathbf{Z}_m$ contains exactly m elements. However, each element of $\mathbf{Z}_m$ can be denoted in many ways, e.g.,

$$\lfloor 0 \rfloor = \lfloor m \rfloor = \lfloor 2m \rfloor = \lfloor 3m \rfloor = \lfloor -m \rfloor.$$

EXERCISE 1 Prove:

A. The set addition of $\lfloor a \rfloor$ and $\lfloor b \rfloor$ is $\lfloor a + b \rfloor$.

B. The set multiplication of $\lfloor a \rfloor$ and $\lfloor b \rfloor$ is contained in the set $\lfloor ab \rfloor$.

Exercise 1 suggests defining the following binary operations on $\mathbf{Z}_m$:

$$\lfloor a \rfloor + \lfloor b \rfloor = \lfloor a + b \rfloor,$$
$$\lfloor a \rfloor \cdot \lfloor b \rfloor = \lfloor ab \rfloor.$$

We call these operations, addition of residue classes and multiplication of residue classes respectively. Clearly these two operations on $\mathbf{Z}_m$ are commutative. The reader should check that both of these operations satisfy the associative law. Clearly $\lfloor a \rfloor + \lfloor 0 \rfloor = \lfloor a \rfloor$, and $\lfloor a \rfloor + \lfloor -a \rfloor = \lfloor 0 \rfloor$, for all a in $\mathbf{Z}$; hence $\mathbf{Z}_m$ is a group under the operation of addition of residue classes. On the other hand $\mathbf{Z}_m$ is not a group under multiplication of residue classes, since $\lfloor 0 \rfloor \cdot \lfloor a \rfloor = \lfloor 0 \rfloor$, for all a in $\mathbf{Z}$. Henceforth, when we talk of the group $\mathbf{Z}_m$, we shall mean $\mathbf{Z}_m$ under the operation of addition of residue classes.

EXERCISES 2 Compute the group table for $\mathbf{Z}_2$, $\mathbf{Z}_5$, $\mathbf{Z}_8$, and $\mathbf{Z}_{12}$.

3 Prove: If m is composite, then residue class multiplication in $\mathbf{Z}_m$ does not satisfy the cancellation law.

4 Prove: The distributive law holds for residue class addition and multiplication.

It is clear that $\lfloor a \rfloor \lfloor 1 \rfloor = \lfloor a \rfloor = \lfloor 1 \rfloor \cdot \lfloor a \rfloor$. Now recall that the congruence $ax \equiv b \pmod{m}$ has a solution if and only if $(a, m) \mid b$. Hence if m is a prime and $(a, m) = 1$, then there is an x such that $\lfloor a \rfloor \lfloor x \rfloor = \lfloor 1 \rfloor$. It follows that, if m is a prime, then the set $\{\lfloor 1 \rfloor, \lfloor 2 \rfloor, \ldots, \lfloor m - 1 \rfloor\}$ of nonzero residue classes modulo m is a group under multiplication.

Observe that, if $(a, m) = 1$ and $\lfloor a \rfloor = \lfloor c \rfloor$, then $(c, m) = 1$. Thus the set

$$\mathbf{Z}'_m = \{\lfloor a \rfloor \text{ in } \mathbf{Z}_m \mid (a, m) = 1\}$$

is a well-defined subset of $\mathbf{Z}_m$.

OPOSITION 2 *The set $\mathbf{Z}'_m$ is a group under multiplication.*

The proof is left to the reader.

Since $\mathbf{Z}'_m$ does not contain $\lfloor 0 \rfloor$, it cannot be a group under addition. Henceforth, when we speak of the group $\mathbf{Z}'_m$, we shall mean the set $\mathbf{Z}'_m$ together with the operation of multiplication of residue classes.

XERCISES 5 Prove: If $p_1, \ldots, p_u$ are the distinct prime divisors of m, then the number of elements in $\mathbf{Z}'_m$ is

$$\varphi(m) = m(1 - p_1{}^{-1})(1 - p_2{}^{-1}) \cdots (1 - p_u{}^{-1}).$$

(*Hint:* Chap. 2, Sec. 6, Exercise 2.)

6 Determine the group table of the following: $\mathbf{Z}'_2, \mathbf{Z}'_5, \mathbf{Z}'_8, \mathbf{Z}'_9, \mathbf{Z}'_{12}, \mathbf{Z}'_{17}$.

3 ADDITIONAL EXAMPLES OF GROUPS

We now give several examples of groups from geometry. Consider a square in the xy plane with the center at the origin and sides parallel to the coordinate axis. Consider the set of all rigid motions in three space that will take the square into itself. Suppose the square is centered at the origin and that its sides are parallel to the coordinate axes. Among such motions are the following:

I, the identity map;

R_1, R_2, and R_3, which are the rotations of the plane about the origin of angle 90°, 180°, and 270° respectively;

D_1 and D_2, which are reflections about the lines $y = x$ and $y = -x$ respectively; and

V and H, which are reflections about the lines $x = 0$ and $y = 0$ respectively.

These motions are maps of the square into itself, and so we have the usual product of iteration of maps. The set

$$\mathscr{R} = \{I, R_1, R_2, R_3, D_1, D_2, V, H\}$$

is a group under the operation of iteration. To prove this, we need only show that $\mathscr{R}$ is closed under iteration and the existence of inverses. (Why?) This can be done by computing the group table.

For a rigid motion to transform a square into a square, it must take edges into edges and vertices into vertices (Why?). Hence there are at most eight rigid motions taking a square into a square. Thus $\mathscr{R}$ is exactly the set of all rigid motions of the square into itself.

XERCISES 1 Prove the statements in the preceding paragraph.

2 Compute the group table of the group of rigid motions of a square.

3 Determine the group of rigid motions of an equilateral triangle; of an isosceles triangle; of a nonsquare rectangle.

4 Determine the group of all rigid motions of a regular n-sided polygon.

5 Show that the group of rigid motions of a circle is an infinite group.

4 ORDER OF GROUPS, SUBGROUPS, ORDER OF ELEMENTS

The *order* of a group $\mathscr{G}$ is the order of the set $\mathscr{G}$. Thus

$$|\Pi_m| = m!, \ |\mathbf{Z}| = \infty, \ |\mathbf{Z}_m| = m, \ |\mathbf{Z}'_m| = \varphi(m).$$

Let $\mathscr{G}$ be a group with binary operation $\cdot$. If $\mathscr{H}$ is a subset of $\mathscr{G}$, such that, under the operation $\cdot$, $\mathscr{H}$ is a group, then $\mathscr{H}$ is said to be a *subgroup of* $\mathscr{G}$.

We note that the associative law holds for any subset of a group $\mathscr{G}$; hence in checking whether a subset of a group is a subgroup, we need never worry about the associative law.

If $\mathscr{H}$ is a subgroup of $\mathscr{G}$, then since $\mathscr{H}$ is a group, there exists an element e^* of $\mathscr{H}$ such that $ae^* = a = e^*a$, for all a in $\mathscr{H}$, but then $e^* = e$, the identity of $\mathscr{G}$, since for any a in $\mathscr{G}$ the equation $ax = a$ has in $\mathscr{G}$ only the one solution $x = e$. Thus a subgroup of $\mathscr{G}$ always contains the identity element of $\mathscr{G}$. Similarly if x is in the subgroup $\mathscr{H}$, then the inverse of x in $\mathscr{H}$ is the inverse of x in $\mathscr{G}$, and hence if x is in $\mathscr{H}$, then x^{-1} is in $\mathscr{H}$.

One easily sees that, if a and b are elements of a subgroup $\mathscr{H}$ of a group $\mathscr{G}$, then ab^{-1} is in $\mathscr{H}$. Conversely we have

PROPOSITION 3 *If X is a subset of a group $\mathscr{G}$ with the property that whenever a and b are in X so is ab^{-1}, then X is a subgroup of $\mathscr{G}$.*

PROOF. If x is in X, then $xx^{-1} = e$ is in X, and hence $ex^{-1} = x^{-1}$ is in X. Thus if x and y are in X, then $x(y^{-1})^{-1} = xy$ is in X; i.e., X is closed under the operation of $\mathscr{G}$. Thus we have shown that X is a group and hence a subgroup of $\mathscr{G}$.

The set consisting of the identity element alone is always a subgroup. This subgroup is often called the *identity group*. A group is obviously a subgroup of itself. A *proper subgroup of* $\mathscr{G}$ is a subgroup different from $\mathscr{G}$ and the identity group.

The reader can prove

PROPOSITION 4 *If $\mathscr{H}$ is a subgroup of the group $\mathscr{G}$, and $\mathscr{J}$ is a subgroup of $\mathscr{H}$, then $\mathscr{J}$ is a subgroup of $\mathscr{G}$.*

PROPOSITION 5 *If $\mathscr{H}$ is a subgroup of the group $\mathbf{Z}$ other than $\{0\}$, then $\mathscr{H}$ is the set of all multiples of the smallest positive integer in $\mathscr{H}$. Conversely, a set of all the multiples of an integer is a subgroup of $\mathbf{Z}$.*

COROLLARY *The only subgroup of* $\mathbf{Z}$ *of finite order is* $\{0\}$.

POSITION 6 *For each* $\lambda \in \Lambda$, *let* $\mathscr{H}_\lambda$ *be a subgroup of the group* $\mathscr{G}$; *then the set intersection* $\bigcap_{\lambda \in \Lambda} \mathscr{H}_\lambda$ *is a subgroup of* $\mathscr{G}$.

ERCISES 1 Ascertain that what we previously called a subgroup of $\Pi(M)$ is a subgroup of $\Pi(M)$ under the above definition.

2 Is it correct to say that $\mathbf{Z}'_m$ is a subgroup of $\mathbf{Z}_m$? Explain.

3 A. Let $\mathscr{H} = \{\lfloor a \rfloor \in \mathbf{Z}_{24} \mid 2 \text{ divides } a\}$. Prove that $\mathscr{H}$ is a subgroup of $\mathbf{Z}_{24}$.

B. Prove $\mathbf{Z}_5$ has no proper subgroup.

C. Can you prove a result analogous to that in part B for $\mathbf{Z}_p$, where p is a prime?

4 Determine all subgroups of $\mathbf{Z}_m$.

5 Determine all subgroups of the group of rigid motions of a square.

6 Prove Propositions 4, 5, 6, and the corollary to Proposition 5.

7 Show that the set union of two subgroups of a group need not be a subgroup.

Let S be any nonempty set of elements of a group $\mathscr{G}$; then there exist subgroups of $\mathscr{G}$ that contain S as a subset, e.g., $\mathscr{G}$ itself contains S. Let $\langle S \rangle$ denote the intersection of all subgroups of $\mathscr{G}$ that contain S. By Proposition 6, $\langle S \rangle$ is a subgroup of $\mathscr{G}$ containing S. Obviously no smaller subgroup of $\mathscr{G}$ has that property. Hence $\langle S \rangle$ is the smallest subgroup of $\mathscr{G}$ containing the set S. Every element in $\langle S \rangle$ can be expressed as the finite product of elements from the set S and of inverses of elements of the set S. (Why?) For this reason, we say that $\langle S \rangle$ is the *subgroup of* $\mathscr{G}$ *generated by* S.

We observe the following interesting consequence of linear diophantine equations:

POSITION 7 *If* $x_1, \ldots, x_n \in \mathbf{Z}$, *then* $\langle x_1, x_2, \ldots, x_n \rangle = \langle d \rangle$, *where* $d = (x_1, x_2, \ldots, x_n)$.

If x is an element of a group, by means of induction we can define x^k, where k is in $\mathbf{Z}$, namely,

$$x^0 = e, \qquad x^k = (x^{\operatorname{sgn} k})^{|k|}, \qquad \text{for every nonzero } k \text{ in } \mathbf{Z}.$$

The group $\langle x \rangle$ generated by the single element x of $\mathscr{G}$ is the set of all integral powers of x. Clearly $\langle x \rangle = \langle x^{-1} \rangle$. If x is an element of the group $\mathscr{G}$, the *order of* x, written $o(x)$, is the order of the group $\langle x \rangle$. Thus

$$o(x) = |\langle x \rangle|.$$

ERCISES 8 A. Determine the various subgroups of $\mathbf{Z}_8$, of $\mathbf{Z}'_8$ and of $\mathbf{Z}'_9$ generated by single elements.

B. What is the order of each element in $\mathbf{Z}_8$, $\mathbf{Z}_5$, $\mathbf{Z}'_8$, $\mathbf{Z}'_9$, Π_6?
C. What is the order of each element in the group of rigid motions of a square; of a circle?

9 Prove Proposition 7.

10 Prove:
A. $o(x) = 1$ if and only if $x = e$.
B. If $0 \neq x$ is in $\mathbf{Z}$, then $o(x) = \infty$.
C. If $o(x)$ is finite, then $x^{o(x)} = e$, $x^{-1} = x^{o(x)-1}$.
D. $o(x) = 2$ if and only if $x = x^{-1}$.
E. If x is in $\mathcal{G}$, then $o(x) \leq |\mathcal{G}|$.
F. $o(x) = o(x^{-1})$.
G. If $o(x)$ is finite, then $o(x) = \min \{k \in \mathbf{Z}^+ \mid x^k = e\}$. This statement is often taken as the definition of order of an element.

11 A. Prove: Given a group $\mathcal{G}$, the map $x \xrightarrow{\varphi} x^{-1}$ is a transformation on $\mathcal{G}$ of order two; i.e., $\varphi^2 = \iota_{\mathcal{G}}$.
B. Prove: If ψ is a transformation of order 2 on a set with an even number of elements, then the fixed set for ψ contains an even number of elements.
C. Prove: If 2 divides the order of a finite group $\mathcal{G}$, then the group contains an element of order 2.
D. Find an element of order 2 in each of the following groups: Π_5, $\mathbf{Z}_8$, $\mathbf{Z}'_9$.

We shall eventually generalize Exercise 11c by showing that a prime p divides the order of a finite group if and only if the group contains an element of order p. More generally, we shall show (Sec. 14) that, if p^m divides the order of the finite group $\mathcal{J}$ and p^{m+1} does not, then $\mathcal{J}$ has a subgroup of order p^m.

5 CYCLIC GROUPS, ABELIAN GROUPS

A group $\mathcal{G}$ is said to be *cyclic* if there exists an element x in $\mathcal{G}$ such that $\mathcal{G} = \langle x \rangle$. In this case x is said to be a *generator* of the cyclic group.

EXERCISES 1 Prove: If x is a generator of a cyclic group, then x^{-1} is also a generator.

2 Prove: $\mathbf{Z}$ is a cyclic group. 1 and -1 are the only generators of $\mathbf{Z}$.

3 Prove: For every positive integer m, $\mathbf{Z}_m$ is cyclic.

4 Which of the following are cyclic: $\mathbf{Z}'_5$, $\mathbf{Z}'_8$, $\mathbf{Z}'_9$, $\mathbf{Z}'_{12}$, $\mathbf{Z}'_{13}$, $\mathbf{Z}'_{17}$?

5 Discuss the properties of the group table of a finite cyclic group.

6 A. Prove: If $(a, m) = 1$, then $\lfloor a \rfloor$ is a generator of the cyclic group $\mathbf{Z}_m$.
B. Determine the number of distinct generators of the group $\mathbf{Z}_m$.

7 A. Prove: If $x \in \mathcal{G}$ and $o(x) = |\mathcal{G}| < \infty$, then $\langle x \rangle = \mathcal{G}$.
B. Prove: If $\mathcal{G} = \langle x \rangle$ and $|\mathcal{G}| = k$, then $o(x^s) = k/(k, s)$. Hence $\langle x^s \rangle = \mathcal{G}$ exactly when $(k, s) = 1$.
C. Show that the condition $|\mathcal{G}| < \infty$ is necessary in part A.

Any time we are given a group, we are naturally curious about the nature of its subgroups. For cyclic groups the reader can prove

ROPOSITION 8 *If $\mathcal{H}$ is a subgroup of $\langle x \rangle$, then $\mathcal{H} = \langle x^\mu \rangle$, where $\mu = \min\{k \in \mathbf{Z}^+ \mid x^k \in \mathcal{H}\}$. Hence, every subgroup of a cyclic group is cyclic.*

COROLLARY *If $o(x) < \infty$ and μ is as in Proposition 8, then $\mu \mid o(x)$.*

This proposition and corollary enable us to find all subgroups of a cyclic group.

EXERCISE 8 Determine the number of distinct subgroups of $\mathbf{Z}_m$ as a function of m.

A group is said to be *abelian* or *commutative* provided the binary operation of the group is commutative. Thus $\mathcal{G}$ is abelian exactly when $xy = yx$ for all $x, y \in \mathcal{G}$. One can trivially prove the following:

ROPOSITION 9 *A subgroup of an abelian group is abelian.*

OPOSITION 10 *A cyclic group is abelian.*

OPOSITION 11 *If $\mathcal{G}$ is a group such that the order of each element of $\mathcal{G}$ is at most 2, then $\mathcal{G}$ is abelian.*

PROOF. If $x, y \in \mathcal{G}$, then

$$xy = x(xy)^2 y = x^2(yx)y^2 = yx.$$

XERCISES 9 A. Prove: $\mathbf{Z}$, $\mathbf{Z}_m$, $\mathbf{Z}'_m$ are abelian groups.
B. Prove: If M contains at least three elements, then $\Pi(M)$ is nonabelian.
C. May a subgroup of a nonabelian group be abelian?
D. Is the group of rigid motions of a square abelian?
E. Is the group of rigid motions of a circle abelian?

10 A. If a is an element of a group $\mathcal{G}$, let

$$\mathfrak{Z}(a) = \{x \in \mathcal{G} \mid ax = xa\}.$$

Show that $\mathfrak{Z}(a)$ is a subgroup of $\mathcal{G}$.
B. Does there exist a group $\mathcal{G}$ containing an element a such that $\mathfrak{Z}(a)$ is nonabelian?

11 The set $\mathfrak{Z} = \{x \in \mathscr{G} \mid xy = yx \text{ for all } y \in \mathscr{G}\}$ is called the *center of* $\mathscr{G}$. Prove:

A. $\mathfrak{Z} = \bigcap_{a \in \mathscr{G}} \mathfrak{Z}(a)$.

B. $\mathfrak{Z}$ is an abelian group.

C. $\mathfrak{Z} = \mathscr{G}$ if and only if $\mathscr{G}$ is an abelian group.

D. Compare these ideas with those in Chap. 2, Sec. 14.

12 Suppose $\mathscr{G}$ is a group containing an element x of order 2 and an element y of order 3. Prove: $\langle x \rangle \cap \langle y \rangle = \langle e \rangle$. If x and y commute, determine the group table for the subgroup $\langle x, y \rangle$. When is $\langle x, y \rangle$ cyclic?

13 Prove: If $\mathscr{G}$ is a noncyclic group of order 9, then each $x \in \mathscr{G}$, $x \neq e$, has order 3 and $\mathscr{G}$ is abelian.

14 A. Prove: If S is a nonempty subset of a finite group $\mathscr{G}$ such that, whenever x and y are in S so is xy, then S is a subgroup of $\mathscr{G}$. Compare this result with Proposition 3 and with Exercise 12, Sec. 1.

B. Prove: If S is a nonempty subset of a group $\mathscr{G}$, closed under taking products such that each $x \in S$, is of finite order, then S is a subgroup of $\mathscr{G}$.

C. Show that there exist subsets S of a group $\mathscr{G}$ with the property that $x, y \in S$ implies $xy \in S$, which are not subgroups of $\mathscr{G}$. For this to happen S must, of course, contain elements of infinite order.

15 A. Prove: If $\mathscr{G}$ is an abelian group containing x and y and if $(o(x), o(y)) = 1$, then $o(xy) = o(x)o(y)$.

B. Does the conclusion of part A hold if $\mathscr{G}$ is nonabelian?

6 COSETS OF SUBGROUPS

If $\mathscr{H}$ is a subgroup of a group $\mathscr{G}$ and x is an element of $\mathscr{G}$, the set

$$x\mathscr{H} = \{y \in \mathscr{G} \mid y = xh \text{ for some } h \in \mathscr{H}\}$$

is called a *left coset of* $\mathscr{H}$. The set $x\mathscr{H}$ is the set of all elements of $\mathscr{G}$ obtained by multiplying each element of $\mathscr{H}$ on the left by the element x. Similarly the set

$$\mathscr{H}x = \{y \in \mathscr{G} \mid y = hx \text{ for some } h \in \mathscr{H}\}$$

is called a *right coset of* $\mathscr{H}$.

We note that the set $\mathscr{H}$ is both a right coset and a left coset, for $e\mathscr{H} = \mathscr{H} = \mathscr{H}e$. Clearly x lies in both $x\mathscr{H}$ and in $\mathscr{H}x$. The set $\mathfrak{O}$ of all odd transformations of Π_m is both a left coset and a right coset of the alternating group $\mathfrak{A}_m$, namely, $\mathfrak{O} = \tau\mathfrak{A}_m = \mathfrak{A}_m\tau$, where τ is a transposition. (See Chap. 2, Sec. 13.) Should $\mathscr{H}$ be a subgroup of the center of $\mathscr{G}$, then $x\mathscr{H} = \mathscr{H}x$, for all $x \in \mathscr{G}$. However, in general $x\mathscr{H}$ and $\mathscr{H}x$ are not the same set, and the reader should exhibit examples where $x\mathscr{H} \cap \mathscr{H}x$ consists of the element x alone.

In case $\mathscr{G}$ is an additive group, we denote left cosets by the symbol $x + \mathscr{H}$.

XERCISES 1 A. If $\mathscr{H} = \langle(1\ 2\ 3)\rangle$ is a subgroup of Π_3, determine $(1\ 2)\mathscr{H}$ and $\mathscr{H}(1\ 2)$.

B. If $\mathscr{H}$ is the subgroup of $\mathbf{Z}$ generated by 5, determine what elements lie in $1 + \mathscr{H}$, $2 + \mathscr{H}$, $5 + \mathscr{H}$.

C. If x is an element of $\mathscr{H}$, show that $x\mathscr{H} = \mathscr{H} = \mathscr{H}x$.

D. Show that there is a 1-1 map of $\mathscr{H}$ onto the coset $x\mathscr{H}$.

E. Show that there is a 1-1 map of any coset (left or right) of $\mathscr{H}$ onto any other coset (left or right) of $\mathscr{H}$.

2 A. Prove: If y is in $x\mathscr{H}$, then $y\mathscr{H} = x\mathscr{H}$.

B. Prove: If z is in $\mathscr{H}x$, then $\mathscr{H}z = \mathscr{H}x$.

C. Prove: Either $x\mathscr{H} = y\mathscr{H}$ or $x\mathscr{H} \cap y\mathscr{H} = \varnothing$.

D. Prove: $x^{-1}y \in \mathscr{H}$ if and only if $x\mathscr{H} = y\mathscr{H}$.

E. Prove: $xy^{-1} \in \mathscr{H}$ if and only if $\mathscr{H}x = \mathscr{H}y$.

If $\mathscr{H}$ is any subgroup of a group $\mathscr{G}$, we can define an equivalence relation on the set $\mathscr{G}$ that is analogous to congruence on $\mathbf{Z}$. We shall say that $x \equiv y \pmod{\mathscr{H}}$ exactly when $x^{-1}y \in \mathscr{H}$. Equivalently $x \equiv y \pmod{\mathscr{H}}$ exactly when $x\mathscr{H} = y\mathscr{H}$. One easily checks that this relation in indeed an equivalence relation on $\mathscr{G}$. Clearly the equivalence classes of this relation are exactly the distinct left cosets of $\mathscr{H}$. In particular $\mathscr{G}$ is the disjoint union of all the distinct left cosets of $\mathscr{H}$. (See Theorem 3, Chap. 2.)

The number of distinct left cosets of $\mathscr{H}$ in $\mathscr{G}$ is called the *index of $\mathscr{H}$ in $\mathscr{G}$*, and we denote this index by $[\mathscr{G} : \mathscr{H}]$.

If $\mathscr{G}$ is a finite group, then any subgroup $\mathscr{H}$ of $\mathscr{G}$ is a finite group, and $[\mathscr{G} : \mathscr{H}]$ is finite. In particular, we have

THEOREM 1 *Theorem of LaGrange: If $\mathscr{G}$ is a finite group containing the subgroup $\mathscr{H}$, then $|\mathscr{G}| = |\mathscr{H}|[\mathscr{G} : \mathscr{H}]$.*

When $\mathscr{G}$ is an infinite group, at least one of $|\mathscr{H}|$ and $[\mathscr{H} : \mathscr{H}]$ is infinite, and it is possible that both are.

It follows from Theorem 1, on taking $\mathscr{H} = \langle x\rangle$, that

COROLLARY *If $\mathscr{G}$ is a finite group containing the element x, then $o(x)$ is a divisor of $|\mathscr{G}|$. Consequently $x^{|\mathscr{G}|} = e$ for all x in $\mathscr{G}$.*

The reader is now in a position to prove several famous results from number theory. The first three are actually corollaries of the above corollary.

POSITION 12 *Fermat's little theorem: If p is a prime and $(a, p) = 1$, then $a^{p-1} \equiv 1 \pmod{p}$.*

COROLLARY *If p is a prime, then $b^p \equiv b \pmod{p}$ for all $b \in \mathbf{Z}$.*

POSITION 13 *If $a, m \in \mathbf{Z}^+$ such that $(a, m) = 1$, then $a^{\varphi(m)} \equiv 1 \pmod{m}$.*

PROPOSITION 14 *Wilson's theorem: For any prime p we have* $(p-1)! \equiv -1 \pmod{p}$.

Hint: We can write $(p-1)!$ as $1\cdot(p-1)\cdot a_1a_1^* \ldots a_sa_s^*$, where $s=(p-3)/2$ and a_j^* is the unique positive integer less than p such that $a_ja_j^* \equiv 1 \pmod{p}$.

EXERCISES

3 Prove Theorem 1.

4 Prove:

A. The number of right cosets of $\mathscr{H}$ in $\mathscr{G}$ is $[\mathscr{G}:\mathscr{H}]$.

B. $|\mathscr{G}| = [\mathscr{G}:\langle e\rangle]$.

C. If $\mathscr{G}$, $\mathscr{H}$, and $\mathscr{J}$ are finite groups such that $\mathscr{J} \subset \mathscr{H} \subset \mathscr{G}$, then $[\mathscr{G}:\mathscr{J}] = [\mathscr{G}:\mathscr{H}][\mathscr{H}:\mathscr{J}]$.

5 Prove: If $\mathscr{H}$ is a proper subgroup of $\mathbf{Z}$, then $[\mathbf{Z}:\mathscr{H}]$ is finite.

6 Let $\mathscr{H} = \{\sigma \in \Pi(\mathbf{Z}) \mid x^\sigma = x$ for all but finitely many $x \in \mathbf{Z}\}$. Show that $\mathscr{H}$ is a subgroup of $\Pi(\mathbf{Z})$. Determine $|\mathscr{H}|$ and $[\Pi(\mathbf{Z}):\mathscr{H}]$. List several subgroups of $\Pi(\mathbf{Z})$ of finite index in $\Pi(\mathbf{Z})$.

7 Prove:

A. A group of prime order has no proper subgroup.

B. If $\mathscr{G}$ is a cyclic group and p is a prime dividing $|\mathscr{G}|$, then $\mathscr{G}$ contains an element of order p.

C. If the order of a group is a power of a prime p, then the group contains an element of order p.

8 Prove: If $\mathscr{H}$ and $\mathscr{J}$ are subgroups of a finite group $\mathscr{G}$ of orders s and t respectively and if $u = |\mathscr{J} \cap \mathscr{H}|$ and $v = |\langle \mathscr{J} \cup \mathscr{H}\rangle|$, then $st \le uv$.

9 Prove: If $|\mathscr{J}| < \infty$ and $x \in \mathscr{J}$ is of order p, then p divides $|\mathscr{J}|$.

7 SUBSET MULTIPLICATION, QUOTIENT GROUPS

Let $\mathscr{G}$ be a group. We define a binary operation on the nonempty subsets of $\mathscr{G}$ as follows: If X and Y are subsets of $\mathscr{G}$, then

$$X\cdot Y = \{z \in \mathscr{G} \mid z = xy \text{ for some } x \in X,\ y \in Y\};$$

i.e., $X\cdot Y$ is the set of all possible products of an element from X by an element from Y. We call this operation *subset multiplication.*† If $X=\{x\}$ and Y is a subgroup, then $x\cdot Y = X\cdot Y$ is the left coset of Y containing x. It follows that XY need not equal YX. On the other hand, if $\mathscr{G}$ is an abelian group, then $XY = YX$, for all subsets X and Y of $\mathscr{G}$. Multiplication of subsets is associative; i.e.,

$$(X\cdot Y)\cdot Z = X\cdot(Y\cdot Z), \qquad \text{for any subsets } X,\ Y, \text{ and } Z \text{ in } \mathscr{G}.$$

We have

$$XY = \bigcup_{x\in X} xY = \bigcup_{y \in Y} Xy.$$

† Compare with Chap. 1, Sec. 5; also, with our definition of addition and multiplication of residue classes in Sec. 2.

EXERCISES 1 Let $\mathscr{H}$ be a subgroup of $\mathscr{G}$, and let X, Y be subsets of $\mathscr{G}$. Prove:

A. $X \subset \mathscr{H}$ implies $X\mathscr{H} = \mathscr{H} = \mathscr{H}X$.

B. $X\mathscr{H} \subset Y\mathscr{H}$ exactly when $X \subset Y\mathscr{H}$.

C. $(x\mathscr{H})\mathscr{H} = x\mathscr{H}$, $\mathscr{H}(\mathscr{H}x) = \mathscr{H}x$ for all $x \in \mathscr{G}$.

2 Prove:

A. For each subset X of $\mathscr{G}$ we have $Xe = X = eX$.

B. If $X, Y, W \subset \mathscr{G}$ and if $X \subset Y$, then $XW \subset YW$ and $WX \subset WY$.

C. For each subset X of $\mathscr{G}$ we have $X\mathscr{G} = \mathscr{G} = \mathscr{G}X$.

3 If X is a subset of $\mathscr{G}$, let $X' = \{g \in \mathscr{G} \mid g^{-1} \in X\}$. Prove:

A. If $X \subset Y$, then $X' \subset Y'$.

B. $(XY)' = Y'X'$.

C. If $\mathscr{H}$ is a subgroup, then $\mathscr{H}' = \mathscr{H}$.

D. If $\mathscr{H}$ is a subgroup, then $(g\mathscr{H})' = \mathscr{H}g^{-1}$.

4 Prove: Set multiplication is an associative operation.

Under our definition of multiplication of subsets of $\mathscr{G}$, the set of all nonempty subsets of $\mathscr{G}$ does not form a group. There are many reasons why this is so, the most obvious being $X \cdot \mathscr{G} = \mathscr{G}$, for every subset X. This counterexample suggests the possibility that the set of all proper subsets of $\mathscr{G}$ is a group under set multiplication. The reader should show that such is not the case. However, it is possible that an even more restricted collection of such subsets does form a group.

We remark that, when the group operation is addition instead of subset multiplication, we consider subset addition and write $X + Y = \{z \in \mathscr{G} \mid z = x + y$ for some $x \in X$ and some $y \in Y\}$. We saw in Sec. 2 that the set addition of two residue classes was a residue class. Thus $\mathbf{Z}_m$ is the group of distinct residue classes modulo m under the operation of subset addition. On the other hand a residue class modulo m is but a left coset of the subgroup $m\mathbf{Z}$, the set of all multiples of m. This suggests that we investigate whether the set of distinct left cosets of $\mathscr{H}$ in $\mathscr{G}$ form a group under subset multiplication.

To begin with, we determine when the product of two left cosets lies in a third left coset. Suppose

$$(x\mathscr{H})(y\mathscr{H}) \subset z\mathscr{H}, \tag{3}$$

for some $x, y, z \in \mathscr{G}$ and some subgroup $\mathscr{H}$ of $\mathscr{G}$. Then

$$x\mathscr{H}y \subset z\mathscr{H}$$

and

$$\mathscr{H}y \subset x^{-1}z\mathscr{H}. \tag{4}$$

But $y \in \mathscr{H}y$, and so there must exist an $h \in \mathscr{H}$ such that

$$y = x^{-1}zh,$$

in which case

$$y\mathscr{H} = x^{-1}zh\mathscr{H} = x^{-1}z\mathscr{H}. \tag{5}$$

Combining Eqs. 4 and 5, we have

$$\mathscr{H}y \subset y\mathscr{H}. \tag{6}$$

In order that the left cosets of $\mathscr{H}$ should form a group under set multiplication, for each x, $y \in \mathscr{G}$ there must be a $z \in \mathscr{G}$ so that Eq. 3 holds and hence Eq. 6 must hold for all $y \in \mathscr{G}$.

It follows from Eq. 6, using Exercise 3, that

$$y^{-1}\mathscr{H} \subset \mathscr{H}y^{-1}. \tag{7}$$

Should Eq. 6 hold for all $y \in \mathscr{G}$, then Eq. 7 holds for all $y^{-1} \in \mathscr{G}$. But every element in $\mathscr{G}$ is the inverse of some element in $\mathscr{G}$. Hence if Eq. 7 holds for all $y^{-1} \in \mathscr{G}$, then

$$y\mathscr{H} \subset \mathscr{H}y \tag{8}$$

holds for all $y \in \mathscr{G}$. It follows from Eqs. 6 and 8 that

$$y\mathscr{H} = \mathscr{H}y, \qquad \text{for all } y \in \mathscr{G}. \tag{9}$$

Now if Eq. 9 holds, then

$$(x\mathscr{H})(y\mathscr{H}) = x(\mathscr{H}y)\mathscr{H} = x(y\mathscr{H})\mathscr{H} = xy\mathscr{H}.$$

Thus we have proved

LEMMA 1 *A necessary and sufficient condition that the product of any two left cosets of a subgroup $\mathscr{H}$ of $\mathscr{G}$ should be a left coset of $\mathscr{H}$ is that*

$$y\mathscr{H} = \mathscr{H}y, \qquad \textit{for all } y \in \mathscr{G}. \tag{10}$$

We note that not every subgroup $\mathscr{H}$ of a group $\mathscr{G}$ need satisfy Eq. 10. For example, let $\mathscr{G} = \Pi_4$, and let $\mathscr{H} = \langle(1\ 2\ 3)\rangle$.

A group $\mathscr{H}$ is said to be a *normal subgroup of* $\mathscr{G}$ if

$$x\mathscr{H} = \mathscr{H}x, \qquad \text{for all } x \in \mathscr{G}.$$

Thus a subgroup $\mathscr{H}$ is normal in $\mathscr{G}$ if and only if each left coset of $\mathscr{H}$ is a right coset of $\mathscr{H}$. It is customary to write $\mathscr{H} \lhd \mathscr{G}$ to indicate that $\mathscr{H}$ is a normal subgroup of $\mathscr{G}$. Clearly $\mathscr{H} \lhd \mathscr{G}$ if and only if $y^{-1}\mathscr{H}y = \mathscr{H}$ for all $y \in \mathscr{G}$; i.e., $\mathscr{H}$ is an invariant set under each of the maps $g \longrightarrow y^{-1}gy$ of $\mathscr{G}$ onto $\mathscr{G}$.

If $\mathscr{H} \lhd \mathscr{G}$, then

$$(x\mathscr{H})(y\mathscr{H}) = xy\mathscr{H}, \qquad (x\mathscr{H})\mathscr{H} = x\mathscr{H}, \qquad \mathscr{H}(x\mathscr{H}) = x\mathscr{H},$$

and $(x\mathscr{H})(x^{-1}\mathscr{H}) = xx^{-1}\mathscr{H} = \mathscr{H} = (x^{-1}x)\mathscr{H} = (x^{-1}\mathscr{H})(x\mathscr{H})$.

Thus we have proved

THEOREM 2 *If $\mathscr{H} \lhd \mathscr{G}$, then the collection of left cosets of $\mathscr{H}$ in $\mathscr{G}$ is a group under set multiplication.*

The set of distinct left cosets of a normal subgroup $\mathscr{H}$ in $\mathscr{G}$ with the operation of set multiplication is called the *quotient group of* $\mathscr{G}$ *by* $\mathscr{H}$ and is denoted by the symbol $\mathscr{G}/\mathscr{H}$. Since, for normal subgroups, left cosets are the same as right cosets, we can, if we like, think of $\mathscr{G}/\mathscr{H}$ as a collection of distinct right cosets.

The reader should prove

POSITION 15 *If* $\mathscr{G}$ *is an abelian group, then every subgroup of* $\mathscr{G}$ *is normal in* $\mathscr{G}$.

POSITION 16 *If* $\mathscr{G}$ *is abelian and* $\mathscr{H} \lhd \mathscr{G}$, *then* $\mathscr{G}/\mathscr{H}$ *is abelian. If* $\mathscr{G}$ *is cyclic and* $\mathscr{H} \lhd \mathscr{G}$, *then* $\mathscr{G}/\mathscr{H}$ *is cyclic.*

POSITION 17 *The center of a group is always normal in the group.*

POSITION 18 *The intersection of a set of normal subgroups of* $\mathscr{G}$ *is a normal subgroup of* $\mathscr{G}$.

COROLLARY *Given a subgroup* $\mathscr{H}$ *of* $\mathscr{G}$, *there is a minimal normal subgroup* $\mathscr{N}$ *of* $\mathscr{G}$ *that contains* $\mathscr{H}$.

POSITION 19 *If* $\mathscr{G}$ *is an abelian group and* $\mathscr{T} = \{x \in \mathscr{G} \mid o(x) < \infty\}$, *then* $\mathscr{T}$ *is a normal subgroup of* $\mathscr{G}$, *and each element of* $\mathscr{G}/\mathscr{T}$, *except the identity, has infinite order.*

The group $\mathscr{T}$, of Proposition 19, is called the *torsion subgroup of* $\mathscr{G}$.

XERCISES 5

A. Show that the alternating group $\mathfrak{A}_m$ is a normal subgroup of Π_m, and determine $\Pi_m/\mathfrak{A}_m$.

B. Prove: If $\mathscr{G}/\mathscr{H}$ is the quotient group of a finite group $\mathscr{G}$ by a normal subgroup $\mathscr{H}$, then $|\mathscr{G}/\mathscr{H}|$ is a divisor of $|\mathscr{G}|$. In fact $|\mathscr{G}/\mathscr{H}| = |\mathscr{G}|/|\mathscr{H}|$.

C. Given a group $\mathscr{G}$, prove that the trivial subgroups $\langle e\rangle$ and $\mathscr{G}$ are always normal in $\mathscr{G}$.

D. Is the group $\langle(1\ 2\ 3\ 4\ 5)\rangle$ normal in Π_5?

E. Let $F(m) = \{\sigma \in \Pi_m \mid m^\sigma = m\}$. Is $F(m)$ normal in Π_m?

F. Suppose $\mathscr{N}$ and $\mathscr{H}$ are subgroups of $\mathscr{G}$ and that $\mathscr{N} \lhd \mathscr{G}$. Show that $\mathscr{N} \cap \mathscr{H}$ is normal in $\mathscr{H}$. Is $\mathscr{N} \cap \mathscr{H}$ necessarily normal in $\mathscr{G}$?

G. Let $\mathscr{H} = \{\varphi \in \mathfrak{A}_m \mid m^\varphi = m\}$. Show that $\mathscr{H}$ is normal in $F(m)$.

H. Let $\mathscr{H}$ be a subgroup of $\mathscr{G}$, and let $\mathscr{N} = \bigcap_{x \in \mathscr{G}} x^{-1}\mathscr{H}x$. Show that $\mathscr{N}$ is a normal subgroup in $\mathscr{G}$.

6 Suppose $\langle \iota\rangle \neq \mathscr{N} \lhd \mathfrak{A}_n$, $n > 4$:

A. Prove: If $\mathscr{N}$ contains an element σ such that $o(\sigma) \nmid 6$, then $\sigma = \gamma_1\gamma_2 \cdots \gamma_r$, where the γ_i are disjoint cycles and $\gamma_r = (x_1\ x_2\ \ldots\ x_s)$, with $s > 3$. Set $\delta = (x_{s-2}\ x_{s-1}\ x_s)$, and show that $\sigma\delta\sigma^{-1}\delta^{-1}$ is a cycle of order 3 in $\mathscr{N}$.

B. Prove: If $\mathscr{N}$ contains an element of order 6, then $\mathscr{N}$ contains an element of order 3.

C. If σ is an element of order 2 in $\mathcal{N}$, show that $\sigma = (x_1\ x_2)(x_3\ x_4) \cdots (x_{2s-1}\ x_{2s})$, where $s = 2t > 1$. If $2s < n$, then set $\beta = (x_1\ x_n)$, where x_n is different from $x_1, x_2, \ldots, x_{2s}$, and show that $\sigma\beta^{-1}\sigma\beta$ is a 3 cycle in $\mathcal{N}$.

D. If σ is as in part C but $2s = n$, then $n \geq 8$. Set $\mu = (x_3\ x_4\ x_5) \cdot (x_6\ x_7\ x_8)$, and show that $\sigma\mu^{-1}\sigma\mu$ is an element in $\mathcal{N}$ of order 3.

E. If $\mathcal{N}$ contains an element σ of order 3 that is not a 3 cycle, then $\sigma = (x_1\ x_2\ x_3)(x_4\ x_5\ x_6) \cdots (x_{3s-2}\ x_{3s-1}\ x_{3s})$, where $s \geq 2$. Set $\alpha = (x_6\ x_1\ x_2)$, and show that $\sigma\alpha^{-1}\sigma^{-1}\alpha$ is a 5 cycle in $\mathcal{N}$.

F. Prove: If $\langle\iota\rangle \neq \mathcal{N} \lhd \mathfrak{A}_n$, $n > 4$, then $\mathcal{N}$ contains a 3 cycle.

G. Prove: Any normal subgroup $\mathcal{N}$ of $\mathfrak{A}_n$ that contains a 3 cycle contains all 3 cycles, and hence $\mathcal{N} = \mathfrak{A}_n$.

Exercise 6 is an outline of a proof of

THEOREM 3 *If* $\langle\iota\rangle \neq \mathcal{N} \lhd \mathfrak{A}_n$ and $n \geq 5$, *then* $\mathcal{N} = \mathfrak{A}_n$.

The reader can prove

COROLLARY *If* $n > 4$, *then the only normal subgroups of* Π_n *are* $\langle\iota\rangle$, $\mathfrak{A}_n$, *and* Π_n.

If the trivial subgroups are the only normal subgroups of $\mathcal{G}$, then $\mathcal{G}$ is said to be a *simple group*. Thus $\mathfrak{A}_n$, where $n > 4$, and $\mathbf{Z}_p$, where p is a prime, are simple groups. It is an interesting but difficult problem to determine whether a group is simple.

EXERCISE 7 Determine whether the preceding theorem is true for Π_3 and Π_4.

8 ISOMORPHISM, HOMOMORPHISM

In our study of transformation groups we saw that, if there exists a 1-1 map σ of M onto N, then there exists a 1-1 map Σ of $\Pi(M)$ onto $\Pi(N)$ such that

$$(\pi\delta)^\Sigma = \pi^\Sigma\delta^\Sigma, \qquad \text{for all } \pi, \delta \text{ in } \Pi(M). \tag{11}$$

(Chap. 2, Proposition 41.) The significance of a map satisfying Eq. 11 is seen by considering the group tables of $\Pi(M)$ and $\Pi(N)$. We note that

$$(\pi)^\Sigma = (\iota_M\pi)^\Sigma = \iota_M{}^\Sigma\pi^\Sigma;$$

hence

$$\iota_M{}^\Sigma = \iota_N.$$

Let

$$\iota_M, \pi_2, \pi_3, \ldots$$

be the first row of the group table of $\Pi(M)$, and arrange the first row of the group table of $\Pi(N)$ as follows:

$$\iota_N, \pi_2{}^\Sigma, \pi_3{}^\Sigma, \ldots .$$

Then Eq. 11 tells us that, if λ is the entry in the (i, j) spot of the group table of $\Pi(M)$, then λ^Σ is the entry in the (i, j) spot of the group table of $\Pi(N)$. Thus the group tables of the two groups coincide, and we see that any information that we have about the structure of one group (such as its order, the existence of a group element of order 2, the existence of a nontrivial center, etc.) also applies to the structure of the other group. Because of the existence of this map Σ we saw that, in studying transformation groups on finite sets, it was sufficient to study the groups $\Pi_1, \Pi_2, \Pi_3, \ldots$. We now study such maps for arbitrary groups.

Let $\mathcal{G}$ be a group with the binary operation $(\cdot)$, and let $\mathcal{G}^*$ be a group with the binary operation $(\circ)$. A map φ of $\mathcal{G}$ into $\mathcal{G}^*$ such that

$$(x \cdot y)^\varphi = x^\varphi \circ y^\varphi, \qquad \text{for all } x, y \in \mathcal{G}, \tag{12}$$

is called a *homomorphism* of $\mathcal{G}$ into $\mathcal{G}^*$. A map φ that satisfies Eq. 12 is also called an *operation-preserving map.*

An injective map of $\mathcal{G}$ into $\mathcal{G}^*$ that satisfies Eq. 12 is called a *monomorphism* of $\mathcal{G}$ into $\mathcal{G}^*$. Thus a monomorphism is an injective operation-preserving map. A monomorphism of $\mathcal{G}$ into $\mathcal{G}^*$ has the effect of *embedding* $\mathcal{G}$ in the group $\mathcal{G}^*$.

A map of $\mathcal{G}$ onto $\mathcal{G}^*$ that satisfies Eq. 12 is called an *epimorphism* of $\mathcal{G}$ onto $\mathcal{G}^*$. An epimorphism is a surjective operation-preserving map.

A bijective map of $\mathcal{G}$ onto $\mathcal{G}^*$ that satisfies Eq. 12 is called an *isomorphism* of $\mathcal{G}$ onto $\mathcal{G}^*$. If there is an isomorphism of $\mathcal{G}$ onto $\mathcal{G}^*$, we say *$\mathcal{G}$ is isomorphic to $\mathcal{G}^*$.*

If $n = qm + r$, where $0 \le r < m$, the map $n^\varphi = \lfloor n \rfloor = \lfloor r \rfloor$ is an epimorphism of $\mathbf{Z}$ onto $\mathbf{Z}_m$, since in this case Eq. 12 is equivalent to the fact that, when $n \equiv r \pmod{m}$ and $p \equiv s \pmod{m}$, then $n + p \equiv r + s \pmod{m}$. The map Σ described at the beginning of this section is an isomorphic map of $\Pi(M)$ onto $\Pi(N)$. If α is in Π_m, define

$$\alpha^\varphi = \begin{pmatrix} 1 & 2 & 3 & \cdots & m & m+1 \\ 1^\alpha & 2^\alpha & 3^\alpha & \cdots & m^\alpha & m+1 \end{pmatrix};$$

then φ is a monomorphism of Π_m into Π_{m+1}.

The reader should prove

POSITION 20 *Let σ be a homomorphism of $\mathcal{G}$ into $\mathcal{G}^*$:*

A. *If e is the identity of $\mathcal{G}$, then e^σ is the identity of $\mathcal{G}^*$.*

B. *If x^{-1} is the inverse of x in $\mathcal{G}$, then $(x^{-1})^\sigma$ is the inverse of x^σ in $\mathcal{G}^*$; i.e., $(x^{-1})^\sigma = (x^\sigma)^{-1}$.*

POSITION 21 *If σ is a homomorphism of $\mathcal{G}$ into $\mathcal{H}$ and ψ is a homomorphism of $\mathcal{H}$ into $\mathcal{J}$, then $\sigma\psi$ is a homomorphism of $\mathcal{G}$ into $\mathcal{J}$.*

XERCISES 1 A. Let $\mathcal{H}$ be the multiplicative group consisting of 1 and -1; show that the map $n^\varphi = (-1)^n$ is an epimorphism of $\mathbf{Z}$ onto $\mathcal{H}$.

B. Let S be a finite subset of M. Let $\mathcal{G} = \{\pi \in \Pi(M) \mid S^\pi \subset S\}$. Show that the map $\pi \to \text{res}_S\, \pi$ is an epimorphism of $\mathcal{G}$ onto $\Pi(S)$.

2 A. Show that, if $\mathcal{G}$ is a subgroup of $\mathcal{J}$, there always exists a monomorphism of $\mathcal{G}$ into $\mathcal{J}$.

B. Show that every group can be mapped homomorphically onto the trivial group consisting of the identity alone.

C. Trivially every group can be mapped monomorphically into itself by the identity map. Show that there are infinitely many different monomorphisms of $\mathbf{Z}$ into itself.

D. Show that every group can be mapped isomorphically onto itself.

E. Does each group possess more than one isomorphism of the group onto itself?

3 A. Show that, if $\mathcal{G}$ is isomorphic to $\mathcal{H}$, then $|\mathcal{G}| = |\mathcal{H}|$.

B. Prove: If φ is a homomorphism of $\mathcal{G}$ into $\mathcal{H}$ and x is in $\mathcal{G}$, then the order of x in $\mathcal{G}$ is at least as large as the order of x^φ in $\mathcal{H}$.

C. Is it possible to state a more precise result than that in part B?

D. Prove: If φ is a monomorphism of $\mathcal{G}$ into $\mathcal{H}$ and $x \in \mathcal{G}$, then the order of x in $\mathcal{G}$ is the order of x^φ in $\mathcal{H}$.

4 A. Show that $\mathbf{Z}_4$ is isomorphic to $\mathbf{Z}'_5$ but that $\mathbf{Z}'_8$ is not isomorphic to either of them.

B. Is $\mathbf{Z}'_6$ isomorphic to $\mathbf{Z}'_9$?

C. Is $\mathbf{Z}_6$ isomorphic to Π_3?

PROPOSITION 22 *If φ is a homomorphism of $\mathcal{G}$ into $\mathcal{G}^*$, then the image of $\mathcal{G}$ under φ is a subgroup of $\mathcal{G}^*$.*

PROOF. Since $\mathcal{G}^\varphi$ is a subset of $\mathcal{G}^*$, the elements of $\mathcal{G}^\varphi$ satisfy the associative law. By Proposition 20 we see that $\mathcal{G}^\varphi$ contains the identity and the inverse of each element in $\mathcal{G}^\varphi$. Finally, we see that $\mathcal{G}^\varphi$ is closed under multiplication, since $x^\varphi \cdot y^\varphi = (xy)^\varphi$.

COROLLARY *If φ is a homomorphism of $\mathcal{G}$ into $\mathcal{G}^*$, then φ is an epimorphism of $\mathcal{G}$ onto $\mathcal{G}^\varphi$.*

If φ is a homomorphism of $\mathcal{G}$ into $\mathcal{G}^*$ and e^* is the identity of $\mathcal{G}^*$, the set

$$\mathfrak{K}_\varphi = \{g \in \mathcal{G} \mid g^\varphi = e^*\}$$

is called the *kernel of* φ.

PROPOSITION 23 *The kernel of a homomorphism of $\mathcal{G}$ into $\mathcal{G}^*$ is a normal subgroup of $\mathcal{G}$.*

PROOF. Let φ be the homomorphism of $\mathcal{G}$ into $\mathcal{G}^*$. If $x \in \mathfrak{K}_\varphi$, then $x^\varphi = e^*$, and so by Proposition 20 we have

$$e^* = e^{*-1} = (x^\varphi)^{-1} = (x^{-1})^\varphi.$$

Now if $x, y \in \mathfrak{K}_\varphi$, then $yx^{-1} \in \mathfrak{K}_\varphi$, since

$$(yx^{-1})^\varphi = y^\varphi(x^{-1})^\varphi = e^* \cdot e^* = e^*.$$

It follows from Proposition 3 that $\mathfrak{K}_\varphi$ is a subgroup of $\mathscr{G}$.

Finally we observe, if $x \in \mathfrak{K}_\varphi$, then

$$(g^{-1}xg)^\varphi = (g^{-1})^\varphi x^\varphi g^\varphi = (g^\varphi)^{-1} g^\varphi = e^*,$$

for all $g \in \mathscr{G}$. Hence $\mathfrak{K}_\varphi \lhd \mathscr{G}$.

PROPOSITION 24 *Let φ be a homomorphism of $\mathscr{G}$ into $\mathscr{G}^*$, and let $x, y \in \mathscr{G}$; then $x^\varphi = y^\varphi$, if and only if $x\mathfrak{K}_\varphi = y\mathfrak{K}_\varphi$, where $\mathfrak{K}_\varphi$ is the kernel of φ.*

COROLLARY 1 *A homomorphism φ of $\mathscr{G}$ into $\mathscr{H}$ is injective if and only if $\mathfrak{K}_\varphi = \langle e \rangle$.*

Now by Corollary 1 and Proposition 21 we have

COROLLARY 2 *If φ is a monomorphism of $\mathscr{G}$ into $\mathscr{G}^*$ and ψ is a monomorphism of $\mathscr{G}^*$ into $\mathscr{J}$, then $\varphi\psi$ is a monomorphism of $\mathscr{G}$ into $\mathscr{J}$.*

If φ is an isomorphism of $\mathscr{G}$ onto $\mathscr{H}$, then (see Chap. 2, Sec. 2) there exists a 1-1 map φ^* of $\mathscr{H}$ onto $\mathscr{G}$ such that $\varphi\varphi^* = \iota_\mathscr{G}$, $\varphi^*\varphi = \iota_\mathscr{H}$. We claim that φ^* is an isomorphism of $\mathscr{H}$ onto $\mathscr{G}$. Since φ is bijective given $h, k \in \mathscr{H}$, there is a unique x and a unique y in $\mathscr{G}$ so that $x^\varphi = h$, $y^\varphi = k$, $h^{\varphi^*} = x$, and $k^{\varphi^*} = y$. Then

$$(hk)^{\varphi^*} = (x^\varphi \cdot y^\varphi)^{\varphi^*} = ((xy)^\varphi)^{\varphi^*} = (xy)^{\varphi\varphi^*} = xy = h^{\varphi^*}k^{\varphi^*}.$$

Therefore φ^* is an operation-preserving map and hence an isomorphism.

Now every group is isomorphic to itself (Exercise 2D). We have just proved that, if $\mathscr{G}$ is isomorphic to $\mathscr{H}$, then $\mathscr{H}$ is isomorphic to $\mathscr{G}$, and by Corollary 2 it follows that the relation "is isomorphic to" is a transitive relation. Thus we have

THEOREM 4 *The relation "is isomorphic to" is an equivalence relation on groups.*

We denote the equivalence relation "is isomorphic to" by $\cong$.

EXERCISES 5 Prove Proposition 24 and its corollaries.

6 Let σ be a homomorphism of $\mathscr{G}$ into $\mathscr{H}$:

A. Prove: If $\mathscr{G}$ is abelian, then $\mathscr{G}^\sigma$ is abelian.

B. Prove: If $\mathscr{G}$ is a cyclic group, then $\mathscr{G}^\sigma$ is cyclic.

C. Give examples where $\mathscr{G}$ is nonabelian but $\mathscr{G}^\sigma$ is abelian.

D. Give examples where $\mathscr{G}$ is abelian and $\mathscr{H}$ is nonabelian.

E. Discuss the possibility of an abelian group being isomorphic to a nonabelian group.

F. Prove: If $\mathscr{J} \lhd \mathscr{G}$, then $\mathscr{J}^\sigma \lhd \mathscr{G}^\sigma$.

G. Give examples where $\mathscr{J} \lhd \mathscr{G}$ and $\mathscr{J}^\sigma \ntriangleleft \mathscr{H}$.

H. Prove: The homomorphic image of a simple group is simple.

PROPOSITION 25 *A cyclic group of order m is isomorphic to $\mathbf{Z}_m$. A cyclic group of infinite order is isomorphic to $\mathbf{Z}$.*

PROOF. Let $\mathscr{G} = \langle x \rangle$, where $o(x) = m$. The reader can show that the map

$$x^u \rightarrow \lfloor u \rfloor_m$$

is an isomorphism of $\mathscr{G}$ onto $\mathbf{Z}_m$. Similarly, if $\mathscr{G} = \langle x \rangle$ and $|\mathscr{G}| = \infty$, the map $x^u \rightarrow u$ is an isomorphism of $\mathscr{G}$ onto $\mathbf{Z}$.

This proposition completely characterizes cyclic groups. We can learn everything concerning cyclic groups by studying the groups $\mathbf{Z}$ and $\mathbf{Z}_m$ $(m = 1, 2, \dots.)$.

Consider a group $\mathscr{G}$ of order 4 that is not cyclic. By the corollary to Theorem 1 and Exercise 7A, Sec. 5, if $e \neq g \in \mathscr{G}$, then $o(g) = 2$. We saw in Proposition 11 that such groups are necessarily abelian. Thus there are elements $a, b \in \mathscr{G}$ such that $\mathscr{G} = \{e, a, b, ab\}$. The map

$$e \rightarrow \lfloor 1 \rfloor_8, \qquad a \rightarrow \lfloor 3 \rfloor_8, \qquad b \rightarrow \lfloor 5 \rfloor_8, \qquad ab \rightarrow \lfloor 7 \rfloor_8$$

is an isomorphism of $\mathscr{G}$ onto $\mathbf{Z}'_8$. We have proved

PROPOSITION 26 *If $\mathscr{G}$ is a group of order 4, then either $\mathscr{G} \cong \mathbf{Z}_4$ or $\mathscr{G} \cong \mathbf{Z}'_8$.*

EXERCISES 7 Let p be a prime, and show that, if φ is a homomorphism of $\mathbf{Z}_p$ into $\mathscr{G}$, then either $x^\varphi = e$ for all x or φ is a monomorphism.

8 Prove: A homomorphism of $\mathbf{Z}$ into $\mathbf{Z}$, other than the O map, is necessarily a monomorphism.

9 A. Suppose $\mathscr{G} = \langle S \rangle$, and suppose φ and σ are homomorphisms of $\mathscr{G}$ into $\mathscr{H}$ such that $s^\varphi = s^\sigma$ for all s in S. Prove that $\varphi = \sigma$.

B. Let $\gamma \in \Pi_n$, and show that there exists an isomorphism φ of Π_n into Π_n such that $(1\ \ r)^\varphi = (1^\gamma\ \ r^\gamma)$, for $r = 2, 3, \dots, n$.

10 Let $\mathscr{G}$ be a group; to each x in $\mathscr{G}$ define the map

$$a \rightarrow a^{r_x} = ax$$

of $\mathscr{G}$ into $\mathscr{G}$:

A. Show that r_x is an element of $\Pi(\mathscr{G})$.

B. Prove: If $x \neq y$, then $r_x \neq r_y$.

C. Show that $r_x r_y = r_{xy}$, for all x and y in $\mathscr{G}$.

D. Prove: The set $\mathfrak{R}(\mathscr{G})$ consisting of all the maps r_x, with $x \in \mathscr{G}$, is a subgroup of $\Pi(\mathscr{G})$.

E. Show that the mapping $x^\rho = r_x$ of $\mathscr{G}$ into $\Pi(\mathscr{G})$ is a monomorphism of $\mathscr{G}$ into $\Pi(\mathscr{G})$.

F. Show that $\mathscr{G} \cong \mathfrak{R}(\mathscr{G})$.

In Exercise 10 we have outlined a proof of a theorem of Cayley, namely

THEOREM 5 *Every group $\mathscr{G}$ is isomorphic to a subgroup of a group of transformations. Specifically $\mathscr{G} \cong \mathfrak{R}(\mathscr{G}) \subset \Pi(\mathscr{G})$.*

This theorem is a rather interesting result. We started our study of groups by studying groups of transformations. We then decided it would be to our advantage to study abstract groups, i.e., a set with a binary operation satisfying a few simple rules. We have now come full circle and have shown that each abstract group is isomorphic to a subgroup of a group of transformations. Does this mean we can forget about abstract groups altogether? The answer is no, and the reasons many. For one, we have embedded the abstract group $\mathscr{G}$ into the transformation group $\Pi(\mathscr{G})$. But $\Pi(\mathscr{G})$ has extremely large order compared with $\mathscr{G}$, and we know very little about groups of large order. So far we have found only a few properties of a group that are inherited by subgroups (being cyclic and being abelian are two inheritable properties), so that even though we know much about $\Pi(\mathscr{G})$, we cannot use this information to tell us about the properties of $\mathscr{G}$. One final example: The information that all groups of order 4 can be embedded in Π_4 is very marginal compared with the information contained in Proposition 26.

Let M be a countable set, and let S be the set of all 3 cycles in $\Pi(M)$. Set $\mathfrak{A}(M) = \langle S \rangle$. In the next exercise the reader will find a proof of a generalization of Theorem 3, namely

THEOREM 6 $\mathfrak{A}(\mathbf{Z})$ *is a simple group.*

XERCISE 11

A. Show: If γ is a 3 cycle in $\Pi(M)$ and λ is in $\Pi(M)$, then $\lambda^{-1}\gamma\lambda$ is a 3 cycle in $\Pi(M)$.

B. Prove $\mathfrak{A}(M) \lhd \Pi(M)$.

C. Let $X_n = \{1, 2, \ldots, n\} \subset \mathbf{Z}^+$. Let S_n be the set of 3 cycles in $\Pi(\mathbf{Z}^+)$ that leave elements not in X_n fixed. Let $\mathfrak{A}(X_n) = \langle S_n \rangle$. Prove: $\mathfrak{A}(X_n) \cong \mathfrak{A}_n$; hence $\mathfrak{A}(X_n)$ is a simple group.

D. Show that, if $\sigma \in \mathfrak{A}(\mathbf{Z}^+)$, then there exists an integer n such that $\sigma \in \mathfrak{A}(X_n)$, and hence $\mathfrak{A}(\mathbf{Z}^+) = \bigcup_{n \in \mathbf{Z}^+} \mathfrak{A}(X_n)$.

E. Prove: If $\mathscr{N}$ is a proper normal subgroup of $\mathfrak{A}(\mathbf{Z}^+)$, then there exists an integer n such that $\mathscr{N} \cap \mathfrak{A}(X_n) \neq \langle \iota \rangle$.

F. Prove $\mathfrak{A}(\mathbf{Z}^+)$ is simple.

G. Prove $\mathfrak{A}(\mathbf{Z}) \cong \mathfrak{A}(\mathbf{Z}^+)$.

H. Prove Theorem 6.

9 HOMOMORPHISMS

We now investigate the concept of a homomorphism in greater detail. The reader can prove

POSITION 27 *If $\mathscr{N} \lhd \mathscr{G}$, then the mapping*

$$x \to x^{\pi} = x\mathscr{N}$$

is an epimorphism of $\mathcal{G}$ onto $\mathcal{G}/\mathcal{N}$, and the kernel of the map π is the subgroup $\mathcal{N}$.

Note that Proposition 27 tells us each normal subgroup is the kernel of a homomorphism. Previously, we saw each kernel was a normal subgroup. Thus the collection of all normal subgroups of $\mathcal{G}$ and the collection of all kernels of homomorphisms of $\mathcal{G}$ are the same.

Now Proposition 23 suggests we investigate the validity of the converse of Proposition 27. The converse would be that, if σ is a homomorphism of $\mathcal{G}$ onto $\mathcal{H}$ with kernel $\mathcal{N}$, then $\mathcal{G}/\mathcal{N}$ is $\mathcal{H}$. This is too much to expect, but we can show that $\mathcal{G}/\mathcal{N} \cong \mathcal{H}$.

Suppose σ is a homomorphism of $\mathcal{G}$ onto $\mathcal{H}$ with kernel $\mathcal{N}$. Define

$$(x\mathcal{N})^{\Sigma} = x^{\sigma}, \qquad x \in \mathcal{G}.$$

Then Σ is a mapping of $\mathcal{G}/\mathcal{N}$ into $\mathcal{H}$, since (as we saw in Proposition 24) $x\mathcal{N} = y\mathcal{N}$ if and only if $x^{\sigma} = y^{\sigma}$.

Furthermore

$$((x\mathcal{N})(y\mathcal{N}))^{\Sigma} = (xy\mathcal{N})^{\Sigma} = (xy)^{\sigma} = x^{\sigma}y^{\sigma} = (x\mathcal{N})^{\Sigma}(y\mathcal{N})^{\Sigma}.$$

Hence Σ is an operation-preserving map. Consequently Σ is a homomorphism of $\mathcal{G}/\mathcal{N}$ into $\mathcal{H}$.

If

$$(x\mathcal{N})^{\Sigma} = e = \text{the identity of } \mathcal{H},$$

then

$$x^{\sigma} = e^{*},$$

and consequently $x \in \mathcal{N}$. It follows that the kernel of Σ consists of the identity of $\mathcal{G}/\mathcal{N}$ alone. Hence Σ is injective. Since σ is onto, so is Σ. Thus we have shown that Σ is a bijective operation-preserving map, proving

THEOREM 7 *If σ is an epimorphism (homomorphism) of $\mathcal{G}$ onto $\mathcal{H}$, then $\mathcal{G}/\mathcal{N} \cong \mathcal{H}$, where $\mathcal{N}$ is the kernel of σ.*

This theorem is of great import, for it says that to within isomorphism the only homomorphic images of a group are its quotient groups. Thus the three concepts of homomorphism, quotient group, and normal subgroup are intimately related.

We now prove a result about quotient groups that helps justify the name and the notation. We shall need a lemma whose proof is straightforward and is left to the reader.

LEMMA *Let $\mathcal{J}$ be a subgroup of $\mathcal{H}$ that in turn is a subgroup of $\mathcal{G}$. If $\mathcal{J}$ and $\mathcal{H}$ are normal subgroups of $\mathcal{G}$, then $\mathcal{J} \lhd \mathcal{H}$, and $\mathcal{H}/\mathcal{J} \lhd \mathcal{G}/\mathcal{J}$.*

THEOREM 8 *Let $\mathcal{J}$ be a subgroup of $\mathcal{H}$ that in turn is a subgroup of $\mathcal{G}$. If $\mathcal{J}$ and $\mathcal{H}$ are normal subgroups of $\mathcal{G}$, then $\mathcal{G}/\mathcal{H} \cong (\mathcal{G}/\mathcal{J})/(\mathcal{H}/\mathcal{J})$.*

PROOF. By Proposition 27 there is an epimorphism σ of $\mathcal{G}$ onto $\mathcal{G}/\mathcal{J}$ and an epimorphism τ of $\mathcal{G}/\mathcal{J}$ onto $(\mathcal{G}/\mathcal{J})/(\mathcal{H}/\mathcal{J})$. Hence by Proposition 21, $\sigma\tau$ is an epimorphism of $\mathcal{G}$ onto $(\mathcal{G}/\mathcal{J})/(\mathcal{H}/\mathcal{J})$. Now the kernel of $\sigma\tau$ is the set

$$(e^*)^{\tau^{-1}\sigma^{-1}} = (\mathcal{H}/\mathcal{J})^{\sigma^{-1}} = \mathcal{H}.$$

Hence by Theorem 7, we have

$$\mathcal{G}/\mathcal{H} \cong (\mathcal{G}/\mathcal{J})/(\mathcal{H}/\mathcal{J}).$$

EXERCISE 1 Let $\mathcal{N} \lhd \mathcal{G}$. Let $N = \{\mathcal{H} \mid \mathcal{N} \subset \mathcal{H} \subset \mathcal{G}\}$. Let M be the set of subgroups of $\mathcal{G}/\mathcal{N}$. Prove that there is a bijection δ of N onto M such that:

A. $\mathcal{N} \subset \mathcal{H}_1 \subset \mathcal{H}_2$ if and only if $\mathcal{H}_1^{\ \delta} \subset \mathcal{H}_2^{\ \delta}$.
B. $\mathcal{N} \subset \mathcal{H} \lhd \mathcal{G}$ if and only if $\mathcal{H}^\delta \lhd \mathcal{G}/\mathcal{N}$.
C. If $\mathcal{N} \subset \mathcal{H} \lhd \mathcal{G}$, then $\mathcal{G}/\mathcal{H} \cong \mathcal{G}^\delta/\mathcal{H}^\delta$.
D. If $\mathcal{H} \in N$, then $[\mathcal{G} : \mathcal{H}] = [\mathcal{G}^\delta : \mathcal{H}^\delta]$.

The reader should prove

OPOSITION 28 *If $\mathcal{H}$ and $\mathcal{J}$ are subgroups of a group $\mathcal{G}$ and one of $\mathcal{H}$ and $\mathcal{J}$ is normal in $\mathcal{G}$, then $\mathcal{H}\mathcal{J} = \mathcal{J}\mathcal{H} = \langle \mathcal{H} \cup \mathcal{J} \rangle$.*

OPOSITION 29 *If $\mathcal{H} \lhd \mathcal{G}$ and $\mathcal{J}$ is a subgroup of $\mathcal{G}$, then $\mathcal{H} \cap \mathcal{J} \lhd \mathcal{J}$ and $\mathcal{H} \lhd \mathcal{J}\mathcal{H}$.*

OPOSITION 30 *If $\mathcal{H} \lhd \mathcal{G}$ and $\mathcal{J}$ is a subgroup of $\mathcal{G}$, then $\mathcal{J}/\mathcal{H} \cap \mathcal{J} \cong \mathcal{H}\mathcal{J}/\mathcal{H}$.*

XERCISES 2 Let $\mathcal{G}$ be a group; let

$$\mathfrak{C} = \{x \in \mathcal{G} \mid x = uvu^{-1}v^{-1} \text{ for some } u, v \in \mathcal{G}\}.$$

The elements of $\mathfrak{C}$ are called *commutators*. Set

$$\mathcal{G}' = \langle \mathfrak{C} \rangle.$$

$\mathcal{G}'$ is called the *commutator subgroup of* $\mathcal{G}$ or the *derived group of* $\mathcal{G}$. Prove:

A. $\mathcal{G}' \lhd \mathcal{G}$.
B. $\mathcal{G}/\mathcal{G}'$ is abelian.
C. If φ is a homomorphism of $\mathcal{G}$ into an abelian group $\mathcal{G}^*$, then the kernel of φ contains $\mathcal{G}'$.
D. Find examples where

$$\mathcal{G} \underset{\neq}{\supset} \mathcal{G}' \underset{\neq}{\supset} (\mathcal{G}')'.$$

3 Give examples to show Proposition 28 is false if neither $\mathcal{H}$ nor $\mathcal{J}$ is normal in $\mathcal{G}$.

10 AUTOMORPHISMS

An isomorphism of a group $\mathscr{G}$ onto itself is called an *automorphism of* $\mathscr{G}$. The identity map $\iota_{\mathscr{G}}$ is always an automorphism of $\mathscr{G}$. If $\mathscr{G}$ is an abelian group, the map $x^\rho = x^{-1}$ is always an automorphism of $\mathscr{G}$. In particular, the map $x^\rho = -x$ is an automorphism of the additive group of integers. Note, here we must use the additive inverse, since our operation is addition.

If σ and τ are automorphisms of $\mathscr{G}$, then $\sigma\tau$ is bijective, and so by Proposition 21 $\sigma\tau$ is an automorphism of $\mathscr{G}$. Also if σ is an automorphism of $\mathscr{G}$, then by the argument preceding Theorem 4, σ^{-1} is also an automorphism of $\mathscr{G}$. Thus we have proved

PROPOSITION 31 *The set $\mathscr{A}(\mathscr{G})$ of all automorphisms of a group is a subgroup of $\Pi(\mathscr{G})$, the set of transformations on $\mathscr{G}$.*

Since $e^\sigma = e$, for any σ in $\mathscr{A}(\mathscr{G})$, we can actually say that $\mathscr{A}(\mathscr{G}) \subset F(e) = \{\sigma \in \Pi(\mathscr{G}) \mid e^\sigma = e\}$.

EXERCISES

1. Show that the map $x^\rho = x^{-1}$ is an automorphism of an abelian group, but not an automorphism of a nonabelian group. For an abelian group $\mathscr{G}$, show that $\rho = \iota_{\mathscr{G}}$ if and only if the order of each element of $\mathscr{G}$ does not exceed 2.
2. Prove $\mathscr{A}(\mathbf{Z}) \cong \mathbf{Z}_2$.
3. Determine the automorphism group of $\mathbf{Z}_3$, of $\mathbf{Z}_4$, of $\mathbf{Z}_5$, and of $\mathbf{Z}_6$.
4. Prove:
   A. If $\mathscr{G}$ is an abelian group, then $\langle\rho\rangle$ is a normal subgroup of $\mathscr{A}(\mathscr{G})$.
   B. If $\mathscr{G} = \langle x\rangle$ and $\sigma \in \mathscr{A}(\mathscr{G})$, then $\mathscr{G} = \langle x^\sigma\rangle$. Conversely, if $\langle x\rangle = \langle y\rangle = \mathscr{G}$, then the map μ, given by $(x^r)^\mu = y^r$ for r in $\mathbf{Z}$, is an automorphism of $\mathscr{G}$. Hence if $\mathscr{G}$ is cyclic, then $|\mathscr{A}(\mathscr{G})|$ is the number of generators of $\mathscr{G}$.

The reader can now prove

PROPOSITION 32 $\mathscr{A}(\mathbf{Z}_m) \cong \mathbf{Z}'_m$.

PROPOSITION 33 If $\mathscr{G} \cong \mathscr{H}$, then $\mathscr{A}(\mathscr{G}) \cong \mathscr{A}(\mathscr{H})$.

Is the converse of this last proposition true?

Suppose that $\mathscr{G}$ is a multiplicative group, and let a be an element of $\mathscr{G}$; then the map

$$x^{\gamma_a} = a^{-1}xa, \qquad x \in \mathscr{G},$$

is an automorphism of $\mathscr{G}$. This map is bijective, since $\gamma_a \cdot \gamma_{a^{-1}} = \iota_{\mathscr{G}} = \gamma_{a^{-1}} \cdot \gamma_a$. Also

$$(xy)^{\gamma_a} = a^{-1}(xy)a = a^{-1}xaa^{-1}ya = x^{\gamma_a}y^{\gamma_a}.$$

Thus for each $a \in \mathcal{G}$, γ_a is an automorphism of $\mathcal{G}$.

If σ is an automorphism of $\mathcal{G}$ and there exists an element $a \in \mathcal{G}$ such that $\sigma = \gamma_a$, then σ is said to be an *inner automorphism of* $\mathcal{G}$. An automorphism that is not inner is sometimes called an *outer automorphism.* We denote the set of all inner automorphisms of $\mathcal{G}$ by $\mathcal{I}(\mathcal{G})$. $\mathcal{I}(\mathcal{G})$ is a group, and the following propositions hold:

OPOSITION 34 $\mathcal{I}(\mathcal{G}) \cong \mathcal{G}/\mathfrak{Z}$, where $\mathfrak{Z}$ is the center of $\mathcal{G}$.

OPOSITION 35 $\mathcal{I}(\mathcal{G}) \lhd \mathcal{A}(\mathcal{G})$.

EXERCISES 5 Prove Proposition 34. (*Hint:* Show $\gamma_a = \iota_{\mathcal{G}}$ if and only if $a \in \mathfrak{Z}(\mathcal{G})$.)

6 A. Prove: If $\varphi \in \mathcal{A}(\mathcal{G})$, then $\varphi^{-1}\gamma_a\varphi = \gamma_b$, where $b = a^\varphi$.

B. Prove Proposition 35.

7 Show that the set of outer automorphisms of a group $\mathcal{G}$ does not form a subgroup of $\mathcal{A}(\mathcal{G})$.

Two subsets X_1, X_2 of $\mathcal{G}$ are said to be *conjugate* if there exists a $g \in \mathcal{G}$ such that

$$X_1^{\gamma_g} = g^{-1}X_1g = X_2.$$

It is easily seen that "being conjugate" is an equivalence relation on the set of all subsets of $\mathcal{G}$. If X_1 and X_2 are conjugate, we denote this equivalence by

$$X_1 \sim X_2.$$

Clearly $\qquad X_1 \sim X_2 \qquad$ implies $\qquad |X_1| = |X_2|,$

and $X \sim \mathcal{H}$, where $\mathcal{H}$ is a subgroup, implies X is a subgroup. Thus "being conjugate" is an equivalence relation on the set of all subgroups of $\mathcal{G}$. It is also an equivalence relation on the set $\mathcal{G}$ itself.

Given a set $X \subset \mathcal{G}$, we shall denote the equivalence class of sets conjugate to X by $\mathfrak{c}(X)$. Hence

$$\mathfrak{c}(X) = \{Y \subset \mathcal{G} \mid Y = X^\gamma \text{ for some } \gamma \in \mathcal{I}(\mathcal{G})\}.$$

If $x \in \mathcal{G}$, the set $\mathfrak{c}(x)$ is called a *conjugate class of* $\mathcal{G}$.

A set $X \subset \mathcal{G}$ is said to be *self-conjugate* if $g^{-1}Xg = X$, for all $g \in \mathcal{G}$. Thus normal subgroups constitute the collection of self-conjugate subgroups.

An automorphism σ of $\mathcal{G}$ induces a transformation on $S(\mathcal{G})$, the set of all subsets of $\mathcal{G}$, namely,

$$X \to X^\sigma.$$

A normal subgroup $\mathcal{H}$ of $\mathcal{G}$ is one for which

$$\mathcal{H}^\sigma = \mathcal{H}, \qquad \text{for all } \sigma \in \mathcal{I}(\mathcal{G}).$$

For this reason, normal subgroups are often called *invariant subgroups.* We note in passing that a subgroup $\mathscr{H}$ of $\mathscr{G}$ is said to be a *characteristic subgroup* provided

$$\mathscr{H}^\sigma = \mathscr{H}, \qquad \text{for all } \sigma \in \mathscr{A}(\mathscr{G}).$$

EXERCISES 8 Prove:

A. If $x \in \mathscr{G}$, $\mathfrak{c}(x) = \{x\}$ if and only if $x \in \mathfrak{Z}(\mathscr{G})$.
B. If $X, Y \subset \mathscr{G}$, $X \sim Y$, $\varphi \in \mathscr{A}(\mathscr{G})$, then $X^\varphi \sim Y^\varphi$.
C. If $x \in \mathscr{G}$, then the set $\mathfrak{c}(x)$ is self-conjugate.
D. If X is a self-conjugate set and $\varphi \in \mathscr{A}(\mathscr{G})$, then X^φ is self-conjugate.
E. If $x \sim y$, then $o(x) = o(y)$.
F. If $\varphi \in \mathscr{A}(\Pi_n)$, then $(1\ 2)^\varphi$ is the product of disjoint transpositions.

9 A. Prove: If $\tau = (1\ 2) \in \Pi_n$, then the conjugate class of τ is the set of all transpositions in Π_n.
B. Does part A extend? That is, is it true that the conjugate class of a cycle of length k in Π_n is the set of all cycles of length k?
C. Prove: If $\alpha \sim \beta$ and α is the product of k disjoint cycles, then β is the product of k disjoint cycles.
D. If $\pi = \gamma_1\gamma_2 \cdots \gamma_s$, where the γ_i are disjoint cycles in Π_n, determine which elements lie in $\mathfrak{c}(\pi)$.
E. Show that the number of conjugate classes in Π_n is equal to the number of distinct integral solutions of the equation $n = x_1 + \cdots + x_n$, subject to the restraint that $x_1 \geq x_2 \geq \cdots \geq x_n \geq 0$.
F. Show that the number of elements in the conjugate class that contains the element $(1\ 2)(3\ 4) \cdots (2k-1\ 2k)$ is $n!/2^k(k!)(n-2k)!$.
G. Determine the number of elements in the conjugate class of Π_n that contains $\pi = \gamma_1 \cdots \gamma_s$, where the γ_i are disjoint cycles.

If $X \subset \mathscr{G}$, the set

$$N(X) = \{g \in \mathscr{G} \mid X^{\gamma_g} = g^{-1}Xg = X\}$$

is called the *normalizer of* X, and the set

$$\mathfrak{Z}(X) = \bigcap_{x \in X} N(x)$$

is called the *centralizer of* X. We see immediately that, when $x \in \mathscr{G}$, then

$$\mathfrak{Z}(x) = N(x).$$

In general $\mathfrak{Z}(X) \subset N(X)$. The centralizer of $\mathscr{G}$ is the center of $\mathscr{G}$.

EXERCISE 10 A. Prove: The sets $N(X)$ and $\mathfrak{Z}(X)$ are subgroups of $\mathscr{G}$.
B. Prove: A subgroup $\mathscr{H}$ is normal in $\mathscr{G}$ if and only if $N(\mathscr{H}) = \mathscr{G}$.

As noted above, a subset of $\mathscr{G}$ that is conjugate to X must be of the form $g^{-1}Xg$, for some $g \in \mathscr{G}$. If $g \in N(X)h$, i.e., $g = nh$, for some $n \in N(X)$, then

$$g^{-1}Xg = (nh)^{-1}X(nh) = h^{-1}(n^{-1}Xn)h = h^{-1}Xh.$$

Consequently, elements of the same right coset of the group $N(X)$ determine the same conjugate class. On the other hand, if $g^{-1}Xg = k^{-1}Xk$, then $gk^{-1} \in N(X)$, and so $g \in N(X)k$. Hence there are exactly as many distinct subsets of $\mathscr{G}$ conjugate to X as there are right cosets of $N(X)$ in $\mathscr{G}$. Thus we have proved

POSITION 36 *If X is a subset of $\mathscr{G}$, then the number of distinct subsets of $\mathscr{G}$ conjugate to X is $[\mathscr{G}:N(X)]$.*

The reader should prove

COROLLARY *If $x \in \mathscr{G}$, then $|\mathfrak{c}(x)|$ is a divisor of $|\mathscr{G}|$.*

Now the group $\mathscr{G}$ is the disjoint union of the various conjugate classes $\mathfrak{c}(x)$. If $|\mathscr{G}|$ is a prime power, say p^m, let

$$\mathscr{G} = \bigcup_{i=1}^{r} \mathfrak{c}(x_i),$$

for some $x_1, x_2, \ldots, x_r \in \mathscr{G}$, where the $\mathfrak{c}(x_i)$ are pairwise disjoint. Furthermore $|\mathfrak{c}(x)| = 1$ if and only if $x \in \mathfrak{Z}(\mathscr{G})$. It follows that

$$p^m = \sum_{i=1}^{r} |\mathfrak{c}(x_i)| = |\mathfrak{Z}(\mathscr{G})| + \sum |\mathfrak{c}(x_i)|,$$

where the last sum is over those $x_i \notin \mathfrak{Z}(\mathscr{G})$. By the above corollary, $|\mathfrak{c}(x_i)|$ is a divisor of p^m, and if $x \notin \mathfrak{Z}(\mathscr{G})$, then p is a divisor of $|\mathfrak{c}(x_i)|$. Hence p is a divisor of $|\mathfrak{Z}(\mathscr{G})|$. As $|\mathfrak{Z}(\mathscr{G})| \geq 1$, we have proved

POSITION 37 If $|\mathscr{G}|$ *is a power of a prime, then $\mathfrak{Z}(\mathscr{G})$ is not the identity group.*

If $|\mathscr{G}| = p^2$, then $\mathfrak{Z}(\mathscr{G}) \neq \langle e \rangle$. Suppose $\mathscr{G}$ is not abelian; then $|\mathfrak{Z}(\mathscr{G})| = p$, and so $\mathfrak{Z}(\mathscr{G}) = \langle x \rangle$, for some $x \in \mathscr{G}$. Then there is a $y \in \mathscr{G} - \mathfrak{Z}(\mathscr{G})$. The order of each element of $\mathscr{G}$ must be a divisor of p^2. If $o(y) = p^2$, then $\mathscr{G} = \langle y \rangle$, and $\mathscr{G}$ would be abelian. Hence $o(y) = p$. But x commutes with every element of $\mathscr{G}$; hence $xy = yx$. In this case $\mathscr{G} = \{x^i y^j \mid i, j = 0, 1, \ldots, p-1\}$, and $(x^i y^j)(x^s y^t) = (x^s y^t)(x^i y^j)$. Consequently we have proved

POSITION 38 *If $|\mathscr{G}|$ is the square of a prime, then $\mathscr{G}$ is abelian.*

The reader should show that the hypothesis of Proposition 38 does not imply that $\mathscr{G}$ is cyclic.

We have seen in Exercise 2 that $\mathscr{A}(\mathbf{Z})$ is very small. We have also seen that

$$\mathscr{A}(\mathscr{G}) \subset F(e) = \{\varphi \in \Pi(\mathscr{G}) \mid e^\varphi = e\}.$$

We now give an example for which $\mathscr{A}(\mathscr{G}) = F(e)$.

Consider the group $\mathbf{Z}_8' = \{\lfloor 1 \rfloor, \lfloor 3 \rfloor, \lfloor 5 \rfloor, \lfloor 7 \rfloor\}$, and let $M = \{\lfloor 3 \rfloor, \lfloor 5 \rfloor, \lfloor 7 \rfloor\}$. It is easily seen that M is exactly the set of all elements of $\mathbf{Z}_8'$ of order 2. The product of distinct elements of M is the third element. Hence any two elements of M generate $\mathbf{Z}_8'$. Because of the operation-preserving property of automorphisms, it follows that an automorphism of $\mathbf{Z}_8'$ is completely determined by a map of $\{\lfloor 3 \rfloor, \lfloor 5 \rfloor\}$ into $\mathbf{Z}_8'$. Since automorphisms preserve the order of elements, the map must take $\lfloor 3 \rfloor$ and $\lfloor 5 \rfloor$ into elements of order 2, and hence into M. As automorphisms are injective, the images of $\lfloor 3 \rfloor$ and $\lfloor 5 \rfloor$ must be different. It follows that each injection of $\{\lfloor 3 \rfloor, \lfloor 5 \rfloor\}$ into M determines a unique automorphism of $\mathbf{Z}_8'$. Thus

$$|\mathscr{A}(\mathbf{Z}_8')| = 6.$$

But

$$\mathscr{A}(\mathbf{Z}_8') \subset F(e) \cong \Pi_3,$$

and so, on comparing orders, we see that

$$\mathscr{A}(\mathbf{Z}_8') = F(e) \cong \Pi_3.$$

Now Π_3 is generated by any two of the transpositions in the set

$$Q = \{(1\ \ 2), (1\ \ 3), (2\ \ 3)\}$$

(see Chap. 2, Sec. 13, Exercise 2). Hence each injection of $N = \{(1\ \ 2), (1\ \ 3)\}$ into Q determines a unique automorphism on Π_3 (see Sec. 8, Exercise 9). Each injection of N into Q can be extended in only one way to an injection of Q into Q. Hence there is a bijective map of the set of injections of N into Q onto the set $\Pi(Q)$. Thus there is an injection λ of $\Pi(Q)$ into $\mathscr{A}(\Pi_3)$.

But $Q = \{\pi \in \Pi_3 \,|\, o(\pi) = 2\}$, and $\varphi \in \mathscr{A}(\Pi_3)$ implies $\text{res}_Q\, \varphi \in \Pi(Q)$. Furthermore, since $\langle Q \rangle = \Pi_3$, we have

$$\varphi = \psi.$$

whenever $\qquad \text{res}_Q\, \varphi = \text{res}_Q\, \psi, \qquad \varphi, \psi \in \mathscr{A}(\Pi_3).$

Thus the map

$$\varphi \xrightarrow{\ \rho\ } \text{res}_Q\, \varphi$$

is an injection of $\mathscr{A}(\Pi_3)$ into $\Pi(Q)$. But then $\rho\lambda$ is an injection of the finite set $\mathscr{A}(\Pi_3)$ into itself, and therefore (see Chap. 2, Sec. 3, Exercise 8) $\rho\lambda$ is bijective. It follows that ρ and λ are each bijective. Furthermore

$$(\varphi\psi)^\rho = \text{res}_Q(\varphi\psi) = \text{res}_Q(\varphi)\, \text{res}_Q(\psi) = \varphi^\rho \psi^\rho.$$

Hence ρ is an isomorphism of $\mathscr{A}(\Pi_3)$ onto $\Pi(Q)$. Since Q is a three-element set, we have

$$\Pi(Q) \cong \Pi_3.$$

Thus we have shown

$$\mathscr{A}(\Pi_3) \cong \Pi_3.$$

Now $\mathfrak{Z}(\Pi_3) = \langle e \rangle$, and hence by Proposition 34, we have

$$\mathscr{I}(\Pi_3) \cong \Pi_3/\langle e \rangle \cong \Pi_3 \cong \mathscr{A}(\Pi_3).$$

But $\mathscr{I}(\Pi_3)$ is a subgroup of the finite group $\mathscr{A}(\Pi_3)$, and hence

$$\mathscr{I}(\Pi_3) = \mathscr{A}(\Pi_3) \cong \Pi_3.$$

This phenomenon holds for other transformation groups also. More generally we shall prove

THEOREM 9 *If $n \geq 3$ and $n \neq 6$, then $\mathscr{A}(\Pi_n) = \mathscr{I}(\Pi_n) \cong \Pi_n$.*

PROOF. Using Proposition 34 and the corollary to Theorem 8, Chap. 2, the reader should show that $\mathscr{I}(\Pi_n) \cong \Pi_n$, for $n \geq 3$. There remains to show that to each $\varphi \in \mathscr{A}(\Pi_n)$ there is an $\alpha \in \Pi_n$ such that $\pi^\varphi = \alpha^{-1}\pi\alpha$, for all $\pi \in \Pi_n$.

The set T of all transpositions in Π_n is a class of conjugates of order 2, and hence the set T^φ must be a class of conjugates all of order 2. In particular each element of T^φ is the product of the same number of disjoint transpositions, say k. There are $A_k = (n!)/2^k(k!)(n-2k)!$ distinct elements in Π_n that are the product of k disjoint transpositions; hence T^φ contains exactly A_k elements. (All these results are implied by Exercises 8 and 9.) As φ is a one-to-one map of Π_n onto Π_n, φ must be a one-to-one map of T onto T^φ, and therefore T and T^φ contain exactly the same number of elements of Π_n. As T contains $n(n-1)/2$ elements, we have $A_k = n(n-1)/2$; i.e.,

$$\frac{n(n-1)}{2} = \frac{n!}{2^k k!(n-2k)!}.$$

This equation is possible only if $k = 1$ or if $n = 6$ and $k = 3$. Hence if $n \neq 6$, then $T = T^\varphi$.

Now suppose that $(1\ r)^\varphi = (a_r\ b_r)$ for $r = 2, 3, \ldots, n$. If $r \neq 2$, then

$$[(1\ 2)(1\ r)]^\varphi = (1\ 2\ r)^\varphi = (a_2\ b_2)(a_r\ b_r),$$

is an element of order 3; and hence, for each $r > 2$, $(a_2\ b_2)$ and $(a_r\ b_r)$ have an element in common. Suppose r and s are distinct and exceed 2, and suppose

$$(1\ r)^\varphi = (a_2\ b_r) \qquad \text{and} \qquad (1\ s)^\varphi = (a_s\ b_2);$$

then

$$\begin{aligned}[(2\ r)(1\ s)]^\varphi &= [(1\ 2)(1\ r)(1\ 2)(1\ s)]^\varphi \\ &= (a_2\ b_2)(a_2\ b_r)(a_2\ b_2)(a_s\ b_2) \\ &= (b_2\ b_r\ a_s),\end{aligned}$$

which is a contradiction, since $o[(2\ r)(1\ s)] = 2$ and $o(b_2\ b_r\ a_s) = 3$. Thus without loss of generality, we can suppose that

$$(1\ r)^{\varphi} = (a\ b_r), \qquad \text{for } r = 2, 3, \ldots, n.$$

We note that $a \neq b_r$, for $r = 2, 3, \ldots, n$. Since φ is an automorphism, if $r \neq s$, then $b_r \neq b_s$. Hence

$$\alpha = \begin{pmatrix} 1 & 2 & \cdots & n \\ a & b_2 & \cdots & b_n \end{pmatrix}$$

is an element of Π_n. It is easily seen that

$$(1\ r)^{\gamma_\alpha} = \alpha^{-1}(1\ r)\alpha = (a\ b_r) = (1\ r)^{\varphi}, \qquad \text{for } r = 2, 3, \ldots, n.$$

As $\Pi_n = \langle(1\ 2), (1\ 3), \ldots, (1\ n)\rangle$, we must have $\varphi = \gamma_\alpha$. (Explain.) This completes the proof that $\mathscr{A}(\Pi_n) = \mathscr{I}(\Pi_n)$ if $n \neq 6$ and so completes the proof of Theorem 9.

EXERCISES 11 Prove: If n, $k \in \mathbf{Z}^+$ and $n(n-1)/2 = n!/2^k(k!)(n-2k)!$, then either $k = 1$ or $n = 6$ and $k = 3$.

12 Examine the situation for Π_6, and decide whether this is truly an exceptional case or whether the exception arose only because of the method of our proof.

13 Prove $\mathscr{A}(\Pi(\mathbf{Z})) = \mathscr{I}(\Pi(\mathbf{Z}))$.
(The proof of this result is more involved than that of Theorem 9.)

11 GENERAL COMMENTS

The concepts of homomorphism, isomorphism, and automorphism are of fundamental importance in the study of groups. Their importance derives from their common property of being operation-preserving maps and from the intrinsic property of groups as a set with a binary operation. On first meeting these maps, one cannot hope to see in all detail the significant role they play. We shall comment on a few of these roles, and as we continue to develop our subject, their importance will become more evident.

In studying the structure of a group, one can always study the structure of any isomorphic group. This is of considerable importance when we realize that groups can appear in many different formats, e.g., the following are just a few examples of groups containing four elements: $\mathbf{Z}_4$, $\mathbf{Z}_8'$, $\langle\sqrt{-1}\rangle$, the group of rotations of a square, the group of rigid motions of a nonsquare rectangle, the group of transformations on the set $\{\pm \sin x, \pm \cos x\}$ generated by the derivative. Now, Proposition 26 says that all these groups behave either like $\mathbf{Z}_4$ or like $\mathbf{Z}_8'$; hence in studying groups of order 4, it is enough to study these two only.

Another advantage that accrues to us because of isomorphism is that, in doing certain computations, we can always go to an isomorphic group in which we may know a quick and speedy method of calculation.

A homomorphism often enables us to infer information concerning a group by looking at a homomorphic image of the group that is smaller and possibly simpler.

Automorphisms give us information regarding the inner symmetry of a group. If $\mathscr{A}(\mathscr{G})$ is large, then there is considerable symmetry; i.e., many elements have similar behavior, for example, if $\mathscr{A}(\mathscr{G})$ is large, then many elements of $\mathscr{G}$ have the same order. $\mathscr{I}(\mathscr{G})$ is a measure of how close the group $\mathscr{G}$ is to being commutative, since $\mathscr{G}/\mathfrak{Z}(\mathscr{G}) \cong \mathscr{I}(\mathscr{G})$.

Mappings like homomorphism, isomorphism, etc., appear throughout mathematics. In one aspect of geometry we are interested in which sets intersect and in the manner of the intersection. When considering such questions, it is customary to consider projections; e.g., consider the map π of three space into a plane that is not parallel to the z axis given by mapping all points on a line parallel to the z axis onto the point where the line and the plane intersect. The map π preserves intersections; i.e., if S and T are subsets in three space that intersect, the S^π and T^π intersect. Of course, if S^π and T^π intersect, S and T need not intersect. Thus the mapping π that we described is a type of homomorphism of three space onto a plane.

In the study of Euclidean geometry, congruency plays a major role. A little reflection will recall that two sets S and T are said to be congruent if there exists a 1-1 map σ of the space onto itself that preserves distance, for which $S^\sigma = T$. In Euclidean geometry, distance between points is the property that one wants to preserve, and thus a 1-1 map of the plane onto itself that preserves distance may be considered a type of automorphism on the Euclidean plane. Thus we can say the sets in the plane that are congruent to a fixed set S are the sets S^σ as σ runs over all "automorphisms of the plane." The congruent sets play a role that is similar to that played by conjugate subgroups.

We should offer one word of caution. Although isomorphic groups have the same group structure, properties that arise from a particular realization may not be held by all isomorphic groups. A trivial example would be the color of ink with which the symbols are written. Of more significance is the fact that two subgroups of $\Pi(M)$ may be isomorphic and have quite different effects on the elements of M. For example, let $\mathscr{H} = \langle \iota, (1\ 2)(3\ 4), (1\ 3)(2\ 4), (1\ 4)(2\ 3) \rangle$ and let $\mathscr{H}' = \langle \iota, (1\ 2), (3\ 4), (1\ 2)(3\ 4) \rangle$. These two sets are subgroups of Π_4 that are isomorphic to $\mathbf{Z}_8'$. The group $\mathscr{H}$ has the property that, if x and y are any two elements from the set $\{1, 2, 3, 4\}$, then there is an element of $\mathscr{H}$, say $\sigma = \sigma_{xy}$ depending on x and y, such that $x^\sigma = y$. On the other hand there is no element of $\mathscr{H}'$ that takes 1 into 3.

Given any two ordered sets of k distinct elements of a set M, say $\{x_1, x_2, \ldots, x_k\}$ and $\{y_1, y_2, \ldots, y_k\}$, if there exists an element σ in a subgroup $\mathscr{H}$ of $\Pi(M)$ such that $x_i^\sigma = y_i$, for $i = 1, 2, \ldots, k$, we say that $\mathscr{H}$ is *k-fold transitive.* One abbreviates the phrase "1-fold transitive group" to "a transitive group." The group $\mathscr{H}$ mentioned above is transitive, and the group $\mathscr{H}'$ is intransitive. The property of being transitive is not preserved under isomorphism.

EXERCISES 1 Show that Π_n is n-fold transitive.

2 Determine the maximum k such that $\mathfrak{A}_n$ is k-fold transitive.

3 Discuss the transitivity of $\langle(1, 2, \ldots, k)\rangle$ on the set $\{1, 2, \ldots, k\}$.

If $\mathscr{H}$ is a subgroup of $\Pi(M)$, the set

$$\mathfrak{O}_{\mathscr{H}}(x) = \{y \in M \mid y = x^\sigma \text{ for some } \sigma \in \mathscr{H}\}$$

is called the *$\mathscr{H}$ orbit of x*, and the set

$$S_{\mathscr{H}}(x) = \{\sigma \in \mathscr{H} \mid x^\sigma = x\}$$

is called the *stabilizing set of x in $\mathscr{H}$.*

EXERCISES 4 A. Prove $S_{\mathscr{H}}(x)$ is a subgroup of $\mathscr{H}$.

B. Prove: $S_{\mathscr{H}}(x)$ is normal in $\mathscr{H}$ if and only if

$$S_{\mathscr{H}}(x) = \bigcap_{y \in \mathfrak{O}_{\mathscr{H}}(x)} S_{\mathscr{H}}(y).$$

5 Prove:

A. "Being in the same $\mathscr{H}$ orbit" is an equivalence relation on M.

B. $\mathscr{H}$ is transitive on M if and only if M is an $\mathscr{H}$ orbit.

C. If $\sigma \in \Pi(M)$, determine the $\langle\sigma\rangle$ orbits in M. (*Hint:* What if σ is a cycle?)

6 Prove:

A. $\mathfrak{O}_{\mathscr{H}}(x) = \mathfrak{O}_{\mathscr{H}}(y)$ if and only if $S_{\mathscr{H}}(x)$ and $S_{\mathscr{H}}(y)$ are conjugate subgroups.

B. If M is a finite set and $\mathscr{H} \subset \Pi(M)$, then

$$|\mathfrak{O}_{\mathscr{H}}(x)| \cdot |S_{\mathscr{H}}(x)| = |\mathscr{H}|, \qquad \text{for each } x \in M.$$

7 Prove: If $\mathscr{G}$ is a group, then $\mathfrak{R}(\mathscr{G})$ is a transitive group on the set $\mathscr{G}$. (See Exercise 10, Sec. 8, for the definition of $\mathfrak{R}(\mathscr{G})$.)

12 CARTESIAN PRODUCT OF GROUPS

In mathematics, one often constructs a new system from two other systems by forming the set of ordered pairs of elements, one from each system. The most common example of this phenomena is the formation of two-dimensional space $\mathbf{R}^{(2)}$ by taking the set of all ordered pairs of real numbers and defining a formula for the distance between points. This method of combining systems to get a new system is usually referred to as a *cartesian* operation, in honor of Réné Descartes, who was the first to introduce the technique.

If $\mathscr{G}$ and $\mathscr{H}$ are two groups with $\cdot$ and $\circ$ as their respective binary operations, we let

$$\mathscr{G} \times \mathscr{H} = \{(g, h) \mid g \text{ in } \mathscr{G} \text{ and } h \text{ in } \mathscr{H}\}$$

and define
$$(g, h)(g', h') = (g \cdot g', h \circ h').$$

Under this binary operation $\mathscr{G} \times \mathscr{H}$ is indeed a group, and this group is called the *cartesian product of* $\mathscr{G}$ *and* $\mathscr{H}$. In case both operations are addition, we may speak of the new group as the *cartesian sum of* $\mathscr{G}$ *and* $\mathscr{H}$ and write $\mathscr{G} + \mathscr{H}$.

EXERCISES 1 A. Determine the identity of $\mathscr{G} \times \mathscr{H}$.

B. Determine the inverse of (g, h) in $\mathscr{G} \times \mathscr{H}$.

C. Prove that $\mathscr{G} \times \mathscr{H}$ is a group.

D. Prove: $\mathscr{G} \times \langle e \rangle \cong \mathscr{G}$.

2 A. Construct the group tables of the following:

$$G_1 = \mathbf{Z}_2 + \mathbf{Z}_2,\ G_2 = \mathbf{Z}_2 + \mathbf{Z}_3,\ G_3 = \mathbf{Z}_2 + \mathbf{Z}_4,$$
$$G_4 = \mathbf{Z}_2 \times \mathbf{Z}_6',\ G_5 = \mathbf{Z}_3 \times \mathbf{Z}_8',\ G_6 = \mathbf{Z}_2 \times \Pi_3.$$

B. Which of the above groups are cyclic? Which are abelian?

C. Show that $\mathscr{G} \times \mathscr{H}$ is cyclic only if $\mathscr{G}$ and $\mathscr{H}$ are cyclic.

D. Determine a necessary and sufficient condition on $\mathscr{G}$ and $\mathscr{H}$ so that $\mathscr{G} \times \mathscr{H}$ is abelian.

3 A. Prove: If $\mathscr{G}$ and $\mathscr{H}$ are finite groups, then $|\mathscr{G} \times \mathscr{H}| = |\mathscr{G}|\,|\mathscr{H}|$.

B. Prove: If $\mathscr{G}$ and $\mathscr{H}$ are finite groups, then $o(g, h) = \text{l.c.m. } \{o(g), o(h)\}$.

C. Determine a necessary and sufficient condition on m and n so that $\mathbf{Z}_m + \mathbf{Z}_n$ is a cyclic group.

D. Prove: If $|\mathscr{J}| = p^2$, p a prime, then either $\mathscr{J} \cong \mathbf{Z}_{p^2}$ or $\mathscr{J} \cong \mathbf{Z}_p + \mathbf{Z}_p$. (*Hint:* Examine the proof of Proposition 37.)

E. Prove: If $(m, n) = 1$, then $\mathbf{Z}_{mn} \cong \mathbf{Z}_m + \mathbf{Z}_n$. (*Hint:* Consider the map $(\lfloor a \rfloor_m, \lfloor b \rfloor_n) \rightarrow \lfloor na + mb \rfloor_{mn}$.)

The reader can easily prove

PROPOSITION 39 $\mathscr{G} \times \mathscr{H} \cong \mathscr{H} \times \mathscr{G}$.

PROPOSITION 40 *If* $\mathscr{G} \cong \mathscr{J}$, *then* $\mathscr{G} \times \mathscr{H} \cong \mathscr{J} \times \mathscr{H}$.

One might naturally suspect that the converse of Proposition 40 is also true. However, to date no one has been able to prove or disprove the converse of Proposition 40 for finite groups. We shall eventually do so for finite abelian groups. (See Corollary 1 of Theorem 13.)

Let

$$\mathcal{G}^* = \{(g, e_{\mathcal{H}}) \mid g \in \mathcal{G},\ e_{\mathcal{H}} = \text{identity of } \mathcal{H}\},$$

$$\mathcal{H}^* = \{(e_{\mathcal{G}}, h) \mid h \in \mathcal{H},\ e_{\mathcal{G}} = \text{identity of } \mathcal{G}\}.$$

The reader should prove

LEMMA $g^*h^* = h^*g^*$ *for all* $g^* \in \mathcal{G}^*$, $h^* \in \mathcal{H}^*$.

PROPOSITION 41 $\mathcal{G} \cong \mathcal{G}^*$, $\mathcal{G}^* \lhd \mathcal{G} \times \mathcal{H}$, $(\mathcal{G} \times \mathcal{H})/\mathcal{G}^* \cong \mathcal{H}$, *and* $\mathcal{G} \times \mathcal{H} = \mathcal{G}^*\mathcal{H}^*$.

If $\mathcal{G} \cong \mathcal{G}^* \lhd \mathcal{E}$ and $\mathcal{E}/\mathcal{G}^* \cong \mathcal{H}$, we say that $\mathcal{E}$ is an *extension of* $\mathcal{G}$ *by* $\mathcal{H}$. Clearly $\mathcal{G} \times \mathcal{H}$ is always an extension of $\mathcal{G}$ by $\mathcal{H}$. On the other hand not every extension of $\mathcal{G}$ by $\mathcal{H}$ need be isomorphic to $\mathcal{G} \times \mathcal{H}$. For consider the following example: $\mathbf{Z}_4$ contains the normal group $\mathcal{G}^* = \langle \boxed{2} \rangle \cong \mathbf{Z}_2$ and $\mathbf{Z}_4/\mathcal{G}^* \cong \mathbf{Z}_2$, and hence $\mathbf{Z}_4$ is an extension of $\mathbf{Z}_2$ by $\mathbf{Z}_2$. However $\mathbf{Z}_4$ is a cyclic group, but $\mathbf{Z}_2 + \mathbf{Z}_2$ is not; hence they are not isomorphic. It is an interesting and extremely difficult problem to determine the totality of possible nonisomorphic extensions of one group by another. We shall not discuss the problem further at this time.

EXERCISES 4 Verify the statements in the preceding paragraph.

5 A. Show that Π_n is an extension of $\mathfrak{A}_n$ by $\mathbf{Z}_2$.

B. Is Π_n an extension of $\mathbf{Z}_2$ by $\mathfrak{A}_n$?

6 If $\lambda \in \mathcal{A}(\mathcal{G})$ and $\mu \in \mathcal{A}(\mathcal{H})$, define

$$(g, h)^{(\lambda, \mu)} = (g^\lambda, h^\mu).$$

A. Show that (λ, μ) is an element of $\mathcal{A}(\mathcal{G} \times \mathcal{H})$.

B. Show $\mathcal{A}(\mathcal{G}) \times \mathcal{A}(\mathcal{H})$ is isomorphic to a subgroup of $\mathcal{A}(\mathcal{G} \times \mathcal{H})$.

C. If $(p, q) = 1$, show that

$$\mathcal{A}(\mathbf{Z}_{pq}) \cong \mathcal{A}(\mathbf{Z}_p + \mathbf{Z}_q) \cong \mathcal{A}(\mathbf{Z}_p) \times \mathcal{A}(\mathbf{Z}_q),$$

whence $$\mathbf{Z}'_{pq} \cong \mathbf{Z}'_p \times \mathbf{Z}'_q.$$

D. Show that $\mathcal{A}(\mathbf{Z}_2 + \mathbf{Z}_2) \not\cong \mathcal{A}(\mathbf{Z}_2) \times \mathcal{A}(\mathbf{Z}_2)$.

E. Use part C to derive the multiplicative property of the Euler phi function $\varphi(n)$. (See Proposition 20, Chap. 2.)

7 Let $H(\mathcal{L}, \mathcal{M})$ denote the set of homomorphisms of the group $\mathcal{L}$ into the group $\mathcal{M}$. Prove:

A. If $\mathcal{J}$ is an abelian group and $\sigma \in H(\mathcal{G} \times \mathcal{H}, \mathcal{J})$, then there exist $\pi \in H(\mathcal{G}, \mathcal{J})$, $\lambda \in H(\mathcal{H}, \mathcal{J})$ such that $(g, e_{\mathcal{H}})^\sigma = g^\pi$, $(e_{\mathcal{G}}, h) = h^\lambda$, and

$$(g, h)^\sigma = g^\pi h^\lambda = (g, h)^{(\pi, \lambda)}.$$

B. If $\mathscr{J}$ is abelian, then there is a bijective map of $H(\mathscr{G} \times \mathscr{H}, \mathscr{J})$ onto the set $H(\mathscr{G}, \mathscr{J}) \times H(\mathscr{H}, \mathscr{J})$.

C. If $\mathscr{I}$, $\mathscr{J}$, and $\mathscr{H}$ are groups, not necessarily abelian, then

$$H(\mathscr{I}, \mathscr{J} \times \mathscr{H}) \cong H(\mathscr{I}, \mathscr{J}) \times H(\mathscr{I}, \mathscr{H}).$$

We note that $(\mathscr{G}_1 \times \mathscr{G}_2) \times \mathscr{G}_3$ and $\mathscr{G}_1 \times (\mathscr{G}_2 \times \mathscr{G}_3)$ are well defined, since the cartesian product is defined for any pair of groups. We can further define

$$\mathscr{G}_1 \times \mathscr{G}_2 \times \mathscr{G}_3 = \{(g_1, g_2, g_3) \mid g_i \text{ in } \mathscr{G}_i, (i = 1, 2, 3)\}$$

with

$$(g_1, g_2, g_3)(g_1', g_2', g_3') = (g_1 g_1', g_2 g_2', g_3 g_3').$$

Under this binary operation $\mathscr{G}_1 \times \mathscr{G}_2 \times \mathscr{G}_3$ is a group. Furthermore one can easily prove that

$$\mathscr{G}_1 \times \mathscr{G}_2 \times \mathscr{G}_3 \cong (\mathscr{G}_1 \times \mathscr{G}_2) \times \mathscr{G}_3 \cong \mathscr{G}_1 \times (\mathscr{G}_2 \times \mathscr{G}_3).$$

Analogously, given any finite set of groups $\mathscr{G}_1, \mathscr{G}_2, \ldots, \mathscr{G}_n$, we can define their cartesian product. The reader should check that the cartesian product of groups satisfies the generalized associative law.

Let $\mathfrak{C}_0 = \langle e \rangle, \mathfrak{C}_1, \mathfrak{C}_2, \ldots$ be classes of isomorphic groups, and let $\mathbf{G}$ be the set of all such classes. Define

$$\mathfrak{C}_1 \mathfrak{C}_2 = \{\mathscr{M} \mid \mathscr{M} \cong \mathscr{H} \times \mathscr{J}, \text{ for some } \mathscr{H} \in \mathfrak{C}_1, \mathscr{J} \in \mathfrak{C}_2\}.$$

Clearly $\mathbf{G}$ is closed under this binary product. The reader should check that the product is associative and commutative. We also have, by Exercise 1D, that $\mathfrak{C}_0 \mathfrak{C} = \mathfrak{C} = \mathfrak{C}\mathfrak{C}_0$, for all $\mathfrak{C} \in \mathbf{G}$. Hence this product has an identity in $\mathbf{G}$. However, $\mathbf{G}$ is not a group, since $\mathfrak{C}_1 \mathfrak{C}_2 = \mathfrak{C}_0$ if and only if $\mathfrak{C}_0 = \mathfrak{C}_1 = \mathfrak{C}_2$. A set with a binary operation that is associative and commutative is called a *semigroup*. Thus relative to multiplication, $\mathbf{Z}^+$ is a semigroup with identity, and $\mathbf{G}$ is a semigroup with identity relative to the above binary operation.

The semigroup $\mathbf{G}$ does have some of the structure of the positive integers under multiplication. It does not have all the properties of such a structure, since the cancellation law does not hold. However, following this analogy to the integers, we might next seek to determine what groups play the role of the primes. A group $\mathscr{G}$ is said to be *decomposable* if $\mathscr{G}$ is isomorphic to the cartesian product of two groups, each of order >1. A group of order >1 that is not decomposable is said to be *indecomposable*. Two isomorphic groups are either both decomposable or both indecomposable. Thus the isomorphism classes of indecomposable groups play the role of the primes in the semigroup $\mathbf{G}$. By Proposition 41, the decomposable groups have nontrivial normal subgroups. Hence a simple group is always indecomposable. However there are indecomposable groups that are not simple. Cyclic groups of prime power order are indecomposable groups, and only those of prime order are simple. (See Proposition 43 and Exercise 4, Sec. 14.)

It is a very difficult task to determine when a group is indecomposable. This should not be too surprising, for it is also a formidable task to determine when a large integer is a prime. No attempt will be made here to determine criteria for indecomposable groups.

We shall see that there are infinite groups that are not isomorphic to the cartesian product of finitely many groups. Hence for infinite groups we do not have a factorization theorem. However, in Sec. 15 we shall determine all indecomposable finite abelian groups, and we shall show that each finite abelian group is isomorphic to the cartesian product of finitely many indecomposable groups. Thus we shall have a factorization theorem for the semigroup consisting of the isomorphism classes of abelian groups.

In our discussion so far, we have considered only cartesian products of finitely many groups. Actually there is no need for such a limitation. Let Λ be some set, and suppose to each λ in Λ there is associated a group $\mathcal{G}_\lambda$. Let

$$\underset{\lambda\in\Lambda}{\times} \mathcal{G}_\lambda = \{f = (\ldots, f_\lambda, \ldots) \mid f_\lambda \in \mathcal{G}_\lambda\};$$

i.e., if $f \in \times\mathcal{G}_\lambda$, then f is a map from Λ into $\bigcup\mathcal{G}_\lambda$ such that, for each λ, $f(\lambda) = f_\lambda$ is an element of $\mathcal{G}_\lambda$. Define $fg = (\ldots, f_\lambda g_\lambda, \ldots)$. Under this definition $\times\mathcal{G}_\lambda$ is a group, and we call it the cartesian product of the $\mathcal{G}_\lambda$'s. Compare this definition with that for the cartesian product of three groups.

If f is in $\times\mathcal{G}_\lambda$, let

$$X(f) = \{\lambda \in \Lambda \mid f_\lambda \text{ is not the identity of } \mathcal{G}_\lambda\}.$$

Let

$$r\!\times\mathcal{G}_\lambda = \{f \in \times\mathcal{G}_\lambda \mid X(f) \text{ is a finite set}\}.$$

The set $r\!\times\mathcal{G}_\lambda$ is a normal subgroup of $\times\mathcal{G}_\lambda$ and is called the *restricted cartesian product of the* $\mathcal{G}_\lambda$. If Λ is a finite set, then the cartesian product and the restricted cartesian product are the same; otherwise the one is a proper subgroup of the other.

EXERCISES

8 Prove: $r\!\times\mathcal{G}_\lambda \lhd \times\mathcal{G}_\lambda$.

9 Show that $\mathbf{Z}$ is indecomposable.

10 Is the group of rigid motions of a square indecomposable?

11 Show that there are infinite groups all of whose elements have order at most 2.

12 Prove:

$$H(\mathcal{I}, \underset{\lambda\in\Lambda}{\times} \mathcal{I}_\lambda) \cong \underset{\lambda\in\Lambda}{\times} H(\mathcal{I}, \mathcal{I}_\lambda).$$

XERCISE 13 A. Show that the map $(x, y) \to (ax + \alpha y, bx + \beta y)$ is an automorphism of $\mathbf{Z} + \mathbf{Z}$ if and only if $a\beta - b\alpha = \pm 1$ and $a, b, \alpha, \beta \in \mathbf{Z}$.

B. Are there other automorphisms of $\mathbf{Z} + \mathbf{Z}$ besides those mentioned in part A?

13 DIRECT PRODUCT OF GROUPS

A group $\mathscr{G}$ is said to be a *direct product* of normal subgroups $\mathscr{M}$ and $\mathscr{N}$ if $\mathscr{M} \cap \mathscr{N} = \langle e \rangle$ and $\mathscr{G} = \mathscr{M}\mathscr{N}$ (set multiplication). In this event we write

$$\mathscr{G} = \mathscr{M}\mathscr{N} \text{ (direct)},$$

and the subgroups $\mathscr{M}$ and $\mathscr{N}$ are called *direct factors* of $\mathscr{G}$. Note that $\mathscr{G} = \mathscr{M}\mathscr{N}$ (direct) implies $\mathscr{G} = \mathscr{N}\mathscr{M}$ (direct).

Direct products and cartesian products are intimately related. In fact, in the exercises below we outline a proof of

POSITION 42 *If $\mathscr{G} = \mathscr{M} \times \mathscr{N}$, then $\mathscr{G} = \mathscr{M}^*\mathscr{N}^*$ (direct), where $\mathscr{M}^* = \{(g, e_{\mathscr{N}}) \mid g \in \mathscr{M}\}$ and $\mathscr{N}^* = \{(e_{\mathscr{M}}, h) \mid h \in \mathscr{N}\}$. If $\mathscr{G} = \mathscr{M}\mathscr{N}$ (direct), then $\mathscr{G} \cong \mathscr{M} \times \mathscr{N}$.*

XERCISES 1 Prove: If $\mathscr{G} = \mathscr{M}\mathscr{N}$ (direct), then $mn = nm$, for all $m \in \mathscr{M}$ and $n \in \mathscr{N}$. (*Hint:* $mnm^{-1}n^{-1} = m_1n_1$, for some $m_1 \in \mathscr{M}$, $n_1 \in \mathscr{N}$. Show $m_1 = n_1 = e$.)

2 Prove: If $\mathscr{G} = \mathscr{M}\mathscr{N}$ (direct) and $mn = m_1n_1$, then $m = m_1$, $n = n_1$.

3 Using Exercises 1 and 2 and Proposition 41, prove Proposition 42.

4 Are there other direct summands of $\mathbf{Z}_4 + \mathbf{Z}_2$ of order 4 besides $\mathbf{Z}_4^*$?

5 Prove or disprove: If $\mathscr{N} \lhd \mathscr{G}$, then $\mathscr{N}$ is a direct factor of $\mathscr{G}$.

6 A. Prove: If $\mathscr{M}$ and $\mathscr{N}$ are subgroups of $\mathscr{G}$ such that each $g \in \mathscr{G}$ can be expressed as $g = mn$, with $m \in \mathscr{M}$ and $n \in \mathscr{N}$, in exactly one and only one way, then

$$\mathscr{G} = \mathscr{M}\mathscr{N} = \mathscr{N}\mathscr{M} \quad \text{and} \quad \mathscr{M} \cap \mathscr{N} = \langle e \rangle.$$

B. Show that the hypothesis of part A does not imply $\mathscr{G} = \mathscr{M}\mathscr{N}$ (direct).

7 Prove: If $\mathscr{M}$ and $\mathscr{N}$ are subgroups of $\mathscr{G}$ such that $mn = nm$ for all $m \in \mathscr{M}$, $n \in \mathscr{N}$ and if each $g \in \mathscr{G}$ can be expressed in one and only one way as $g = mn$, with $m \in \mathscr{M}$ and $n \in \mathscr{N}$, then $\mathscr{G} = \mathscr{M}\mathscr{N}$ (direct). Prove the converse is also true.

Just as we wished to speak of the cartesian product of many groups, so we wish to speak of the direct product of many groups. We give two definitions, which the reader should show are equivalent.

DEFINITION 1 $\mathcal{G}$ is the *direct product* of the subgroups $\mathcal{H}_1, \mathcal{H}_2, \ldots, \mathcal{H}_r$ if:

A. $\mathcal{G} = \mathcal{H}_1\mathcal{H}_2 \cdots \mathcal{H}_r$ (set multiplication).

B. Each $\mathcal{H}_i \lhd \mathcal{G}$.

C. For each $i = 1, 2, \ldots, r$, $\mathcal{H}_i \cap \mathcal{H}_1 \cdots \mathcal{H}_{i-1}\mathcal{H}_{i+1} \cdots \mathcal{H}_s = \langle e \rangle$.

DEFINITION 2 $\mathcal{G}$ is the *direct product* of the subgroups $\mathcal{H}_1, \ldots, \mathcal{H}_r$ if:

A. $x \in \mathcal{H}_i$ and $y \in \mathcal{H}_j$ with $i \neq j$, implying that $xy = yx$.

B. Each $g \in \mathcal{G}$ can be expressed in one and only one way as $g = x_1x_2 \cdots x_r$ with $x_i \in \mathcal{G}_i$ $(i = 1, \ldots, r)$.

In either case we write

$$\mathcal{G} = \mathcal{H}_1 \cdots \mathcal{H}_r \text{ (direct)} = \prod_{i=1}^{r} \mathcal{H}_i \text{ (direct)}.$$

More generally, if to each $\lambda \in \Lambda$ there is a normal subgroup $\mathcal{H}_\lambda$ of $\mathcal{G}$ such that

$$\mathcal{G} = \bigcup_S \left(\prod_{\lambda \in S} \mathcal{H}_\lambda \right),$$

where the union is over all finite subsets S of Λ, and if

$$\mathcal{H}_\lambda \cap \prod_{\mu \in S} \mathcal{H}_\mu = \langle e \rangle \text{ when } S \text{ is a finite subset of } \Lambda \text{ and } \lambda \notin S,$$

then $\mathcal{G}$ is said to be the direct product of the subgroups $\mathcal{H}_\lambda$, and we write

$$\mathcal{G} = \prod_{\lambda \in \Lambda} \mathcal{H}_\lambda \text{ (direct)}.$$

EXERCISES 8 A. Prove: If $\mathcal{G} = \prod_{\lambda \in \Lambda} \mathcal{H}_\lambda$ (direct), then $\mathcal{G} \cong \underset{\lambda \in \Lambda}{\times} \mathcal{H}_\lambda$.

B. If $\mathcal{G} = \times \mathcal{H}_\lambda$, then $\mathcal{G} = \prod_{\lambda \in \Lambda} \mathcal{H}_\lambda^*$ (direct), where

$$\mathcal{H}_\lambda^* = \{ f \in \mathcal{G} \mid f_\mu = e \text{ if } \mu \neq \lambda \}.$$

9 A. Prove: If $\mathcal{G} = \prod_{\lambda \in \Lambda} \mathcal{H}_\lambda$ (direct), then each $x \in \mathcal{G}$, $x \neq e$, can be represented uniquely as a product of finitely many elements, none of which is e and no two lie in the same $\mathcal{H}_\lambda$.

B. Formulate a definition of $\mathcal{G} = \prod_{\lambda \in \Lambda} \mathcal{H}_\lambda$ (direct) analogous to Definition 2. Show that your definition is equivalent to the one given above.

10 A. Prove: If $\mathcal{G} = \mathcal{M}\mathcal{N}$ (direct) and $\mathcal{N} = \mathcal{R}\mathcal{S}$ (direct), then $\mathcal{G} = \mathcal{M}\mathcal{R}\mathcal{S}$ (direct).

B. Is it true that $\mathcal{G} = \mathcal{M}\mathcal{N}$ (direct) and $\mathcal{H} \lhd \mathcal{G}$ imply

$$\mathcal{H} = (\mathcal{M} \cap \mathcal{H})(\mathcal{N} \cap \mathcal{H}) \text{ (direct)?}$$

Exercise 8 shows us that the study of when a group is isomorphic to the cartesian product of finitely many indecomposable groups is equivalent to the study of the decomposition of a group into indecomposable direct factors. The latter is somewhat preferable, since we always remain within the given group.

As we remarked earlier, there are indecomposable groups that are not simple. The following proposition provides us with such examples.

POSITION 43 *A cyclic group of prime power order is indecomposable.*

PROOF. Let $|\mathscr{G}| = p^m$, $m \geq 1$. Suppose $\mathscr{G} = \mathscr{H}_1 \cdots \mathscr{H}_r$ (direct), where $\mathscr{H}_i \neq \langle e \rangle$ and $r \geq 2$. Then for each i, we have

$$|\mathscr{H}_i| = p^{m_i}, \qquad \text{with } m_i \geq 1,$$

such that

$$\sum m_i = m.$$

Thus $2 \leq r \leq m$ and $1 \leq m_i < m$ for each i.

Let $M = \max\{m_i\}$; then $M < m$, and $x \in \mathscr{G}$ implies $x^{p^M} = 1$, contrary to the hypothesis that $\mathscr{G}$ is cyclic.

We now prove a theorem that uses our extended definition of direct product.

THEOREM 10 *If $\mathscr{G}$ is an abelian group without elements of infinite order, then*

$$\mathscr{G} = \prod_p \mathscr{G}(p) \ (direct),$$

where

$$\mathscr{G}(p) = \{x \in \mathscr{G} \mid o(x) \text{ is a power of } p\}.$$

and p ranges over all the primes.

In order to prove this theorem, we need a lemma whose proof we leave to the reader:

LEMMA *If x, y are elements of a group and $xy = yx$, then $o(xy)$ is a divisor of $o(x)o(y)$.*

PROOF OF THEOREM 10. In view of the lemma, it is easily seen that each $\mathscr{G}(p)$ is a subgroup of $\mathscr{G}$. Since $\mathscr{G}$ is abelian, each subgroup of $\mathscr{G}$ is normal in $\mathscr{G}$. Suppose

$$x_p = x_{q_1} x_{q_2} \cdots x_{q_r}, \qquad \text{where } x_p \in \mathscr{G}(p),\ x_{q_j} \in \mathscr{G}(q_j),$$

and $p_1, q_1, \ldots, q_r$ are a set of $r + 1$ distinct primes. Then $o(x_p) = o(x_{q_1} \cdots x_{q_r})$. It follows from the lemma that $x_p = e$. Thus we have

$$\mathscr{G}(p) \cap \prod_{q \in S} \mathscr{G}(q) = \langle e \rangle \tag{13}$$

when S is any finite set of primes not including p.

Now given $x \in \mathscr{G}$, suppose

$$o(x) = n = \prod_{i=1}^{r} p_i^{e_i} > 1,$$

with $e_i \geq 0$. Set

$$m_i = n/p_i^{e_i}, \qquad i = 1, 2, \ldots, r,$$

and put $y_i = x_i^{m_i}, \quad i = 1, 2, \ldots, r;$

then $y_i \in \mathcal{G}(p_i), \quad i = 1, 2, \ldots, r.$

As $(m_1, m_2, \ldots, m_r) = 1,$

there exist integers $s_1, s_2, \ldots, s_r$ such that

$$\sum_{i=1}^{r} s_i m_i = 1.$$

Hence
$$x = x^{\sum_{i=1}^{r} s_i m_i} = \prod_{i=1}^{r} (x^{m_i})^{s_i} = \prod_{i=1}^{r} y_i^{s_i} \in \mathcal{G}(p_1) \cdots \mathcal{G}(p_r). \tag{14}$$

Thus we have

$$\mathcal{G} = \bigcup_S \left(\prod_{p \in S} \mathcal{G}(p) \right),$$

where the union is over all finite sets S. Equations 13 and 14 imply that $\mathcal{G}$ is the direct product of the $\mathcal{G}(p)$.

A group is said to be a *p group* if each element of the group has order a power of the prime p. We note that $\mathcal{G}(p)$ is the maximal p subgroup of the abelian group $\mathcal{G}$. For if $\mathcal{H}$ is a p subgroup, then by the definition of $\mathcal{G}(p)$, each element of $\mathcal{H}$ lies in $\mathcal{G}(p)$; i.e.,

$$\mathcal{H} \subset \mathcal{G}(p).$$

Theorem 10 states that every abelian group without elements of infinite order can be decomposed into the direct product of p subgroups. These p subgroups may not be indecomposable. Consequently, as yet, we do not have a decomposition theorem for abelian groups without elements of infinite order into the direct product of indecomposable groups. Nevertheless, the decomposition given in Theorem 10 is a strong one, for we have

PROPOSITION 44 *If θ is an isomorphism of an abelian group $\mathcal{G}$ onto $\mathcal{J}$, then $\mathcal{G}(p)^\theta$ is the maximal p subgroup (for the prime p) in $\mathcal{J}$.*

EXERCISES

11 Prove the lemma to Theorem 10.

12 A. Determine the maximal p subgroups of $\mathbf{Z}_{24}$.

B. If $\mathcal{G} = \mathbf{Z}_n$, determine the $\mathcal{G}(p)$ to within isomorphism.

13 A. Prove: If $\mathcal{G}$ is a cyclic p group, then $\mathcal{G}$ is a finite group.

B. Give an example of a p group that is not cyclic.

14 Prove: If $|\mathcal{G}| = p^m$, then $\mathcal{G}$ is a p group.

15 Prove: A homomorphic image of a p group is a p group.

16 Prove Proposition 44.

There are infinite abelian groups without elements of infinite order for which each $\mathcal{G}(p)$ is a nontrivial subgroup of $\mathcal{G}$. One of the simplest examples is the set of all roots of unity. We shall discuss such groups in the next chapter. When $|\mathscr{G}|$ is finite, we have

POSITION 45 *Let $\mathscr{G}$ be a finite abelian group, and let S denote the set of primes that divide $|\mathscr{G}|$. Then*

$$|\mathscr{G}(p)| \neq 1, \qquad \textit{if and only if } p \in S,$$

and

$$\mathscr{G} = \prod_{p \in S} \mathscr{G}(p) \ (\textit{direct}).$$

To prove this proposition, we need to know

LEMMA *If $\mathscr{G}$ is a finite abelian group and p is a prime dividing $|\mathscr{G}|$, then there is an $x \in \mathscr{G}$ of order p.*

PROOF. Our proof is by induction on $|\mathscr{G}|$. If $|\mathscr{G}| = 1$, then no prime divides $|\mathscr{G}|$, and the conclusion holds vacuously. Suppose the conclusion holds for groups of order less than $|\mathscr{G}|$. Let $e \neq y \in \mathscr{G}$. If $p \mid o(y)$, then $o(y) = pm$, and y^m has order p.

So suppose $(p, o(y)) = 1$. Since $\mathscr{G}$ is abelian, $\langle y \rangle$ is a normal subgroup of $\mathscr{G}$, and $\mathscr{G}/\langle y \rangle$ is an abelian group. Let $\mathscr{H} = \mathscr{G}/\langle y \rangle$; then

$$o(y)|\mathscr{H}| = |\mathscr{G}|.$$

Hence $|\mathscr{H}| < |\mathscr{G}|$, and since $(p, o(y)) = 1$ and p divides $|\mathscr{G}|$, we have that p divides $|\mathscr{H}|$. It follows from the induction hypothesis that $\mathscr{H}$ contains an element of order p. Let this element be $z\langle y \rangle$. If z has order m in $\mathscr{G}$, then

$$[z\langle y \rangle]^m = z^m\langle y \rangle = \langle y \rangle.$$

But then $p \mid m$. It follows as above that some power of z has order p. This completes the proof of the lemma.

The reader should now complete the proof of Proposition 45. He can also prove

OROLLARY 1 *If $\mathscr{G}$ is a finite abelian group such that p^m divides $|\mathscr{G}|$ but p^{m+1} does not, then there is a unique p subgroup of order p^m.*

OROLLARY 2 *A finite abelian group $\mathscr{G}$ is a p group if and only if $|\mathscr{G}|$ is a power of the prime p.*

14 SYLOW SUBGROUPS

Given a finite group $\mathscr{G}$, a subgroup $\mathscr{P}$ of $\mathscr{G}$ is said to be a *Sylow p subgroup of $\mathscr{G}$* if $\mathscr{P}$ is a p group and $\mathscr{P}$ is not contained in a larger p subgroup of $\mathscr{G}$. Obviously every finite group has a Sylow p subgroup.

In the previous section we proved: *A finite abelian group $\mathscr{G}$ has a unique Sylow p subgroup $\mathscr{G}(p)$, for each prime p, and $|\mathscr{G}(p)|$ is the maximal* *power of p that divides* $|\mathcal{G}|$. It is natural to investigate whether we can prove such a result for nonabelian groups and, if not, to see how close we can come.

We shall need several tools, which we now develop.

A. Let $\mathfrak{M}$ be a collection of nonempty subsets of a finite group $\mathcal{G}$. We shall say $\mathfrak{M}$ is closed provided

$$gM \in \mathfrak{M} \qquad \text{whenever} \qquad g \in \mathcal{G},\ M \in \mathfrak{M}. \tag{15}$$

If A is a subset of $\mathfrak{M}$, let

$$\mathfrak{K}_A = \{M \in \mathfrak{M} \mid M = gA \text{ for some } g \in \mathcal{G}\}.$$

Then $\mathfrak{K}_A$ is a collection of subsets from $\mathfrak{M}$, $\mathfrak{K}_A$ is closed, and $\mathfrak{K}_A = \mathfrak{K}_B$ if and only if $A = gB$, for some $g \in \mathcal{G}$. In case A is a one-element set $\{a\}$, $\mathfrak{K}_A$ is the $\mathcal{G}$ orbit of a. Let $\|\mathfrak{K}_A\|$ denote the number of distinct subsets of $\mathfrak{M}$ in the collection $\mathfrak{K}_A$.

If $A \in \mathfrak{M}$, let

$$\mathcal{F}_A = \{g \in \mathcal{G} \mid A = gA\}.$$

Clearly $\mathcal{F}_A$ is a subgroup of $\mathcal{G}$.

The reader should prove the following results:

LEMMA 1 *If $\mathfrak{M}$ is closed, then either $\mathfrak{K}_A = \mathfrak{K}_B$ or there is no set common both to $\mathfrak{K}_A$ and to $\mathfrak{K}_B$. Thus the classes $\mathfrak{K}_A$ form a partition of $\mathfrak{M}$.*

LEMMA 2 *If $g \in \mathcal{G}$ and A is a nonempty subset of $\mathcal{G}$, then*

$$g\mathcal{F}_A = \{y \in \mathcal{G} \mid yA = gA\} \tag{16}$$

and

$$\mathcal{F}_{gA} = g\mathcal{F}_A g^{-1}. \tag{17}$$

Because of Eq. 16 we have

COROLLARY *If $\mathfrak{M}$ is closed, then $\|\mathfrak{K}_A\| = [\mathcal{G}:\mathcal{F}_A]$.*

LEMMA 3 *If $\mathfrak{M}$ is closed and $A \in \mathfrak{M}$, then there is a subset $A_0 \in \mathfrak{K}_A$ such that $e \in A_0$.*

LEMMA 4 *If A is a nonempty subset of $\mathcal{G}$, then A is the union of some, not necessarily all, of the right cosets of $\mathcal{F}_A$ in $\mathcal{G}$. Hence for some positive integer t, we have*

$$|A| = t|\mathcal{F}_A| \tag{18}$$

$$\|\mathfrak{K}_A\| = \frac{t|\mathcal{G}|}{|A|}. \tag{19}$$

PROOF. Clearly $\mathcal{F}_A \cdot A \subset A$. Also $A = eA \subset \mathcal{F}_A A$. Hence $A = \mathcal{F}_A A$. But $\mathcal{F}_A A$ is the union of some of the right cosets of $\mathcal{F}_A$. If A is the union of t disjoint right cosets of $\mathcal{F}_A$, we clearly have Eq. 18, and Eq. 19 follows from Eq. 18 and the corollary to Lemma 2.

LEMMA 5 *Suppose $\mathfrak{M}$ is closed. $|\mathscr{F}_A| = |A|$ if and only if A_0 is a subgroup. If A_0 is a subgroup, then $A_0 = \mathscr{F}_{A_0}$ and $\mathfrak{K}_A$ is the entire collection of all left cosets of A_0.*

PROOF. From Lemma 3, we have $|A| = |A_0|$, and from Lemma 2 we have $|\mathscr{F}_A| = |\mathscr{F}_{A_0}|$. Since $e \in A_0$, we have

$$\mathscr{F}_{A_0} = \mathscr{F}_{A_0} \cdot e \subset \mathscr{F}_{A_0} A_0 = A_0.$$

If $|\mathscr{F}_A| = |A|$, we would necessarily have $\mathscr{F}_{A_0} = A_0$, and hence A_0 would be a subgroup.

Conversely, suppose that A_0 is a subgroup. Then $A_0 A_0 = A_0$, and so $A_0 \subset \mathscr{F}_{A_0}$. But it is easily shown that $\mathscr{F}_{A_0} \subset A_0$, and it follows that $\mathscr{F}_{A_0} = A_0$, whence $|\mathscr{F}_A| = |A|$. This information, together with Eqs. 18 and 19, implies that $\|\mathfrak{K}_A\| = |\mathscr{G}|/|\mathscr{F}_{A_0}| = [\mathscr{G}: \mathscr{F}_{A_0}]$. The last relation tells us that $\mathfrak{K}_A$ contains all the left cosets of the subgroup $\mathscr{F}_{A_0}$ in $\mathscr{G}$. This completes the proof of Lemma 5.

OROLLARY 1 *If $A \in \mathfrak{M}$ and $\mathfrak{M}$ is closed, then the set $\mathfrak{K}_A$ contains a subgroup of $\mathscr{G}$ if and only if A_0 is a subgroup.*

PROOF. Suppose $gA \in \mathfrak{K}_A$ and that gA is a subgroup of $\mathscr{G}$. Since $\mathfrak{K}_A = \mathfrak{K}_{gA}$, it follows from Lemma 5 that $\mathfrak{K}_A$ consists of the distinct left cosets of gA. In particular, the sets in $\mathfrak{K}_A$ are pairwise disjoint. But $e \in A_0 \cap gA$ and $A_0 \in \mathfrak{K}_A$. Hence $gA = A_0$ is a subgroup. The converse is obvious.

OROLLARY 2 *If $A \in \mathfrak{M}$ and $\mathfrak{M}$ is closed, then at most one of the sets in $\mathfrak{K}_A$ is a subgroup of $\mathscr{G}$.*

PROOF. If $\mathfrak{K}_A$ contains a subgroup, then $\mathfrak{K}_A$ consists of the entire set of left cosets of that group. It is impossible for two distinct left cosets of a subgroup both to be subgroups.

B. Let $\mathscr{H}$ be a subgroup of a finite group $\mathscr{G}$. Let $\mathfrak{N}$ be a collection of subgroups of $\mathscr{G}$ such that

$$h\mathscr{I}h^{-1} \in \mathfrak{N}, \qquad \text{whenever } \mathscr{I} \in \mathfrak{N} \text{ and } h \in \mathscr{H}. \tag{20}$$

$\mathfrak{N}$ is closed under conjugation by elements of $\mathscr{H}$.

Let

$$\mathfrak{C}_{\mathscr{I}} = \{\mathscr{B} \subset \mathfrak{N} \mid \mathscr{B} = h\mathscr{I}h^{-1} \text{ for some } h \in \mathscr{H}\}.$$

Then $\mathfrak{C}_{\mathscr{I}}$ is some collection of subgroups conjugate to $\mathscr{I}$. The class $\mathfrak{C}_{\mathscr{I}}$ satisfies property (20) with $\mathfrak{N} = \mathfrak{C}_{\mathscr{I}}$. If $\mathscr{H} \neq \mathscr{G}$ then $\mathfrak{C}_{\mathscr{I}}$ need not contain all the subgroups conjugate to $\mathscr{I}$. Let $\|\mathfrak{C}_{\mathscr{I}}\|$ denote the number of distinct subgroups in $\mathfrak{C}_{\mathscr{I}}$. If $\mathscr{H} = \mathscr{G}$, then $\mathfrak{C}_{\mathscr{I}} = \mathfrak{c}(\mathscr{I})$.

Let

$$\mathscr{L}_{\mathscr{I}} = \{h \in \mathscr{H} \mid h\mathscr{I}h^{-1} = \mathscr{I}\}.$$

Clearly $\mathscr{L}_{\mathscr{I}}$ is a subgroup of $\mathscr{H}$ that contains the group $\mathscr{I} \cap \mathscr{H}$. Let

$$N(\mathscr{I}) = \{g \in \mathscr{G} | g\mathscr{I}g^{-1} = \mathscr{I}\};$$

then
$$\mathscr{L}_{\mathscr{I}} = \mathscr{H} \cap N(\mathscr{I}). \tag{21}$$

The reader can easily prove

LEMMA 6 *Either $\mathfrak{C}_{\mathscr{I}} = \mathfrak{C}_{\mathscr{B}}$, or there is no subgroup of $\mathfrak{N}$ common to $\mathfrak{C}_{\mathscr{I}}$ and to $\mathfrak{C}_{\mathscr{B}}$. Thus the classes $\mathfrak{C}_{\mathscr{I}}$ form a partition of $\mathfrak{N}$.*

LEMMA 7 *If $\mathscr{I}$ is a subgroup of $\mathscr{G}$, then*

$$y\mathscr{L}_{\mathscr{I}} = \{h \in \mathscr{H} | h\mathscr{I}h^{-1} = y\mathscr{I}y^{-1}\}, \tag{22}$$

and
$$\mathscr{L}_{h\mathscr{I}h^{-1}} = h^{-1}\mathscr{L}_{\mathscr{I}}h. \tag{23}$$

COROLLARY 1 *If $\mathscr{G} = \mathscr{H}$, then $\|\mathfrak{C}_{\mathscr{I}}\|$ is a divisor of $[\mathscr{G}:\mathscr{I}]$.*

PROOF. By Eq. 22 all elements of a left coset of $\mathscr{L}_{\mathscr{I}}$ determine the same conjugate group. Conversely if $g\mathscr{I}g^{-1} = y\mathscr{I}y^{-1}$, then $g \in y\mathscr{L}_{\mathscr{I}}$. Thus, when $\mathscr{G} = \mathscr{H}$, we have $\|\mathfrak{C}_{\mathscr{I}}\| = [\mathscr{G}:\mathscr{L}_{\mathscr{I}}]$. On the other hand $\mathscr{I} \subset \mathscr{L}_{\mathscr{I}}$. Hence $[\mathscr{G}:\mathscr{L}_{\mathscr{I}}]$ is a divisor of $[\mathscr{G}:\mathscr{I}]$. This completes the proof of Corollary 1.

COROLLARY 2 *If $\mathscr{H} \subset \mathscr{G}$, then $\|\mathfrak{C}_{\mathscr{I}}\|$ is a divisor of $|\mathscr{H}|$.*

The proof consists in showing that $\|\mathfrak{C}_{\mathscr{I}}\| = [\mathscr{H}:\mathscr{L}_{\mathscr{I}}]$. The reader should provide the proof.

We also need

LEMMA 8 If $(p, q) = 1$ and $r \geq 1$, then

$$\binom{p^r q}{p^r} \equiv q \pmod{pq}. \tag{24}$$

PROOF. If $1 \leq s < p^r$, then $p^r q/s = pAL_s^{-1}$, where $(A, L_s) = 1$ and $L_s \not\equiv 0 \pmod p$. Hence

$$\prod_{s=1}^{p^r-1} \left(\frac{p^r q}{s} - 1\right) = (-1)^{p^r-1} + pML^{-1},$$

where $(M, L) = 1$ and $L \not\equiv 0 \pmod p$. If p is odd, then $(-1)^{p^r-1} = 1$, but if $p = 2$, then $(-1) \equiv 1 \pmod 2$. Thus we have

$$\prod_{s=1}^{p^r-1} \left(\frac{p^r q}{s} - 1\right) \equiv 1 \pmod p. \tag{25}$$

But

$$\binom{p^r q}{p^r} = q\binom{p^r q - 1}{p^r - 1} = q\left(\frac{p^r q - 1}{1}\right)\cdots\left(\frac{p^r q - p^r + 1}{p^r - 1}\right) = q\prod_{s=1}^{p^r-1}\left(\frac{p^r q}{s} - 1\right). \tag{26}$$

Combining Eqs. 25 and 26 we obtain Eq. 24.

We now apply these lemmas and corollaries to the study of p subgroups of a finite group $\mathscr{G}$. We assume

$$|\mathscr{G}| = n = p^m q, \tag{27}$$

where $(p, q) = 1$, $m \geq 1$, p a prime.

In the first instance, we let $\mathfrak{M}$ be the collection of all subsets of $\mathscr{G}$ of order p^m. Clearly $\mathfrak{M}$ has property (15), and hence we can apply the results in (A). It follows from Proposition 9, Chap. 2, that

$$\|\mathfrak{M}\| = \binom{n}{p^m}. \tag{28}$$

From Eq. 19 we see that, if $A \in \mathfrak{M}$, then $\|\mathfrak{K}_A\| = t\dfrac{|\mathscr{G}|}{|A|} = tq$, with $t \geq 1$. On the other hand, by Eq. 18 we see that t is a divisor of $|A| = p^m$. Therefore

$$t = p^\nu, \qquad \text{with } \nu \geq 0.$$

If $\mathfrak{K}_A$ contains a subgroup, then, by Lemma 5 and its corollaries, we have $|\mathscr{F}_A| = |A|$, whence $t = 1$. Conversely if $t = 1$ for some $A \in \mathfrak{M}$, then $|A| = |\mathscr{F}_A| = p^m$, and by Lemma 5 and its corollaries, $\mathfrak{K}_A$ contains exactly one subgroup of $\mathscr{G}$. The order of this subgroup is p^m. Furthermore, when $t = 1$, we have $\|\mathfrak{K}_A\| = q$.

Next, suppose for some $A \in \mathfrak{M}$ we have $t = p^\nu > 1$. Then no element of $\mathfrak{K}_A$ is a subgroup of $\mathscr{G}$, and by Eq. 19, we have $\|\mathfrak{K}_A\| \equiv 0 \pmod{pq}$. By Lemma 1, the set $\mathfrak{M}$ is partitioned by the distinct classes $\mathfrak{K}_A$. Hence

$$\|\mathfrak{M}\| = \sum_{\mathfrak{K}_A \text{ distinct}} \|\mathfrak{K}_A\| = \Sigma'\|\mathfrak{K}_A\| + \Sigma''\|\mathfrak{K}_A\|,$$

where Σ' is the sum taken over those classes $\mathfrak{K}_A$ that contain a subgroup of $\mathscr{G}$, and Σ'' is the sum taken over the other classes. Then $\Sigma''\|\mathfrak{K}_A\| \equiv 0 \pmod{pq}$. Let P denote the number of distinct subgroups of $\mathscr{G}$ of order p^m. Since each $\mathfrak{K}_A$ contains at most one subgroup and since all subgroups of $\mathscr{G}$ of order p^m are in $\mathfrak{M}$, we have $\Sigma' = Pq$. It follows that $\|\mathfrak{M}\| \equiv Pq \pmod{pq}$. Combining this result with Eqs. 24 and 28, we obtain

$$P \equiv 1 \pmod{p}.$$

Thus we have proved

POSITION 46 *Let $\mathscr{G}$ be a group such that $|\mathscr{G}| = p^m q$, where $(p, q) = 1$, p a prime, $m \geq 1$. If P is the number of subgroups of $\mathscr{G}$ order p^m, then*

$$P \equiv 1 \pmod{p}.$$

In particular, Proposition 46 tells us there exist subgroups of $\mathscr{G}$ of order p^m. Clearly there are no subgroups of $\mathscr{G}$ or order p^s, where

$s > m$, since the order of a subgroup is a divisor of $|\mathscr{G}|$. Thus these subgroups of order p^m are exactly the Sylow p subgroups of $\mathscr{G}$.

When $\mathscr{G}$ is abelian, $P = 1$. However when $\mathscr{G}$ is nonabelian, P can be larger than 1. For example Π_3 has three subgroups of order 2, which are Sylow 2 subgroups of Π_3.

COROLLARY 1 *Let $\mathscr{G}$ be a group such that $|\mathscr{G}| = p^m q$, where p is a prime, $(p, q) = 1$, and $m \geq 1$. Then at least one Sylow p subgroup has s distinct conjugates with $(p, s) = 1$.*

PROOF. Let $\mathfrak{N}$ be the set of all Sylow p subgroups of $\mathscr{G}$ and take $\mathscr{H} = \mathscr{G}$. Then $\mathfrak{N}$ has property (20), and we can apply results in (**B**). Suppose $\|\mathfrak{C}_{\mathscr{I}}\| \equiv 0 \pmod p$, for each $\mathscr{I} \in \mathfrak{N}$. Then, since by Lemma 6 the sets $\mathfrak{C}_{\mathscr{I}}$ form a partition of $\mathfrak{N}$, we have $P = \|\mathfrak{N}\| = \Sigma\|\mathfrak{C}_{\mathscr{I}}\| \equiv 0$ (mod p), the sum being taken over distinct $\mathfrak{C}_{\mathscr{I}}$. This contradicts Proposition 46.

LEMMA 9 *Let $\mathscr{G}$ be a group such that $|\mathscr{G}| = p^m q$, where p is a prime, $(p, q) = 1$, and $m \geq 1$. Let $\mathscr{P}$ be a Sylow p subgroup that has $s \not\equiv 0 \pmod p$ distinct conjugates in $\mathscr{G}$. Let $\mathscr{H}$ be a p subgroup of $\mathscr{G}$. Then there is a Sylow p subgroup $\mathscr{B}$ of $\mathscr{G}$ such that*

$$\mathscr{B} = g\mathscr{P}g^{-1}, \qquad \textit{for some } g \in \mathscr{G}, \tag{29}$$

and

$$\mathscr{B} = h\mathscr{B}h^{-1}, \qquad \textit{for all } h \in \mathscr{H}. \tag{30}$$

PROOF. Let $\mathfrak{N}$ be those subgroups of $\mathscr{G}$ which are conjugate to $\mathscr{P}$ under an inner automorphism of $\mathscr{G}$. By hypothesis

$$\|\mathfrak{N}\| = s \not\equiv 0 \pmod p.$$

Now $\mathfrak{N}$ satisfies property (20) when $\mathscr{H}$ is the p subgroup of the hypothesis, and so we can apply the results of (**B**).

Since the subsets $\mathfrak{C}_{\mathscr{I}}$ of $\mathfrak{N}$ form a partition of $\mathfrak{N}$, we must have at least one $\mathscr{B} \in \mathfrak{N}$ such that

$$\|\mathfrak{C}_{\mathscr{B}}\| = t \not\equiv 0 \pmod p.$$

But Corollary 2 of Lemma 7 assures us that t is a divisor of $|\mathscr{H}| = p^u$. Hence t must be 1. Thus there is one class $\mathfrak{C}_{\mathscr{B}}$ in $\mathfrak{N}$ containing but one group. This proves Eq. (30). The relation in Eq. (29) holds, since $\mathscr{P}$ and $\mathscr{B}$ are in $\mathfrak{N}$.

PROPOSITION 47 *There exists a Sylow p group $\mathscr{P}$ of $\mathscr{G}$ such that each p subgroup of $\mathscr{G}$ is contained in some conjugate of $\mathscr{P}$.*

PROOF. Let $\mathscr{H}$ be a p subgroup of $\mathscr{G}$, say $|\mathscr{H}| = p^r$, $(r \leq m)$. Let $\mathscr{P}$ be a Sylow p subgroup of $\mathscr{G}$ satisfying the hypothesis of Lemma 9. Then, by Lemma 9, there is a Sylow p subgroup $\mathscr{B}$ of $\mathscr{G}$ satisfying Eqs. 29 and 30. The set $\mathscr{H}\mathscr{B}$ is easily shown to be a subgroup of $\mathscr{G}$, and

$$|\mathscr{H}\mathscr{B}| = \frac{|\mathscr{H}||\mathscr{B}|}{|\mathscr{H} \cap \mathscr{B}|} = p^{r+m-u},$$

where $|\mathscr{H} \cap \mathscr{B}| = p^u$. Clearly $u \leq \min(r, m)$. Now $|\mathscr{H}\mathscr{B}|$ is a divisor of $|\mathscr{G}|$, and hence $r + m - u \leq m$. Thus $r \leq u$. Consequently $r = u$. As $\mathscr{H} \cap \mathscr{B} \subset \mathscr{H}$ and $|\mathscr{H} \cap \mathscr{B}| = |\mathscr{H}|$, we have

$$\mathscr{H} \cap \mathscr{B} = \mathscr{H};$$

and so

$$\mathscr{H} \subset \mathscr{B} = g\mathscr{P}g^{-1}, \qquad \text{for some } g \in \mathscr{G}.$$

This is what we set out to prove.

OPOSITION 48 *All Sylow p subgroups of a group are conjugate.*

PROOF. It follows from Proposition 47 that there is a Sylow subgroup $\mathscr{P}$ such that each p subgroup of $\mathscr{G}$ lies in some conjugate of $\mathscr{P}$. Suppose $\mathscr{H}$ is a Sylow p subgroup of $\mathscr{G}$; then, as observed,

$$\mathscr{H} \subset g\mathscr{P}g^{-1}, \qquad \text{for some } g \in \mathscr{G}.$$

But $\mathscr{H}$ is a maximal p subgroup, and so

$$\mathscr{H} = g\mathscr{P}g^{-1}, \qquad \text{for some } g \in \mathscr{G}.$$

This proves the proposition.

OPOSITION 49 *If* $|\mathscr{G}| = p^m q$, *where p is a prime*, $(p, q) = 1$, $m \geq 1$, *then the number of Sylow p subgroups of* $\mathscr{G}$ *is a divisor of q.*

PROOF. This proposition is immediately deducible from Proposition 48 and Corollary 1, Lemma 7. Let $\mathfrak{N}$ be the set of all Sylow p groups in $\mathscr{G}$. Then $\mathfrak{N}$ satisfies (**B**) with $\mathscr{H} = \mathscr{G}$. By Corollary 1, Lemma 7, for each $\mathscr{J} \in \mathfrak{N}$, $\|\mathfrak{C}_{\mathscr{J}}\|$ is a divisor of $[\mathscr{G}:\mathscr{J}] = q$. However, it follows from Proposition 48 that $\mathfrak{N} = \mathfrak{C}_{\mathscr{P}}$; i.e., $\mathfrak{N}$ is but one class. Hence $P = \|\mathfrak{N}\|$ is a divisor of q.

OROLLARY 1 *If* $P = 1$, *then the unique Sylow p subgroup of* $\mathscr{G}$ *is a normal subgroup of* $\mathscr{G}$.

The proof is obvious.

Propositions 46 and 49 give us congruence conditions on P, the number of Sylow p subgroups in $\mathscr{G}$, namely,

$$P \equiv 1 \pmod{p}, \qquad q \equiv 0 \pmod{P}.$$

Often these conditions may be used to show that P must be 1. Such is indeed the case of a group of order pq, where $q < p$ are primes.

XERCISES 1 Let $\mathscr{B}$ and $\mathscr{H}$ be subgroups of $\mathscr{G}$ such that $\mathscr{B} = h\mathscr{B}h^{-1}$ for all $h \in \mathscr{H}$. Prove $\mathscr{H}\mathscr{B}$ is a subgroup of $\mathscr{G}$ and $|\mathscr{H}\mathscr{B}||\mathscr{H} \cap \mathscr{B}| = |\mathscr{H}||\mathscr{B}|$.

2 Let $\mathscr{H}$ be a finite group, and suppose p^r divides $|\mathscr{G}|$. Let P_r denote the number of subgroups of $\mathscr{G}$ of order p^r. Prove:

A. $P_r \equiv 1 \pmod{p}$; hence $\mathscr{G}$ has subgroups of order p^r.

B. There is a subgroup of order p^r with $s \not\equiv 0 \pmod{p}$ distinct conjugates.

(*Hint:* Modify the proofs for Proposition 46 and its corollary.)

3 Show that the group $\mathscr{G} = \langle(1\ 2)(3\ 4), (1\ 2\ 3)\rangle$ is a group of order 12 and has no subgroup of order 6. This result shows that we cannot extend the results in Exercise 2 to any divisor of $|\mathscr{G}|$.

4 Let $\mathscr{G}$ be a group such that $|\mathscr{G}| = p^m$, p a prime. Let I_r denote the number of normal subgroups of $\mathscr{G}$ of order p^r $(r \le m)$. Prove:

A. $I_r \equiv 1 \pmod{p}$.

B. Every subgroup of $\mathscr{G}$ of order p^{m-1} is normal in $\mathscr{G}$.

(*Hint:* Let $\mathfrak{N}$ be the set of all subgroups of order p^r and apply (**B**)).

5 Suppose $|\mathscr{G}| = p^m$, p a prime. Let $\mathscr{H}$ be a proper subgroup of $\mathscr{G}$, say $|\mathscr{H}| = p^s$, with $s < m$. Prove: There is a subgroup $\mathscr{J}$ of $\mathscr{G}$ such that

$$\mathscr{H} \subset \mathscr{J} \subset \mathscr{G} \text{ and } |\mathscr{J}| = p^{s+1}.$$

(*Hint:* By Exercise 4 there is a normal subgroup $\mathscr{U}$ of $\mathscr{G}$ with $|\mathscr{U}| = p$. Suppose the result holds for p groups of order $<p^m$. If $\mathscr{U} \subset \mathscr{H}$, then consider $\mathscr{G}/\mathscr{U}$ and $\mathscr{H}/\mathscr{U}$. If $\mathscr{U} \not\subset \mathscr{H}$, examine $\mathscr{U}\mathscr{H}$.)

6 Suppose $|\mathscr{G}| = p^m$, and suppose $\mathscr{G} \supset \mathscr{H}_1 \supset \mathscr{H}_2$, where $\mathscr{H}_1$ and $\mathscr{H}_2$ are normal subgroups of $\mathscr{G}$. Say $|\mathscr{H}_1| = p^{r_1}$, $|\mathscr{H}_2| = p^{r_2}$ with $r_1 \ge r_2 + 2$. Prove: There is a normal subgroup $\mathscr{H}$ of $\mathscr{G}$ such that

$$\mathscr{H}_2 \subset \mathscr{H} \subset \mathscr{H}_1$$
$$|\mathscr{H}| = p^{r_1 - 1}.$$

(*Hint:* Consider $\mathscr{H}_1/\mathscr{H}_2$ and apply Exercise 4.)

7 Prove: If $|\mathscr{G}| = p^m$, then there is a sequence of groups

$$\mathscr{G} = \mathscr{H}_0 \supset \mathscr{H}_1 \supset \cdots \supset \mathscr{H}_m = \langle e\rangle,$$

where each $\mathscr{H}_i \lhd \mathscr{G}$ and $|\mathscr{H}_i/\mathscr{H}_{i+1}| = p$.

8 Suppose $|\mathscr{G}| = p^m q$, where p is a prime, $(p, q) = 1$, $m \ge 1$. Prove: If $\mathscr{H} \lhd \mathscr{G}$ such that $(|\mathscr{G}/\mathscr{H}|, p) = 1$, then each Sylow p group of $\mathscr{G}$ is a Sylow p group of $\mathscr{H}$.

9 Prove: If $\mathscr{G}$ is a finite group containing a normal p subgroup $\mathscr{H}$, then each Sylow p subgroup of $\mathscr{G}$ contains $\mathscr{H}$.

Our proofs of the Sylow propositions involved the collecting of information concerning a group $\mathscr{G}$ by studying the action of the elements of $\mathscr{G}$ on a collection of sets $\mathfrak{M}$. This type of argument, and generalizations of it, occur frequently throughout the study of algebra. We shall not dwell further on these methods at this time but shall use them on the appropriate occasion.

We shall now give a few examples of the use of the preceding propositions on p groups to classify finite groups whose orders are not too highly composite.

Recall that a group of prime order is cyclic and isomorphic to $\mathbf{Z}_p$. Secondly recall that we proved (Proposition 37) that *every p group has a nontrivial center* and deduced from this that *every group of order p^2 is abelian and is isomorphic either to $\mathbf{Z}_{p^2}$ or to $\mathbf{Z}_p + \mathbf{Z}_p$*. (See Exercise 3D, Sec. 12.)

Groups of order p^3. We first sketch the proof of the following result.

POSITION 50 *An abelian group of order p^3 is isomorphic to one of the following nonisomorphic groups:*

$$\mathbf{Z}_{p^3}, \qquad \mathbf{Z}_{p^2} + \mathbf{Z}_p, \qquad \mathbf{Z}_p + \mathbf{Z}_p + \mathbf{Z}_p.$$

PROOF. The reader should prove that the groups listed in the Proposition are nonisomorphic.

Given a group $\mathcal{G}$ of order p^3, let

$$m = \max \{o(x) \mid x \in \mathcal{G}\}.$$

Then $m = p$, p^2, or p^3. If $m = p^3$, then $\mathcal{G} \cong \mathbf{Z}_{p^3}$. Suppose $m = p^2$. Let $x \in \mathcal{G}$ of order p^2. Let $y \in \mathcal{G} - \langle x \rangle$; then $y\langle x \rangle \neq \langle x \rangle$. Hence

$$\mathcal{G} = \langle x \rangle \cup y\langle x \rangle \cup \cdots \cup y^{p-1}\langle x \rangle. \tag{31}$$

But then $y^p \in \langle x \rangle$, say $y^p = x^s$. If $(s, p) = 1$, then $o(y) = p^3 > m$, a contradiction. Consequently $y^p = e$ or x^p. If $y^p = x^p$, we can replace y by yx without disturbing the relation in Eq. 31. Hence we can assume

$$\mathcal{G} = \langle x, y \rangle, \qquad \text{where } x^{p^2} = e,\ y^p = e,\ xy = yx.$$

But then $$\mathcal{G} = \langle x \rangle \langle y \rangle \text{ (direct)} \cong \mathbf{Z}_{p^2} + \mathbf{Z}_p.$$

Finally suppose $m = p$. Let $x \in \mathcal{G}$ of order p. Then $\langle x \rangle \lhd \mathcal{G}$, and each element of $\mathcal{G}/\langle x \rangle$ is of order p. Hence

$$\mathcal{G}/\langle x \rangle \cong \mathbf{Z}_p + \mathbf{Z}_p,$$

and $\mathcal{G}$ is mapped homomorphically onto $\mathbf{Z}_p + \mathbf{Z}_p$. Say φ is that homomorphic map. Let $y, z \in \mathcal{G}$ such that $y^\varphi = (1, 0)$, $z^\varphi = (0, 1)$. Then $\mathcal{G} = \langle x, y, z \rangle$ with $x^p = y^p = z^p = e$. It follows that $\mathcal{G} \cong \mathbf{Z}_p + \mathbf{Z}_p + \mathbf{Z}_p$. This proves Proposition 50.

When we come to nonabelian groups of order p^3, we need to distinguish between $p = 2$ and p an odd prime.

Suppose $|\mathcal{G}| = 8$ and $\mathcal{G}$ is nonabelian. Then no element is of order 8, and some element must have order 4 (see Proposition 11). Say $x \in \mathcal{G}$, with $o(x) = 4$. Let $y \in \mathcal{G} - \langle x \rangle$. Then $\mathcal{G} = \langle x \rangle \cup y\langle x \rangle$ and $y^2 \in \langle x \rangle$. Say $y^2 = x^\mu$. If $(\mu, 2) = 1$, then $o(y) = 8$, a contradiction. So $\mu = 0, 2$. By Exercise 4B, $\langle x \rangle \lhd \mathcal{G}$. So $y^{-1}xy = x^v$ and $v = 1$ or 3, since $o(yxy^{-1}) = 4$. If $yxy^{-1} = x$, we would have $xy = yx$, and hence $\mathcal{G}$ would be abelian. Hence

$$xy = yx^3.$$

Thus we see that $\mathscr{G}$ is of one of two types:

$$\mathscr{A} = \langle x, y \rangle, \qquad \text{where } x^4 = e,\ x^2 = y^2, \text{ and } xy = yx^3,$$

$$\mathscr{B} = \langle x, y \rangle, \qquad \text{where } x^4 = e,\ y^2 = e, \text{ and } xy = yx^3.$$

The reader should verify that $\mathscr{A}$ and $\mathscr{B}$ are indeed groups of order 8 and that they are not isomorphic. Thus we have

PROPOSITION 51 *If $|\mathscr{G}| = 8$ and $\mathscr{G}$ is nonabelian, then there exist $x, y \in \mathscr{G}$ such that either $\mathscr{G} = \langle x, y \rangle$, where $x^4 = e$, $x^2 = y^2$, and $xy = yx^3$, or $\mathscr{G} = \langle x, y \rangle$, where $x^4 = e$, $y^2 = e$, and $xy = yx^3$.*

Suppose p odd, and some $x \in \mathscr{G}$ is of order p^2. Then by Exercise 4B we have $\langle x \rangle \lhd \mathscr{G}$. Let $y \in \mathscr{G} - \langle x \rangle$; then $y\langle x \rangle \neq \langle x \rangle$, and

$$\mathscr{G} = \langle x \rangle \cup \cdots \cup y^{p-1}\langle x \rangle \qquad \text{(disjoint union)}.$$

Thus $y^p \in \langle x \rangle$. Furthermore

$$xy = yx^r, \qquad \text{for some } r,\ 0 < r < p^2. \tag{32}$$

Clearly $r \neq 1$; otherwise $\mathscr{G}$ would be abelian. Repeated application of Eq. 32 gives

$$xy^s = y^s x^{r^s}, \qquad s = 1, 2, \ldots .$$

Since $y^p \in \langle x \rangle$, we have

$$x = y^{-p} x y^p = x^{r^p}.$$

This implies

$$r^p \equiv 1 \pmod{p^2}.$$

But Proposition 12 (Fermat's little theorem) tells us that

$$r^p \equiv r \pmod{p},$$

and so $r \equiv 1 \pmod{p}$.

Set

$$r = 1 + kp.$$

Then $k \not\equiv 0 \pmod{p}$; else $r = 1$ and $\mathscr{G}$ is abelian. Let s be chosen so that

$$ks \equiv 1 \pmod{p}, \qquad 0 < s < p.$$

Then
$$y^{-s} x y^s = x^{r^s} = x^{(1+kp)^s}.$$

But
$$(1 + kp)^s \equiv 1 + ksp \equiv 1 + p \pmod{p^2}.$$

Thus
$$y^{-s} x y^s = x^{1+p}.$$

Since $y^s \notin \langle x \rangle$, we could have used y^s instead of y. If we do, we shall have

$$\mathscr{G} = \{x^\alpha y^\beta \mid 0 \le \alpha < p^2,\ 0 \le \beta < p\},$$

where $xy = yx^{1+p}$, and $y^p = x^t$.

If $(t, p) = 1$, then $o(y) = p^3$ and $\mathscr{G}$ would be abelian. Hence $t = up$, for some $u \in \mathbf{Z}$. Now

$$y^{-1}x^{-1} = (xy)^{-1} = (yx^{1+p})^{-1} = x^{-1-p}y^{-1},$$

whence

$$x^{-1}y = yx^{-1-p},$$

and

$$(yx^{-u})^p = y^p x^{-u[1+(1+p)+(1+p)^2+\cdots+(1+p)^{p-1}]}$$

$$= x^{up-u[1+\cdots+(1+p)^{p-1}]}. \tag{33}$$

But

$$1 + r + \cdots + r^{p-1} = \frac{r^p - 1}{r - 1}.$$

Hence the exponent of x on the right-hand side of Eq. 33 is

$$up - u\,\frac{(1+p)^p - 1}{p},$$

which is congruent to 0 modulo p^2. Thus

$$(yx^{-u})^p = e.$$

We now set $z = yx^{-u}$. Then $z^p = e$, and $z^{-1}xz = x^{1+p}$. It follows that

$$\mathscr{G} = \langle x, z \rangle, \qquad \text{where } x^{p^2} = e,\ z^p = e,\ xz = zx^{1+p}. \tag{34}$$

Suppose p odd, $\mathscr{G}$ nonabelian, and each $x \in \mathscr{G}$ is of order $\leq p$. The reader can verify that the center $\mathfrak{Z}(\mathscr{G})$ could not have order p^2; else $\mathscr{G}$ would be abelian. Hence $\mathscr{G}/\mathfrak{Z}(\mathscr{G})$ is a group of order p^2 with no element of order p^2; that is,

$$\mathscr{G}/\mathfrak{Z}(\mathscr{G}) \cong \mathbf{Z}_p + \mathbf{Z}_p.$$

Hence there is a homomorphism φ of $\mathscr{G}$ onto $\mathbf{Z}_p + \mathbf{Z}_p$ with kernel $\mathfrak{Z}(\mathscr{G})$. Let x and y be elements of $\mathscr{G}$ such that $x^\varphi = (1, 0)$ and $y^\varphi = (0, 1)$. Let $\mathfrak{Z}(\mathscr{G}) = \langle z \rangle$. Then $\mathscr{G} = \langle x, y, z \rangle$, where $xz = zx$, $yz = zy$. Now $(xyx^{-1}y^{-1})^\varphi = (0, 0)$; hence $xyx^{-1}y^{-1} = z^s$. If $s \equiv 0 \pmod{p}$, then $xy = yx$ and $\mathscr{G}$ is abelian. If $s \not\equiv 0 \pmod{p}$, then $\mathfrak{Z}(\mathscr{G}) = \langle z^s \rangle$. Hence we can replace z by z^s. Thus we have $\mathscr{G} = \langle x, y, z \rangle$, where

$$x^p = y^p = z^p = e \qquad xz = zx,\ yz = zy,\ xy = zyx. \tag{35}$$

The reader should prove that the groups in Eqs. 34 and 35 are nonisomorphic. We have proved

OPOSITION 52 *If $|\mathscr{G}| = p^3$, p an odd prime, and $\mathscr{G}$ is nonabelian, then there exist x, y, $z \in \mathscr{G}$ such that either*

$$\mathscr{G} = \langle x, y \rangle, \qquad \textit{where } x^{p^2} = y^p = e,\ xy = yx^{1+p},$$

or $\mathscr{G} = \langle x, y, z \rangle$, *where* $x^p = y^p = z^p = e$, $xz = zx$, $yz = zy$, $xy = zyx$.

EXERCISES 10 Prove: If p and q are primes such that $q \geq p$ and $q \not\equiv 1 \pmod{p}$, then a group of order pq is cyclic. (*Hint:* Show there is but one Sylow p subgroup and but one Sylow q subgroup.)

11 Prove: If $\mathscr{G}$ is a nonabelian group of order pq, where $q > p$ are primes, then $p \mid q - 1$. If r is any positive integer such that

$$r^p \equiv 1 \pmod{q}, \qquad r \equiv 1 \pmod{q},$$

then $\mathscr{G}$ is isomorphic to the group $\langle x, y \rangle$, where $x^p = 1$, $y^q = 1$, $xy = y^r x$. Show that different r's give isomorphic groups.

12 Prove: A group of order pq, where $p < q$ are primes, is either cyclic or it is isomorphic to the group specified in Exercise 11.

13 Prove: If p and q are primes such that $q > p$ and $q \not\equiv \pm 1 \pmod{p}$, then a group of order pq^2 is abelian. Must such groups be cyclic?

14 Find the number of distinct isomorphic classes of groups of order 1965. Can you generalize your result to groups of order pqn, where p, q, *and* n are primes and $n > pq$?

One can use these techniques to find all the classes of isomorphic groups whose order does not involve too many factors, e.g., $|\mathscr{G}| = p^4$ or p^3q or p^2q^2. However, experiments will soon show that the work is exceedingly tedious, and furthermore it does not help predict what will happen for groups whose orders involve many prime factors.

15 THE DECOMPOSITION THEOREM FOR FINITE ABELIAN GROUPS

In this section we shall prove that a finite abelian group can be decomposed into the direct product of finitely many cyclic p subgroups in a unique way. By Proposition 43 such groups are indecomposable. To attain such a decomposition is as much as one could desire. It tells us that for the semigroup of isomorphic classes of finite abelian groups we have the equivalent of a unique factorization theorem. Furthermore this theorem will enable us to say whether two finite abelian groups are isomorphic.

If $|\mathscr{G}| < \infty$, then there is a minimal number of elements of $\mathscr{G}$ that generate $\mathscr{G}$; denote this number by $r = r(\mathscr{G})$.

EXERCISE 1 Prove:

A. $r(\mathscr{G}) = 1$ exactly when $\mathscr{G}$ is cyclic.

B. $r(\mathscr{G}) < |\mathscr{G}|$ if $\mathscr{G} \neq \langle e \rangle$.

C. $\mathscr{G} \cong \mathscr{H}$ implies $r(\mathscr{G}) = r(\mathscr{H})$. Is the converse true?

D. $r(\mathscr{G} \times \mathscr{H}) \leq r(\mathscr{G}) + r(\mathscr{H})$. Give examples where the inequality holds.

Throughout this section we assume $\mathscr{G}$ is an abelian group. Many of the lemmas, propositions, and theorems stated in this section are false for nonabelian groups.

A set $r = r(\mathscr{G})$ elements from $\mathscr{G}$, which generate $\mathscr{G}$, is said to be a *minimal generating set of* $\mathscr{G}$. Given a minimal generating set M and an ordering of the elements of M, say

$$M = \{g_1, g_2, \ldots, g_r\},$$

there exists ordered r-tuples of integers $(n_1, n_2, \ldots, n_r)$ such that

$$g_1^{n_1} g_2^{n_2} \cdots g_r^{n_r} = e.$$

For example, take $n_i = o(g_i)$ or $n_i = 0$. Let

$$\mathscr{N}(g_1, g_2, \ldots, g_r) = \{(n_1, \ldots, n_r) \,|\, n_i \in \mathbf{Z} \text{ and } g_1^{n_1} \cdots g_r^{n_r} = e\}.$$

One can easily show that $\mathscr{N}(g_1, \ldots, g_r)$ is an additive subgroup of $\mathbf{Z}^{(r)}$, the cartesian sum of $\mathbf{Z}$ with itself r times.

Let

$$\mathscr{N} = \bigcup \mathscr{N}(g_1, \ldots, g_r),$$

where the union is taken over all possible orderings $g_1, g_2, \ldots, g_r$ of all possible minimal generating sets of $\mathscr{G}$. We observe the following facts.

LEMMA 1 *If* $(n_1, \ldots, n_r) \in \mathscr{N}$ *and* $\pi \in \Pi_r$, *then* $(n_{1\pi}, \ldots, n_{r\pi}) \in \mathscr{N}$.

If $\{g_1, g_2, \ldots, g_r\}$ is a minimal generating set, then $\{g_1, \ldots, g_{i-1}, g_i g_j^s, g_{i+1}, \ldots, g_r\}$, with $i \neq j$ and $s \in \mathbf{Z}$, is a minimal generating set. Hence

LEMMA 2 *If* $(n_1, \ldots, n_r) \in \mathscr{N}$, *then* $(n_1, \ldots, n_{j-1}, n_j - sn_i, n_{j+1}, \ldots, n_r) \in \mathscr{N}$.

Let n be the minimal positive integer appearing in any r-tuple in $\mathscr{N}$. This integer is uniqely determined by the group $\mathscr{G}$, and we shall sometimes indicate this by writing $n = n(\mathscr{G})$.

EXERCISE 2 Prove:

A. $n(\langle e \rangle) = 1$.

B. If $\mathscr{G} \neq \langle e \rangle$, then $n(\mathscr{G}) > 1$.

C. If $\mathscr{G}$ is a cyclic group, then $n(\mathscr{G}) = |\mathscr{G}|$.

D. $n(\mathscr{G}) \leq |\mathscr{G}|$.

E. If $\mathscr{G} \cong \mathscr{H}$, then $n(\mathscr{G}) = n(\mathscr{H})$.

We continue to make observations on the set $\mathscr{N}$.

LEMMA 3 *If* $(n_1, \ldots, n_r) \in \mathscr{N}$ *and some* $n_i = n = n(\mathscr{G})$, *then* n *is a divisor of each* n_i, $(i = 1, 2, \ldots, r)$.

PROOF. Suppose that $n_i = n$ and that $n_j = nq + m$ with $0 < m < n$. By Lemma 2, m appears as a coordinate of $\mathscr{N}$, contrary to the definition of n.

By Lemma 1, we can assume there is a minimal generating set and an ordering of that set, say $g_1, g_2, \ldots, g_r$, such that there exist $n_1, \ldots, n_r$, with $n_1 = n$ and $g_1{}^{n_1} g_2{}^{n_2} \cdots g_r{}^{n_r} = e$. By Lemma 3 the other n_j are divisible by n. Consequently, by repeated applications of Lemma 2, we see that $(n, 0, \ldots, 0) \in \mathcal{N}$. Finally we observe that n must be the order of g_1. Thus we have

LEMMA 4 *There exists a minimal generating set* $\{g_1, \ldots, g_r\}$ of $\mathcal{G}$ *with* $o(g_1) = n(\mathcal{G})$.

By letting $g_1, \ldots, g_n$ be as in Lemma 4 and by applying Lemma 3 to the n-tuple $(o(g_1), \ldots, o(g_n))$, the conclusion of Lemma 4 can be strengthened to read

$$o(g_1) = n(\mathcal{G}) \geq 2 \qquad \text{and} \qquad n \mid o(g_i), \qquad i = 1, 2, \ldots, r. \tag{36}$$

More generally we have

LEMMA 5 *Let* $\{g_1, \ldots, g_r\}$ *be a minimal generating set for* $\mathcal{G}$ *such that*

$$o(g_1) = n(\mathcal{G}) = n \geq 2. \tag{37}$$

If $g_1^{m_1} \cdots g_r^{m_r} = e$, *then* $n \mid m_i$, $(i = 1, 2, \ldots, r)$.

PROOF. Suppose $m_1 = nq + u$, $0 < u < n$. Then

$$g_1{}^{-nq} g_1{}^{m_1} \cdots g_r{}^{m_r} = g_1{}^{u} g_2{}^{m_2} \cdots g_r{}^{m_r} = e.$$

Hence $(u, m_1, \ldots, m_r) \in \mathcal{N}$, contrary to the definition of $n(\mathcal{G})$. Thus $n \mid m_1$. It follows that

$$g_1{}^{n} g_2{}^{m_2} \cdots g_r{}^{m_r} = e,$$

and hence by Lemma 3, we have $n \mid m_i$, $(i = 2, \ldots, r)$.

We can now prove

PROPOSITION 53 *If* $\mathcal{G}$ *is a finite, noncyclic, abelian group, then* $\mathcal{G} = \mathcal{H}\mathcal{J}$ *(direct), where* $\mathcal{H}$ *is cyclic of order* $n(\mathcal{G})$, *and* $\mathcal{J}$ *is such that*

$$r(\mathcal{J}) = r(\mathcal{G}) - 1 \qquad \textit{and} \qquad n(\mathcal{G}) \mid n(\mathcal{J}).$$

PROOF. By Lemma 4, $\mathcal{G}$ has a generating set $\{g_1, \ldots, g_r\}$, with $o(g_1) = n \geq 2$. Put

$$\mathcal{H} = \langle g_1 \rangle, \qquad \mathcal{J} = \langle g_2, \ldots, g_r \rangle.$$

Clearly $\mathcal{H}$ and $\mathcal{J}$ are proper normal subgroups of $\mathcal{G}$ for which $\mathcal{G} = \mathcal{H}\mathcal{J}$. Furthermore $\mathcal{H} \cap \mathcal{J} = \langle e \rangle$, for suppose

$$g_1{}^{m_1} = g_2{}^{m_2} \cdots g_r{}^{m_r}.$$

Then by Lemma 5

$$n \mid m_i, \qquad i = 1, 2, \ldots, r,$$

and so $g_1{}^{m_1} = e$. Thus

$$\mathcal{G} = \mathcal{H}\mathcal{J} \quad \text{(direct)}.$$

By Exercise 1,

$$r(\mathcal{G}) \le r(\mathcal{H}) + r(\mathcal{J}) = 1 + r(\mathcal{J}).$$

Hence
$$r(\mathcal{G}) - 1 \le r(\mathcal{J}).$$

However, by construction $r(\mathcal{J}) \le r(\mathcal{G}) - 1$. Consequently

$$r(\mathcal{G}) - 1 = r(\mathcal{J}).$$

By Lemma 4, $\mathcal{J}$ has a minimal generating set $\{g_2^*, \ldots, g_r^*\}$, with $o(g_2^*) = n(\mathcal{J})$. Then $\{g_1, g_2^*, \ldots, g_r^*\}$ is a minimal generating set of $\mathcal{G}$. It follows from Eq. 36 that

$$n(\mathcal{G}) \mid o(g_2^*);$$

i.e.,
$$n(\mathcal{G}) \mid n(\mathcal{J}).$$

This completes the proof of the proposition.

We next prove that $\mathcal{G}$ can be decomposed into the direct product of cyclic groups. Specifically, we prove

THEOREM 11 *If $\mathcal{G}$ is a finite abelian group, then*

$$\mathcal{G} = \langle x_1 \rangle \langle x_2 \rangle \cdots \langle x_r \rangle \text{ (direct),}$$

where $r = r(\mathcal{G})$, $o(x_1) = n(\mathcal{G})$ and $o(x_i) \mid o(x_{i+1})$ $\quad i = 1, 2, \ldots, r-1$.

PROOF. The proof is by induction on r. The theorem is obviously true for cyclic groups, i.e., for $r = 1$. We assume the theorem is valid for groups $\mathcal{H}$ having $r(\mathcal{H}) < r = r(\mathcal{G})$. We can suppose $r \ge 2$. Then, by Proposition 53, we have

$$\mathcal{G} = \langle x_1 \rangle \mathcal{J} \text{ (direct),}$$

where $o(x_1) = n(\mathcal{G}) = n$, and where $r(\mathcal{J}) = r - 1$ and $n \mid n(\mathcal{J})$. It follows from the induction hypothesis that

$$\mathcal{J} = \langle x_2 \rangle \cdots \langle x_r \rangle \text{ (direct),}$$

where $o(x_i) \mid o(x_{i+1})$, for $i = 2, 3, \ldots, r-1$. Since $n(\mathcal{J}) = o(x_2)$, the conclusion of the theorem now follows.

Using Theorem 11 and Proposition 45 we now obtain the converse of Proposition 43:

COROLLARY *If $\mathcal{G}$ is a finite indecomposable abelian group, then $\mathcal{G}$ is a cyclic p group.*

Thus we have

THEOREM 12 *The set of finite indecomposable abelian groups is exactly the set of all cyclic p groups.*

If we decompose a finite abelian group of order greater than 1 into its nontrivial Sylow subgroups (see Theorem 10) and then apply

Theorem 11 to each of these p subgroups, we see that each finite abelian group can be expressed as the direct product of finitely many indecomposable groups. Thus we have a result analogous to the decomposition of an integer greater than 1 into a finite product of primes (indecomposable integers). Is this decomposition of groups unique; that is, can we express a finite abelian group as a direct product of indecomposable groups in two different ways?

We note that in direct products the order of the factors is not important. Given a decomposition of a finite abelian group $\mathscr{G}$ into indecomposable groups, we group all those groups belonging to the same prime p. The direct product of these p groups must be $\mathscr{G}(p)$, since $\mathscr{G}(p)$ is exactly the set of elements of $\mathscr{G}$, the orders of which are powers of p. Now $\mathscr{G}(p)$ is uniquely determined by $\mathscr{G}$ and the prime p, and consequently different decompositions of $\mathscr{G}$ must lead to the same $\mathscr{G}(p)$. Thus to prove the uniqueness of decomposition, it is sufficient to prove that the decomposition of abelian p groups into the direct product of cyclic groups is unique.

We need some additional notation. If $\mathscr{G}$ is an abelian group, and $m \in \mathbf{Z}^+$ the map

$$g \to g^m$$

is a homomorphism of $\mathscr{G}$ into $\mathscr{G}$. We denote the kernel of this homomorphism by $\mathscr{G}_m$ and the image by $\mathscr{G}^m$. Then

$$\mathscr{G}_m = \{g \in \mathscr{G} \mid o(g) \text{ divides } m\},$$

$$\mathscr{G}^m = \{g \in \mathscr{G} \mid g = x^m \text{ for some } x \in \mathscr{G}\},$$

and

$$|\mathscr{G}_m|\,|\mathscr{G}^m| = |\mathscr{G}|.$$

Thus we see that $\mathscr{G}_m$ and $\mathscr{G}^m$ are completely determined by $\mathscr{G}$ and m and do not depend in any way on possible decomposition of $\mathscr{G}$.

In particular, we note that, when $\mathscr{G}$ is a cyclic group of order k, say $\mathscr{G} = \langle g \rangle$, then

$$\mathscr{G}^m = \langle g^m \rangle = \langle g^{(m,k)} \rangle,$$

and

$$\mathscr{G}_m = \langle g^{k/(m,k)} \rangle.$$

Also note that $\mathscr{G}^m = \langle e \rangle$ if and only if for each $g \in \mathscr{G}$, $o(g) \mid m$.

Since elements from different direct factors commute, we see that, if

$$\mathscr{G} = \mathscr{G}_1 \mathscr{G}_2 \cdots \mathscr{G}_r \quad \text{(direct)},$$

then

$$\mathscr{G}^m = \mathscr{G}_1{}^m \cdots \mathscr{G}_r{}^m \quad \text{(direct)},$$

and

$$\mathscr{G}_m = (\mathscr{G}_1)_m \cdots (\mathscr{G}_r)_m \quad \text{(direct)}.$$

LEMMA 1 *If $\mathscr{G}$ is a finite abelian p group, then $r = r(\mathscr{G})$ is the number of nontrivial cyclic factors in any decomposition of $\mathscr{G}$ into indecomposable groups.*

PROOF. Suppose $\mathscr{G}_i$, $\mathscr{H}_i$ are cyclic groups of order greater than 1 such that

$$\mathscr{G} = \mathscr{G}_1 \cdots \mathscr{G}_r \quad \text{(direct)} \quad = \mathscr{H}_1 \cdots \mathscr{H}_s \quad \text{(direct)}.$$

Since each $\mathscr{G}_i$ and $\mathscr{H}_j$ is a cyclic p group, the groups $(\mathscr{G}_i)_p$ and $(\mathscr{H}_j)_p$ are cyclic of order p. Thus $|\mathscr{G}_p| = p^r = p^s$, whence $r = s$.

LEMMA 2 *If $\mathscr{G}$ is a finite abelian p group such that*

$$\mathscr{G} = \mathscr{G}_1 \cdots \mathscr{G}_r \quad \text{(direct)} \quad = \mathscr{H}_1 \cdots \mathscr{H}_r \quad \text{(direct)},$$

where the $\mathscr{G}_i$ and $\mathscr{H}_j$ are cyclic groups such that $o(\mathscr{G}_i) \mid o(\mathscr{G}_{i+1})$ and $o(\mathscr{H}_i) \mid o(\mathscr{H}_{i+1})$, $(i = 1, 2, \ldots, r-1)$, then $\mathscr{G}_i \cong \mathscr{H}_i$, $(i = 1, 2, \ldots, r)$.

PROOF. The proof is by induction on r. If $r = 1$, then $\mathscr{G}$ is cyclic, and $\mathscr{G} = \mathscr{G}_1 = \mathscr{H}_1$. Suppose the lemma is true for p groups with fewer than r generators. Since the $\mathscr{G}_i$ and $\mathscr{H}_i$ are cyclic, we can prove $\mathscr{G}_i \cong \mathscr{H}_i$ by showing $|\mathscr{G}_i| = |\mathscr{H}_i|$. Suppose $|\mathscr{G}_1| \neq |\mathscr{H}_1|$, say $n = |\mathscr{G}_1| < |\mathscr{H}_1|$; then

$$r(\mathscr{G}^n) = r(\mathscr{G}_1{}^n \cdots \mathscr{G}_r{}^n) < r = r(\mathscr{H}_1{}^n \cdots \mathscr{H}_r{}^n) = r(\mathscr{G}^n),$$

a contradiction. Hence $\mathscr{G}_1 \cong \mathscr{H}_1$. Furthermore

$$\mathscr{G}^n = \mathscr{G}_{s+1}{}^n \cdots \mathscr{G}_r{}^n \text{ (direct)} = \mathscr{H}_{t+1}{}^n \cdots \mathscr{H}_r{}^n \qquad \text{(direct)},$$

where s is such that

$$|\mathscr{G}_s| = n < |\mathscr{G}_{s+1}|,$$

and t is such that

$$|\mathscr{H}_t| = n < |\mathscr{H}_{t+1}|.$$

It follows from Lemma 1 that $r - s = r - t$; i.e., $s = t$. Hence

$$\mathscr{G}_i \cong \mathscr{H}_i, \qquad 1 \leq i \leq s. \tag{38}$$

Since $r(\mathscr{G}^n) < r$, it follows from the induction hypothesis that

$$\mathscr{G}_j{}^n \cong \mathscr{H}_j{}^n, \qquad j = s+1, s+2, \ldots, r.$$

Since $n | o(\mathscr{G}_i)$ and $n | o(\mathscr{H}_j)$, we have $|(\mathscr{G}_i)_n| = |(\mathscr{H}_j)_n| = n$. Hence

$$|\mathscr{G}_j| = |\mathscr{G}_j{}^n|\,|(\mathscr{G}_j)_n| = |\mathscr{G}_j{}^n| \cdot n,$$

$$|\mathscr{H}_j| = |\mathscr{H}_j{}^n|\,|(\mathscr{H}_j)_n| = |\mathscr{H}_j{}^n| \cdot n.$$

Therefore $|\mathscr{G}_j| = |\mathscr{H}_j|$, $(j = s+1, \ldots, r)$. But then

$$\mathscr{G}_j \cong \mathscr{H}_j, \qquad j = s+1, \ldots, r. \tag{39}$$

Clearly Eqs. 38 and 39 cover the entire range $j = 1, \ldots, r$. Thus we have proved Lemma 2.

Another way to express Lemmas 1 and 2 is the following: If $\mathscr{G} = \mathscr{G}_1 \cdots \mathscr{G}_r$ (direct) $= \mathscr{H}_1 \cdots \mathscr{H}_s$ (direct) are two decompositions of an abelian p group into the direct product of cyclic p groups, then $r = s$, and after a rearrangement of the factors, we have $\mathscr{G}_i \cong \mathscr{H}_i, (i = 1, \ldots, r)$.

It should be noted that we cannot expect to say $\mathscr{G}_i = \mathscr{H}_i$, $(i = 1, \ldots, r)$. For example,

$$\mathbf{Z}_8' = \langle \lfloor 3 \rfloor \rangle \langle \lfloor 5 \rfloor \rangle \text{ (direct)} = \langle \lfloor 3 \rfloor \rangle \langle \lfloor 7 \rfloor \rangle \text{ (direct)},$$

and $\langle \lfloor 5 \rfloor \rangle \cap \langle \lfloor 7 \rfloor \rangle = \langle \lfloor 1 \rfloor \rangle$.

Combining Lemmas 1 and 2 and the fact that for each prime p there is exactly one Sylow p subgroup of an abelian group, we obtain

THEOREM 13 *If $\mathscr{G}$ is a finite abelian group and if*

$$\mathscr{G} = \mathscr{G}_1 \cdots \mathscr{G}_r \text{ (direct)} = \mathscr{H}_1 \cdots \mathscr{H}_s \text{ (direct)},$$

where the $\mathscr{G}_i$ and $\mathscr{H}_j$ are indecomposable groups, then $r = s$, and after a rearrangement of the components $\mathscr{G}_i \cong \mathscr{H}_i$, $(i = 1, \ldots, r)$.

This is the promised theorem on the decomposition of a finite abelian group into indecomposable groups. It is a unique factorization theorem for the semigroup of isomorphism classes of finite abelian groups.

Theorem 13 is often called the *fundamental theorem for finite abelian groups*. In general, we cannot prove an analogous theorem for general abelian groups. However, the conclusion of Theorem 13 remains valid if we replace the assumption that "$\mathscr{G}$ is a finite abelian group" by "$\mathscr{G}$ is a finitely generated abelian group." The reader should examine our proof to see if it is adequate for the stronger theorem. When we consider countably generated abelian groups, we must allow the possibility that the group can be expressed as the direct product of infinitely many groups. If we do so, we can obtain something like a unique factorization theorem. These results are achieved by using Ulm invariants. The interested reader should investigate books specializing in infinite abelian groups.

The reader can immediately deduce two corollaries to Theorem 13:

COROLLARY 1 *If $\mathscr{G}$, $\mathscr{H}$, and $\mathscr{J}$ are finite abelian groups such that $\mathscr{G} \times \mathscr{H} \cong \mathscr{G} \times \mathscr{J}$, then $\mathscr{H} \cong \mathscr{J}$.*

COROLLARY 2 *If n is a square-free integer, then all abelian groups of order n are isomorphic.*

Corollary 1 is a cancellation law for the cartesian product of finite abelian groups.

EXERCISES 3 Prove the two corollaries.

4 A. Determine the number of distinct isomorphic classes of abelian groups of order 144.

B. If $n = \prod_{1}^{r} p_i^{e_i}$, determine the number of distinct isomorphism classes of abelian groups of order n.

5 Determine the number of distinct automorphisms of an abelian group whose order is square-free.

6 Prove: If $\mathscr{H}$ is a subgroup of an abelian p group $\mathscr{G}$, then $r(\mathscr{H}) \leq r(\mathscr{G})$. (*Hint:* Examine $\mathscr{H}_p$ and $\mathscr{G}_p$.)

7 Prove: If $\mathscr{G}$ is an abelian p group and $\mathscr{G} = \langle x_1 \rangle \cdots \langle x_r \rangle$ (direct), where $o(x_i) \mid o(x_{i+1})$, $(i = 1, \ldots, r-1)$, then $\mathscr{G}$ has a subgroup $\mathscr{H} = \langle y_1 \rangle, \cdots, \langle y_s \rangle$ (direct), where $o(y_j) \mid o(y_{j+1})$, $(j = 1, \ldots, s-1)$ if and only if $s \leq r$ and $o(x_i) \geq o(y_i)$, $(i = 1, \ldots, s)$. (*Hint:* Examine the case $\mathscr{G} = \Pi\langle x_i \rangle$ (direct), where $o(x_i) = p$. Then try induction.)

8 Determine the number of subgroups of order p^2 in $\mathbf{Z}_{p^3} \times \mathbf{Z}_{p^2} \times \mathbf{Z}_p$.

9 Prove: If $\mathscr{G}$ is an abelian p group, then $\mathscr{G}$ is cyclic if and only if the number of elements $x \in \mathscr{G}$ satisfying $x^p = e$ is exactly p.

10 Exhibit an infinite abelian group whose elements all have order ≤ 2.

11 An abelian group is said to be *torsion-free* if the identity is the only element of finite order. Suppose that $\mathscr{G}$ is a torsion-free abelian group and that $g_1, \ldots, g_n$ are a minimal set of generators for $\mathscr{G}$. Prove:

A. If $g_1^{n_1} \cdots g_n^{n_n} = e$, then $n_1 = \cdots = n_n = 0$.

B. $\mathscr{G} \cong \mathbf{Z}^{(n)}$, where $\mathbf{Z}^{(n)}$ is the cartesian sum of $\mathbf{Z}$ with itself n times.

C. An indecomposable torsion-free abelian group is isomorphic to $\mathbf{Z}$.

CHAPTER FOUR

RINGS, INTEGRAL DOMAINS, FIELDS

1 ENDOMORPHISMS OF GROUPS

Let M be a nonempty set, and let $\mathscr{G}$ be a multiplicative group. We now consider the set of all maps of M into $\mathscr{G}$ and denote this set by $\mathscr{T} = \mathscr{T}(M, \mathscr{G})$. If $\alpha, \beta \in \mathscr{T}$, then the map $x \to x^\alpha x^\beta$ is in $\mathscr{T}$. We denote this map by the symbol $\alpha + \beta$; thus

$$x^{\alpha+\beta} = x^\alpha x^\beta, \qquad \text{for all } x \in M.$$

This operation of addition of maps from $\mathscr{T}$ is a binary operation on $\mathscr{T}$. Since the multiplicative operation on $\mathscr{G}$ is associative, we have

$$(\alpha + \beta) + \gamma = \alpha + (\beta + \gamma), \qquad \text{for all } \alpha, \beta, \gamma \in \mathscr{T}.$$

Thus the addition operation on $\mathscr{T}$ is associative. Similarly the addition operation on $\mathscr{T}$ is commutative if and only if the multiplication operation on $\mathscr{G}$ is commutative. We let 0 denote the map that sends each element of M onto e, the identity element of $\mathscr{G}$; i.e.,

$$x^0 = e, \qquad \text{for all } x \in M.$$

Then
$$\alpha + 0 = \alpha = 0 + \alpha, \qquad \text{for all } \alpha \in \mathscr{T}$$

Finally, if $\alpha \in \mathscr{T}$, we let $-\alpha$ denote the map

$$x \to (x^\alpha)^{-1}.$$

One easily checks that

$$\alpha + (-\alpha) = 0 = (-\alpha) + \alpha, \qquad \text{for all } \alpha \in \mathscr{T}.$$

We have thus shown

PROPOSITION 1 *If M is a nonempty set and $\mathscr{G}$ is a group, then $\mathscr{T}(M, \mathscr{G})$ is a group. $\mathscr{T}(M, \mathscr{G})$ is an abelian group if and only if $\mathscr{G}$ is abelian.*

If we let $M = \mathscr{G}$, then $\mathscr{T}(\mathscr{G}) = \mathscr{T}(\mathscr{G}, \mathscr{G})$ is an additive group that is also closed under the usual product of maps. As soon as we have two operations, it is desirable to check whether they satisfy the distributive laws. Specifically, we ask whether $\alpha(\beta + \gamma) = \alpha\beta + \alpha\gamma$, $(\beta + \gamma)\alpha = \beta\alpha + \gamma\alpha$, for all $\alpha, \beta, \gamma \in \mathscr{T}(\mathscr{G})$.

Given $\alpha, \beta, \gamma \in \mathscr{T}(\mathscr{G})$, we have

$$x^{\alpha(\beta+\gamma)} = (x^\alpha)^{\beta+\gamma} = (x^\alpha)^\beta (x^\alpha)^\gamma = x^{\alpha\beta} x^{\alpha\gamma} = x^{\alpha\beta+\alpha\gamma}, \qquad \text{for all } x \in \mathscr{G}.$$

Hence we do have the left distributive law. To each $u \in \mathscr{G}$ there is a map $\rho_u \in \mathscr{T}(\mathscr{G})$ such that $x^{\rho_u} = u$ for all $x \in \mathscr{G}$. Then

$$x^{(\rho_u + \rho_v)\alpha} = (x^{\rho_u} x^{\rho_v})^\alpha = (uv)^\alpha,$$

and
$$x^{\rho_u\alpha + \rho_v\alpha} = x^{\rho_u\alpha} x^{\rho_v\alpha} = u^\alpha v^\alpha,$$

for all $u, v \in \mathscr{G}$ and all $\alpha \in \mathscr{T}(\mathscr{G})$. But this means that, if $\mathscr{T}(\mathscr{G})$ satisfies the right distributive law, then each $\alpha \in \mathscr{T}(\mathscr{G})$ must satisfy the functional equation

$$(uv)^\alpha = u^\alpha v^\alpha, \qquad \text{for all } u, v \in \mathscr{G}; \tag{1}$$

i.e., each $\alpha \in \mathscr{T}(\mathscr{G})$ would need to be a homomorphism of $\mathscr{G}$ into $\mathscr{G}$. If $|\mathscr{G}|$ is at least 2, there are $\alpha \in \mathscr{T}(\mathscr{G})$ that are not homomorphisms of $\mathscr{G}$. Thus we see that, in general, the set $\mathscr{T}(\mathscr{G})$ does not satisfy the right distributive law.

A homomorphism of a group $\mathscr{G}$ into itself is called an *endomorphism of $\mathscr{G}$*. We denote the set of endomorphisms of $\mathscr{G}$ by $\mathscr{E}(\mathscr{G})$. The set of automorphisms of $\mathscr{G}$ is a subset of $\mathscr{E}(\mathscr{G})$.

XERCISES 1 Prove:

A. If $m \in \mathbf{Z}$, the map $x \to mx$ is an endomorphism of $\mathbf{Z}$.

B. If $\alpha \in \mathscr{E}(\mathbf{Z})$, then there is an integer m such that $x^\alpha = mx$, for all $x \in \mathbf{Z}$.

C. The map $\rho_a \in \mathscr{T}(\mathscr{G})$ is an endomorphism of $\mathscr{G}$ if and only if a is the identity of $\mathscr{G}$.

2 Prove:

A. If $\alpha, \beta \in \mathscr{E}(\mathscr{G})$, then $\alpha\beta \in \mathscr{E}(\mathscr{G})$; furthermore this operation is associative.

B. The maps $x \xrightarrow{\iota} x$, $x \xrightarrow{0} e$ both lie in $\mathscr{E}(\mathscr{G})$. Furthermore $\alpha\iota = \alpha = \iota\alpha$, $\alpha + 0 = \alpha = 0 + \alpha$, for all $\alpha \in \mathscr{E}(\mathscr{G})$.

C. The automorphism group of $\mathscr{G}$ is exactly the set of elements of $\mathscr{E}(\mathscr{G})$ that possess a multiplicative inverse in $\mathscr{E}(\mathscr{G})$.

D. If $\alpha \in \mathscr{E}(\mathscr{G})$, then $\mathscr{G}^\alpha$ is a subgroup of $\mathscr{G}$.

E. If $\alpha \in \mathscr{E}(\mathscr{G})$, $\beta, \gamma \in \mathscr{T}(\mathscr{G})$, then $(\beta + \gamma)\alpha = \beta\alpha + \gamma\alpha$ and $\alpha(\beta + \gamma) = \alpha\beta + \alpha\gamma$.

We next ask whether $\mathscr{E}(\mathscr{G})$ is closed under addition. Suppose $\alpha, \beta \in \mathscr{E}(\mathscr{G})$; then

$$(uv)^{\alpha+\beta} = (uv)^\alpha(uv)^\beta = u^\alpha v^\alpha u^\beta v^\beta,$$

for all $u, v \in \mathscr{G}$. If in addition $\alpha + \beta \in \mathscr{E}(\mathscr{G})$, then

$$(uv)^{\alpha+\beta} = u^{\alpha+\beta}v^{\alpha+\beta} = u^\alpha u^\beta v^\alpha v^\beta,$$

for all $u, v \in \mathscr{G}$, and we would have

$$v^\alpha u^\beta = u^\beta v^\alpha, \qquad \text{for all } u, v \in \mathscr{G}. \tag{2}$$

Conversely, if $\alpha, \beta \in \mathscr{E}(\mathscr{G})$ satisfy Eq. 2, then $\alpha + \beta \in \mathscr{E}(\mathscr{G})$. We have thus shown

LEMMA 1 *Let $\alpha, \beta \in \mathscr{E}(\mathscr{G})$; then $\alpha + \beta \in \mathscr{E}(\mathscr{G})$ if and only if each element of $\mathscr{G}^\alpha$ commutes with each element of $\mathscr{G}^\beta$.*

The reader can prove

LEMMA 2 *Let $\alpha \in \mathscr{E}(\mathscr{G})$; then $-\alpha \in \mathscr{E}(\mathscr{G})$ if and only if $\mathscr{G}^\alpha$ is a commutative group.*

Clearly we obtain from the above lemmas

LEMMA 3 *If $\mathscr{G}$ is an abelian group, then $\mathscr{E}(\mathscr{G})$ is an abelian group under addition.*

Combining Lemma 3 and Exercise 2, we obtain

OPOSITION 2 *If $\mathscr{G}$ is an abelian group, then* (A) *$\mathscr{E}(\mathscr{G})$ is an abelian group under addition,* (B) *$\mathscr{E}(\mathscr{G})$ is closed under a product which is associative and which has a multiplicative identity, and* (C) *$\mathscr{E}(\mathscr{G})$ satisfies both distributive laws.*

The reader should compare this proposition with the properties listed for **Z**. In $\mathscr{E}(\mathscr{G})$ the product may but need not be commutative.

EXERCISES 3 Determine the addition and multiplication tables for $\mathscr{E}(\mathbf{Z}_2 + \mathbf{Z}_2)$. Show that the product in $\mathscr{E}(\mathbf{Z}_2 + \mathbf{Z}_2)$ is not commutative.

4 Prove: If $\mathscr{G}$ is a cyclic group, then $\mathscr{E}(\mathscr{G})$ has a commutative product.

5 Examine the abelian groups of order 8, and determine for which of these groups $\mathscr{E}(\mathscr{G})$ has a commutative product.

6 Prove or give a counterexample to the statement: If the product in $\mathscr{E}(\mathscr{G})$ is commutative, then $\mathscr{G}$ is a cyclic group.

7 Prove:

A. If $|\mathscr{G}| \geq 2$, then $\mathscr{E}(\mathscr{G})$ is never a group under multiplication.

B. The nonzero endomorphisms of an abelian group $\mathscr{G}$ form a multiplicative group if and only if $\mathscr{G}$ is a simple group.

2 RINGS

In our study of groups we first discussed groups of transformation and then abstract groups, i.e., sets of objects with a binary operation satisfying certain properties. In the study of transformation groups one obtained information that was a consequence, not only of these properties, but also of the properties of the underlying space. In the study of abstract groups the information obtained was derived using only the group properties and as such was applicable to all systems having these properties. Since the study of abstract groups was so fruitful, it is advisable for us also to examine the abstract case of a set with two binary operations. If one is to get more information than he would expect to obtain by studying each operation separately, there must be a property or rule relating the two operations. One such property is the distributive law, and it is this property which distinguishes the algebraic systems that we will study in this chapter.

A *ring* $\mathscr{R}$ is a set of elements with two binary operations, usually denoted by $+$ and $\cdot$, such that (A) $\mathscr{R}$ is an abelian group under $+$, (B) $\mathscr{R}$ is closed under the associative operation $\cdot$, and (C) $\mathscr{R}$ satisfies the distributive laws: $x(y+z) = xy + xz$, $(y+z)x = yx + zx$, for all $x, y, z \in \mathscr{R}$.

The additive identity of a ring is usually denoted by 0, and the additive inverse of an element x by $-x$. It follows from the distributive laws that $0 \cdot x = 0 = x \cdot 0$, for all $x \in \mathscr{R}$.

As examples of rings we have $\mathbf{Z}$, $m\mathbf{Z}$, $\mathbf{Z}_m$, and $\mathscr{E}(\mathscr{G})$ when $\mathscr{G}$ is an abelian group. There is one very trivial ring that consists only of the additive identity 0. This ring is called the *zero ring*.

Since a ring $\mathscr{R}$ is closed under $+$ and $\cdot$, it follows that, if $x \in \mathscr{R}$ and $\mathbf{n} \in \mathbf{Z}^+$, then $\mathbf{n}x = x + \cdots + x$ (the addition of x to itself $\mathbf{n}$ times) and

$x^{\mathbf{n}} = x \cdots x$ (the product of x by itself **n** times) are defined and lie in $\mathscr{R}$. If **0** is the zero of **Z**, we define $\mathbf{0}x = 0$ for all $x \in \mathscr{R}$. Also we define $(-\mathbf{n})x = -(\mathbf{n}x)$, for all $\mathbf{n} \in \mathbf{Z}^+$ and $x \in \mathscr{R}$. Thus, if $\mathbf{n} \in \mathbf{Z}$, $x \in \mathscr{R}$, then $\mathbf{n}x$ is defined and lies in $\mathscr{R}$. Note this "product" is defined even though **n** need not lie in $\mathscr{R}$. Whenever confusion may arise, we shall distinguish elements of **Z** from elements of a ring $\mathscr{R}$ by indicating the elements of **Z** in boldface. This is needed especially when we have to distinguish between the 0 of $\mathscr{R}$ and the **0** of **Z**.

XERCISES 1 Prove: In a ring $\mathscr{R}$ the usual algebraic rules of sign hold: i.e., $x \cdot 0 = 0 = 0 \cdot x$, $(-x)y = -(xy) = x(-y)$, $(-x)(-y) = xy$, for all $x, y \in \mathscr{R}$.

2 Determine the addition and multiplication tables of all rings having two, three, and four elements.

From our examples we see that some rings satisfy additional properties. Among these are the following:

A. The ring $\mathscr{R}$ contains a two-sided multiplicative identity that is different from 0. This element is usually denoted by 1 and is called the *unity of* $\mathscr{R}$. We have $x \cdot 1 = x = 1 \cdot x$, for all $x \in \mathscr{R}$. A ring has at most one unity. Clearly **Z**, $\mathbf{Z}_m$, and $\mathscr{E}(\mathscr{G})$ ($\mathscr{G}$ abelian) are rings with unity. If $\mathscr{R}$ possesses a unity, we define $x^{\mathbf{0}} = 1$.

B. The operation $\cdot$ in $\mathscr{R}$ is commutative. A ring satisfying this condition is called a *commutative ring*.

If a subset $\mathscr{S}$ of a ring $\mathscr{R}$ is a ring under the operations of $\mathscr{R}$, then $\mathscr{S}$ is called a *subring* of $\mathscr{R}$. The reader should show that the intersection of subrings is again a subring. If R is a subset of a ring $\mathscr{R}$, then the set $\langle R \rangle = \bigcap \mathscr{R}_\lambda$, where the intersection is over all subrings $\mathscr{R}_\lambda$ that contain the set R, is the minimal subring of $\mathscr{R}$ containing the set R. We say that R generates the subring $\langle R \rangle$.

XERCISES 3 Prove: A ring has at most one unity.

4 If x is an element of a ring $\mathscr{R}$, show that the ring generated by x is the additive subgroup generated by the set $\{x, x^2, \ldots\}$.

5 If $\mathscr{R}$ is a ring with unity, show that the additive subgroup generated by 1 is a commutative subring with unity.

6 Determine all subrings of **Z** and of $\mathbf{Z}_m$.

7 Prove: A subring of a commutative ring is commutative.

Let $\mathscr{R}$ be a ring with unity. An element u of $\mathscr{R}$ for which there is an element v in $\mathscr{R}$ such that $uv = 1 = vu$ is called a *unit of* $\mathscr{R}$. Thus 1, -1 are always units of a ring $\mathscr{R}$. They are the only units of **Z**. But some rings, e.g., $\mathbf{Z}_m$, have many units. The units of $\mathbf{Z}_m$ are the elements in $\mathbf{Z}'_m$.

EXERCISES 8 Prove: The units of $\mathcal{E}(\mathcal{G})$ are the automorphisms of $\mathcal{G}$.

9 Prove: The set of units of a ring with unity is a multiplicative group.

10 Prove: If $\mathcal{R}$ is a ring with unity and $\mathcal{R}$ is either a finite ring or a commutative ring, then u is a unit exactly when there is a $v \in \mathcal{R}$ such that $uv = 1$. (*Hint:* The map $x \xrightarrow{\lambda} ux$ maps $\mathcal{R}$ onto $\mathcal{R}$, since $vy \xrightarrow{\lambda} y$.)

If $\mathcal{R}_1$ and $\mathcal{R}_2$ are rings, then we can define their *cartesian sum* $\mathcal{R}_1 + \mathcal{R}_2$ in the usual way; namely, $\mathcal{R}_1 + \mathcal{R}_2 = \{(x, y) \mid x \in \mathcal{R}_1, y \in \mathcal{R}_2\}$ with $(x, y) = (u, v)$ exactly when $u = x$ and $v = y$. If we define

$$(x, y) + (u, v) = (x + u, y + v), \qquad (x, y)(u, v) = (xu, yv),$$

then under these operations $\mathcal{R}_1 + \mathcal{R}_2$ is a ring. In an entirely analogous way we can define the cartesian sum of any number of rings. Let Λ be a set, and suppose to each $\lambda \in \Lambda$ there is associated a ring $\mathcal{R}_\lambda$. Let $\sum \mathcal{R}_\lambda = \{\mathbf{x} = (\ldots, x_\lambda, \ldots) \mid x_\lambda \in \mathcal{R}_\lambda\}$; define $\mathbf{x} + \mathbf{y} = (\ldots, x_\lambda + y_\lambda, \ldots)$, $\mathbf{xy} = (\ldots, x_\lambda y_\lambda, \ldots)$. Then $\sum \mathcal{R}_\lambda$ is a ring called the *cartesian sum of the* $\mathcal{R}_\lambda$. Similarly, we can define the *restricted cartesian sum of the* $\mathcal{R}_\lambda$:

$$r\sum \mathcal{R}_\lambda = \{\mathbf{x} = (\ldots, x_\lambda, \ldots) \mid x_\lambda \in \mathcal{R}_\lambda, x_\lambda = 0 \text{ for all but finitely many } \lambda.\}$$

Clearly $r\sum \mathcal{R}_\lambda$ is a subring of $\sum \mathcal{R}_\lambda$.

EXERCISES 11 A. Determine the necessary conditions for the cartesian sum $\mathcal{R}_1 + \mathcal{R}_2$ to be a ring with unity.

B. If Λ is an infinite set, show that $r\sum \mathcal{R}_\lambda$ is never a ring with unity.

C. Determine the necessary and sufficient conditions for the cartesian sum $\sum \mathcal{R}_\lambda$ to be a commutative ring.

12 A. Give an example of a proper subring $\mathcal{S}$ of a ring $\mathcal{R}$ such that $\mathcal{S}$ has a unity and $\mathcal{R}$ does not.

B. Give an example of a nonzero subring $\mathcal{S}$ of a ring $\mathcal{R}$ such that $\mathcal{R}$ has a unity but $\mathcal{S}$ does not.

C. Give an example of a proper nonzero subring $\mathcal{S}$ of a ring $\mathcal{R}$ such that each has a unity but the unity of $\mathcal{S}$ is not the unity of $\mathcal{R}$.

13 A. Determine the units of $\mathbf{Z} + \mathbf{Z}$.

B. If the $\mathcal{R}_\lambda$ are rings with unity, determine the group of units of $\sum \mathcal{R}_\lambda$ in terms of the groups of units of $\mathcal{R}_\lambda$.

14 Let $\mathcal{G}$ be the direct sum of $\mathbf{Z}$ by itself a countable number of times. Show that there exist $\alpha, \beta \in \mathcal{E}(\mathcal{G})$ such that $\alpha\beta = 1$, but $\beta\alpha \neq 1$. Compare this result with that in Exercise 10.

Just as for groups, we have the various morphisms of one ring into another. A *homomorphism* of a ring $\mathcal{R}_1$ into $\mathcal{R}_2$ is a map φ of $\mathcal{R}_1$ into $\mathcal{R}_2$ such that

$$(x + y)^\varphi = x^\varphi + y^\varphi, \qquad (xy)^\varphi = x^\varphi y^\varphi, \qquad \text{for all } x, y \in \mathcal{R}_1.$$

As for groups, a *monomorphism* is an injective homomorphism, and an *isomorphism* is a bijective homomorphism. As usual, we let $\cong$ denote the equivalence relation of being isomorphic.

EXERCISES 15 Prove or give a counterexample to the following:

A. If φ is a homomorphism of a ring $\mathscr{R}_1$ onto a ring $\mathscr{R}_2$ and $\mathscr{R}_1$ has a unity, then $\mathscr{R}_2$ has a unity.

B. If φ is a monomorphism of $\mathscr{R}_1$ into $\mathscr{R}_2$ and $\mathscr{R}_1$ has a unity, then $\mathscr{R}_2$ has a unity.

16 Prove: $\mathscr{E}(\mathbf{Z}) \cong$ the ring $\mathbf{Z}$, $\mathscr{E}(\mathbf{Z}_m) \cong$ the ring $\mathbf{Z}_m$.

17 Prove: If φ is a homomorphism of a commutative ring $\mathscr{R}_1$ onto $\mathscr{R}_2$, then $\mathscr{R}_2$ is commutative.

As with groups, if φ is a homomorphism of a ring $\mathscr{R}_1$ into $\mathscr{R}_2$, we call the set $\mathscr{I} = \{x \in \mathscr{R}_1 \mid x^\varphi = 0\}$ the *kernel of* φ. Since φ is a homomorphism of the additive group $\mathscr{R}_1$ into the additive group $\mathscr{R}_2$, the kernel $\mathscr{I}$ is a subgroup of $\mathscr{R}_1$. But φ has an additional property; namely, if $x \in \mathscr{I}$ and $r \in \mathscr{R}_1$, then rx and xr are in $\mathscr{I}$. Thus we see that the kernel $\mathscr{I}$ of a homomorphism is a subring of $\mathscr{R}_1$ with the property that $\mathscr{R}_1\mathscr{I}$ and $\mathscr{I}\mathscr{R}_1$ are subsets of $\mathscr{I}$. A subset $\mathscr{I}$ of a ring $\mathscr{R}$ such that $\mathscr{I}$ is an additive subgroup of $\mathscr{R}$ and such that $\mathscr{I}\mathscr{R} \subset \mathscr{I}$, $\mathscr{R}\mathscr{I} \subset \mathscr{I}$ is called an *ideal of* $\mathscr{R}$. The ideals of $\mathbf{Z}$ are exactly the sets $m\mathbf{Z}$ that we studied in Chap. 1. Ideals of rings play a role in ring theory analogous to that of normal subgroups in group theory.

XERCISES 18 Determine all the ideals of the rings $m\mathbf{Z}$, $\mathbf{Z} + \mathbf{Z}$, $\mathbf{Z}_m$.

19 Prove: A homomorphism of a ring $\mathscr{R}$ with unity is the 0 map if and only if 1 is in the kernel of the homomorphism.

There are theorems and propositions concerning homomorphisms of rings that are analogous to Theorem 7 and Proposition 27 of Chap. 3. The reader should prove

ROPOSITION 3 *If $\mathscr{R}$ is a ring and $\mathscr{I}$ is an ideal in $\mathscr{R}$, then the collection of additive cosets $r + \mathscr{I}$, $r \in \mathscr{R}$ forms a ring under the operations $(r + \mathscr{I}) + (s + \mathscr{I}) = r + s + \mathscr{I}$, $(r + \mathscr{I})(s + \mathscr{I}) = rs + \mathscr{I}$. Let $\mathscr{R}/\mathscr{I}$ denote this ring of cosets; then there is a homomorphism of $\mathscr{R}$ onto $\mathscr{R}/\mathscr{I}$ with kernel $\mathscr{I}$. If $\mathscr{R}$ has a unity and $\mathscr{R} \neq \mathscr{I}$, then $\mathscr{R}/\mathscr{I}$ has a unity.*

The ring of cosets $\mathscr{R}/\mathscr{I}$ is called a *factor ring* or a *difference ring*.

OPOSITION 4 *If φ is an homomorphism of $\mathscr{R}_1$ onto $\mathscr{R}_2$ and $\mathscr{I}$ is the kernel of φ, then $\mathscr{R}_2 \cong \mathscr{R}_1/\mathscr{I}$.*

PROPOSITION 5 *If $\mathscr{I}$ is an ideal in $\mathscr{R}$ and $\mathscr{S}$ is a subring of $\mathscr{R}$, then $\mathscr{S} \cap \mathscr{I}$ is an ideal in $\mathscr{S}$. The set $\mathscr{I} + \mathscr{S} = \{x \in \mathscr{R} \mid x = a + s, a \in \mathscr{I}, s \in \mathscr{S}\}$ is a subring of $\mathscr{R}$ that has $\mathscr{I}$ as an ideal. The rings $\mathscr{S}/(\mathscr{S} \cap \mathscr{I})$ and $(\mathscr{I} + \mathscr{S})/\mathscr{I}$ are isomorphic.*

PROPOSITION 6 *Isomorphism is an equivalence relation on rings.*

EXERCISES 20 If $\mathscr{I}$ is an ideal of a ring $\mathscr{R}$ and $\mathscr{S}$ is a subring of $\mathscr{R}$ such that $\mathscr{I} \cap \mathscr{S} = 0$, then $\mathscr{R}/\mathscr{I}$ contains a subring isomorphic to $\mathscr{S}$.

21 An element x of a ring $\mathscr{R}$ is said to be *nilpotent* if there is an integer n such that $x^n = 0$. Prove: The set $\mathscr{N}$ of all nilpotent elements of $\mathscr{R}$ is an ideal of $\mathscr{R}$, and the only nilpotent element of $\mathscr{R}/\mathscr{N}$ is $0 + \mathscr{N}$.

A ring $\mathscr{R}'$ is said to be an *extension of* $\mathscr{R}$ if $\mathscr{R}$ is a subring of $\mathscr{R}'$. We next prove a useful result concerning extensions and monomorphisms.

PROPOSITION 7 *If φ is a monomorphism of a ring $\mathscr{R}$ into a ring $\mathscr{S}$, then there is an extension $\mathscr{R}'$ of $\mathscr{R}$ and an isomorphism Φ of $\mathscr{R}'$ onto $\mathscr{S}$ such that $\operatorname{res}_{\mathscr{R}} \Phi = \varphi$.*

PROOF. To each $x \in \mathscr{S} - \mathscr{R}^{\varphi}$ form the symbol x', where $x' \neq y'$ if $x \neq y$ and where none of the symbols x' is in the set $\mathscr{R}$. Let $\mathscr{U} = \{x' \mid x \in \mathscr{S} - \mathscr{R}^{\varphi}\}$. Let $\mathscr{R}'$ be the union of the disjoint sets $\mathscr{R}$ and $\mathscr{U}$. Let

$$r^{\Phi} = r^{\varphi} \quad \text{if } r \in \mathscr{R}, \qquad x'^{\Phi} = x \quad \text{if } x' \in \mathscr{U}.$$

Then Φ is a bijective map of the set $\mathscr{R}'$ onto the set $\mathscr{S}$ such that $\operatorname{res}_{\mathscr{R}} \Phi = \varphi$. Consider the following binary operations on $\mathscr{R}'$:

$$(y + z) = (y^{\Phi} + z^{\Phi})^{\Phi^{-1}}, \qquad (yz) = (y^{\Phi} z^{\Phi})^{\Phi^{-1}}.$$

Now
$$(y + z) + w = \{[(y^{\Phi} + z^{\Phi})^{\Phi^{-1}}]^{\Phi} + w^{\Phi}\}^{\Phi^{-1}}$$
$$= \{(y^{\Phi} + z^{\Phi}) + w^{\Phi}\}^{\Phi^{-1}}.$$

Similarly
$$y + (z + w) = \{y^{\Phi} + (z^{\Phi} + w^{\Phi})\}^{\Phi^{-1}}.$$

Since $\mathscr{S}$ has an associative addition, these two expressions are equal. Therefore the operation of addition on $\mathscr{R}'$ is associative. In analogous ways one can show that the addition on $\mathscr{R}'$ is commutative, that the multiplication on $\mathscr{R}'$ is associative, and that the distributive law holds for these two operations. Also

$$y + 0 = (y^{\Phi} + 0^{\Phi})^{\Phi^{-1}} = (y^{\Phi} + 0^{\varphi})^{\Phi^{-1}} = (y^{\Phi})^{\Phi^{-1}} = y,$$

for all $y \in \mathscr{R}'$. If $y \in \mathscr{R}$, then y has an additive inverse in $\mathscr{R}$ and hence an additive inverse in $\mathscr{R}'$. If $y \in \mathscr{U}$, then $y = x'$ for some $x \in \mathscr{S} - \mathscr{R}^{\varphi}$. In this case $-x \in \mathscr{S} - \mathscr{R}^{\varphi}$, for $\mathscr{R}^{\varphi}$ is a subring of $\mathscr{S}$, and if $-x \in \mathscr{R}^{\varphi}$, then $x \in \mathscr{R}^{\varphi}$, contrary to the assumption. Hence $(-x)' \in \mathscr{U}$, and

$$x' + (-x)' = (x + (-x))^{\Phi^{-1}} = 0.$$

Thus every element of $\mathscr{R}'$ has an additive inverse. We have shown that $\mathscr{R}'$ is a ring under the given operations. Clearly the map Φ is an isomorphism of $\mathscr{R}'$ onto $\mathscr{S}$.

The value of this proposition lies in the fact that, if you can embed a ring $\mathscr{R}$ into a ring $\mathscr{S}$, where the ring $\mathscr{S}$ has certain properties, then there is an extension of $\mathscr{R}$ that has the same properties. For example, if φ is a monomorphism of the ring $\mathbf{Z}$ into a ring $\mathscr{S}$ and if there is an element $x \in \mathscr{S}$ such that $x^2 = 2$, then there is an extension $\mathscr{R}'$ of $\mathbf{Z}$ that contains an element whose square is 2.

3 ADDITIONAL EXAMPLES OF RINGS

Let M be a nonempty set, and let $\mathscr{R}$ be a ring. Let $\mathscr{T} = \mathscr{T}(M, \mathscr{R})$ be the set of all maps of M into $\mathscr{R}$. Let us use the functional notation in describing elements of $\mathscr{T}$; then $f \in \mathscr{T}$ is the map

$$x \to f(x), \qquad \text{for all } x \in M.$$

Denote the map $x \to 0$ by 0. If $f, g \in \mathscr{T}$, denote the map $x \to f(x) + g(x)$ by $f + g$, the map $x \to f(x)\,g(x)$ by fg, and the map $x \to -f(x)$ by $-f$. The reader can easily check that under these operations of addition and multiplication $\mathscr{T}$ is a ring.

ERCISES 1 A. Show that $\mathscr{T}$ is a ring.

B. Show that, when $|M| \geq 2$, then $\mathscr{T}$ contains $f \neq 0, g \neq 0$ such that $fg = 0$.

2 Prove:

A. $\mathscr{T}$ is a commutative ring if and only if $\mathscr{R}$ is a commutative ring.

B. $\mathscr{T}$ has a unity if and only if $\mathscr{R}$ has a unity.

3 A. If $\mathscr{R}$ has a unity, determine the units of $\mathscr{T}$.

B. Let $\mathscr{S} = \{f \in \mathscr{T} \mid f(0) = 0\}$. Show that $\mathscr{S}$ is a subring of $\mathscr{R}$. If $\mathscr{R}$ has a unity, does $\mathscr{S}$ have a unity? Is $\mathscr{S}$ an ideal in $\mathscr{R}$?

4 If $f \in \mathscr{T}$, let $\mathscr{A}(f) = \{g \in \mathscr{T} \mid gf = 0\}$. Show that $\mathscr{A}(f)$ is a subring of $\mathscr{T}$. Give examples where $\mathscr{A}(f)$ is the zero ring. Give examples where $\mathscr{A}(f)$ is infinite. If $\mathscr{R}$ is a commutative ring, is $\mathscr{A}(f)$ an ideal in $\mathscr{T}$?

5 Let $\mathscr{F} = \{f \in \mathscr{T} \mid f(m) = 0 \text{ for all but finitely many } m \in M\}$:

A. Show that $\mathscr{F}$ is a subring of $\mathscr{T}$ and $\mathscr{F}$ has no unity if M is infinite.

B. If $\mathscr{R}$ is a commutative ring, is $\mathscr{F}$ an ideal in $\mathscr{T}$?

C. Prove: $\mathscr{T}$ is isomorphic to the cartesian sum of $\mathscr{R}$ by itself $|M|$ times.

D. Prove: $\mathcal{F}$ is isomorphic to the restricted cartesian sum of $\mathcal{R}$ by itself $|M|$ times.

If m is an element of a commutative ring $\mathcal{R}$, let $\mathcal{R}|m|$ be the set $\{[a, b] \mid a, b \in \mathcal{R}\}$ with the operations

$$[a, b] + [s, t] = [a + s, b + t], \qquad [a, b][s, t] = [as + mbt, at + bs].$$

The reader should prove that $\mathcal{R}|m|$ is a commutative ring.

EXERCISE 6 Prove:

A. $\mathcal{R}|m|$ has a unity if and only if $\mathcal{R}$ does.

B. There is a monomorphism of $\mathcal{R}$ into $\mathcal{R}|m|$.

C. If there is an element $a \in \mathcal{R}$ such that $a^2 = m$, then $\mathcal{R}|m|$ contains nonzero elements u and v such that $uv = 0$.

D. Given a commutative ring $\mathcal{R}$ and an element $m \in \mathcal{R}$, there is an extension of $\mathcal{R}$ containing an x for which $x^2 = m$.

As additive groups $\mathbf{Z} + \mathbf{Z}$ and $\mathbf{Z}|m|$ are identical. Certainly they are not identical as rings. Could they be ring isomorphic? Any isomorphism of the ring $\mathbf{Z}|m|$ onto $\mathbf{Z} + \mathbf{Z}$ is an automorphism of the additive group $\mathbf{Z} + \mathbf{Z}$. Hence we will first determine all automorphisms of $\mathbf{Z} + \mathbf{Z}$ and then investigate if any could be the desired ring isomorphism.

Let $\varphi \in \mathcal{A}(\mathbf{Z} + \mathbf{Z})$. Say $(1, 0)^\varphi = (U, V)$, $(0, 1)^\varphi = (S, T)$, where $U, V, S, T \in \mathbf{Z}$. Since $(a, b) = \mathbf{a}(1, 0) + \mathbf{b}(0, 1)$, we have

$$\begin{aligned}(a, b)^\varphi &= \mathbf{a}(1, 0)^\varphi + \mathbf{b}(0, 1)^\varphi \\ &= (aU + bS, aV + bT), \qquad \text{for all } a, b \in \mathbf{Z}.\end{aligned}$$

Since φ is surjective, for any $a_o, b_o \in \mathbf{Z}$ we must be able to determine $a, b \in \mathbf{Z}$ such that

$$aU + bS = a_o, \qquad aV + bT = b_o.$$

On taking $a_o = b_o = 1$, we see that $(U, S) = (V, T) = 1$. On taking $a_o = 1$, $b_o = 0$, we see that $a(UT - SV) = T$, $b(SV - UT) = V$. Consequently $UT - SV = D$ is a divisor of T and V, and hence $D = \pm 1$. When $D = \pm 1$, then

$$a = D(a_oT - b_oS), \qquad b = D(b_oU - a_oV),$$

and we see that for any given (a_o, b_o) there is exactly one (a, b) such that $(a, b)^\varphi = \mathbf{a}(S, T) + \mathbf{b}(U, V) = (a_o, b_o)$. Clearly such a map is an operation-preserving map of $\mathbf{Z} + \mathbf{Z}$ into itself. Thus we have proved

PROPOSITION 8 *The map $(a, b)^\varphi = (aU + bS, aV + bT)$ is an automorphism of the group $\mathbf{Z} + \mathbf{Z}$ if and only if $UT - SV = \pm 1$.*

Now suppose φ is a ring isomorphism of $\mathbf{Z}|m|$ onto $\mathbf{Z}+\mathbf{Z}$. In $\mathbf{Z}|m|$ we have $[0, 1]^2 = [m, 0]$, and hence $\{[0, 1]^{\varphi}\}^2 = [m, 0]^{\varphi}$; i.e., $(S, T)^2 = (S^2, T^2) = (mU, mV)$. Thus we have $mU = S^2$, $mV = T^2$. As $UT - VS = \pm 1$, we have $(T, S) = 1$, and hence $m = \pm 1$. But then $U = mS^2$, $V = mT^2$ and

$$\pm 1 = UT - SV = mS^2T - mST^2 = mST(S - T).$$

But then $|S - T| = |S| = |T| = 1$, which is impossible. Thus we have proved

OROLLARY 1 *For all $m \in \mathbf{Z}$, the rings $\mathbf{Z}|m|$ and $\mathbf{Z} + \mathbf{Z}$ are nonisomorphic.*

ERCISES 7 Prove: If $n \neq m$, then $\mathbf{Z}|m|$ and $\mathbf{Z}|n|$ are nonisomorphic.

8 Determine all the automorphisms of the ring $\mathbf{Z} + \mathbf{Z}$.

9 If p is a prime, determine all the automorpisms of the ring $\mathbf{Z}_p + \mathbf{Z}_p$.

10 Determine the units of $\mathbf{Z}|m|$.

Let $\mathscr{R}$ be a ring. Let $\mathscr{R}_*$ be the set $\{(x, \mathbf{n}) \mid x \in \mathscr{R}, \mathbf{n} \in \mathbf{Z}\}$ with the binary operations

$$(x, \mathbf{n}) + (y, \mathbf{m}) = (x + y, \mathbf{n} + \mathbf{m}),$$

$$(x, \mathbf{n})(y, \mathbf{m}) = (xy + \mathbf{n}y + \mathbf{m}x, \mathbf{nm}).$$

As the reader can show, $\mathscr{R}_*$ is a ring, and

$$(x, \mathbf{n})(0, \mathbf{1}) = (x, \mathbf{n}) = (0, \mathbf{1})(x, \mathbf{n}).$$

Hence $\mathscr{R}_*$ is a ring with unity. The map $x \to (x, \mathbf{0})$ is a monomorphism of $\mathscr{R}$ into $\mathscr{R}_*$. Thus we have proved

OPOSITION 9 *Every ring can be embedded in a ring with unity.*

It follows from Propositions 7 and 9 that

COROLLARY *Every ring is a subring of a ring with unity.*

ERCISE 11 A. If $\mathscr{R} = 2\mathbf{Z}$, is the ring $\mathscr{R}_*$, defined above, isomorphic to $\mathbf{Z}$?

B. Under what conditions is the ring $\mathscr{R}_*$ commutative?

C. Given a ring $\mathscr{R}$, can you always embed the ring $\mathbf{Z}$ into the ring $\mathscr{R}_*$?

D. Show that the set $\{(x, \mathbf{0}) \mid x \in \mathscr{R}\}$ is an ideal of $\mathscr{R}_*$.

E. Prove: Every ring is a proper ideal of a ring with unity.

We now prove a result for rings that is analogous to that of Cayley's theorem for groups (Theorem 5, Chap. 3).

POSITION 10 *If $\mathscr{R}$ is a ring with unity, then $\mathscr{R}$ can be embedded in a ring of endomorphisms of an abelian group.*

PROOF. The set of endomorphisms of the additive group of $\mathscr{R}$ is a ring with unity. Denote this ring by $\mathscr{E} = \mathscr{E}(\mathscr{R})$. If $x \in \mathscr{R}$, let λ_x be the map $r \to rx$. It follows from the right distributive law for $\mathscr{R}$ that the map λ_x is in $\mathscr{E}$. Furthermore, the associative law for multiplication tells us that $\lambda_x \lambda_y = \lambda_{xy}$, and the left distributive law tells us that $\lambda_x + \lambda_y = \lambda_{x+y}$. Thus the map $x \xrightarrow{\Lambda} \lambda_x$ is a homomorphism of $\mathscr{R}$ into $\mathscr{E}$. If x and y are unequal elements of $\mathscr{R}$, then $\lambda_x \neq \lambda_y$, since

$$1^{\lambda_x} = x \neq y = 1^{\lambda_y}.$$

Hence the map Λ is one-to-one. This completes the proof of Proposition 10.

The reader should prove

COROLLARY *Every ring can be embedded in a ring of endomorphisms of an abelian group.*

4 INTEGRAL DOMAINS

Some rings have the following property:

C. If $x, y \in \mathscr{R}$ and $xy = 0$, then at least one of x and y are 0. However, as we have seen, not all rings have this property. If x and y are nonzero elements of a ring $\mathscr{R}$ such that $xy = 0$, we say that x and y are *zero divisors* or *divisors of zero.*

EXERCISES

1 A. Determine the m such that $\mathbf{Z}_m$ has no zero divisors.

B. Prove: A subring of a ring without zero divisors has no zero divisors.

C. Prove: The cartesian sum of two or more rings has zero divisors.

2 A. Show that, if $a \in \mathbf{Z}$, then $Z|a^2|$ has zero divisors.

B. Prove: If $\mathscr{R}$ is commutative and there is an $a \in \mathscr{R}$ such that there are more than two distinct elements $x \in \mathscr{R}$ for which $x^2 = a$, then $\mathscr{R}$ has zero divisors.

C. State and prove a general statement concerning the $m \in \mathbf{Z}^+$ such that $\mathbf{Z}|m|$ has no zero divisors.

3 Prove:

A. If a is a zero divisor of a ring $\mathscr{R}$, then to each x there is a $y \in \mathscr{R}$ such that $x \neq y$ and $ax = ay$.

B. If a is not a zero divisor of $\mathscr{R}$, then $ax = ay$ implies $x = y$. Thus in rings the cancellation law holds for nondivisors of zero.

4 Let $\mathscr{R}$ be a ring with unity and without zero divisors. Suppose $u, v \in \mathscr{R}$ such that $uv = 1$. Prove:

A. The map $x \xrightarrow{\lambda} xv$ is a bijective map of $\mathscr{R}$ onto $\mathscr{R}$.

B. The map $x \xrightarrow{\mu} xu$ is a left inverse of λ.

C. $vu = 1$.

(Compare this result with Exercises 10 and 14, Sec. 2.)

We have seen that we can have rings with unity $\mathscr{R}$ and $\mathscr{S}$ such that $\mathscr{S}$ is a subring of $\mathscr{R}$ and the unity of $\mathscr{S}$ is not the unity of $\mathscr{R}$. Such a situation cannot occur with rings without zero divisors.

POSITION 11 *Let $\mathscr{R}$ be a ring with unity and without zero divisors. If $\mathscr{S}$ is a subring of $\mathscr{R}$ and $\mathscr{S}$ has a unity, then the unity of $\mathscr{S}$ is the unity of $\mathscr{R}$.*

PROOF. If I were the unity of $\mathscr{S}$ and $I \neq 1$, then we would have $I1 = I = II$. Since $\mathscr{S}$ is not the zero ring, by Exercise 3A we get $I = 1$.

A commutative ring with unity and without zero divisors is called an *integral domain.*† The best known example of an integral domain is the ring of integers **Z**, hence the terminology. Note that an integral domain always contains at least two elements, 0 and 1. As usual a subset $\mathscr{D}'$ of an integral domain $\mathscr{D}$ that is an integral domain under the operations of $\mathscr{D}$ is called a *subdomain of* $\mathscr{D}$. By Proposition 11, every subdomain of $\mathscr{D}$ contains the unity of $\mathscr{D}$. It is easily seen that any subring of an integral domain $\mathscr{D}$ containing the unity of $\mathscr{D}$ is a subdomain. The additive group $\mathscr{D}_0$ generated by the unity of an integral domain $\mathscr{D}$ is closed under multiplication and is a subdomain of $\mathscr{D}$.

XERCISES 5 Prove:

A. $\mathbf{Z}_m$ is an integral domain if and only if m is a prime.

B. The domains **Z** and $\mathbf{Z}_p$ (p a prime) have no proper subdomains.

C. If $\mathscr{G}$ is a group of prime order, then $\mathscr{E}(\mathscr{G})$ is an integral domain.

6 Prove or give a counterexample:

A. If $\mathscr{R}$ is a commutative ring without zero divisors, then $\mathscr{R}_*$ is an integral domain.

B. If a ring $\mathscr{R}$ is isomorphic to an integral domain, then $\mathscr{R}$ is an integral domain.

C. If there is a homomorphism of a ring $\mathscr{R}$ onto an integral domain, then $\mathscr{R}$ is an integral domain.

D. If there is a monomorphism of a ring $\mathscr{R}$ into an integral domain, then $\mathscr{R}$ is an integral domain.

E. If there is a homomorphism of an integral domain onto a ring $\mathscr{R}$, then $\mathscr{R}$ is an integral domain.

F. The cancellation law for multiplication holds in an integral domain.

7 Prove: If $m < 0$ or if m is a nonsquare integer, then $\mathbf{Z}|m|$ is an integral domain.

Given an integral domain $\mathscr{D}$, let $c(\mathscr{D}) = \{\mathbf{n} \in \mathbf{Z}^+ \mid \mathbf{n}1 = 0\}$. We define the *characteristic of* $\mathscr{D}$ to be 0 if $c(\mathscr{D})$ is empty and to be the min $c(\mathscr{D})$ otherwise. We will write "char $\mathscr{D}$" for "characteristic of $\mathscr{D}$."

† Some authors do not require that an integral domain have a unity.

EXERCISE 8 Prove:

A. char $\mathbf{Z} = 0$.
B. char $\mathbf{Z}_p = p$.
C. If char $\mathcal{D} \neq 0$, then char $\mathcal{D}$ is a prime.
D. If char $\mathcal{D} \neq 0$, the additive order of each $a \in \mathcal{D} (a \neq 0)$ is char $\mathcal{D}$.
E. If char $\mathcal{D} = 0$, then $|\mathcal{D}| = \infty$.

Using Exercise 8D and Proposition 45 of Chap. 3, the reader can now prove

PROPOSITION 12 *A finite integral domain has prime characteristic and its order is a power of the characteristic.*

EXERCISE 9 Prove:

A. The intersection of subdomains of an integral domain $\mathcal{D}$ is a subdomain of $\mathcal{D}$.
B. Every integral domain $\mathcal{D}$ has a unique minimal subdomain $\mathcal{D}_0$ such that $\mathcal{D}_0$ lies in every subdomain of $\mathcal{D}$. The subdomain $\mathcal{D}_0$ is the ring generated by the unity of $\mathcal{D}$.

10 Prove: Let $\mathcal{D}_0$ be the integral domain generated by the unity of $\mathcal{D}$. If char $\mathcal{D} = 0$, then $\mathcal{D}_0 \cong \mathbf{Z}$. If char $\mathcal{D} = p$, then $\mathcal{D}_0 \cong \mathbf{Z}_p$.

Exercises 5B, 8, 9, and 10 imply

PROPOSITION 13 *Every integral domain $\mathcal{D}$ contains a unique minimal subdomain $\mathcal{D}_0$ such that $\mathcal{D}_0$ lies in each subdomain of $\mathcal{D}$, and $\mathcal{D}_0$ has no proper subdomains. $\mathcal{D}_0 \cong \mathbf{Z}_p$ or $\mathbf{Z}$, depending on the characteristic of $\mathcal{D}$.*

Thus one has

COROLLARY *If $\mathcal{D}$ is a subdomain of an integral domain $\mathcal{E}$, then char $\mathcal{D}$ = char $\mathcal{E}$.*

Just as we did in $\mathbf{Z}$, we can define the relation "divides" in an integral domain $\mathcal{D}$. If $a, b \in \mathcal{D}$, we say *a divides b in $\mathcal{D}$* if and only if there is an element $c \in \mathcal{D}$ such that $ac = b$.† We shall use the usual notation $a \mid b$. Results like Exercises 1 to 5, Sec. 7, Chap. 1, can be proved, and the reader should do so.

Let $\mathcal{D}$ be an integral domain. If $a, b \in \mathcal{D}$ and if $a = bu$, where u is a unit of $\mathcal{D}$, we say that a is an *associate* of b. The relation of being an associate is an equivalence relation on $\mathcal{D}$. Two elements of $\mathcal{D}$ are associates if and only if each divides the other. If $b \mid c$, then every associate of

† It should be noted that, if $\mathcal{D}$, $\mathcal{E}$ are integral domains with $\mathcal{D} \subset \mathcal{E}$, there may exist $a, b \in \mathcal{D}$ such that there is no $c \in \mathcal{D}$ with $ac = b$ but there is a $c' \in \mathcal{E}$ such that $ac' = b$. For example, 2 does not divide 1 in $\mathbf{Z}$ but it does in the ring of rational numbers. Thus the relation "divides" is a relative one.

b divides c. We say that a nonzero element $\pi \in \mathscr{D}$ is an irreducible element of $\mathscr{D}$ if π is not a unit and the only divisors of π in $\mathscr{D}$ are the associates of 1 and of π. With this definition -2 is an irreducible element of **Z**. An integral domain may not have irreducible elements. For example, all nonzero elements in the domain $\mathbf{Z}_p$ are units. Also, an integral domain $\mathscr{D}$ with the property that for each $a \in \mathscr{D}$ there is an element $x \in \mathscr{D}$ such that $x^2 = a$, has no irreducible elements. In contrast with $\mathbf{Z}_p$ such a domain may very well have nonzero elements that are not units. Examples of such an integral domain will be given later.

If u is a unit of $\mathscr{D}$ other than 1 and if $a, b, c \in \mathscr{D}$ are such that $a = bc$, then $a = (bu)(cu^{-1})$; e.g., in **Z**, $14 = 2 \cdot 7 = (-2)(-7)$. Hence we cannot express each element of $\mathscr{D}$ uniquely as a product of irreducible elements. In the case of **Z** we got a unique factorization by requiring the irreducible factors to be positive primes. That is, from each class of associate irreducible elements we chose one, the positive one, and showed that each integer was the unique product of a unit (± 1) and finitely many of the positive primes. Suppose that $\mathscr{D}$ is an integral domain with irreducible elements, and suppose by some choice map we choose one element from each class of associate irreducible elements of $\mathscr{D}$. Call these elements representatives of the class, and let $\mathscr{P}$ be the set of representatives. If each $0 \neq a \in \mathscr{D}$ can be expressed uniquely (to within order of multiplication) as a unique product of a unit of $\mathscr{D}$ and finitely many elements from $\mathscr{P}$, then we say that $\mathscr{D}$ is a *unique factorization domain*. One can show that, if one set of representatives leads to a unique factorization, so does any other such set. However, some sets may suggest easier proofs. Our proof that **Z** was a unique factorization domain relied heavily on the well-ordering principle. Most integral domains do not possess such a principle, and hence our proof does not carry over to most domains. In unique factorization domains we have the property that, if π is an irreducible element and $\pi \mid ab$, then either $\pi \mid a$ or $\pi \mid b$. Irreducible elements π of an integral domain satisfying this last property are called *primes*. In particular, irreducible elements of a unique factorization domain are called primes.

There are integral domains in which each element can be factored into irreducible elements and which is not a unique factorization domain. For example, in the ring $\mathbf{Z}|-5|$ we have

$$[9, 0] = [3, 0]^2 = [2, 1][2, -1].$$

The reader can check that $[3, 0], [2, 1], [2, -1]$ are nonassociated irreducible elements in $\mathbf{Z}|-5|$.

Let $\{a_1, \ldots, a_n\}$ be a subset of an integral domain $\mathscr{D}$. If $d \in \mathscr{D}$ is a common divisor in $\mathscr{D}$ of $a_1, \ldots, a_n$ and if each common divisor in $\mathscr{D}$ of $a_1, \ldots, a_n$ is a divisor in $\mathscr{D}$ of d, then d is said to be a *greatest common divisor in* $\mathscr{D}$ of the set $\{a_1, \ldots, a_n\}$. The greatest common divisor of a finite set of integers as defined in Chap. 1 is also a greatest common divisor by the definition above. However, in contrast to the integer case, where the greatest common divisor was defined so that it was unique, our new definition allows a set to have many greatest common divisors. The reader can show: If d and d' are greatest common divisors in $\mathscr{D}$ of $a_1, \ldots, a_n$, then d and d' are associates in $\mathscr{D}$. Thus the greatest common divisor of a finite set is unique to within a multiple of a unit of $\mathscr{D}$. If $m \in \mathscr{D}$ is a multiple in $\mathscr{D}$ of each a_i and if every x that is a multiple in $\mathscr{D}$ of each a_i is also a multiple in $\mathscr{D}$ of m, then m is said to be *a least common multiple in* $\mathscr{D}$ of $\{a_1, \ldots, a_n\}$. The set of associates of m in $\mathscr{D}$ is exactly the set of all the least common multiples in $\mathscr{D}$ of $a_1, \ldots, a_n$. Although examples are not easily obtainable, the reader should know there are integral domains $\mathscr{D}$ containing finite sets that have neither a greatest common divisor nor a least common multiple in $\mathscr{D}$.

If $\mathscr{D}$ is a unique factorization domain, let $\mathscr{P}$ be a set of representatives of the classes of associated primes. Suppose

$$a_\nu = u_\nu \prod_{p \in \mathscr{P}} p^{\alpha_\nu(p)}, \qquad \nu = 1, \ldots, n,$$

where u_ν is a unit, and the $\alpha_\nu(p)$ are nonnegative integers of which all but finitely many are 0. Put

$$d = d_{\mathscr{P}} = \prod_{p \in \mathscr{P}} p^{\min\{\alpha_1(p), \ldots, \alpha_n(p)\}},$$

$$m = m_{\mathscr{P}} = \prod_{p \in \mathscr{P}} p^{\max\{\alpha_1(p), \ldots, \alpha_n(p)\}}.$$

Clearly d divides each of the a_ν and each a_ν divides m in $\mathscr{D}$. Also, one can check that any common divisor in $\mathscr{D}$ of $a_1, \ldots, a_n$ is a divisor of d and any common multiple in $\mathscr{D}$ of $a_1, \ldots, a_n$ is a multiple of m. Thus d is a *greatest common divisor* of the set $a_1, \ldots, a_n$ and m is a *least common multiple* of the set. It should be noted that d and m are uniquely determined by $\mathscr{P}$. However, if we used a different set of representatives of the classes, say $\mathscr{P}'$, then $d_{\mathscr{P}}$ and $d_{\mathscr{P}'}$, might not be equal, but they would be associates. Thus for unique factorization domains the greatest common divisor (and the least common multiple) of a finite set $\{a_1, \ldots, a_n\}$ always exists.

The reader should show that in a unique factorization domain one always has the proposition that, if $a \mid bc$ and the greatest common divisor of a and b is a unit, then $a \mid c$.

Our discussion has shown that, although integral domains have some of the arithmetic properties of **Z**, in general they have very few. It is impossible to develop a theory for the arithmetic of a general integral domain. To obtain a substantial theory one needs to impose restrictions on the domain. In some of the remaining sections of this chapter we shall examine some special cases where we do have a substantial theory.

5 SKEWFIELDS AND FIELDS

Some rings satisfy the following property:

D. The ring has a unity, and every nonzero element of the ring is a unit.

When p is a prime, the ring $\mathbf{Z}_p$ is one such ring. If a ring satisfies property D, then it has no zero divisors, for if $ua = 1$ and $ab = 0$, then $b = uab = 0$. A ring satisfying property D is called a *skewfield* or a *sfield.* The nonzero elements of a skewfield, being units of that ring, form a multiplicative group. A commutative ring satisfying property D is called a *field.* Every field is a skewfield, and every field is an integral domain. Consequently, we may speak of the characteristic of a field. Clearly the characteristic of a field is either 0 or a prime. The reader can prove

POSITION 14 *A finite integral domain is a field.*

ERCISES 1 A. Prove: $\mathbf{Z}_3|2|$ is a field.

B. For what m is $\mathbf{Z}_p|m|$ a field?

C. Are any of the rings $\mathbf{Z}|m|$ fields?

2 Prove:

A. The cancellation law for multiplication holds in skewfields.

B. A skewfield is a ring whose nonzero elements are a group under multiplication.

3 Prove: All nonzero elements of a skewfield have the same additive order.

It follows from Exercise 3 that we can define a characteristic of a skewfield just as we did for an integral domain; namely, the characteristic of a skewfield is the additive order of 1, if that order is finite, and is 0 otherwise. The subring of a skewfield generated by the unity of that skewfield is an integral domain, and its characteristic is the characteristic of the skewfield. Hence the characteristic of a skewfield is either 0 or a prime. It follows from theorems for finite groups that

POSITION 15 *The order of a finite skewfield is a power of a prime.*

In a skewfield $\mathscr{S}$, to each nonzero element a there is an $x \in \mathscr{S}$ such that $ax = 1$. Since the nonzero elements of $\mathscr{S}$ form a group, x is uniquely determined by a, and we have $ax = xa = 1$. It is customary to denote this element by a^{-1}. The element a^{-1} is called the *reciprocal* or the *multiplicative inverse* of a.

ERCISES 4 A. Determine $\lfloor 2 \rfloor^{-1}$, $\lfloor 4 \rfloor^{-1}$ in $\mathbf{Z}_7$.

B. Determine $[1, 1]^{-1}$ in the field $\mathbf{Z}_3|2|$.

C. Prove: If $a \neq 0$ and b are elements of a skewfield, then there is a unique element x in that skewfield such that $ax = b$. Must $xa = b$?

5 Prove:

A. A subring of a skewfield is a ring without zero divisors.

B. If a subring $\mathcal{R}$ of a field $\mathcal{F}$ contains the unity of $\mathcal{F}$, then $\mathcal{R}$ is an integral domain.

C. If $\mathcal{D}$ is a subintegral domain of a field $\mathcal{F}$, then char $\mathcal{D}$ = char $\mathcal{F}$.

D. If a is a nonzero element of a field $\mathcal{F}$, the additive cyclic group generated by a need not be a subring of $\mathcal{F}$.

6 Prove that in a skewfield we have:

A. $b \cdot a^{-1} = d^{-1}c$ if and only if $ca = db$.

B. $b \cdot a^{-1} = 0$ if and only if $b = 0$.

C. $b \cdot a^{-1} \neq 0$ implies that $(b \cdot a^{-1})^{-1} = a \cdot b^{-1}$.

D. If $bc = cb$, then $b^{-1}c = c \cdot b^{-1}$.

E. If $bd = db$, then $a \cdot b^{-1} + c \cdot d^{-1} = (ad + cb) \cdot (db)^{-1}$.

F. If $bc = cb$, then $(a \cdot b^{-1})(c \cdot d^{-1}) = (ac)(db)^{-1}$.

G. $(-b) \cdot a^{-1} = b \cdot (-a)^{-1} = -(b \cdot a^{-1})$.

In a field $ab = ba$, and hence $ab^{-1} = b^{-1}a$. We often denote the element $a \cdot b^{-1}$ by a/b. In a skewfield it may be that $a^{-1}b \neq b \cdot a^{-1}$, and hence the symbol a/b would be ambiguous if used in skewfields.

The following proposition and corollaries are of considerable importance and are easily proved. The proofs are left to the reader.

PROPOSITION 16 *The only ideals in a skewfield $\mathcal{S}$ are the trivial ideals $\{0\}$ and $\mathcal{S}$.*

COROLLARY 1 *Every nonzero homomorphism of a skewfield into a ring is injective.*

COROLLARY 2 *If there is a homomorphism of a skewfield onto a ring $\mathcal{R}$, then $\mathcal{R}$ is a skewfield.*

As usual, we say that a subset $\mathcal{T}$ of a skewfield $\mathcal{S}$ is a *subskewfield* of $\mathcal{S}$ if $\mathcal{T}$ is a skewfield under the operations of $\mathcal{S}$. Similarly, we speak of a subfield of a field. The intersection of subskewfields of a skewfield is again a subskewfield. Hence each skewfield contains a unique minimal subskewfield. This minimal subskewfield obviously contains the integral domain $\langle 1 \rangle$ generated by 1. In case the characteristic of the skewfield is a prime p, the minimal subskewfield is isomorphic to the field $\mathbf{Z}_p$.

Now suppose the characteristic of the skewfield $\mathcal{S}$ is 0. Then the integral domain $\langle 1 \rangle$ is isomorphic to $\mathbf{Z}$. For this isomorphism, denote the image of the integer $\mathbf{n}$ by $\mathbf{n}'$. Thus $\mathbf{n}' = \mathbf{n}1' \in \mathcal{S}$. If $\mathbf{n}' \neq \mathbf{0}'$, there is a unique element $\mathbf{n}'^{-1} \in \mathcal{S}$ such that $\mathbf{n}'(\mathbf{n}'^{-1}) = (\mathbf{n}'^{-1})\mathbf{n}' = 1'$. Since $(\mathbf{nm})' = \mathbf{n}'\mathbf{m}' = \mathbf{m}'\mathbf{n}' = (\mathbf{mn})'$, we see that $\mathbf{m}'(\mathbf{n}'^{-1}) = (\mathbf{n}')^{-1}\mathbf{m}'$. Let

$$\mathbf{Q}' = \{s \in \mathcal{S} \mid s = \mathbf{m}'(\mathbf{n}'^{-1}), \mathbf{0}' \neq \mathbf{n}', \mathbf{m}' \in \langle 1 \rangle\}.$$

Clearly the subset $\mathbf{Q}'$ is contained in the minimal subskewfield of $\mathcal{S}$. Using Exercise 6, the reader can show that $\mathbf{Q}'$ is indeed a field. It follows that $\mathbf{Q}'$ is the minimal subskewfield of $\mathcal{S}$.

The reader should note that *the minimal subskewfield of a skewfield is always a field.*

So far we have gathered a certain amount of information concerning skewfields of characteristic 0, but we have not exhibited any such skewfield. The preceding discussion and exercises suggest how to construct a field of characteristic 0.

Let W be the set of all ordered pairs of integers $a \mid b$, with $b \neq 0$. On W we have the equivalence relation: $a \mid b \sim c \mid d$ if and only if $ad = cb$. Relative to this equivalence relation, denote the equivalence class containing the element $a \mid b$ by $\lfloor a \mid b \rfloor$. Thus $\lfloor 1 \mid 2 \rfloor = \lfloor 3 \mid 6 \rfloor = \lfloor -1 \mid -2 \rfloor$. Let $\mathcal{Q}$ be the set of all these equivalence classes together with the operations

$$\lfloor a \mid b \rfloor + \lfloor c \mid d \rfloor = \lfloor ad + bc \mid bd \rfloor, \qquad \lfloor a \mid b \rfloor \lfloor c \mid d \rfloor = \lfloor ac \mid bd \rfloor.$$

These operations depend only on the equivalence class and not on any particular element in the class, for if $a \mid b$ and $c \mid d$ are in the same class, then $(ay + bx) \mid by$ and $(cy + dx) \mid dy$ are equivalent as are $ax \mid by$ and $cx \mid dy$. The reader can now show that $\mathcal{Q}$ is a field of characteristic 0.

The unity of the field $\mathcal{Q}$ is the class $\lfloor 1 \mid 1 \rfloor$, and the integral domain generated by this element is the set $\mathcal{D}_0 = \{\lfloor n \mid 1 \rfloor \mid n \in \mathbf{Z}\}$. $\mathcal{D}_0$ and $\mathbf{Z}$ are isomorphic. Furthermore each element $\lfloor a \mid b \rfloor$ is the ratio of two elements of $\mathcal{D}_0$. By Proposition 7 there is a ring $\mathbf{Q}$ that contains $\mathbf{Z}$ as a subdomain and an isomorphism σ of $\mathbf{Q}$ onto $\mathcal{Q}$ such that $n^\sigma = \lfloor n \mid 1 \rfloor$ for all $n \in \mathbf{Z}$. It would then follow that each element of $\mathbf{Q}$ is a ratio of two integers from $\mathbf{Z}$. By Corollary 2 of Proposition 16, $\mathbf{Q}$ is a field. This field is the smallest field containing $\mathbf{Z}$, since any field containing $\mathbf{Z}$ must contain all ratios of integers. This minimal field $\mathbf{Q}$ is called the *field of rational numbers*. Note that $\mathbf{Q}$ is just the set of fractions under the usual operations.

A quick examination of the $\mathbf{Q}$ shows that $\mathbf{Q}$ has no proper subfield. One also notes that the minimal subfield $\mathbf{Q}'$ of a skewfield of characteristic 0 is isomorphic to $\mathbf{Q}$. The fields $\mathbf{Z}_p$ and $\mathbf{Q}$ are called *prime fields*, since they contain no proper subfields and each skewfield contains an isomorphic replica of exactly one of the fields $\mathbf{Z}_p$ (p a prime), $\mathbf{Q}$.

We can now give an example of a skewfield that is not a field. Let $\mathbf{Q}$ be a field of rational numbers, and let $\mathcal{H}$ be the set of all 4-tuples of rational numbers together with the operations

$$(a, b, c, d) + (x, y, z, w) = (a + x, b + y, c + z, d + w),$$

$$(a, b, c, d)(x, y, z, w) = (ax - by - cz - dw, bx + ay - dz + cw,$$
$$cx + dy + az - bw, dx - cy + bz + aw).$$

Then $\mathcal{H}$ is a skewfield that is not a field. $\mathcal{H}$ is called the *quaternion algebra* or the *Hamilton ring*. One can prove that a finite skewfield is always a field. Actually $\mathcal{H}$ is the simplest skewfield.

EXERCISES 7 Prove that $\mathbf{Q}$ is a field of characteristic 0 without a proper subfield.

8 Prove that $\mathscr{H}$ is a skewfield of characteristic 0 that is not a field.

9 Prove: If m is a nonsquare integer, then $\mathbf{Q}|m|$ is a field of characteristic 0 that is not isomorphic to $\mathbf{Q}$.

10 Prove: If φ is a homomorphism of a prime field $\mathscr{F}$ into itself, then either $x^\varphi = 0$ for all $x \in \mathscr{F}$ or $x^\varphi = x$ for all $x \in \mathscr{F}$. Show that such is not the case for $\mathbf{Q}|2|$.

11 Prove: If $\mathscr{F}$ is a field of characteristic p, then the map $a \to a^p$ is an automorphism of $\mathscr{F}$.

12 If $\mathscr{D}$ is an integral domain, let $W(\mathscr{D})$ be the set of all ordered pairs, $\alpha \mid \beta$, of elements from $\mathscr{D}$ with $\beta \neq 0$. On $W(\mathscr{D})$ define the equivalence relation $\alpha|\beta \sim \gamma|\delta$ if and only if $\alpha\delta = \beta\gamma$. Let $\lfloor \alpha|\beta \rfloor$ denote the equivalence class that contains $\alpha \mid \beta$. Let $\mathscr{Q}(\mathscr{D})$ be the set of these equivalence classes together with the operations

$$\lfloor \alpha \mid \beta \rfloor + \lfloor \gamma \mid \delta \rfloor = \lfloor \alpha\delta + \beta\gamma \mid \beta\delta \rfloor,$$
$$\lfloor \alpha \mid \beta \rfloor \lfloor \gamma \mid \delta \rfloor = \lfloor \alpha\gamma \mid \beta\delta \rfloor .$$

Prove:

A. $\mathscr{Q}(\mathscr{D})$ is a field with $\lfloor 1 \mid 1 \rfloor$ as its unity.

B. There is an monomorphism of $\mathscr{D}$ into $\mathscr{Q}(\mathscr{D})$.

C. char $\mathscr{Q}$ = char $\mathscr{Q}(\mathscr{D})$.

D. If $\mathscr{F}$ is a field containing a subdomain isomorphic to $\mathscr{D}$, then $\mathscr{F}$ contains a subfield isomorphic to $\mathscr{Q}(\mathscr{D})$. Thus, up to isomorphism $\mathscr{Q}(\mathscr{D})$ is the minimal field containing an isomorphic replica of the integral domain $\mathscr{D}$.

A field that contains an integral domain as a subdomain and such that no proper subfield does is called a *quotient field for the integral domain.* Each element of a quotient field of an integral domain $\mathscr{D}$ can be expressed as the quotient of two elements of $\mathscr{D}$. Hence a quotient field of an integral domain is unique. The field $\mathbf{Q}$ is a quotient field for $\mathbf{Z}$.

As a consequence of Exercise 12 we have

PROPOSITION 17 *Every integral domain has a quotient field.*

EXERCISES 13 Prove:

A. An integral domain and its quotient field have the same characteristic.

B. The quotient field of a field is that field.

14 Let a be a nonzero element of $\mathbf{Q}$. Let $a^{-1}\mathbf{Z} = \{x \in \mathbf{Q} \mid xa \in \mathbf{Z}\}$. Prove:

A. $a^{-1}\mathbf{Z}$ is an additive cyclic group.

B. Let $J_m = \bigcup_u m^{-u}\mathbf{Z}$. Prove that J_m is not an additive cyclic group but is an integral domain.

C. Prove or disprove: Every proper subgroup of J_m is an additive cyclic group.
D. Prove: $\mathbf{Q}$ is the quotient field for J_m.
E. Determine the units and primes in J_m.

15 Prove: If m is a nonsquare integer, the quotient field of the integral domain $\mathbf{Z}|m|$ is $\mathbf{Q}|m|$.

16 Suppose that $\mathscr{F}$ is a field containing $\mathbf{Q}$ as a subfield. Suppose that m is a nonsquare integer such that there is an $\alpha \in \mathscr{F}$ with $\alpha^2 = m$. Prove:
A. $\alpha \notin \mathbf{Q}$.
B. The minimal subfield that contains α is isomorphic to $\mathbf{Q}|m|$. This minimal field is usually denoted by $\mathbf{Q}(\alpha)$.
C. If m and m' are nonsquare integers whose ratio is not the square of a rational number, then $\mathbf{Q}|m|$ and $\mathbf{Q}|m'|$ are not isomorphic. Hence there exist infinitely many fields of characteristic 0.

Using the same construction as in Exercise 12, the reader can prove

POSITION 18 *Given a commutative ring $\mathscr{R}$ without zero divisors, there is a field $\mathscr{F}$ such that $\mathscr{R}$ is a subring of $\mathscr{F}$.*

6 INDETERMINATES AND POLYNOMIAL RINGS

Let $\mathscr{S}$ be a ring containing a subring $\mathscr{R}$ and an element x. There are subrings of $\mathscr{S}$ that contain $\{x\} \cup \mathscr{R}$; e.g., $\mathscr{S}$ is one such ring. The intersection of all such rings is again a ring that contains $\{x\} \cup \mathscr{R}$. Furthermore, it is the minimal subring of $\mathscr{S}$ that contains the set $\{x\} \cup \mathscr{R}$. We denote this ring by $\mathscr{M} = \mathscr{M}(\mathscr{R}, x)$. Since $\mathscr{M}$ is closed under multiplication, $\mathscr{M}$ contains all elements of $\mathscr{S}$ of the form ax^n, with $a \in \mathscr{R}$, $n \in \mathbf{Z}^+$. In particular $0x^n = 0$ is in $\mathscr{M}$. Since $\mathscr{M}$ is closed under addition, $\mathscr{M}$ contains all finite sums of the form

$$a_0 + a_1x + a_2x^2 + \cdots + a_nx^n, \qquad a_i \in \mathscr{R}. \tag{3}$$

Expressions of the form (3) are said to be *polynomials in x with coefficients from $\mathscr{R}$* or *polynomials in x over $\mathscr{R}$*.

Let $\mathscr{R}[x]$ be the set of all polynomials in x with coefficients from $\mathscr{R}$. Clearly $\mathscr{R} \subset \mathscr{R}[x] \subset \mathscr{M}(\mathscr{R}, x)$. As $ax^n + bx^n = (a+b)x^n$ and $ax^n + bx^m = bx^m + ax^n$, we see that $\mathscr{R}[x]$ is an additive abelian subgroup of $\mathscr{S}$. However $\mathscr{R}[x]$ need not be closed under multiplication. The trouble arises when there is an element $a \in \mathscr{R}$ such that xa is not of the form (3). This problem does not occur when $xa = ax$ for all $a \in \mathscr{R}$, and in that case the product of two polynomials in x is given by

$$(a_0 + \cdots + a_nx^n)(b_0 + \cdots + b_mx^m)$$
$$= a_0b_0 + (a_1b_0 + a_0b_1)x + \cdots + \left(\sum_{\nu=0}^{r} a_{r-\nu}b_\nu\right)x^r + \cdots + a_nb_mx^{n+m}. \tag{4}$$

We have

PROPOSITION 19 *If $\mathscr{R}$ is a subring of a ring $\mathscr{S}$ and $x \in \mathscr{S}$ such that $ax = xa$ for all $a \in \mathscr{R}$, then $\mathscr{R}[x]$ is a ring.*

It should be noted that in Proposition 19, although we assume the x commutes with each element of $\mathscr{S}$, we do not assume $\mathscr{R}$ itself is commutative.

In case $\mathscr{R}$ does not contain the unity of $\mathscr{S}$, we cannot be certain that $x \in \mathscr{R}[x]$. However, the following is easily shown:

PROPOSITION 20 *If $\mathscr{R}$ is a subring of a ring $\mathscr{S}$ with unity, such that $\mathscr{R}$ contains the unity of $\mathscr{S}$ and $ax = xa$ for all $a \in \mathscr{R}$, then $\mathscr{R}[x]$ is the minimal ring containing $\{x\} \cup \mathscr{R}$.*

It should be observed that two different polynomial expressions in x with coefficients from $\mathscr{R}$ may be equal. For example, let $m \in \mathscr{R}$; then $a \xrightarrow{\varphi} [a, 0]$ is a monomorphism of $\mathscr{R}$ into $\mathscr{R}|m|$ and

$$(-m)^{\varphi} + 1^{\varphi}[0, 1]^2 \qquad \text{and} \qquad 0^{\varphi}$$

are two polynomials in the element [0, 1] over the ring $\mathscr{R}^{\varphi}$ that are equal as elements of the ring $\mathscr{R}|m|$.

Let x be an element of a ring $\mathscr{S}$, and let $\mathscr{R}$ be a subring of $\mathscr{S}$ such that $ax = xa$ for all $a \in \mathscr{R}$. We say x is *algebraic over* $\mathscr{R}$ if there is a finite set $a_0, a_1, \ldots, a_n \in \mathscr{R}$, not all 0, such that $a_0 + a_1x + \cdots + a_nx^n = 0$. If x is not algebraic over $\mathscr{R}$, we say x is a *transcendental* (or an *indeterminate*) over $\mathscr{R}$. Thus x is a transcendental (or an indeterminate) over $\mathscr{R}$ provided there is a ring $\mathscr{S}$ such that (A) $x \in \mathscr{S}$, (B) $\mathscr{R}$ is a subring of $\mathscr{S}$, (C) x commutes with each element of $\mathscr{R}$, and (D) a polynomial in x over $\mathscr{R}$ is 0 only if all the coefficients are 0. If we are given a ring $\mathscr{S}$ with a subring $\mathscr{R}$ and we are classifying the elements of $\mathscr{S}$ relative to $\mathscr{R}$, the term "transcendental" is customarily used. The term "indeterminate" is customarily used when one is studying the existence of nonalgebraic elements over a ring $\mathscr{R}$. However, as indicated above, the two terms "transcendental" and "indeterminate" may be used interchangeably.

Obviously each element of $\mathscr{R}$ is algebraic over $\mathscr{R}$. It is easily shown that each element of $\mathscr{R}|m|$ is algebraic over the ring $\mathscr{R}$. Examples of indeterminate elements are less easily given. It is usually a very difficult task to show that a particular element of a ring $\mathscr{S}$ is transcendental over $\mathscr{R}$; e.g., it is not easy to show that the real numbers e and π are transcendental over **Z**. In high school algebra the existence of indeterminates is taken for granted. In time we shall show that each ring has arbitrarily many indeterminates. Before doing so, we shall determine a few properties of indeterminates, assuming they exist.

The next two propositions are easily proved and the proofs are left to the reader.

POSITION 21 *If x is an indeterminate over a ring $\mathcal{R}$ and if $a_0 + a_1x + \cdots + a_nx^n = b_0 + b_1x + \cdots + b_mx^m$, $a_\nu, b_\nu \in \mathcal{R}$, $m, n \in \mathbf{Z}$, then $m = n$ and $a_\nu = b_\nu$, $\nu = 0, 1, \ldots, n$.*

POSITION 22 *If $\mathcal{R}_1$ is a subring of a ring $\mathcal{R}$ and if x is an indeterminate over $\mathcal{R}$, then x is an indeterminate over $\mathcal{R}_1$ and $\mathcal{R}[x] \supset \mathcal{R}_1[x]$.*

The converse of Proposition 22 is false, for if x is an indeterminate over a ring $\mathcal{R}$, then $\mathcal{R}[x] = \mathcal{R}_1 \supset \mathcal{R}$, and x is algebraic over $\mathcal{R}_1$.

If A is a nonzero polynomial in the indeterminate x with coefficients from $\mathcal{R}$, then there is a minimal nonnegative integer $d = d(A)$ such that

$$A = a_0 + a_1x + \cdots + a_dx^d.$$

Since d is minimal, $a_d \neq 0$. We call a_d the *leading coefficient* of the polynomial A, and we call $d = d(A)$ the *degree of A*. We note $d(A) = 0$ if and only if $0 \neq A \in \mathcal{R}$. We define $d(0) = -\infty$. Then $A \to d(A)$ is a map of $\mathcal{R}[x]$ into $\mathbf{Z} \cup \{-\infty\}$. We shall adopt the usual practice of defining

$$\begin{aligned} -\infty &< n && \text{for all } n \in \mathbf{Z}, \\ (-\infty) + n &= -\infty && \text{for all } n \in \mathbf{Z}, \\ (-\infty)n &= -\infty && \text{for all } n \in \mathbf{Z}^+. \end{aligned}$$

We have

POSITION 23 A. *$d(A + B) \leq \max\{d(A), d(B)\}$, with equality holding unless $d(A) = d(B)$ and the leading coefficient of A is the negative of the leading coefficient of B.*

B. *$d(AB) \leq d(A)d(B)$, with equality holding if $\mathcal{R}$ has no zero divisors.*

Part A is easily obtained, and part B follows from Eq. 4.

XERCISE 1 Give an example to show that the inequality can occur in part B.

As a direct consequence of our definition of an indeterminate we have

POSITION 24 *If x is an indeterminate over $\mathcal{R}$, then any polynomial in x, with coefficients from $\mathcal{R}$, of positive degree, is an indeterminate over $\mathcal{R}$.*

POSITION 25 *Let $\mathcal{R}$ be a subring of a ring $\mathcal{S}$. Let φ be a monomorphism of $\mathcal{S}$ into a ring $\mathcal{S}'$. If $x \in \mathcal{S}$ is an indeterminate over $\mathcal{R}$, then $x^\varphi \in \mathcal{S}'$ is an indeterminate over $\mathcal{R}^\varphi$.*

The reader should prove

POSITION 26 *Let x be an indeterminate over $\mathcal{R}$:*

A. *$\mathcal{R}[x]$ is commutative if and only if $\mathcal{R}$ is commutative.*

B. *$\mathcal{R}[x]$ has a unity if and only if $\mathcal{R}$ has a unity.*

C. *$\mathscr{R}[x]$ has divisors of zero if and only if $\mathscr{R}$ has divisors of zero.*
D. *$\mathscr{R}[x]$ is an integral domain if and only if $\mathscr{R}$ is an integral domain.*
E. *If $\mathscr{R}$ is an integral domain, then char $\mathscr{R}$ = char $\mathscr{R}[x]$, and the units of $\mathscr{R}[x]$ are the units of $\mathscr{R}$.*
F. *For no ring $\mathscr{R}$ is $\mathscr{R}[x]$ a field.*

Since the operation of addition is a binary operation on a ring, we have given meaning only to finite sums of elements from a ring. However, it is sometimes convenient to permit ourselves the convention of speaking of infinite sums when all but finitely many of the summands are 0. In that case the infinite sum is merely the sum of the nonzero summands. We shall adopt this convention. Then a polynomial in x with coefficients in $\mathscr{R}$ can be considered an infinite sum of the form

$$A = a_0 + \sum_{\nu=1}^{\infty} a_\nu x^\nu = a_0 + a_1 x + \cdots + a_n x^n + \cdots, \qquad a_\nu \in \mathscr{R},$$

where all but finitely many a_ν are 0. It follows that $d(A) = \max\{n \in \mathbf{Z} \mid a_n \neq 0\}$, and

$$\left(a_0 + \sum_{\nu=1}^{\infty} a_\nu x^\nu\right) + \left(b_0 + \sum_{\nu=1}^{\infty} b_\nu x^\nu\right) = (a_0 + b_0) + \sum_{\nu=1}^{\infty} (a_\nu + b_\nu) x^\nu,$$

$$\left(a_0 + \sum_{\nu=1}^{\infty} a_\nu x^\nu\right)\left(b_0 + \sum_{\nu=1}^{\infty} b_\nu x^\nu\right) = a_0 b_0 + \sum_{\nu=1}^{\infty} \left(\sum_{\mu=0}^{\nu} a_{\nu-\mu} b_\mu\right) x^\nu.$$

We note that, if $a_\nu = 0$ for $\nu > N$ and $b_\nu = 0$ for $\nu > M$, then $a_\nu + b_\nu = 0$ and $\sum_{\mu=0}^{\nu} a_{\nu-\mu} b_\mu = 0$ for $\nu > M + N$. Hence the expressions on the right-hand side in the equations above have the desired property that all coefficients with large subscript are 0.

Let $T(\mathscr{R})$ be the restricted cartesian sum of $\mathscr{R}$ by itself a denumerable number of times. Then $\mathbf{a} \in T(\mathscr{R})$ has the form

$$\mathbf{a} = (a_0, a_1, \ldots), \qquad a_\nu \in \mathscr{R},$$

where all but finitely many $a_\nu = 0$. $T(\mathscr{R})$ is an additive abelian group. Define a multiplication on $T(\mathscr{R})$ as follows:

$$(a_0, a_1, \ldots)(b_0, b_1, \ldots) = \left(a_0 b_0, \ldots, \sum_{\nu=0}^{n} a_{n-\nu} b_\nu, \ldots\right).$$

The reader should prove

LEMMA 1 *Under the multiplication above, the additive abelian group $T(\mathscr{R})$ is a ring.*

We have obviously defined the multiplication in $T(\mathscr{R})$ so that the map $a_0 + \sum_{\nu=1}^{\infty} a_\nu x^\nu \xrightarrow{\tau} \mathbf{a} = (a_0, a_1, \ldots)$ is an operation-preserving map of $\mathscr{R}[x]$ into the ring $T(\mathscr{R})$. Since τ is clearly bijective, we have

PROPOSITION 27 *If x is an indeterminate over $\mathscr{R}$, then the ring $\mathscr{R}[x]$ is isomorphic to the ring $T(\mathscr{R})$.*

As a corollary to Proposition 27 we have

COROLLARY 1 A. *Let x be an indeterminate over the ring $\mathscr{R}$. If $\mathscr{R}$ is not the zero ring, then $\mathscr{R}[x]$ is an infinite ring.*

B. *If $\mathscr{R}$ is a countable ring, then $\mathscr{R}[x]$ is a countable ring.*

On examining the proof of Proposition 27, we see that

PROPOSITION 28 *If x and y are indeterminates over the ring $\mathscr{R}$, then there is an isomorphism φ of $\mathscr{R}[x]$ onto $\mathscr{R}[y]$ such that $a^\varphi = a$ for all $a \in \mathscr{R}$.*

EXERCISES 2 Let x and y be indeterminates over an integral domain $\mathscr{D}$. Prove: If λ is an isomorphism of $\mathscr{D}[x]$ onto $\mathscr{D}[y]$ such that $a^\lambda = a$ for all $a \in \mathscr{D}$, then x^λ is a polynomial in y of degree 1 and leading coefficient a unit of $\mathscr{D}$.

3 If x is an indeterminate over $\mathbf{Z}$, determine all automorphisms of $\mathbf{Z}[x]$.

4 Let x, y be indeterminates over $\mathbf{Z}_9$. Let λ be an operation-preserving map of $\mathbf{Z}_9[x]$ into $\mathbf{Z}_9[y]$ such that $a^\lambda = a$ for $a \in \mathbf{Z}_9$, $x^\lambda = 3y^2 - y$. Show that λ is an isomorphism of $\mathbf{Z}_9[x]$ onto $\mathbf{Z}_9[y]$.

5 Let x be an indeterminate over $\mathscr{R}$. Prove: If $y \in \mathscr{R}[x]$, then x is algebraic over $\mathscr{R}[y]$.

6 Prove: If $\mathscr{R}$ is a ring, then the ring $\mathscr{T}(\mathbf{Z}^+, \mathscr{R})$ of Sec. 3 and the ring $T(\mathscr{R})$ are not isomorphic.

We now prove that every ring has an indeterminate. Given a ring, we can always construct the ring $T(\mathscr{R})$. One easily checks that $T(\mathscr{R})$ contains a ring $\mathscr{R}_1 = \{(a, 0, \ldots) \mid a \in \mathscr{R}\}$ that is isomorphic to $\mathscr{R}$. Suppose $b \neq 0$ is a nondivisor of zero of $\mathscr{R}$ such that $ab = ba$ for all $a \in \mathscr{R}$. Then $(a, 0, 0, \ldots)(0, b, 0, 0, \ldots) = (0, b, 0, 0, \ldots)(a, 0, 0, \ldots)$ and

$$(0, b, 0, 0, \ldots)^n = \Big(\underbrace{0, 0, 0, \ldots, 0}_{n}, b^n, 0, 0, \ldots\Big).$$

Consider $\alpha = (a_0, 0, \ldots) + \sum_{\nu=1}^{n} (a_\nu, 0, 0, \ldots)(0, b, 0, \ldots)^\nu \in T(\mathscr{R})$. Clearly

$$\alpha = (a_0, a_1 b, \ldots, a_n b^n, 0, 0, \ldots).$$

If $\alpha = 0$, we must have $a_0 = a_1 b = \cdots = a_n b^n = 0$, whence

$$a_0 = a_1 = \cdots = a_n = 0.$$

Thus it follows that $(0, b, 0, 0, \ldots)$ is an indeterminate over $\mathscr{R}_1$. It follows from Proposition 7 that there is a ring $\mathscr{S}$ that contains $\mathscr{R}$ and an isomorphism δ of $\mathscr{S}$ onto $T(\mathscr{R})$ such that $a^\delta = (a, 0, 0, \ldots)$ for all $a \in \mathscr{R}$. Let x be that element in $\mathscr{S}$ such that $x^\delta = (0, b, 0, 0, \ldots)$. By Proposition 25, x is an indeterminate over the ring $\mathscr{R}$.

If $\mathscr{R}$ has a unity, that unity satisfies the assumptions imposed on b in the preceding paragraph. Hence

LEMMA 2 *If $\mathscr{R}$ is a ring with unity, then there exist extensions of $\mathscr{R}$ that contain indeterminates over $\mathscr{R}$.*

But as we saw in Proposition 9, every ring is embeddable in a ring $\mathscr{R}_*$ with unity. By Proposition 22, every indeterminate over $\mathscr{R}_*$ is an indeterminate over $\mathscr{R}$. Thus we have

PROPOSITION 29 *Each ring $\mathscr{R}$ has an extension that contains indeterminates over $\mathscr{R}$.*

We need to extend our notation a bit. Let $\mathscr{R}$ be a subring, and let X be a subset (possibly infinite) of a ring $\mathscr{S}$. There exists a unique minimal subring $\mathscr{M}(\mathscr{R}, X)$ of $\mathscr{S}$ that contains $\mathscr{R} \cup X$. By a *monomial* in the elements of X over $\mathscr{R}$ we mean an element of $\mathscr{R}$ or a finite product of the form

$$ax \cdots x_m, \qquad a \in \mathscr{R},\ x_\nu \in X\ (x_\nu \text{ not necessarily distinct}).$$

By a polynomial in X over $\mathscr{R}$ we mean a finite sum of monomials of X over $\mathscr{R}$. If the set X is such that

$$xy = yx, \qquad ax = xa, \qquad \text{for } x,\ y \in X,\ a \in \mathscr{R},$$

then the set of all polynomials in X over $\mathscr{R}$ is a subring of $\mathscr{S}$. We denote this ring by $\mathscr{R}[X]$. If $\mathscr{R}$ contains the unity of $\mathscr{S}$, then $\mathscr{R}[X] = \mathscr{M}(\mathscr{R}, X)$.

The typical element of $\mathscr{R}[x_1, \ldots, x_r]$ is of the form

$$a_{0,\ldots,0} + \sum_{n=1}^{\infty} \sum_{\nu_1+\cdots+\nu_r=n} a_{\nu_1\cdots\nu_r} x_1{}^{\nu_1} \cdots x_r{}^{\nu_r}, \tag{5}$$

where the $a_{\nu_1 \ldots \nu_r} \in \mathscr{R}$, and all but finitely many are 0.

We have seen that, if $\mathscr{R}$ is a ring, we can find an indeterminate over $\mathscr{R}$, say x. Applying our proposition to the ring $\mathscr{R}[x]$, we see there exists an indeterminate over $\mathscr{R}[x]$, say y. By Proposition 22, y is an indeterminate over $\mathscr{R}$, and by definition $xy = yx$. We now show that x is an indeterminate over $\mathscr{R}[y]$.

Suppose

$$p_0 + p_1 x + \cdots + p_n x^n = 0,$$

where $$p_\nu = a_{\nu 0} + \sum_{\mu=1}^{\infty} a_{\nu\mu} y^\mu \in \mathscr{R}[y], \qquad \nu = 0, 1, \ldots, n.$$

Let $m \geq \max\{d(p_0), d(p_1), \ldots, d(p_n)\}$. Then using the associative properties of the ring and the commutative properties of x and y, we get

$$0 = \left(a_{00} + \sum_{\nu=1}^{n} a_{\nu 0} x^\nu\right) + \left(a_{01} + \sum_{\nu=1}^{n} a_{\nu 1} x^\nu\right) y + \cdots + \left(a_{0m} + \sum_{\nu=1}^{n} a_{\nu m} x^\nu\right) y^m.$$

As y is an indeterminate over $\mathcal{R}[x]$, we must have

$$a_{0\mu} + \sum_{\nu=1}^{n} a_{\nu\mu}x^{\nu} = 0, \qquad \mu = 0, 1, \ldots, m.$$

But x is an indeterminate over $\mathcal{R}$, and hence

$$a_{\nu\mu} = 0, \qquad \mu = 0, 1, \ldots, m, \qquad \nu = 0, 1, \ldots, n,$$

whence $p_0 = p_1 = \cdots = p_n = 0$.

It is immediately obvious from the commutative properties of indeterminates and from the associative law for rings that

$$\mathcal{R}[x][y] = \mathcal{R}[x, y] = \mathcal{R}[y][x].$$

The reader should show that a polynomial in x and y over $\mathcal{R}$ in the form (5) is 0 if and only if each $a_{\nu_1\nu_2} = 0$.

Let $X = \{x_1, \ldots, x_r\}$ be a finite subset and $\mathcal{R}$ be a subring of a ring $\mathcal{S}$. We say that the set $\{x_1, \ldots, x_r\}$ is a set of *algebraically independent indeterminates over* $\mathcal{R}$ provided:

A. $ax = xa$, $xy = yx$ for all $a \in \mathcal{R}$ and all $x, y \in X$, and

B. An expression of the form (5) is 0 if and only if each $a_{\nu_1 \cdots \nu_r} = 0$.

More generally if X is a subset and $\mathcal{R}$ is a subring of a ring $\mathcal{S}$, we say that X is a set of *algebraically independent indeterminates over* $\mathcal{R}$ provided every finite subset of X is a set of algebraically independent indeterminates over $\mathcal{R}$.

We have shown that every ring has a set of two algebraically independent indeterminates. Proceeding inductively, we could show that each ring has any prescribed finite number of algebraically independent indeterminates. We shall now show there is no limit to the order of the sets of algebraically independent indeterminate over a fixed ring. As in Proposition 29, it is sufficient to prove the result for rings with a unity.

We have seen that $T(\mathcal{R})$ is an isomorphic model of the ring $\mathcal{R}[x]$. Similarly, if $\{x, y\}$ is a set of algebraically independent indeterminates over a ring $\mathcal{R}$ with unity, we can construct a model of $\mathcal{R}[x, y]$. Let J_2 be the set of all ordered pairs of nonnegative integers. J_2 is closed under coordinatewise addition, although it is not an additive group. Let K_2 be the set of all maps of J_2 into $\mathcal{R}$. Let

$$\mathcal{S}_2 = \{\alpha \in K_2 \mid \alpha(u, v) = 0 \text{ for all but finitely many pairs } (u, v) \in J_2\}.$$

(Note that we are using the functional notation for maps.) Define

$$(u, v) \xrightarrow{\alpha+\beta} \alpha(u, v) + \beta(u, v),$$

$$(u, v) \xrightarrow{\alpha\times\beta} \sum_{\substack{u_1+u_2=u \\ v_1+v_2=v}} \alpha(u_1, v_1)\beta(u_2, v_2).^{\dagger}$$

† Products of this type are often called the *convolution* of the two maps α and β.

If $\alpha, \beta \in \mathscr{S}_2$, then $\alpha(u, v) \neq 0$ for only finitely many pairs and $\beta(u, v) \neq 0$ for only finitely many pairs. Consequently the right-hand sides of the two relations above are nonzero for only finitely many pairs (u, v). Thus $\mathscr{S}_2$ is closed under the defined addition and multiplication. The reader can check that $\mathscr{S}_2$ is a ring.

To each $a \in \mathscr{R}$ there is a map

$$\alpha_a(u, v) = \begin{cases} a & \text{if } (u, v) = (0, 0), \\ 0 & \text{otherwise,} \end{cases}$$

in $\mathscr{S}_2$. The map $a \to \alpha_a$ of $\mathscr{R}$ into $\mathscr{S}_2$ is a monomorphism. In $\mathscr{S}_2$, we also have the maps

$$\beta_1(u, v) = \begin{cases} 1 & \text{if } (u, v) = (1, 0), \\ 0 & \text{otherwise,} \end{cases}$$

$$\beta_2(u, v) = \begin{cases} 1 & \text{if } (u, v) = (0, 1), \\ 0 & \text{otherwise.} \end{cases}$$

There is an obvious isomorphism φ of $\mathscr{R}[x, y]$ onto $\mathscr{S}_2$ where φ maps the polynomial A given in the form (5) into the function α given by $(u, v) \xrightarrow{\alpha} a_{uv}$. As β_1, β_2 are the images of x and y under φ, they are a set of two algebraically independent indeterminates over $\mathscr{R}^\varphi$. Thus $\mathscr{S}_2$ is an isomorphic model of $\mathscr{R}[x, y]$.

We shall now treat the general case. Let M be any set, and let J be the set of all maps of M into $\mathbf{Z}^+ \cup 0$. We shall use the functional notation for elements of J. In J we define an addition operation as follows:

$$m \xrightarrow{j_1 + j_2} j_1(m) + j_2(m).$$

J is closed under this operation. Let K be the set of all maps of J into the ring $\mathscr{R}$, which we suppose has a unity. Let

$$\mathscr{S} = \{\alpha \in K \mid \alpha(j) = 0 \text{ for all but finitely many } j \in J\}.$$

In $\mathscr{S}$ we define

$$j \xrightarrow{\alpha + \beta} \alpha(j) + \beta(j),$$

$$j \xrightarrow{\alpha \times \beta} \sum_{j_1 + j_2 = j} \alpha(j_1)\beta(j_2).$$

Under these operations $\mathscr{S}$ is a ring.

Let j_0 be the map such that

$$j_0(m) = 0, \qquad \text{for all } m \in M.$$

To each $m \in M$ let j_m be the map

$$j_m(n) = \begin{cases} 1 & \text{if } n = m, \\ 0 & \text{otherwise.} \end{cases}$$

To each $a \in \mathscr{R}$ let α_a be the element of $\mathscr{S}$ such that

$$\alpha_a(j) = \begin{cases} a & \text{if } j = j_0, \\ 0 & \text{otherwise.} \end{cases}$$

The map $a \to \alpha_a$ is a monomorphism of $\mathscr{R}$ into $\mathscr{S}$. To each $m \in M$ let β_m be the map

$$\beta_m(j) = \begin{cases} 1 & \text{if } j = j_m, \\ 0 & \text{otherwise.} \end{cases}$$

Clearly

$$\beta_m\beta_n = \beta_n\beta_m, \qquad \alpha_a\beta_m = \beta_m\alpha_a, \qquad \text{for } m, n \in M, a \in \mathscr{R}.$$

Also, if $m \in M$ and $\mathbf{s} \in \mathbf{Z}^+ \cup 0$, then

$$\beta_m^{\mathbf{s}}(j) = \begin{cases} 1 & \text{if } j = \mathbf{s}j_m, \\ 0 & \text{otherwise.} \end{cases}$$

Let $\{\beta_{m_1}, \beta_{m_2}, \ldots, \beta_{m_r}\}$ be any finite subset from $\{\beta_m \mid m \in M\}$. Let

$$\theta = \sum_{n=0}^{\infty} \sum_{v_1 + \cdots + v_r = n} \alpha_{a_{v_1 \ldots v_r}} \times \beta_{m_1}{}^{v_1} \times \cdots \times \beta_{m_r}{}^{v_r},$$

where $a_{v_1 \ldots v_r} = 0$ for all but finitely many $(v_1, \ldots, v_r)$. Then

$$\theta(j) = \begin{cases} a_{s_1 s_2 \cdots s_r} & \text{if } j = \mathbf{s}_1 j_{m_1} + \cdots + \mathbf{s}_r j_{m_r} \ (\mathbf{s}_j \in \mathbf{Z}^+ \cup 0), \\ 0 & \text{if } j \text{ is not of the form } \mathbf{s}_1 j_{m_1} + \cdots + \mathbf{s}_r j_{m_r}. \end{cases}$$

If $\theta = 0$, we see that $a_{v_1 \ldots v_r} = 0$ for all r-tuples $(v_1, \ldots, v_r)$. Hence we have shown that $\{\beta_{m_1}, \ldots, \beta_{m_r}\}$ is a set of algebraically independent indeterminates over $\mathscr{R}^\varphi$. Since this is true for any such finite set, we see that $\{\beta_m \mid m \in M\}$ is a set of algebraically independent indeterminates over $\mathscr{R}^\varphi$. Now applying Proposition 7, we obtain

OPOSITION 30 *Given a ring $\mathscr{R}$ and a set M, there exists a set X of algebraically independent indeterminates over $\mathscr{R}$ such that there is an one-to-one correspondence between M and X.*

Each polynomial $A \in \mathscr{R}[X]$ can be expressed in the form (5) for some finite set of indeterminates $\{x_1, \ldots, x_r\}$ from X. Consequently: *If X is a set of algebraic independent indeterminates over $\mathscr{R}$, then $\mathscr{R}[X] = \bigcup \mathscr{R}[Y]$, where the union is over all finite subsets Y of X.* The *degree of a polynomial A*, expressed as in (5), is the max $\{v_1 + \cdots + v_r | a_{v_1 \cdots v_r} \neq 0\}$.

Analogous to Proposition 26, the reader can prove: If *X is a set of algebraically independent indeterminates over an integral domain $\mathscr{D}$, then $\mathscr{D}[X]$ is an integral domain.* We denote the quotient field of the domain $\mathscr{D}[X]$ by $\mathscr{D}(X)$. The following result is easily proved:

OPOSITION 31 *Let X be a set of algebraically independent indeterminates over an integral domain $\mathscr{D}$. Let $\mathscr{Q}$ be the quotient field of $\mathscr{D}$. Then $\mathscr{D}(X) \supset \mathscr{Q}$, X is a set of algebraically independent indeterminates over $\mathscr{Q}$ and $\mathscr{Q}(X) = \mathscr{D}(X)$.*

EXERCISES 7 Prove: If X is a finite set of algebraically independent indeterminates over a countable field $\mathscr{F}$, then $\mathscr{F}(X)$ is a denumerable set.

8 Let x be an indeterminate over a field $\mathscr{F}$. Prove: An operation-preserving map φ of $\mathscr{F}(x)$ into $\mathscr{F}(x)$ such that $a^\varphi = a$ for all $a \in \mathscr{F}$, $x^\varphi = x^{-1}$ is an automorphism of $\mathscr{F}(x)$.

9 Prove: If $\mathscr{D}$ is an integral domain, $\mathscr{Q}$ its quotient field, and φ is an automorphism of $\mathscr{D}$, then there is a unique automorphism Φ on $\mathscr{Q}$ such that $\operatorname{res}_{\mathscr{D}} \Phi = \varphi$.

10 Prove: If x is an indeterminate over the field of rational numbers $\mathbf{Q}$, then any automorphism of $\mathbf{Q}(x)$ is such that $a^\varphi = a$, for all $a \in \mathbf{Q}$, and either $x^\varphi = cx + b$ or $x^\varphi = b + cx^{-1}$, with $c \neq 0$, $b \in \mathbf{Q}$.

7 ZEROS OF POLYNOMIALS

Throughout this section we assume that $\{x_1, x_2, \ldots, x_n\}$ is a set of algebraically independent indeterminates over an integral domain $\mathscr{D}$. Although some of our results hold for arbitrary rings, others do not. The interested reader can examine the various propositions to see whether they hold for rings satisfying weaker conditions than those for an integral domain. A few of the results could be given meaning for the case of infinitely many algebraically independent indeterminates.

Let $\mathscr{D}^{(n)}$ denote the cartesian sum of $\mathscr{D}$ by itself n times. To each $\mathbf{c} = (c_1, \ldots, c_n) \in \mathscr{D}^{(n)}$ there is a map $\sigma_\mathbf{c}$ of $\mathscr{D}[x_1, \ldots, x_n]$ into $\mathscr{D}$ given by

$$A = \sum_{m=0}^{\infty} \sum_{\nu_1 + \cdots + \nu_n = m} a_{\nu_1 \cdots \nu_n} x_1^{\nu_1} \cdots x_n^{\nu_n} \xrightarrow{\sigma\mathbf{c}} \sum_{m=0}^{\infty} \sum_{\nu_1 + \cdots + \nu_n = m} a_{\nu_1 \cdots \nu_n} c_1^{\nu_1} \cdots c_n^{\nu_n}.$$

We usually denote the right-hand side of this relation by $A(\mathbf{c})$. The map $\sigma_\mathbf{c}$ is called a *specialization of* $\mathscr{D}[x_1, \ldots, x_n]$ *at* $\mathbf{c}$. Clearly $a \xrightarrow{\sigma\mathbf{c}} a$, for all $a \in \mathscr{D}$. Hence the map $\sigma_\mathbf{c}$ is surjective. However, $\sigma_\mathbf{c}$ is never injective, since all the polynomials $(x_1 - c_1)B$, $B \in \mathscr{D}[x_1, \ldots, x_n]$ are mapped into 0. We also have

$$(A + B)^{\sigma\mathbf{c}} = A^{\sigma\mathbf{c}} + B^{\sigma\mathbf{c}},$$

$$(AB)^{\sigma\mathbf{c}} = A^{\sigma\mathbf{c}} B^{\sigma\mathbf{c}}.$$

Hence $\sigma_\mathbf{c}$ is a homomorphism of the ring $\mathscr{D}[x_1, \ldots, x_n]$ onto $\mathscr{D}$. If $A(\mathbf{c}) = 0$, we say that $\mathbf{c}$ is a *zero of* A.

Following our usual convention, if $A, B \in \mathscr{D}[x_1, \ldots, x_n]$ are such that $B = AC$ for some $C \in [\mathscr{D}x_1, \ldots, x_n]$, we say that *$A$ divides B in* $\mathscr{D}[x_1, \ldots, x_n]$, and we write $A \mid B$.

EXERCISE 1 Let $A, B, C \in \mathscr{D}[x_1, \ldots, x_n]$. Prove:

A. If $A \mid B$, $A \mid C$, then $A \mid (UB + VC)$, for all $U, V \in \mathscr{D}[x_1, \ldots, x_n]$.

B. If $A \mid B$, $B \mid C$, then $A \mid C$.

C. If $A \mid B$, then either $B = 0$ or $d(A) \leq d(B)$.

D. If $A \mid B$ and $d(A) = d(B)$, then there is a $b \in \mathscr{D}$ such that $B = bA$.

We now prove a result analogous to the division algorithm for integers:

ROPOSITION 32 *If $A, B \in \mathscr{D}[x]$ and the leading coefficient of B is a unit of $\mathscr{D}$, then there exist unique polynomials $Q, T \in \mathscr{D}[x]$ such that*

$$A = BQ + T, \qquad d(T) < d(B).$$

PROOF. The proof is by induction on $d(A)$. If $d(A) < d(B)$, we take $Q = 0$, $T = A$. Suppose the result is true for fixed B and arbitrary A of degree less than k. Suppose

$$A = ax^k + \cdots + a_0, \qquad a \neq 0,$$

$$B = bx^m + \cdots + b_0, \qquad b \text{ a unit of } \mathscr{D},$$

then $A - ab^{-1}x^{k-m}B$ is a polynomial of degree less than k. By the induction hypothesis there are Q_1, T_1 such that

$$A - ab^{-1}x^{n-m}B = BQ_1 + T_1, \qquad d(T_1) < d(B).$$

Consequently, $A = B(Q_1 + ab^{-1}x^{n-m}) + T_1 = BQ + T_1$ as desired.

As for the uniqueness, we observe that, if

$$A = BQ + T = BQ' + T',$$

then $B \mid (T - T')$ and hence $T - T' = 0$, whence $T = T'$, $Q = Q'$.

EXERCISE 2 A. Prove: If $A = BQ + T$, $d(T) < d(B) \leq d(A)$, then the leading coefficient of B is a divisor (in $\mathscr{D}$) of the leading coefficient of A.

B. Let $A = 2x^3 - 3x^2 + 1$, $B = 2x^2 + 4x - 1$. Show that we cannot express A as $BQ + T$ where $Q, T \in \mathbf{Z}[x]$ and $d(T) < d(B)$.

C. Discuss the possibility of dropping the assumption in Proposition 32 that the leading coefficient of B is a unit.

The following corollaries are immediately derivable from Proposition 32:

COROLLARY 1 *If $A \in \mathscr{D}[x]$ and $c \in \mathscr{D}$ is a zero of A, then $(x - c) \mid A$.*

COROLLARY 2 *If $A, B \in \mathscr{D}[x]$ such that $(x - c) \mid AB$ and $(x - c) \nmid A$, then $(x - c) \mid B$.*

By repeated use of the corollaries above we obtain

PROPOSITION 33 *If $A \in \mathscr{D}[x]$ and $c_1, \ldots, c_r \in \mathscr{D}$ are distinct zeros of A, then* $\prod_{\nu=1}^{r} (x - c_\nu) \mid A$.

The reader should prove

COROLLARY 1 *A nonzero polynomial $A \in \mathscr{D}[x]$ has at most $d(A)$ distinct zeros in $\mathscr{D}$.*

COROLLARY 2 *If $A, B \in \mathscr{D}[x]$ and there exist $c_0, \ldots, c_n \in \mathscr{D}$ such that $A(c_\nu) = B(c_\nu)$* where $n \geq \max \{d(A), d(B)\}$, *then $A = B$.*

PROPOSITION 34 *If $\mathbf{c} \in \mathscr{D}^{(n)}$ is a zero of a polynomial $A \in \mathscr{D}[x_1, \ldots, x_n]$, then there exist $B_1, \ldots, B_n \in \mathscr{D}[x_1, \ldots, x_n]$ such that* $A = \sum_{\nu=1}^{n} (x_\nu - c_\nu)B_\nu$.

PROOF. The proof is by induction on n. If $n = 1$ this is Corollary 1 to Proposition 32. Assume that the proposition holds if we have less than n indeterminates. We can consider A to be a polynomial in x_n over the integral domain $\mathscr{D}[x_1, \ldots, x_{n-1}]$. By Proposition 32 we have

$$A = (x_n - c_n)B_n + T_n,$$

where $\qquad B_n \in \mathscr{D}[x_1, \ldots, x_n], \qquad T_n \in \mathscr{D}[x_1, \ldots, x_{n-1}].$

Now $T_n(c_1, \ldots, c_{n-1}) = 0$, and by the induction hypothesis we find $T_n = \sum_{\nu=1}^{n-1} (x_\nu - c_\nu)B_\nu$. This completes the proof of the proposition.

PROPOSITION 35 *If $A \in \mathscr{D}[x_1, \ldots, x_n]$ and $c_0, \ldots, c_{d(A)} \in \mathscr{D}$ such that $A(\mathbf{c}) = 0$ for every ordered n-tuple $\mathbf{c}$ with entries from $\{c_0, \ldots, c_{d(A)}\}$, then $A = 0$.*

PROOF. The proof is by induction on n. The case $n = 1$ is Corollary 1 of Proposition 33. Let $m = d(A)$; then

$$A = x_n{}^m B_m + x_n{}^{m-1} B_{m-1} + \cdots + B_0,$$

where the $B_\nu \in \mathscr{D}[x_1, \ldots, x_{n-1}]$ and some of the B_ν, including B_m, may be 0. For each choice of $c_1, \ldots, c_{n-1}$ the polynomial $A(c_1, \ldots, c_{n-1}, x_n)$ is of degree at most m with $m + 1$ zeros, and hence it must be the 0 polynomial. That is

$$B_\nu(c_1, \ldots, c_{n-1}) = 0, \qquad \nu = 0, 1, \ldots, m, \qquad \text{when } c_\nu \in \{c_o, \ldots, c_{d(A)}\}.$$

As $d(B\gamma) \leq d(A)$, by induction each B_ν is the zero polynomial.

EXERCISE 3

A. Prove: If $A, B \in \mathbf{Z}[x]$ and $A \mid B$, then the leading coefficient of A is a divisor of the leading coefficient of B and $A(0) \mid B(0)$.

B. If $A \in \mathbf{Z}[x]$ and $A(s/t) = 0$, then $s \mid A(0)$, and t divides the leading coefficient of A.

C. Determine all rational zeros of the polynomials

$$12x^4 - 6x^2 + 7x + 15, \qquad x^5 + 2x^2 - x.$$

8 THE ARITHMETIC OF POLYNOMIAL DOMAINS

Again we let $\{x_1, \ldots, x_n\}$ be a set of algebraically independent indeterminates over an integral domain $\mathscr{D}$. The additive group of $\mathscr{D}[x_1, \ldots, x_n]$ is isomorphic to the cartesian sum of $\mathscr{D}$ by itself denumerably many times. However, the multiplicative structure of $\mathscr{D}[x_1, \ldots, x_n]$ is not so easily resolved. We have seen, in Exercise 1 of the last section, that, if b is a nonzero constant polynomial in $\mathscr{D}[x_1, \ldots, x_n]$, then all the divisors of b in $\mathscr{D}[x_1, \ldots, x_n]$ already lie in $\mathscr{D}$. Hence the multiplicative structure of $\mathscr{D}[x_1, \ldots, x_n]$ contains all the information concerning the multiplicative structure of $\mathscr{D}$. In particular, irreducible elements of $\mathscr{D}$ are irreducible elements of $\mathscr{D}[x_1, \ldots, x_n]$. If $\mathscr{D}[x_1, \ldots, x_n]$ is a unique factorization ring, then $\mathscr{D}$ is also. We shall show that the converse of this last statement is also true.

A polynomial $A \in \mathscr{D}[x_1, \ldots, x_n]$ of positive degree is *irreducible over* $\mathscr{D}$ if it is not the product of two polynomials of $\mathscr{D}[x_1, \ldots, x_n]$ of positive degree. The property of being irreducible over a domain is relative to the domain; i.e., if x is an indeterminate over $\mathscr{D}'$ and $\mathscr{D}$ is a subdomain of $\mathscr{D}'$, then there can exist $A \in \mathscr{D}[x]$ that are irreducible over $\mathscr{D}$ and reducible over $\mathscr{D}'$. One such example is $x^2 - 2$; it is irreducible over $\mathbf{Q}$ but reducible over $\mathbf{Q}|2|$. Obviously, a polynomial of degree 1 is always irreducible. An irreducible polynomial (over $\mathscr{D}$) may be an irreducible element of $\mathscr{D}[x_1, \ldots, x_n]$, but it need not be; e.g., $A = 2x + 6$ is irreducible over $\mathbf{Z}$, but it is not an irreducible element of $\mathbf{Z}[x]$, since 2 and $x + 3$ are not units of $\mathbf{Z}[x]$. To avoid confusion between polynomials irreducible over $\mathscr{D}$ and polynomials that are irreducible elements of $\mathscr{D}[x_1, \ldots, x_n]$, we shall refer to the latter as primes of $\mathscr{D}[x_1, \ldots, x_n]$. This choice of terminology is consistent with our remarks in Sec. 4.

A polynomial $A \in \mathscr{D}[x]$ having leading coefficient 1 is called a *monic* polynomial. Every monic polynomial of first degree over $\mathscr{D}$ is a prime of $\mathscr{D}[x]$.

We begin our study of the arithmetic of $\mathscr{D}[x_1, \ldots, x_n]$ with the simplest case: the ring of polynomials in one indeterminate x over a field $\mathscr{F}$. Since every nonzero element of $\mathscr{F}$ is a unit of $\mathscr{F}$, $\mathscr{F}$ is trivially a unique factorization domain. Each $0 \neq A \in \mathscr{F}[x]$ can be expressed uniquely as $A = aA'$, where $a \in \mathscr{F}$ and A' is a monic polynomial of $\mathscr{F}[x]$. Thus, each nonzero polynomial $A \in \mathscr{F}[x]$ is the associate of a unique monic polynomial over $\mathscr{F}$.

XERCISES 1 Prove:

A. If A is a monic polynomial and A is reducible in $\mathscr{F}[x]$, then A is the product of monic polynomials of positive degree.

B. Two monic polynomials of $\mathscr{F}[x]$ are associates if and only if they are equal.

2 Prove: An irreducible polynomial of positive degree over $\mathscr{F}$ is a prime of $\mathscr{F}[x]$.

Now, using the exercises above and induction on the degree of the polynomial, the reader can prove

PROPOSITION 36 *If x is an indeterminate over a field $\mathscr{F}$, each monic polynomial of $\mathscr{F}[x]$ can be expressed as a finite product of monic irreducible polynomials over $\mathscr{F}$.*

If $A, B \in \mathscr{F}[x]$, not both zero, let

$$\mathscr{S}(A, B) = \{C \in \mathscr{F}[x] \mid C \mid A \text{ and } C \mid B\}.$$

Clearly $\mathscr{S}(A, B) \supset 1$. If $Q \in \mathscr{F}[x]$, then $\mathscr{S}(A, B) = \mathscr{S}(A - BQ, B)$. Hence, using Proposition 32 (the division algorithm), we can construct a finite sequence of nonzero polynomials $T_1, \ldots, T_k$ such that $d(B) > d(T_1) > \cdots > d(T_k)$ and $\mathscr{S}(A, B) = \mathscr{S}(B, T_1) = \mathscr{S}(T_1, T_2) = \cdots = \mathscr{S}(T_k, 0)$. Let D be the unique monic associate of T_k. Then $D \mid A$ and $D \mid B$. Furthermore if $E \mid A$ and $E \mid B$, then $E \mid T_k$. Hence D is a *greatest common divisor* in $\mathscr{F}[x]$ of A and B. If E is a common divisor of A and B, then $d(E) \leq d(B)$. Clearly D is the monic polynomial of maximal degree in $\mathscr{F}[x]$, which divides both A and B. Thus D is unique. We write $D = (A, B)$. Summarizing, we have

PROPOSITION 37 *Each pair $A, B \in \mathscr{F}[x]$, not both zero, has a greatest common divisor D in $\mathscr{F}[x]$, where D is the monic polynomial in $\mathscr{F}[x]$ of maximal degree dividing both A and B.*

The polynomials T_ν, which appeared in the argument above, could all be expressed in the form

$$T_\nu = AU_\nu + BV_\nu, \qquad U_\nu, V_\nu \in \mathscr{F}[x].$$

Hence we have the first part of

PROPOSITION 38 *To each pair $A, B \in \mathscr{F}[x]$, not both zero, there exist $U, V \in \mathscr{F}[x]$ such that $AU + BV = D = (A, B)$. Furthermore, there exist $U, V \in \mathscr{F}[x]$ such that $d(U) < d(B)$, $d(V) < d(A)$, and in that case, U, V are unique.*

The reader should verify the last sentence of Proposition 38.

EXERCISE 3 Let $A = 5x^{10} + 3x^8 - 6x^5 - x + 3$, $B = x^3 - 5x + 4$:

A. Find a greatest common divisor of A, B in $\mathbf{Q}[x]$.
B. Find the U, V in $\mathbf{Q}[x]$ such that $AU + BV = (A, B)$ with $d(U) < d(B)$.
C. Find a greatest common divisor of A, B in $\mathbf{Z}_3[x]$.
D. Find the $U, V \in \mathbf{Z}_3[x]$ such that $AU + BV = (A, B)$ with $d(U) < d(B)$.

If A, $B \in \mathscr{F}[x]$ and if 1 is a greatest common divisor of A, B in $\mathscr{F}[x]$, we say that A and B are *relatively prime over* $\mathscr{F}$. The reader should prove

POSITION 39 *Let x be an indeterminate over a field $\mathscr{E}$ containing a field $\mathscr{F}$. If A, $B \in \mathscr{F}[x]$, then A and B are relatively prime over $\mathscr{E}$ if and only if they are relatively prime over $\mathscr{F}$.*

It follows from the proposition above that the property of being relatively prime over a field is independent of the field.

We now have the tools with which to prove that $\mathscr{F}[x]$ is a unique factorization domain. The proofs are exactly as for **Z** and are left to the reader.

POSITION 40 *If A, B, C are nonzero polynomials of $\mathscr{F}[x]$ such that $(A, B) = 1$ and $A \mid BC$, then $A \mid C$.*

POSITION 41 *If A is a monic polynomial of positive degree in $\mathscr{F}[x]$, then A is a unique product (to within order) of monic irreducible polynomials over $\mathscr{F}$.*

COROLLARY *Each polynomial of positive degree over a field $\mathscr{F}$ can be expressed uniquely as the product of an element of $\mathscr{F}$ and finitely many monic irreducible polynomials of positive degree over $\mathscr{F}$.*

Summarizing, we have shown

POSITION 42 *If x is an indeterminate over a field $\mathscr{F}$, then the integral domain $\mathscr{F}[x]$ is a unique factorization domain.*

The selection of the monic irreducible polynomials is a simple and natural way of selecting representatives for each class of associate primes of $\mathscr{F}[x]$. With this set of representatives, the proof of the unique factorization theorem is simple. For general unique factorization domains one should not expect always to make such a natural selection of the representatives.

Except for a few fields, the problem of determining the set of monic irreducible polynomials is an impossibility. For finite fields we can give a process for determining whether a given polynomial is irreducible, which is analogous to the sieve method of determining whether or not an integer is a prime. We use the following: (A) polynomials of degree 1 are irreducible; (B) if a polynomial A is reducible, then A is divisible by an irreducible polynomial of degree at most $d(A)/2$. Since there are only finitely many polynomials of given degree over a finite field, we can list the monic irreducible polynomials of degree 1, then of degree 2, then of degree 3, etc., continuing until we have reached those of degree $d(A)/2$. We can then check whether A is irreducible.

When we come to polynomials over infinite fields, this process will not work, since there are infinitely many monic polynomials of degree 1, and the technique described above cannot even be used to determine the irreducible quadratic polynomials. Later we shall show how this technique can be modified so that we can determine whether a given monic polynomial over **Q** is irreducible over **Q**.

EXERCISES 4 A. Prove: A polynomial of degree 2 or 3 is reducible over a field if and only if the polynomial has a zero in $\mathscr{F}$.

B. Find all the irreducible polynomials in $\mathbf{Z}_3[x]$ of degree ≤ 5.

5 Which of the following polynomials are irreducible over $\mathbf{Q}$: $x^3 - 2$, $x^2 - 17$, $x^2 + 4$, $x^3 - 8x + 3$, $2x^3 - x^2 + 14$, $x^4 + 1$?

6 Prove: There are infinitely many monic irreducible polynomials over an integral domain.

Now let $\mathscr{D}$ be a unique factorization domain, and let $\mathscr{Q}$ be its quotient field. Let x be an indeterminate over $\mathscr{Q}$. We have seen that $\mathscr{Q}[x]$ is a unique factorization domain, and we now prove that $\mathscr{D}[x]$ is also a unique factorization domain. Let $\mathscr{P}$ be a fixed set of representatives of the classes of associate primes of $\mathscr{D}$. If $A = a_0 + \cdots + a_n x^n \in \mathscr{D}[x]$, let $\mathfrak{c}_{\mathscr{P}}(A) = \mathfrak{c}(A)$ be a greatest common divisor in $\mathscr{D}$ of the set $a_0, \ldots, a_n$. By definition, the set $\mathscr{P}$ determines $\mathfrak{c}(A)$ uniquely. The polynomial A is said to be *primitive* if $\mathfrak{c}(A)$ is a unit of $\mathscr{D}$. We have

$$A = \mathfrak{c}(A)A',$$

where A' is a primitive polynomial over $\mathscr{D}$.

LEMMA 1 *The product of primitive polynomials is primitive.*

PROOF. Suppose $A = a_0 + \cdots + a_n x^n$, $B = b_0 + \cdots + b_m x^m$ are primitive and that $p \in \mathscr{P}$ divides $\mathfrak{c}(AB)$. Since $\mathfrak{c}(A)$ is a unit, there is a minimal integer $r \leq n$ such that $p \nmid a_r$. Similarly there is a minimum $s \leq m$ such that $p \nmid b_s$. On the other hand p divides each coefficient of AB, and in particular p divides

$$a_0 b_{r+s} + \cdots + a_r b_s + \cdots + a_0 b_{r+s}.$$

Because of the minimality of r and of s this implies that $p \mid a_r b_s$. But in a unique factorization ring, if a prime divides the product, it must divide at least one of the factors. Consequently p divides at least one of a_r and b_s, contrary to the choice of r and s.

The reader can now prove

COROLLARY 1 *If $A, B \in \mathscr{D}[x]$, then $\mathfrak{c}(AB) = \mathfrak{c}(A)\mathfrak{c}(B)$.*

COROLLARY 2 *Any divisor of positive degree of a primitive polynomial is primitive.*

LEMMA 2 *Suppose $a \in \mathscr{D}$ and $A \in \mathscr{D}[x]$, then:*

A. *$\mathfrak{c}(aA)$ and $a\mathfrak{c}(A)$ are associates.*

B. *If a divides A in $\mathscr{D}[x]$, then a divides $\mathfrak{c}(A)$ in $\mathscr{D}$.*

It follows from Lemma 2 and Corollary 2 of Lemma 1 that

LEMMA 3 *The primes of $\mathscr{D}[x]$ are the primes of $\mathscr{D}$ and the primitive irreducible polynomials over $\mathscr{D}$.*

LEMMA 4 *If $B \in \mathscr{Q}[x]$, then there exists $m \in \mathscr{Q}$ such that mB is a primitive polynomial over $\mathscr{D}$. If B is monic, m can be chosen from $\mathscr{D}$.*

PROOF. Let $B = a_0/b_0 + \cdots + (a_n/b_n)x^n$, where $a_\nu, b_\nu \in \mathscr{D}$, and we can require (for each ν) that the greatest common divisor of a_ν and b_ν is a unit of $\mathscr{D}$. Let b be the least common multiple of the set $b_0, \ldots, b_n$. Then $dB \in \mathscr{D}[x]$. Put $c = \mathfrak{c}(bB)$. Put $m = b/c$. By construction mB is a primitive polynomial over $\mathscr{D}$. If B is monic over $\mathscr{Q}$, then c divides b in $\mathscr{D}$ and $m \in \mathscr{D}$.

LEMMA 5 *$A \in \mathscr{D}[x]$ is irreducible over $\mathscr{D}$ if and only if A is irreducible over $\mathscr{Q}$.*

PROOF. Since $\mathscr{Q} \supset \mathscr{D}$, if A is irreducible over $\mathscr{Q}$, it is irreducible over $\mathscr{D}$. Now suppose A is irreducible over $\mathscr{D}$ and $A = B_1 B_2$, where B_1, B_2 are polynomials over $\mathscr{Q}$ of positive degree. We apply Lemma 4. Let $r_1, s_1, r_2, s_2 \in \mathscr{D}$ be such that the greatest common divisor of r_1 and s_1 is a unit of $\mathscr{D}$ and the greatest common divisor of r_2 and s_2 is a unit of $\mathscr{D}$ and $(r_1/s_1)B_1 = C_1$ and $(r_2/s_2)B_2 = C_2$ are primitive polynomials over $\mathscr{D}$. Then $d(C_\nu) > 0$, $(\nu = 1, 2)$, and $r_1 r_2 A = s_1 s_2 C_1 C_2$. It follows from Lemma 2 that $r_1 r_2 \mathfrak{c}(A) = s_1 s_2 u$, where u is a unit of $\mathscr{D}$. Now $\mathscr{D}$ is a unique factorization domain, and hence r_1 is a divisor of s_2 and r_2 is a divisor of s_1. Put $E_1 = [(s_1 s_2)/(r_1 r_2)]C_1$; then $E_1, C_2 \in \mathscr{D}[x]$ and $A = E_1 C_2$, contrary to the hypothesis. This completes the proof of the lemma. This lemma is often referred to in the literature as Gauss' lemma.

By Lemma 4 each class of associates of a monic irreducible polynomial over $\mathscr{Q}$ contains a primitive polynomial that, by Lemma 5, is irreducible over $\mathscr{D}$. If A and B are primitive irreducible polynomials over $\mathscr{D}$ that are associates in $\mathscr{Q}[x]$, then there are $s, t \in \mathscr{D}$ such that s and t are relatively prime in $\mathscr{D}$ and $sA = tB$. As $\mathfrak{c}(A)$ and $\mathfrak{c}(B)$ are units, it must be that s and t are associates in $\mathscr{D}$, and hence A and B are associates in $\mathscr{D}[x]$.

We have thus shown that each class of associate primes in $\mathscr{Q}[x]$ contains exactly one class of associate primitive irreducible polynomials over $\mathscr{D}$. Thus a set $\mathscr{P}'$ of representatives for the classes of associate primitive irreducible polynomials over $\mathscr{D}$ is a set of representatives for the classes of associate primes in $\mathscr{Q}[x]$.

Let $\mathscr{P}^* = \mathscr{P} \cup \mathscr{P}'$. Since an element from $\mathscr{P}$ and an element from $\mathscr{P}'$ have different degrees, they cannot be associate in $\mathscr{D}[x]$. It follows from Lemma 3 that $\mathscr{P}^*$ is a set of representatives for the classes of associate primes in $\mathscr{D}[x]$.

Now let A be any nonzero polynomial from $\mathscr{D}[x]$. Having fixed $\mathscr{P}$, we can write $A = \mathfrak{c}(A)A'$, where $\mathfrak{c}(A)$ is a unique† element in $\mathscr{D}$ and A' is a unique primitive polynomial. By hypothesis, $\mathfrak{c}(A)$ can be expressed uniquely as the product of a unit of $\mathscr{D}$ and finitely many elements from $\mathscr{P}$. By Proposition 42 A' can be expressed uniquely as the product of a unit α of $\mathscr{Q}[x]$ and finitely many elements from $\mathscr{P}'$. Since A' and the elements from $\mathscr{P}'$ are primitive, it follows from Lemma 2 that the α, which is in $\mathscr{Q}$, must indeed be a unit of $\mathscr{D}$. Combining these two statements, we obtain the result that A can be expressed uniquely, as the product of a unit of $\mathscr{D}[x]$, i.e., a unit of $\mathscr{D}$, and finitely many elements of $\mathscr{P}^*$, thus proving

PROPOSITION 43 *If x is an indeterminate over a unique factorization domain $\mathscr{D}$, then $\mathscr{D}[x]$ is a unique factorization domain.*

Finally we prove

THEOREM 1 *If $\{x_1, \ldots, x_n\}$ is a set of algebraically independent indeterminates over a unique factorization domain $\mathscr{D}$, then $\mathscr{D}[x_1, \ldots, x_n]$ is a unique factorization domain.*

PROOF. The proof is by induction on n. The case $n = 1$ is Proposition 43. Suppose the theorem is valid for less than n indeterminates. Then we can view $\mathscr{D}[x_1, \ldots, x_n]$ as the set of polynomials in x_n over the integral domain $\mathscr{D}[x_1, \ldots, x_{n-1}]$. By induction hypothesis $\mathscr{D}[x_1, \ldots, x_{n-1}]$ is a unique factorization domain, and we can now apply Proposition 43 to obtain the theorem.

EXERCISE 7 Let $\mathscr{D}$ be a subdomain of an integral domain $\mathscr{D}_1$. Let $\mathscr{Q}$ and $\mathscr{Q}_1$ be the quotient fields of $\mathscr{D}$ and $\mathscr{D}_1$, respectively; then $\mathscr{Q}_1 \supset \mathscr{Q}$. Let x be an indeterminate over $\mathscr{Q}_1$. Prove:

A. If $A, B \in \mathscr{Q}[x]$ and $A = BC$, for some $C \in \mathscr{Q}_1[x]$, then $C \in \mathscr{Q}[x]$.

B. Let $\mathscr{D}$ be a unique factorization domain. If $A, B \in \mathscr{D}[x]$, B a primitive polynomial over $\mathscr{D}$ and $A = BC$ for some $C \in \mathscr{Q}_1[x]$, then $C \in \mathscr{D}[x]$.

Exercise 7 shows that, if $A, B \in \mathscr{D}[x]$ and B divides A in some larger domain, then B divides A in $\mathscr{D}[x]$.

9 PRINCIPAL IDEAL DOMAINS

Let $\mathscr{R}$ be a ring. The reader will recall (see Sec. 2) that an ideal $\mathscr{I}$ of $\mathscr{R}$ is an additive subgroup of $\mathscr{R}$ such that $\mathscr{I}\mathscr{R}$ and $\mathscr{R}\mathscr{I}$ lie in $\mathscr{I}$. Given any subset $A \subset \mathscr{R}$, there are ideals of $\mathscr{R}$ containing the set A, e.g., $\mathscr{R}$ itself. The intersection of all such ideals is an ideal containing A. It is obviously

† As noted in the concluding paragraphs of Sec. 4 (page 154), $\mathfrak{c}(A)$ is uniquely determined once we fix $\mathscr{P}$.

the smallest ideal containing A. We denote this ideal by the symbolism (A), and we say that the ideal (A) is *generated by the set A*. If $\mathscr{R}$ has no unity, the typical element of (A) is a finite sum of the form

$$\sum_{j=1}^{k} (r_{1j}a_j + a_j r_{2j} + r_{3j}a_j r_{4j} + \mathbf{n}_{1j}a_j + \mathbf{n}_{2j}\gamma_{4j}a_j + \mathbf{n}_{3j}a_j\gamma_{5j} + \mathbf{n}_{4j}\gamma_{6j}a_j\gamma_{7j}),$$

where $a_1, \ldots, a_k \in A$, $r_{ij} \in \mathscr{R}$, $\mathbf{n}_{ij} \in \mathbf{Z}$. If $\mathscr{R}$ is a commutative ring with unity, the typical elements of (A) can be expressed as a finite sum of the form

$$\sum_{j=1}^{k} r_j a_j, \qquad \text{where } r_j \in \mathscr{R},\ a_j \in A.$$

If $\mathscr{R}$ is a commutative ring with unity, an ideal that is generated by a single element is said to be a *principal ideal*. An integral domain in which every ideal is a principal ideal is called a *principal ideal domain*. A field $\mathscr{F}$ is always a principal ideal domain, since its only ideals are (0) and $(1) = \mathscr{F}$.

We have seen (Theorem 12, Chap. 1) that $\mathbf{Z}$ is a principal ideal domain. This was proved using the division algorithm. The reader can similarly prove

ROPOSITION 44 *If x is an indeterminate over a field $\mathscr{F}$, then $\mathscr{F}[x]$ is a principal ideal domain.*

On the other hand, if x is an indeterminate over $\mathbf{Z}$, then the ideal $(2, x)$ is not a principal ideal in the domain $\mathbf{Z}[x]$. For suppose $(2, x) = (P)$, where P is a polynomial over $\mathbf{Z}$. Then P divides both 2 and x, but they are nonassociate primes in $\mathbf{Z}[x]$, and hence P must be a unit of $\mathbf{Z}[x]$. But then 1 is in the ideal $(2, x)$; i.e., $1 = 2(a_0 + a_1x + \cdots + a_nx^n) + x(b_0 + \cdots b_mx^m)$, whence 2 would be a divisor of 1 in $\mathbf{Z}$; an impossibility.

XERCISES 1 If x and y are algebraically independent indeterminates over a field $\mathscr{F}$, show that the ideal (x, y) is not a principal ideal in the integral domain $\mathscr{F}[x, y]$.

2 Prove: If A is a subset of an integral domain $\mathscr{D}$ such that (A) is a principal ideal in $\mathscr{D}$, say $(A) = (d)$, then d is the greatest common divisor in $\mathscr{D}$ of the elements of A.

3 Prove: If $\mathscr{I}_1 \subset \mathscr{I}_2 \subset \cdots \mathscr{I}_n \subset \cdots$ is a sequence of ideals in a ring $\mathscr{R}$, then $\mathscr{I} = \bigcup_{n=1}^{\infty} \mathscr{I}_n$ is an ideal of $\mathscr{R}$.

We are particularly interested in principal ideal domains because of the following propositions:

POSITION 45 *If $\mathscr{D}$ is a principal ideal domain, then $\mathscr{D}$ is a unique factorization domain.*

In proving this proposition we shall need several lemmas:

LEMMA 1 *Let $\mathscr{D}$ be a principal ideal domain. If a, b, $p \in \mathscr{D}$ are such that p is an irreducible element of $\mathscr{D}$ that divides ab, then p divides at least one of a and b. Thus irreducible elements of a principal ideal domain are primes.*

PROOF. Consider the ideal (a, p). By assumption it is principal, say $(a, p) = (d)$. Then $d \mid p$, and hence d is either a unit or an associate of p. In the latter case, since $d \mid a$, we would have $p \mid a$, If d is a unit, then $1 \in (a, p)$, and hence $1 = au + pv$, for some u, $v \in \mathscr{D}$. But then, $b = abu + pbv$, and hence $p \mid b$.

LEMMA 2 *Let $\mathscr{D}$ be a principal ideal domain. If $\mathscr{I}_\lambda (\lambda \in \Lambda)$ is some collection of proper ideals of $\mathscr{D}$, then there exists $\lambda_0 \in \Lambda$ such that $\mathscr{I}_{\lambda_0}$ is not a proper subset of any $\mathscr{I}_\lambda$,* where $\lambda_0 \neq \lambda \in \Lambda$.

PROOF. We assume the lemma is false and obtain a contradiction. If $\mathscr{I}_\lambda (\lambda \in \Lambda)$ is a collection of proper ideals and none satisfies the conclusion of the lemma, then there is an increasing subcollection

$$\mathscr{I}_1 \subsetneq \mathscr{I}_2 \subsetneq \mathscr{I}_3 \subsetneq \cdots \subsetneq \mathscr{I}_n \subsetneq \cdots$$

taken from the original set $\mathscr{I}_\lambda$, $(\lambda \in \Lambda)$.† Put $\mathscr{I} = \bigcup_{n=1}^{\infty} \mathscr{I}_n$. By Exercise 3, $\mathscr{I}$ is an ideal of $\mathscr{D}$. Since $\mathscr{D}$ is a principal ideal domain, we have $\mathscr{I} = (d)$ for some $d \in \mathscr{D}$. Hence there is a minimal integer n such that $d \in \mathscr{I}_n$, i.e., $(d) \subset \mathscr{I}_n$. But then $\mathscr{I} = (d) = \mathscr{I}_n$. It follows that $\mathscr{I}_n = \mathscr{I}_{n+1} = \ldots$, contrary to the choice of the $\mathscr{I}_n$.

LEMMA 3 *If $\mathscr{D}$ is a principal ideal domain, then each nonunit of $\mathscr{D}$ is expressible as a finite product of primes from $\mathscr{D}$.*

PROOF. Suppose there are nonunits of $\mathscr{D}$ that are not expressible as a finite product of primes from $\mathscr{D}$. Let Λ be the set of all such nonunits. Consider the collection of ideals (x), $x \in \Lambda$. By Lemma 2 there is an $a \in \Lambda$ such that (a) is not properly contained in any of the (x), $a \neq x \in \Lambda$. Since $a \in \Lambda$, a is not a prime, nor is it expressible as a finite product of primes. Since a is not a prime, we have $a = bc$, where b and c are nonunits of $\mathscr{D}$. Now (b) and (c) each contain (a) properly; hence b, $c \notin \Lambda$. But then b and c are expressible as a finite product of primes, and hence so is a, contrary to our assumption.

PROOF OF PROPOSITION 45. Let $\mathscr{P}$ be a set of representatives for the classes of associate primes of $\mathscr{D}$. It follows from Lemma 3 that each $0 \neq a \in \mathscr{D}$ can be expressed as the product of a unit and finitely many primes from $\mathscr{P}$. To each such a there is a nonnegative integer r such that

† In making this step, we have implicitly made use of the axiom of choice, for we have assumed we can always choose an ideal from the set of ideals properly containing $\mathscr{I}_n$.

a is expressible as a product involving r factors from $\mathscr{P}$ and is not expressible with fewer factors from $\mathscr{P}$. Suppose this expression for a is not unique (to within order of multiplication). Then

$$a = up_1p_2 \cdots p_r = u'p_1' \cdots p_s',$$

where u, u' are units, $p_j, p_j' \in \mathscr{P}$ and $0 \le r \le s$.

The proof will be by induction on r. If $r = 0$, then $s = 0$, for otherwise we would have a prime dividing a unit contrary to the definition of primes. It then follows that $u = u' = a$, whenever $r = s = 0$.

Now suppose that each $0 \ne a \in \mathscr{D}$ expressible with less than r primes from $\mathscr{P}$ is expressible uniquely as a product of a unit and finitely many elements of $\mathscr{P}$. We have seen this assumption is true for $r = 0$. Now $p_1 \mid a$, and by Lemma 1 it follows that p_1 must divide one of $p_1', \ldots, p_s'$, say $p_1 \mid p_1'$. Since p_1 and p_1' are both primes, they must be associates, and since they are both in $\mathscr{P}$, they must be equal. We then cancel p_1 and obtain

$$a' = up_2 \cdots p_r = u'p_2' \cdots p_s'.$$

Now a' satisfies the induction hypothesis, and we can therefore conclude that $r = s$; that, after rearranging terms, $p_j = p_j'$ $(j = 2, \ldots, r)$; and $u = u'$. This completes the proof of the proposition.

The converse to Proposition 45 is false, for as we know, $\mathbf{Z}[x]$ is a unique factorization domain that is not a principal ideal domain.

It is reasonable to ask if there are other principal ideal domains besides $\mathbf{Z}$ and $\mathscr{F}[x]$. We have noticed that these were principal ideal domains because they each possessed a division algorithm. The essential feature of the algorithm lies in the existence of a weight function that permits us to compare elements. In the case of the ring of integers the weight function was the absolute value, and in the case of $\mathscr{F}[x]$ the weight function was the degree map. In the case of $\mathscr{F}[x]$, instead of using the degree map, we might have used the following map:

$$g(A) = \begin{cases} 2^{d(A)}, & \text{if } A \ne 0, \\ 0\ \ , & \text{if } A = 0. \end{cases}$$

The map g is such that $g(A)$ is a nonnegative integer that is 0 only when $A = 0$; $g(AB) = g(A)g(B)$; and given A, $B \in \mathscr{F}[x]$, $B \ne 0$, there is a $Q \in \mathscr{F}[x]$ such that $g(A - BQ) < g(B)$. These are also properties of the absolute value on the domain $\mathbf{Z}$.

We shall say that an integral domain $\mathscr{D}$ is a *Euclidean domain* if there is a map g of $\mathscr{D}$ into $\mathbf{Z}^+ \cup \{0\}$ such that

A. $g(a) = 0$ if and only if $a = 0$.
B. $g(ab) = g(a)g(b)$, for all $a, b \in \mathscr{D}$.
C. Given $a, b \in \mathscr{D}$, $b \ne 0$, there exists $q \in \mathscr{D}$ such that $g(a - bq) < g(b)$.

PROPOSITION 46 *The ring* $\mathbf{Z}|-1|$ *is a Euclidean domain.*

PROOF. Let $g[a, b] = a^2 + b^2$. Clearly g is a map of $\mathbf{Z}|-1|$ into the nonnegative integers that satisfies condition A. Since

$$(ac - bd)^2 + (bc + ad)^2 = (a^2 + b^2)(c^2 + d^2),$$

we have

$$g([a, b][c, d]) = g[a, b]g[c, d], \qquad \text{for all } [a, b], [c, d] \in \mathbf{Z}|-1|.$$

As we saw in Exercise 15, Sec. 5, $\mathbf{Z}|-1|$ is a subdomain of the field $\mathbf{Q}|-1|$. Now g may be viewed as a map of $\mathbf{Q}|-1|$ into $\mathbf{Q}$. Given $[a, b], [u, v] \neq [0, 0]$ in $\mathbf{Z}|-1|$, there are $\alpha, \beta \in \mathbf{Q}$ such that

$$[a, b] = [\alpha, \beta][u, v].$$

We can then choose integers x and y such that $\alpha - x = e$, $\beta - y = f$ are rational numbers of absolute value at most $\frac{1}{2}$. Then $[x, y] \in \mathbf{Z}|-1|$,

$$[a, b] = [\alpha, \beta][u, v] = [x, y][u, v] + [e, f][u, v]$$

and $$g([e, f][u, v]) = g[eu - fv, ev + fu] = (eu - fv)^2 + (ev + fu)^2$$

$$\leq \tfrac{1}{4}[(u - v)^2 + (u + v)^2] = \tfrac{1}{2}[u^2 + v^2].$$

Hence $$g([a, b] - [x, y][u, v]) < g[u, v].$$

This completes the proof of the proposition.

The reader can prove

PROPOSITION 47 *A Euclidean domain is a principal ideal domain.*

The converse to this last proposition is false. The ring $\mathbf{Z}|23|$ is a principal ideal domain, but it is not Euclidean. The proof of this fact is beyond the scope of this book.

It can be shown that there are only finitely many square-free integers m such that $\mathbf{Z}|m|$ is Euclidean relative to the map

$$(a, b) \xrightarrow{N} a^2 + mb^2.$$

On the other hand we have seen that there are square-free m, e.g., $\mathbf{Z}|-5|$, for which $\mathbf{Z}|m|$ is not even a unique factorization domain. It is conjectured that for infinitely many m the domain $\mathbf{Z}|m|$ is a unique factorization domain, but this remains unproved. Also unanswered is the question: If $\mathbf{Z}|m|$ is not a Euclidean domain relative to the function N, can it be a Euclidean domain relative to some other weight function g?

EXERCISES 4 Prove: $\mathbf{Z}|2|$, $\mathbf{Z}|-2|$, $\mathbf{Z}|-11|$ are Euclidean domains.

5 Let $\mathscr{D} = 2^{-1}\mathbf{Z}$. Prove: $\mathscr{D}|-7|$ and $\mathscr{D}|-3|$ are Euclidean domains.

10 POLYNOMIAL FUNCTIONS

Let $x_1, \ldots, x_n$ be a set of algebraically independent indeterminates over a commutative ring $\mathscr{R}$. Each $A \in \mathscr{R}[x_1, \ldots, x_n]$ defines a map

$$\mathbf{c} \to A(\mathbf{c})$$

from $\mathscr{R}^{(n)}$ into $\mathscr{R}$. This map need not be injective, surjective, or operation-preserving. A map φ from $\mathscr{R}^{(n)}$ into $\mathscr{R}$ for which there is a polynomial $A \in \mathscr{R}[x_1, \ldots, x_n]$ such that

$$\varphi(\mathbf{c}) = A(\mathbf{c}), \qquad \mathbf{c} \in \mathscr{R}^{(n)},$$

is called a *polynomial function*, and the polynomial A is said to *represent* the function φ. A given polynomial function can be represented by several different polynomials. For example, 0 and $x^p - x$ are polynomials in $\mathbf{Z}_p[x]$ both representing the 0 map of $\mathbf{Z}_p$ into itself. We define the degree of a polynomial function φ to be the $\min\{d(A) \mid A \text{ representing } \varphi\}$.

A map that sends each $\mathbf{c} \in \mathscr{R}^{(n)}$ into the same element of $\mathscr{R}$ is called a *constant function*. A nonzero constant function is a polynomial function of degree 0. A polynomial function of degree 1 is called a *linear function*. A polynomial function of degree 2 is called a *quadratic function*.

EXERCISES 1 (A) Show that a linear function from $\mathscr{R}^{(n)}$ to $\mathscr{R}$ taking $(0, \ldots, 0)$ into 0 is an operation-preserving map. (B) Prove: A linear function from $\mathscr{R}$ to $\mathscr{R}$ is injective if $\mathscr{R}$ has no zero divisors and it is surjective if and only if $\mathscr{R}$ has a unity and any linear polynomial representing it has a unit of $\mathscr{R}$ as its leading coefficient. (C) Is a linear function from $\mathscr{R}^{(2)}$ to $\mathscr{R}$ ever injective?

2 Find polynomials other than the 0 polynomial representing the 0 map from $\mathbf{Z}_p^{(n)}$ into $\mathbf{Z}_p$.

We have seen in Sec. 3 that the set $\mathscr{T}_n(\mathscr{R})$ of all maps of $\mathscr{R}^{(n)}$ into $\mathscr{R}$ with the operations

$$\mathbf{c} \xrightarrow{\varphi+\psi} \varphi(\mathbf{c}) + \psi(\mathbf{c}),$$

$$\mathbf{c} \xrightarrow{\varphi\psi} \varphi(\mathbf{c})\psi(\mathbf{c})$$

is a ring. Let $\mathfrak{P}_n(\mathscr{R})$ be the set of those $\varphi \in \mathscr{T}_n(\mathscr{R})$ such that φ is a polynomial function. The reader can prove

PROPOSITION 48 *The set $\mathfrak{P}_n(\mathscr{R})$ is a subring of the ring $\mathscr{T}_n(\mathscr{R})$. $\mathfrak{P}_n(\mathscr{R})$ contains a subring isomorphic to $\mathscr{R}$.*

Let φ be a polynomial function from an integral domain $\mathscr{D}$ to itself. It follows from Corollary 1 to Proposition 33 that $0^{\varphi^{-1}}$ is a finite set.

If $|\mathscr{D}| = \infty$, then the product of two nonzero polynomial functions from $\mathscr{D}$ to $\mathscr{D}$ is never the zero function. Hence we obtain

PROPOSITION 49 *If $\mathscr{D}$ is an infinite integral domain, then $\mathfrak{P}_1(\mathscr{D})$ is an integral domain and $\mathfrak{P}_1(\mathscr{D})$ is a proper subring of $\mathscr{T}_1(\mathscr{D})$.*

Let

$$\mathfrak{N} = \{A \in \mathscr{R}[x_1, \ldots, x_n] \mid A \text{ represents the 0 map}\}.$$

The reader should prove

LEMMA 1 *$\mathfrak{N}$ is an ideal of $\mathscr{R}[x_1, \ldots, x_n]$.*

LEMMA 2 *$A, B \in \mathscr{R}[x_1, \ldots, x_n]$ represent the same function if and only if A and B belong to the same coset modulo $\mathfrak{N}$.*

PROPOSITION 50 *There is an isomorphism between the rings $\mathfrak{P}_n(\mathscr{R})$ and $\mathscr{R}[x_1, \ldots, x_n]/\mathfrak{N}$.*

COROLLARY 1 *If $\mathscr{R}$ is a countable ring, then $\mathfrak{P}_n(\mathscr{R})$ is a countable ring.*

Thus we have

COROLLARY 2 *If $\mathscr{R}$ is denumerable, then $\mathscr{T}_n(\mathscr{R})$ is nondenumerable and $\mathfrak{P}_n(\mathscr{R})$ is denumerable.*

This shows that, when $\mathscr{R}$ is infinite, the ring of polynomial functions can form only a small part of the ring of all functions from $\mathscr{R}$ to $\mathscr{R}$.

LEMMA 3 *If $A \in \mathfrak{N}$, then A has at least $|\mathscr{R}|$ zeros in $\mathscr{R}$.*

LEMMA 4 *If $\mathscr{R}$ is an infinite integral domain, then $\mathfrak{N} = (0)$.*

PROPOSITION 51 *If $\mathscr{D}$ is an infinite integral domain, then no two polynomials over $\mathscr{D}$ represent the same function. There is a monomorphism of $\mathscr{D}[x_1, \ldots, x_n]$ into $\mathscr{T}_n(\mathscr{D})$.*

Now suppose that $n = 1$ and that our ring is the field $\mathbf{Z}_p$. Each polynomial $A \in \mathfrak{N}$ has $\lfloor 0 \rfloor, \lfloor 1 \rfloor, \ldots, \lfloor p-1 \rfloor$ among its zeros, and hence, by Proposition 33, A must be divisible by

$$x^p - x = (x - \lfloor 0 \rfloor)(x - \lfloor 1 \rfloor) \ldots (x - \lfloor p-1 \rfloor).$$

Hence we have $\mathfrak{N} = (x^p - x)$. We now seek to generalize this to the case $\mathbf{Z}_p^{(n)}$, with $n > 1$.

As an immediate consequence of Proposition 35, we have

LEMMA 5 *If $A = \sum_{m=0}^{p-1} \sum_{\nu_1 + \cdots + \nu_n = m} a_{\nu_1 \cdots \nu_n} x_1^{\nu_1} x_2^{\nu_2} \cdots x_n^{\nu_n}$, $(\nu_i \geq 0,\ i = 1, \ldots, n)$ with $a_{\nu_1 \cdots \nu_n} \in \mathbf{Z}_p$, then A represents the 0 map from $\mathbf{Z}_p^{(n)}$ into $\mathbf{Z}_p$ if and only if each $a_{\nu_1 \cdots \nu_n} = 0$.*

Every polynomial $B \in \mathbf{Z}_p[x_1, \ldots, x_n]$ is of the form

$$B = \sum_{\nu=1}^{n} (x_\nu^p - x_\nu)C_\nu + A,$$

where $C_\nu \in \mathbf{Z}_p[x_1, \dots, x_n]$ and A is as in Lemma 5. Thus it follows that

)POSITION 52 *The set of polynomials that represent the* 0 *map of* $\mathbf{Z}_p^{(n)}$ *into* $\mathbf{Z}_p$ *is the ideal* $(x_1^p - x_1, \dots, x_n^p - x_n)$ *in* $\mathbf{Z}_p[x_1, \dots, x_n]$.

The reader should prove

COROLLARY $|\mathfrak{P}_n(\mathbf{Z}_p)| = p^{(p^n)}$.

To each $\mathbf{c} \in \mathbf{Z}_p^{(n)}$, let $\varphi_\mathbf{c}$ be the polynomial function represented by the polynomial

$$A_\mathbf{c} = \prod_{\nu=1}^{n} [1 - (x_\nu - c_\nu)^{p-1}].$$

Then
$$\varphi_\mathbf{c}(\mathbf{x}) = \begin{cases} 1 & \text{if } \mathbf{x} = \mathbf{c}, \\ 0 & \text{otherwise,} \end{cases}$$

and
$$\varphi_\mathbf{c}\varphi_\mathbf{d} = \begin{cases} \varphi_\mathbf{c} & \text{if } \mathbf{c} = \mathbf{d}, \\ 0 & \text{if } \mathbf{c} \neq \mathbf{d}. \end{cases}$$

Furthermore, if ψ is any function from $\mathbf{Z}_p^{(n)}$ to $\mathbf{Z}_p$, then ψ is represented by the polynomial

$$\sum_{\mathbf{c} \in \mathbf{Z}_p^{(n)}} \psi(\mathbf{c}) A_\mathbf{c}.$$

Thus we have proved

POSITION 53 *Every map from* $\mathbf{Z}_p^{(n)}$ *to* $\mathbf{Z}_p$ *is a polynomial map of degree at most* $p - 1$ *in any indeterminate.*

OROLLARY 1 $\mathfrak{P}_n(\mathbf{Z}_p) = \mathscr{T}_n(\mathbf{Z}_p)$.

Combining this corollary with Proposition 50, we obtain

OROLLARY 2 *There is a noninjective homomorphism of* $\mathbf{Z}_p[x_1, \dots, x_n]$ *onto* $\mathscr{T}_n(\mathbf{Z}_p)$.

The results we have proved here carry over to any finite field. Also some portions of the theory carry over to finite rings. It is interesting and perhaps somewhat unexpected to find such contrasting results for the theory of finite fields and the theory for infinite fields as is contained in the corollaries to Proposition 53 and in Proposition 51.

ERCISES 3 Prove: $\mathfrak{P}_n(\mathbf{Z}_p)$ is isomorphic to the cartesian sum of the ring $\mathbf{Z}_p$ by itself p^n times.

Prove:

4 A. For each $k \in \mathbf{Z}^+$,

$$n \to \binom{n}{k} = \frac{n(n-1)\cdots(n-k+1)}{1 \cdot 2 \cdots k}$$

is a map of $\mathbf{Z}$ into $\mathbf{Z}$.

B. For $k \geq 2$ these maps cannot be represented by polynomials over $\mathbf{Z}$.

C. If φ is a polynomial function of $\mathbf{Q}$ into $\mathbf{Q}$ such that φ maps $\mathbf{Z}$ into $\mathbf{Z}$, then there is an integer N and integers $a_0, a_1, \ldots, a_N \in \mathbf{Z}$, depending on φ, such that φ is the map

$$n \to a_0 + \sum_{k=1}^{N} a_k \binom{n}{k} = a_0 + \sum_{k=1}^{N} a_k \frac{n(n-1)\cdots(n-k+1)}{1\cdot 2\cdots k}.$$

D. There are functions of $\mathbf{Z}$ into $\mathbf{Z}$ that are not represented by polynomials over $\mathbf{Q}$.

We now prove

PROPOSITION 54 *Given a map φ of a field $\mathscr{F}$ into itself and given distinct elements $c_1, c_2, \ldots, c_m \in \mathscr{F}$, there is a polynomial A of degree less than m such that $\varphi(c_\nu) = A(c_\nu)$, $\nu = 1, 2, \ldots, m$.*

PROOF. Let A_ν be the monic polynomial over $\mathscr{F}$ such that $(x - c_\nu)A_\nu = (x - c_1) \cdots (x - c_m)$. Then $A_\nu(c_\nu) \neq 0$, and $A = \sum_{\nu=1}^{m} \frac{\varphi(c_\nu)}{A_\nu(c_\nu)} A_\nu$ has the desired properties.

Again, let $x_1, \ldots, x_n$ be a set of algebraically independent indeterminates over a ring $\mathscr{R}$. To each $\pi \in \prod_n$ there is an automorphism of $\mathscr{R}[x_1, \ldots, x_n]$ into itself given by

$$(x_\nu)^\pi = x_{\nu\pi}, \qquad \nu = 1, 2, \ldots, n,$$

$$a^\pi = a, \qquad \text{for all } a \in \mathscr{R}.$$

A polynomial $A \in \mathscr{R}[x_1, \ldots, x_n]$ is said to be *symmetric* provided $A^\pi = A$ for all $\pi \in \prod$. The polynomials $\sum_{\nu=1}^{n} x_\nu$, $\sum_{\nu=1}^{n} x_\nu^2$, $\sum_{1 \leq \nu < \mu \leq n} x_\nu x_\mu$ are examples of symmetric polynomials. The polynomials

$$\begin{aligned} S_1 &= x_1 + x_2 + \cdots + x_n, \\ S_2 &= x_1x_2 + \cdots + x_1x_n + x_2x_3 + \cdots + x_{n-1}x_n \\ &= \sum_{1 \leq \nu < \mu \leq n} x_\nu x_\mu, \\ &\vdots \\ S_k &= \sum_{1 \leq \nu_1 < \cdots < \nu_k \leq n} x_{\nu_1} x_{\nu_2} \cdots x_{\nu_k}, \\ &\vdots \\ S_n &= x_1 x_2 \cdots x_n, \end{aligned}$$

are called the *elementary symmetric polynomials* of $\mathscr{R}[x_1, \ldots, x_n]$. Clearly any polynomial in $S_1, \ldots, S_n$ over $\mathscr{R}$ is a symmetric polynomial. We now prove a converse for integral domains.

POSITION 55 *If $x_1, \ldots, x_n$ is a set of algebraically independent indeterminates over an integral domain $\mathcal{D}$, then each symmetric polynomial in $\mathcal{D}[x_1, \ldots, x_n]$ is a polynomial in $S_1, \ldots, S_n$ with coefficients in $\mathcal{D}$.*

PROOF. We may assume that the indeterminates are a set of algebraically independent indeterminates over the quotient field $\mathcal{Q}$ of $\mathcal{D}$. The proof will be by induction on n and on the degree of the symmetric polynomial. If $n = 1$, then $S_1 = x_1$, and any polynomial in $\mathcal{D}[x_1]$ is a polynomial in $\mathcal{D}[S_1]$. Also, if $d(A) = 0$, then A is trivially a polynomial in $S_1, \ldots, S_n$. Assume that the proposition is true for rings with less than n indeterminates and for all polynomials of degree less than d from $\mathcal{D}[x_1, \ldots, x_n]$. Let A be a symmetric polynomial of degree d from $\mathcal{D}[x_1, \ldots, x_n]$. We can write

$$A = A' + x_n A'',$$

where $A' \in \mathcal{D}[x_1, \ldots, x_{n-1}]$ and $A'' \in \mathcal{D}[x_1, \ldots, x_n]$. Since $A^\pi = A$ for all $\pi \in \prod_n$, we must have $(A')^\pi = A'$ for all $\pi \in \prod_{n-1}$. Hence, by the induction hypothesis A' is a polynomial in $S'_1 = x_1 + \cdots + x_{n-1}, \ldots, S'_{n-1} = x_1 x_2 \cdots x_{n-1}$. Let B be the polynomial obtained by replacing each S'_ν in A' by S_ν. We have $d(B) = d(A') \le d(A)$. By construction, B is a symmetric polynomial in $\mathcal{D}[x_1, \ldots, x_n]$, as is $C = A - B$. Now $B = A' + x_n B''$, where $B'' \in \mathcal{D}[x_1, \ldots, x_n]$. Thus, we see that $C = x_n D$, $D \in \mathcal{D}[x_1, \ldots, x_n]$. Since C is symmetric, each of $x_1, x_2, \ldots, x_n$ must be a factor of C. But $x_1, \ldots, x_n$ are a set of nonassociate irreducible polynomials in $\mathcal{Q}[x_1, \ldots, x_n]$, and since $\mathcal{Q}[x_1, \ldots, x_n]$ is a unique factorization domain, we have

$$C = x_1 x_2 \cdots x_n E = S_n E, \qquad \text{where } E \in \mathcal{Q}[x_1, \ldots, x_n].$$

As C and $S_n \in \mathcal{D}[x_1, \ldots, x_n]$, we have $E \in \mathcal{D}[x_1, \ldots, x_n]$. Since C and S_n are symmetric, E must also be symmetric. Since $d(E) < d(C) \le d(A)$, it follows from the induction hypothesis that E is a polynomial in $S_1, \ldots, S_n$. But then A is also a polynomial in $S_1, \ldots, S_n$. This completes the proof of the proposition.

POSITION 56 *If a monic polynomial $A \in \mathcal{D}[x]$ splits into a product of distinct linear factors over a field $\mathcal{E} \supset \mathcal{D}$, say $A = \prod_{i=1}^{n} (x - \alpha_i)$, and if $B \in \mathcal{D}[x_1, \ldots, x_n]$ is a symmetric polynomial, then $B(\alpha_1, \ldots, \alpha_n) \in \mathcal{D}$.*

The proof is left to the reader.

ERCISES 5 Express $\sum_{i=1}^{n} x_i^2$ and $\sum_{i=1}^{n} x_i^3$ as polynomials in $S_1, S_2, \ldots, S_n$.

6 Prove: $\{S_1, S_2, \ldots, S_n\}$ is a set of algebraically independent indeterminates over $\mathcal{D}$.

11 TESTS FOR IRREDUCIBILITY

As we saw earlier, in a finite length of time, one can check whether a given polynomial over a finite ring is irreducible over that ring. The method failed when the ring was infinite. We shall now give Kronecker's method for determining, in a finite length of time, whether a polynomial in one indeterminate with integer coefficients is irreducible. Before giving the method, we recall that each polynomial A over $\mathbf{Q}$ is a constant multiple of a primitive polynomial A' over $\mathbf{Z}$. Also, the primitive irreducible polynomials over $\mathbf{Z}$ are exactly a set of representatives of the classes of associate primes of $\mathbf{Q}[x]$. It follows that A is irreducible over $\mathbf{Q}$ if and only if A' is irreducible over $\mathbf{Z}$. Thus the method also resolves the question of irreducibility over the field of rational numbers.

If a polynomial A of degree d over $\mathbf{Z}$ is reducible over $\mathbf{Z}$, it must have a factor of degree at most $d/2$ that is irreducible over $\mathbf{Z}$. If B is such a factor, then for each $n \in \mathbf{Z}$, $B(n)$ and $A(n)$ are integers such that $B(n)$ is a divisor of $A(n)$.

By Proposition 33 there are infinitely many $n \in \mathbf{Z}$ for which $A(n) \neq 0$. Choose $e + 1$ such integers ($e \leq d/2 < e + 1$), say $n_0, n_1, \ldots, n_e$. Then, for each ν, $B(n_\nu)$ must be one of the finite set $\mathscr{A}_\nu = \{a_{\nu 1}, \ldots, a_{\nu N_\nu}\}$ of integral divisors of $A(n_\nu)$. Next form all possible sequences

$$(a_{o\mu_o}, a_{1\mu_1}, \ldots, a_{e\mu_e}),$$

where $a_{\nu\mu_\nu} \in \mathscr{A}_\nu$. By Propositions 51 and 54, to each sequence there is a unique polynomial $B \in \mathbf{Q}[x]$, of degree at most e, such that $B(n_\nu) = a_{\nu\mu_\nu}$. From this set of polynomials we can discard those which do not have integer coefficients. The remaining polynomials are finite in number and include among them all the irreducible factors of the polynomial A. To determine whether A is reducible, one need only check whether any of these constructed polynomials divide A.

The method we have described is certainly effective in determining the irreducibility of a polynomial over $\mathbf{Z}$. To cut down on the time necessary for the determination of the answer, one attempts to select the n_ν so that $A(n_\nu)$ has very few integral divisors. Even so, the method can be extremely tedious.

EXERCISES 1 Determine which, if any, of the following are irreducible over $\mathbf{Z}$:

$$x^4 - 6x^2 + x - 10, \qquad x^5 + x + 1, \qquad x^4 - 17x^2 + 8x + 5.$$

2 If $\mathscr{D}$ is a unique factorization domain, show that Kronecker's method can be adopted for testing for the irreducibility of polynomials over $\mathscr{D}$.

3 Prove that a polynomial in $\mathbf{Z}[x_1, x_2]$ is irreducible over $\mathbf{Z}$ if and only if it is a primitive irreducible polynomial in x_2 over the domain $\mathbf{Z}[x_1]$.

Since Kronecker's method of testing for irreducibility of a polynomial can be exceedingly tedious, it is of value to describe a second method. The second method need not be quicker, but in many cases it is.

Let x be an indeterminate over $\mathbf{Z}$, and for each $m \in \mathbf{Z}^+$ let x_m be an indeterminate over $\mathbf{Z}_m$. There is a homomorphism $\sigma(m)$ of $\mathbf{Z}[x]$ onto $\mathbf{Z}_m[x_m]$, where

$$x^{\sigma(m)} = x_m \text{ and } a^{\sigma(m)} = a + m\mathbf{Z} = \lfloor a \rfloor \text{ for } a \in \mathbf{Z}.$$

Then $d(A^{\sigma(m)}) \leq d(A)$. If A, B, C are polynomials over $\mathbf{Z}$ of positive degree such that $A = BC$, then $A^{\sigma(m)} = B^{\sigma(m)}C^{\sigma(m)}$. If, further, $d(A^{\sigma(m)}) = d(A)$, then $B^{\sigma(m)}$ and $C^{\sigma(m)}$ are of positive degree, and $A^{\sigma(m)}$ is reducible in $\mathbf{Z}_m[x_m]$. Thus we have

)POSITION 57 *If $A \in \mathbf{Z}[x]$ such that $d(A^{\sigma(m)}) = d(A)$ and $A^{\sigma(m)}$ is irreducible over $\mathbf{Z}_m$, then A is irreducible over $\mathbf{Z}$.*

We need the assumption $d(A^{\sigma(m)}) = d(A)$, for consider $A = 5x^2 + 9x - 2 = (5x - 1)(x + 2)$ then $A^{\sigma(5)} = 4x_5 - 2$, which is irreducible over $\mathbf{Z}_5$. We also note that A can be irreducible although $A^{\sigma(m)}$ is reducible; e.g., $A = x^2 + x + 1$, $A^{\sigma(3)} = (x_3 - 1)^2$.

We now show how this proposition may be used to test for irreducibility over $\mathbf{Z}$. Let $A = a_0 + \cdots + a_4x^4$. Suppose $2 \nmid a_4$. If $A^{\sigma(2)}$ is reducible, it must be divisible by an irreducible polynomial over $\mathbf{Z}_2$ of degree not exceeding 2. The only irreducible polynomials over $\mathbf{Z}_2$ of degree at most 2 are

$$x, \qquad x + 1, \qquad x^2 + x + 1.$$

If $A^{\sigma(2)}$ is not divisible in $\mathbf{Z}_2[x]$ by any of these, then A is irreducible over $\mathbf{Z}$. If $A^{\sigma(2)}$ is reducible, let p be an odd prime not dividing a_4. Again, we would list the irreducible polynomials over $\mathbf{Z}_p$ of degree at most 2 and check if any were a factor of $A^{\sigma(p)}$. If $A^{\sigma(p)}$ is irreducible over $\mathbf{Z}_p$, then A is irreducible over $\mathbf{Z}$. If $A^{\sigma(p)}$ is reducible over $\mathbf{Z}_p$, we can draw no conclusion. When that occurs, we should either choose a different prime or try p^2. One case that is nicely handled by going to p^2 is usually referred to as *Eisenstein's criteria for irreducibility*, and we state it as

)POSITION 58 *If $A = a_0 + a_1x + \cdots + a_nx^n \in \mathbf{Z}[x]$ and p is a prime such that $p \mid a_0$, $p \mid a_1, \ldots, p \mid a_{n-1}, p \nmid a_n, p^2 \nmid a_0$, then A is irreducible over $\mathbf{Z}$.*

PROOF. We shall prove $A^{\sigma(p^2)}$ is irreducible over $\mathbf{Z}_{p^2}$. Suppose $A^{\sigma(p^2)} = B^*C^*$, where B^*, C^* have coefficients in $\mathbf{Z}_{p^2}$. Then there exist polynomials B, C, $D \in \mathbf{Z}[x]$ such that

$$A = BC + p^2D,$$

where $\deg(B)\deg(C) > 0$, and the coefficients of B and C are from $\{0, 1, \ldots, p^2 - 1\}$. Let

$$B = b_0 + \cdots + b_s x^s, \qquad C = c_0 + \cdots + c_t x^t,$$

where $b_s c_t \neq 0$. Since $p \nmid a_n$, we have $p \nmid b_s$, $p \nmid c_t$, and $s + t = n$. Since $p \mid a_0$, $p^2 \nmid a_0$, we see that p divides exactly one of b_0 and c_0. Say $p \mid b_0$. Let $r = \min\{v \mid p \nmid b_v\}$. Then $1 \leq r \leq s < n$ and

$$a_r = p^2 d_r + \sum_{v=0}^{r} b_{r-v} c_v,$$

and this implies that $p \mid b_r c_0$, contrary to previous evidence.

Obviously we could list a long array of similar criteria for irreducibility. However, it seems preferable to recommend to the reader that he understand the basic principle and that in any given case he should experiment with different choices of m.

There is a serious drawback to the method we have been describing. It is true that, if A is irreducible over $\mathbf{Z}$, then there is an m (actually a power of some prime) such that $A^{\sigma(m)}$ is irreducible over $\mathbf{Z}_m$ and $d(A) = d(A^{\sigma(m)})$. Thus this method should enable one to decide the question of the irreducibility of A over $\mathbf{Z}$. However, this m may need to be a very large power of a large prime, and it may be exceedingly hard to find. There are polynomials, e.g.; $A = x^4 + 1$, that are irreducible over $\mathbf{Z}$; yet $A^{\sigma(p)}$ is reducible over $\mathbf{Z}_p$ for all primes p.† There does not seem to be any rule or procedure by which we could, on inspection of A, select a finite (possibly very large) set $\{m_1, \ldots, m_k\}$ such that A is irreducible if and only if one of the $A^{\sigma(m_v)}$ is irreducible. Hence, given A, we cannot, as in Kronecker's method, be sure that we will know if A is irreducible after making a certain selected finite number of trials. However, the method is of value in that in many cases one can resolve the irreducibility question in a few minutes. Usually after a short period of experimentation, a satisfactory m can be found.

In testing for irreducibility it is often of value to make a "change of variable" in order to simplify the work. We shall use the following:

PROPOSITION 59 *Let $\mathscr{D}$ be an integral domain. Suppose θ is a homomorphism of $\mathscr{D}[x]$ into itself such that $a^\theta = a$, $a \in \mathscr{D}$, and $x^\theta \notin \mathscr{D}$. If A^θ is an irreducible polynomial in x over $\mathscr{D}$, then A is irreducible over $\mathscr{D}$.*

PROOF. If $B \in \mathscr{D}[x]$ is of positive degree in x, then B^θ is a polynomial in x of positive degree. If $A = BC$, where B, C are polynomials of

† $x^4 + 1 = (x^2 + 1)^2 - 2x^2 = (x^2 - 1)^2 + 2x^2$. This polynomial will factor over $\mathbf{Z}_p$ unless $-1, -2$, and 2 are all nonsquares in $\mathbf{Z}_p$. If p is odd, the set of squares is a multiplicative subgroup of order $(p - 1)/2$. Hence there is a nonzero element a in $\mathbf{Z}_p$ such that each nonsquare can be expressed as ax^2. But then $-1, -2$, and 2 cannot all be nonsquares. The reader can check that $x^4 + 1$ is irreducible over Z_4.

positive degree over $\mathscr{D}$, then $A^\theta = B^\theta C^\theta$, and hence A^θ is a reducible polynomial in $\mathscr{D}[x]$.

We can now apply Propositions 58 and 59 to obtain

COROLLARY *If p is an odd prime, then $1 + x + \cdots + x^{p-1}$ is irreducible over* $\mathbf{Z}$.

PROOF. Let $A = 1 + x + \cdots + x^{p-1}$, and suppose $x^\theta = x + 1$. As $(x-1)A = x^p - 1$, we find

$$xA^\theta = (x+1)^p - 1 = x^p + px^{p-1} + \binom{p}{2}x^{p-2} + \cdots + \binom{p}{p-1}x.$$

Hence
$$A^\theta = x^{p-1} + px^{p-2} + \cdots + p$$

satisfies the hypothesis of Proposition 58 and hence is irreducible over $\mathbf{Z}$. Then, by Proposition 59, we have that A is irreducible over $\mathbf{Z}$.

Finally we note one other way to use the maps $\sigma(m)$ in checking on the irreducibility of a polynomial A. Suppose $A = B_1B_2 \cdots B_r$, where the B_ν are irreducible over $\mathbf{Z}$. Suppose further that $A^{\sigma(m)} = C_1C_2 \cdots C_s$, where the C_ν are irreducible over $\mathbf{Z}_m$ such that $d(A^{\sigma(m)}) = d(A)$. Then there must exist $\mathscr{E}_{\nu\mu} = 0$ or 1 such that

$$\sum_{\mu=1}^{r} \mathscr{E}_{\nu\mu} = 1, \quad \text{and} \quad \sum_{\nu=1}^{s} \mathscr{E}_{\nu\mu} d(C_\nu) = d(B_\mu), \qquad \mu = 1, 2, \ldots, r.$$

We now show by way of example how this information can be used to prove A is irreducible. Suppose that $m \neq n$, that $A^{\sigma(m)}$ splits into the product of two irreducible factors of degree 3 and one of degree 2, and that $A^{\sigma(n)}$ splits into the product of two irreducible factors of degree 4. Let B be an irreducible factor of A. Then there must exist $\mathscr{E}_\nu$, $\mathscr{E}'_\nu = 0$ or 1 such that

$$d(B) = 3\mathscr{E}_1 + 3\mathscr{E}_2 + 2\mathscr{E}_3 = 4\mathscr{E}'_1 + 4\mathscr{E}'_2.$$

Now $3\mathscr{E}_1 + 3\mathscr{E}_2 + 2\mathscr{E}_3$ assumes the values $0, 2, 3, 5, 6, 8$, and $4\mathscr{E}'_1 + 4\mathscr{E}'_2$ assumes the values $0, 4, 8$. Hence $d(B) = 8$, and consequently A is irreducible over $\mathbf{Z}$.

ERCISES 4 Determine the irreducibility over $\mathbf{Z}$ of the following:

$$x^2 + 6x^2 + 5x + 25,$$

$$x^5 - x^2 + 11,$$

$$x^4 + 7x + 49,$$

$$x^4 + 4x^3 + 17x^2 + 3x + 1,$$

$$x^4 + 6x^2 + x - 10,$$

$$x^k + px^2 + pq.$$

5 A. Show that Eisenstein's criteria can be applied to any unique factorization domain.
B. Show that $y^5 + xy^2 + x^3y + x$ is irreducible over $\mathbf{Z}$.
C. Show that $x^{10} + y^2 - 1$ is irreducible over $\mathbf{Z}$.

6 Let A be a polynomial of degree $n > k$. Let p be a prime such that $p \nmid a_n a_k$, $p \mid a_\nu$ for $0 \le \nu < k$, $p^2 \nmid a_0$. Show that A has at least one irreducible factor whose degree is at least k.

12 FIELD EXTENSIONS

If $\mathcal{M}$ is a proper ideal of a ring $\mathcal{R}$ such that $\mathcal{M}$ is not properly contained in any other proper ideal of $\mathcal{R}$, we say that $\mathcal{M}$ is a *maximal ideal* of $\mathcal{R}$. The *maximal ideals* of $\mathbf{Z}$ are exactly the ideals (p), where p is a prime. If x is an indeterminate over a field $\mathcal{F}$, then the maximal ideals of $\mathcal{F}[x]$ are exactly the ideals (P), where P is an irreducible polynomial.

An ideal in a unique factorization domain $\mathcal{D}$ generated by a prime π of $\mathcal{D}$ has the property that, when $ab \in (\pi)$, then at least one of a and b is in (π). Extending this idea, we shall say that an ideal $\mathfrak{p}$ of a ring $\mathcal{R}$ is a *prime ideal* if, whenever $ab \in \mathfrak{p}$ at least one of $a, b \in \mathfrak{p}$. The zero ideal and the whole ring are trivially prime ideals. Prime ideals are not always generated by a prime element; e.g., the ideal (x, y) in $\mathbf{Z}[x, y]$ is a prime ideal and cannot be generated by a single element.

Proper prime ideals and maximal ideals are characterized by

PROPOSITION 60 *Let $\mathcal{R}$ be a commutative ring with unity containing a proper ideal $\mathcal{I}$. $\mathcal{I}$ is a prime ideal if and only if $\mathcal{R}/\mathcal{I}$ is an integral domain. $\mathcal{I}$ is a maximal ideal if and only if $\mathcal{R}/\mathcal{I}$ is a field.*

PROOF. Clearly $\mathcal{R}/\mathcal{I}$ is a nonzero commutative ring with unity. Suppose $\mathcal{I}$ is a prime ideal. If $(a + \mathcal{I})(b + \mathcal{I}) = \mathcal{I}$, then $ab \in \mathcal{I}$, and hence either $a + \mathcal{I}$ or $b + \mathcal{I}$ is $\mathcal{I}$. It follows that $\mathcal{R}/\mathcal{I}$ is an integral domain. Conversely, if $\mathcal{R}/\mathcal{I}$ is an integral domain and $ab \in \mathcal{I}$, then $(a + \mathcal{I})(b + \mathcal{I}) = \mathcal{I}$. Consequently either $a + \mathcal{I} \subset \mathcal{I}$ or $b + \mathcal{I} \subset \mathcal{I}$; i.e., at least one of $a, b \in \mathcal{I}$.

Suppose $\mathcal{I}$ is a maximal ideal. If $a \notin \mathcal{I}$, then $(\mathcal{I}, a) = \mathcal{R} = (1)$. Hence there is an $x \in \mathcal{R}$ and $y \in \mathcal{I}$ so that $y + ax = 1$. It follows that $(a + \mathcal{I})(x + \mathcal{I}) = 1 + \mathcal{I}$. Thus we have shown that each nonzero residue class $a + \mathcal{I}$ has a reciprocal in $\mathcal{R}/\mathcal{I}$; hence $\mathcal{R}/\mathcal{I}$ is a field.

Finally, suppose $\mathcal{R}/\mathcal{I}$ is a field. By Proposition 16, $\mathcal{R}/\mathcal{I}$ has no proper ideals. On the other hand if $\mathcal{I} \subsetneq \mathcal{I}' \subsetneq \mathcal{R}$, then $\mathcal{I}'/\mathcal{I}$ is a proper ideal of $\mathcal{R}/\mathcal{I}$. Since this is contradictory, we must have that $\mathcal{I}$ is a maximal ideal in $\mathcal{R}$.

Since a field is always an integral domain, we have

COROLLARY *In a commutative ring with unity, every maximal ideal is a prime ideal.*

The converse of this corollary is false. For example, if x is an indeterminate over $\mathbf{Z}$, then (x) is a prime ideal in $\mathbf{Z}[x]$, but it is not a maximal ideal, since

$$(x) \subsetneqq (2, x) \subsetneqq \mathbf{Z}[x].$$

Let x be an indeterminate over a field $\mathscr{F}$. As we noted above, if M is an irreducible polynomial over $\mathscr{F}$, then (M) is a maximal ideal in $\mathscr{F}[x]$, and hence, by Proposition 60, $\mathscr{F}[x]/(M)$ is a field. The map

$$a \to a + (M)$$

is a monomorphism of $\mathscr{F}$ into $\mathscr{F}[x]/(M)$. Hence, by Proposition 7, there is a field $\mathscr{E} \supset \mathscr{F}$ such that $\mathscr{E}$ is isomorphic to $\mathscr{F}[x]/(M)$.

If $M = m_0 + m_1 x + \cdots + m_k x^k$, then

$$\sum_{\nu=0}^{k} (m_\nu + (M))(x + (M))^\nu = \sum_{\nu=0}^{k} m_\nu x^\nu + (M) = 0 + (M).$$

Consequently, if $\alpha \in \mathscr{E}$ is the image of $x + (M)$ under the isomorphism, then

$$\sum_{\nu=0}^{k} m_\nu \alpha^\nu = 0.$$

Thus we have shown

LEMMA 1 *If M is an irreducible polynomial in $\mathscr{F}[x]$, then there is a field $\mathscr{E} \supset \mathscr{F}$ that contains a zero of M.*

If M is of degree 1, then $\mathscr{E} = \mathscr{F}$.

Since each polynomial of positive degree has an irreducible factor, we have proved

)POSITION 61 *If M is a polynomial of positive degree in $\mathscr{F}[x]$, then there is a field $\mathscr{E} \supset \mathscr{F}$ that contains a zero of M.*

Now suppose $M, \mathscr{E}, \mathscr{F}$ are as in Proposition 61. Then $M = (x - \alpha_1)M_1$, where α_1 and the coefficients of M_1 are in $\mathscr{E}$. Applying Proposition 61 to M_1 and $\mathscr{E}$, we see there is a field $\mathscr{E}_2 \supset \mathscr{E} \supset \mathscr{F}$ such that

$$M = (x - \alpha_1)(x - \alpha_2)M_2,$$

where α_1, α_2, and the coefficients of M_2 are in $\mathscr{E}_2$. Continuing this process sufficiently many times, we obtain a field $\mathscr{K} \supset \mathscr{F}$ such that M splits into a product of linear factors over $\mathscr{K}$.

If a polynomial M with coefficients in $\mathscr{F}$ splits into a product of linear factors over a field $\mathscr{K} \supset \mathscr{F}$, then $\mathscr{K}$ is said to be *a splitting field over $\mathscr{F}$ for the polynomial M*. If $\mathscr{K}$ is a splitting field over $\mathscr{F}$ for M, and no proper subfield of $\mathscr{K}$ is, then $\mathscr{K}$ is said to be *the* splitting field over $\mathscr{F}$ of M. We shall show that the splitting field over $\mathscr{F}$ of a polynomial is unique to within an isomorphism that is the identity map on $\mathscr{F}$ (see Proposition 65).

If $\mathscr{E} \supset \mathscr{F}$ and $\alpha \in \mathscr{E}$, let

$$\mathscr{I}_\alpha = \{M \in \mathscr{F}[x] \mid M(\alpha) = 0\}.$$

Clearly $\mathscr{I}_\alpha$ is an ideal. If $\mathscr{I}_\alpha = (0)$, then α is a *transcendental* over $\mathscr{F}$. If $\mathscr{I}_\alpha \neq 0$, then α is *algebraic* over $\mathscr{F}$, and since $\mathscr{F}[x]$ is a principal ideal domain, there is a monic polynomial A such that $\mathscr{I}_\alpha = (A)$. The polynomial A is the monic polynomial over $\mathscr{F}$ of least degree having α as a zero, and therefore we speak of A as the *minimal polynomial for* α over $\mathscr{F}$. The reader can prove

LEMMA 2 *If α is algebraic over $\mathscr{F}$, then the minimal polynomial for α over $\mathscr{F}$ is irreducible over $\mathscr{F}$.*

LEMMA 3 *If B is a monic irreducible polynomial over $\mathscr{F}$ and $\alpha \in \mathscr{E}$ is such that* $B(\alpha) = 0$, *then B is the minimal polynomial for α over $\mathscr{F}$.*

Let $\mathscr{F}[\alpha]$ be the collection of polynomials in α over $\mathscr{F}$. Then $\mathscr{F}[\alpha]$ is a subdomain of $\mathscr{E}$. Suppose $\mathscr{I}_\alpha = (A) \neq 0$, where

$$A = x^n + a_{n-1}x^{n-1} + \cdots + a_0 \neq 0.$$

Then
$$\alpha^n = -a_0 - a_1\alpha - \cdots - -a_{n-1}\alpha^{n-1},$$

and consequently each $\beta \in \mathscr{F}[\alpha]$ can be expressed as a polynomial in α over $\mathscr{F}$ of degree less than n. Each $\beta \in \mathscr{F}[\alpha]$ can be so represented in only one way, for if

$$\beta = B(\alpha) = C(\alpha), \qquad \text{with } \deg B < n, \deg C < n,$$

then $B - C \in \mathscr{I}_\alpha$. But then $A|(B - C)$, and hence $B - C = 0$.

If $0 \neq \beta \in \mathscr{F}[\alpha]$, then $\beta = B(\alpha)$ for some $B \in \mathscr{F}[x]$ with $d(B) < n$. Then $(B, A) = 1$; consequently (see Proposition 38) there are polynomials $U, V \in \mathscr{F}[x]$ such that

$$UA + VB = 1, \qquad d(V) < d(A) = n.$$

But then
$$V(\alpha)B(\alpha) = 1,$$

and we see that β has a multiplicative inverse in $\mathscr{F}[\alpha]$. Hence $\mathscr{F}[\alpha]$ is a field. Since $\mathscr{F}[\alpha]$ is the smallest ring containing $\mathscr{F}$ and α, $\mathscr{F}[\alpha]$ is the minimal field containing $\mathscr{F}$ and α.

We have the map

$$\beta = B(\alpha) \to B + (A) = B + \mathscr{I}_\alpha$$

of $\mathscr{F}[\alpha]$ onto $\mathscr{F}[x]/\mathscr{I}_\alpha$. The reader can quickly verify that this is an isomorphism, thus proving

PROPOSITION 62 *If α is algebraic over $\mathscr{F}$ and A is the minimal polynomial for α over $\mathscr{F}$, then there is an isomorphism σ of $\mathscr{F}[\alpha]$ onto $\mathscr{F}[x]/(A)$ such that $a^\sigma =$* $a + (A)$, for all $a \in \mathscr{F}$.

Combining Lemma 3 and Proposition 62, we obtain

COROLLARY *If B is an irreducible polynomial over $\mathscr{F}$ and if α and β are zeros of B, then there is an isomorphism φ of $\mathscr{F}[\alpha]$ onto $\mathscr{F}[\beta]$ such that $\alpha^\varphi = \beta$ and $a^\varphi = a$, for all $a \in \mathscr{F}$.*

The reader can now prove

PROPOSITION 63 *Let φ be an isomorphism of a field $\mathscr{F}_1$ onto $\mathscr{F}_2$. Suppose $\mathscr{E}_1 \supset \mathscr{F}_1$ and $\mathscr{E}_2 \supset \mathscr{F}_2$. Let $A_1 = a_0 + \cdots + a_n x^n$ be an irreducible polynomial over $\mathscr{F}_1$, and let $A_2 = a_0{}^\varphi + \cdots + a_n{}^\varphi x^n$. Then A_2 is an irreducible polynomial over $\mathscr{F}_2$. Suppose $\alpha_\nu \in \mathscr{E}_\nu$ is a zero of A_ν, $(\nu = 1, 2)$. Then there is an isomorphism Φ of $\mathscr{F}_1[\alpha_1]$ onto $\mathscr{F}_2[\alpha_2]$ such that $\operatorname{res}_{\mathscr{F}_1}\Phi = \varphi$ and $\alpha_1{}^\Phi = \alpha_2$.*

Suppose $\alpha_1, \alpha_2 \in \mathscr{E}$ are algebraic over $\mathscr{F}$; then α_2 is algebraic over the field $\mathscr{F}[\alpha_1]$, and hence $\mathscr{F}[\alpha_1][\alpha_2]$ is a field; $\mathscr{F}[\alpha_1, \alpha_2]$, the minimal field containing α_1, α_2, and $\mathscr{F}$. The elements of $\mathscr{F}[\alpha_1, \alpha_2]$ are polynomials in α_1 and α_2 over $\mathscr{F}$. Similarly, if $\alpha_1, \alpha_2, \ldots, \alpha_n \in \mathscr{E}$ are each algebraic over $\mathscr{F}$, then the ring of polynomials in $\alpha_1, \ldots, \alpha_n$ over $\mathscr{F}$ is a field.

Let $\mathscr{E}$ be a splitting field of a polynomial M (over a field $\mathscr{F}$). Then there exist $\alpha_1, \ldots, \alpha_n \in \mathscr{E}$ such that

$$M = a(x - \alpha_1)\cdots(x - \alpha_n), \qquad 0 \neq a \in \mathscr{F}.$$

Since $\mathscr{E}[x]$ is a unique factorization domain, there are no other $\alpha \in \mathscr{E}$ such that $M(\alpha) = 0$. The field

$$\mathscr{K} = \mathscr{F}[\alpha_1, \ldots, \alpha_n]$$

is clearly a splitting field for M. If $\mathscr{E}' \subset \mathscr{E}$ were a splitting field for M, then $\alpha_1, \ldots, \alpha_n \in \mathscr{E}'$, and hence $\mathscr{K} \subset \mathscr{E}'$. Consequently $\mathscr{K}$ is the minimal subfield of $\mathscr{E}$ that splits M.

Let $\mathscr{E}$ be a field containing $\mathscr{F}$. If $\alpha_1, \alpha_2, \ldots, \alpha_n \in \mathscr{E}$ are the zeros of an irreducible polynomial M over a field $\mathscr{F}$, then $\alpha_1, \ldots, \alpha_n$ are said to be *conjugate* to one another (over $\mathscr{F}$).

If A_1, A_2 are related as in Proposition 63, we write $A_1{}^\varphi = A_2$.

PROPOSITION 64 *Let φ be an isomorphism of a field $\mathscr{F}_1$ onto a field $\mathscr{F}_2$. Let M_1 be a polynomial of positive degree over $\mathscr{F}_1$, and let $M_2 = M_1{}^\varphi$. Suppose that $\mathscr{E}_\nu$ is a splitting field over $\mathscr{F}_\nu$ for M_ν and that $\mathscr{K}_\nu$ is the unique minimal subfield of $\mathscr{E}_\nu$ that contains $\mathscr{F}_\nu$ and splits M_ν. There is an isomorphism Φ of $\mathscr{K}_1$ onto $\mathscr{K}_2$ such that $\operatorname{res}_{\mathscr{F}_1}\Phi = \varphi$.*

PROOF. The proof is by induction on $d(M_1)$. If $d(M_1) = 1$, then M_1 has but one zero, say α_1, and $\alpha_1 \in \mathscr{F}_1$, whence $\mathscr{K}_1 = \mathscr{F}_1$. Similarly $\mathscr{K}_2 = \mathscr{F}_2$, and we may take $\Phi = \varphi$.

Now suppose the proposition is true for polynomials of degree less than n. Suppose $d(M_1) = n$. Let N_1 be an irreducible (over $\mathscr{F}_1$) factor of M_1. Then $M_1 = N_1 W_1$ and $M_2 = N_2 W_2$, where $N_1{}^\varphi = N_2$, $W_1{}^\varphi = W_2$, and N_2 is irreducible over $\mathscr{F}_2$. By hypothesis there are $\alpha_\nu \in \mathscr{E}_\nu$ such that $N_\nu(\alpha_\nu) = 0$, $(\nu = 1, 2)$. By Proposition 63 there is an isomorphism Φ' of $\mathscr{F}_1[\alpha_1]$ onto $\mathscr{F}_2[\alpha_2]$ with $\text{res}_{\mathscr{F}_1} \Phi' = \varphi$. Now $N_\nu = (x - \alpha_\nu)U_\nu$, $(\nu = 1, 2)$, where U_ν has coefficients in $\mathscr{F}_\nu[\alpha_\nu]$ and $U_1^{\Phi'} = U_2$. Then $M_\nu = (x - \alpha_\nu)V_\nu$, where V_ν have coefficients in $\mathscr{F}_\nu[\alpha_\nu]$, $d(V_\nu) = n - 1$, and $V_1^{\Phi'} = V_2$. Now, $\mathscr{F}_1[\alpha_1]$ is isomorphic to $\mathscr{F}_2[\alpha_2]$, $\mathscr{K}_\nu \supset \mathscr{F}_\nu[\alpha_\nu]$ and $\mathscr{K}_\nu$ is the minimal field in $\mathscr{E}_\nu$ containing $\mathscr{F}_\nu[\alpha_\nu]$ that splits the polynomial V_ν. Hence, by the induction assumption, there is an isomorphism Φ of $\mathscr{K}_1$ onto $\mathscr{K}_2$ such that $\text{res}_{\mathscr{F}_1[\alpha_1]} \Phi = \Phi'$. But then $\text{res}_{\mathscr{F}_1} \Phi = \varphi$. This proves the proposition.

If we now take $\mathscr{F}_1 = \mathscr{F}_2$ and take φ to be the identity map, we obtain

PROPOSITION 65 *Let M be a polynomial of positive degree over a field $\mathscr{F}$. Let $\mathscr{K}_1$, $\mathscr{K}_2$ be splitting fields for M such that no proper subfield of $\mathscr{K}_\nu$, $(\nu = 1, 2)$ is a splitting field for M. Then there is an isomorphism Φ of $\mathscr{K}_1$ onto $\mathscr{K}_2$ such that* $\text{res}_{\mathscr{F}} \Phi$ *is the identity map.*

We have shown that the splitting field over $\mathscr{F}$ of a polynomial M is unique to within isomorphism.

EXERCISE 1 Let m be a square-free integer. Prove:

A. $\mathbf{Q}|m|$ is isomorphic to $\mathbf{Q}[x]/(x^2 - m)$.

B. $\mathbf{Q}|m|$ is a splitting field for the polynomial $x^2 - [m, 0]$.

If $\mathscr{K}$ is a minimal splitting field for $x^2 - m$, where m is a nonsquare in $\mathscr{F}$, it is customary to designate the zeros of $x^2 - m$ in $\mathscr{K}$ by $\pm\sqrt{m}$. In that case $\mathscr{K} = \mathscr{F}[\sqrt{m}]$, and $\mathscr{F}|m|$ is isomorphic to $\mathscr{F}[\sqrt{m}]$. We caution the reader that $\mathbf{Q}[\sqrt{4}] = \mathbf{Q}$ is not isomorphic to $\mathbf{Q}|4|$; in fact the latter is not even an integral domain. It is also customary to designate $\sqrt{-1}$ by i.

13 ALGEBRAIC CLOSURE

Given a field $\mathscr{F}$, a field $\mathscr{E}$ that is a splitting field for all the polynomials of positive degree over $\mathscr{F}$ is said to be an *algebraic closure for $\mathscr{F}$*. A field $\mathscr{F}$ is said to be *algebraically closed* if it is an algebraic closure for itself. We shall prove

THEOREM 2 *A countable field has an algebraic closure.*

PROOF. Let $\mathscr{F}$ be a countable field. Then the set of all polynomials over $\mathscr{F}$ is a denumerable set, and hence the monic irreducible polynomials over $\mathscr{F}$ can be arranged in a denumerable sequence:

$$P_1, P_2, P_3, \ldots, P_n, \ldots .$$

Let $\mathscr{F}_1$ be a minimal splitting field for P_1 containing $\mathscr{F}$. We can view P_2 as a polynomial over $\mathscr{F}_1$ and let $\mathscr{F}_2$ be a minimal splitting field for P_2 containing $\mathscr{F}_1$. We continue, inductively, to define the fields $\mathscr{F}_\nu$. If $\mathscr{F}_1, \ldots, \mathscr{F}_{r-1}$ have been defined, view P_r as a polynomial over $\mathscr{F}_{r-1}$ and let $\mathscr{F}_r$ be a minimal splitting field for P_r containing $\mathscr{F}_{r-1}$.

We would then have the chain

$$\mathscr{F} \subset \mathscr{F}_1 \subset \mathscr{F}_2 \subset \cdots \subset \mathscr{F}_n \subset \cdots.$$

Put

$$\mathscr{F}^c = \bigcup_{\nu=1}^{\infty} \mathscr{F}_\nu.$$

The set $\mathscr{F}^c$ is a field containing $\mathscr{F}$. For if $a, b \neq 0 \in \mathscr{F}^c$, there is an integer m so that $a, b \in \mathscr{F}_m$. But then $a \pm b$, ab, $ab^{-1} \in \mathscr{F}_m \subset \mathscr{F}^c$. Similarly the commutative, associative, and distributive laws hold for elements of $\mathscr{F}^c$.

If A is a polynomial over $\mathscr{F}$, by the unique factorization theorem (Proposition 41) there is an integer m such that

$$A = aP_1^{n_1} \cdots P_m^{n_m}, \; n_\nu \geq 0.$$

Hence A splits into linear factors with coefficients in $\mathscr{F}_m \subset \mathscr{F}^c$. It follows that each polynomial of positive degree over $\mathscr{F}$ splits into linear factors over $\mathscr{F}^c$. This completes the proof of the theorem.

COROLLARY *The fields* $\mathbf{Q}$ *and* $\mathbf{Z}_p$ *(p a prime) have algebraic closures.*

Assuming that each set has a choice map defined on it, one can prove that every field has an algebraic closure. The usual proof of this fact uses Zorn's lemma, which is equivalent to the existence of a choice map.

Now suppose that $\mathscr{F}$ is countable and that $\mathscr{E}$ is an algebraic closure of $\mathscr{F}$. The irreducible polynomials over $\mathscr{F}$ are countable and so can be arranged in a sequence $P_1, P_2, \ldots$. Then $\mathscr{E}$ contains a unique chain of subfields,

$$\mathscr{E}_1 \subset \mathscr{E}_2 \subset \ldots,$$

where $\mathscr{E}_n \supset \mathscr{F}$ is the minimal splitting field in $\mathscr{E}$ of the polynomial $P_1 \cdots P_n = A_n$. Put

$$\mathscr{E}^* = \bigcup_{\nu=1}^{\infty} \mathscr{E}_\nu.$$

The reader can prove that $\mathscr{E}^*$ is an algebraic closure for $\mathscr{F}$ and that $\mathscr{E} \supset \mathscr{E}^*$.

By Proposition 65 there are isomorphisms Φ_ν of $\mathscr{F}_\nu$ onto $\mathscr{E}_\nu$ such that $\operatorname{res}_{\mathscr{F}_{\nu-1}} \Phi_\nu = \Phi_{\nu-1}$, and Φ_ν is the identity map on $\mathscr{F}$. We can then define a map Φ of $\mathscr{F}^c$ onto $\mathscr{E}^*$ as follows: To each $a \in \mathscr{F}^c$ there is a minimal m such that $a \in \mathscr{F}_m$; put $a^\Phi = a^{\Phi_\nu}$, $(\nu = m, m+1, \ldots)$. If

$a, b \in \mathscr{F}^c$, then there is an m such that $a, b \in \mathscr{F}_m$, and then

$$(a + b)^\Phi = (a + b)^{\Phi_m} = a^{\Phi_m} + b^{\Phi_m} = a^\Phi + b^\Phi,$$
$$(ab)^\Phi = (ab)^{\Phi_m} = (a^{\Phi_m})(b^{\Phi_m}) = (a^\Phi)(b^\Phi).$$

If $a^\Phi = b^\Phi$, then $a^{\Phi_m} = b^{\Phi_m}$; but Φ_m is an isomorphism, and hence $a = b$. Finally given $u \in \mathscr{E}^*$, there is an n such that $u \in \mathscr{E}_n$. Since Φ_n is an isomorphism of $\mathscr{F}_n$ onto $\mathscr{E}_n$, there is an $a \in \mathscr{F}_n \subset \mathscr{F}^c$ such that $a^\Phi = a^{\Phi_n} = u$. Thus we have shown that Φ is an isomorphism. We have

PROPOSITION 66 *If $\mathscr{E}$ is an algebraic closure of a countable field $\mathscr{F}$, then $\mathscr{E}$ contains an isomorphic replica of $\mathscr{F}^c$.*

The reader can prove

PROPOSITION 67 *If $\mathscr{E}_1$ and $\mathscr{E}_2$ are algebraic closures of a countable field $\mathscr{F}$ such that no proper subfield of them is an algebraic closure of $\mathscr{F}$, then $\mathscr{E}_1$ and $\mathscr{E}_2$ are isomorphic.*

Thus to within isomorphism there is but one minimal algebraic closure of a countable field $\mathscr{F}$. Again, assuming the existence of a choice map, it can be shown that the hypothesis that $\mathscr{F}$ is countable is unnecessary.

PROPOSITION 68 *If $\mathscr{F}$ is a countable field, then $\mathscr{F}^c$ is an algebraically closed field.*

This proposition is most easily proved using certain information to be discussed in the next chapter. Specifically, we need to know

LEMMA 1 *If $\mathscr{K}$ is a finite algebraic extension of a field $\mathscr{F}$ and β is algebraic over $\mathscr{K}$, then β is algebraic over $\mathscr{F}$.*†

If we assume this lemma, the proposition is proved as follows: Let $\alpha_0 + \alpha_1 x + \cdots + \alpha_m x^m = A$ be a polynomial over $\mathscr{F}^c$. Since $\mathscr{F}$ is countable, $\mathscr{F}^c = \bigcup_{m=1}^{\infty} \mathscr{F}_m$, where $\mathscr{F}_m \supset \mathscr{F}_{m-1}$ for all m. Consequently there is an integer n so that the coefficients of A lie in $\mathscr{F}_n$. But then each zero of A is algebraic over $\mathscr{F}_n$, and so, by the lemma, each zero of A is algebraic over. $\mathscr{F}$. Consequently, each zero of A is a zero of an irreducible polynomial over $\mathscr{F}$ and hence lies in $\mathscr{F}^c$. It follows that A splits into linear factors over $\mathscr{F}^c$.

The reader should prove

PROPOSITION 69 *If $\mathscr{F}$ is a countable field, then its minimal algebraic closure is also countable.*

EXERCISES 2 *The derivative.* Let x be an indeterminate over an integral domain $\mathscr{D}$.

† This lemma appears as Exercise 17, page 244. This lemma can also be proved using systems of linear equations.

The map

$$a_0 + \cdots + a_n x^n \xrightarrow{\delta} a_1 + \mathbf{2}a_2 x + \cdots + \mathbf{n}a_n x^{n-1}$$

is a map of $\mathscr{D}[x]$ into $\mathscr{D}[x]$ and is called the derivative.†

Let $A, B, \in \mathscr{D}[x]$, $a, c \in \mathscr{D}$. Prove:

A. $\delta(A + B) = \delta(A) + \delta(B)$.
B. $\delta(aA) = a\delta(A)$.
C. $\delta(AB) = \delta(A)B + A\delta(B)$.
D. If char $\mathscr{D} = 0$, $\delta(A) = 0$ if and only if $d(A) \leq 0$.
E. If char $\mathscr{D} = p$, $\delta(A) = 0$ if and only if $A = a_0 + a_1 x^p + \cdots + a_r x^{rp}$, i.e., $A \in \mathscr{D}[x^p]$.
F. If A is irreducible, then $(A, \delta(A)) = 1$.
G. $(A, \delta(A)) > 1$ if and only if A has a multiple factor.

An element c is said to be a multiple zero of A of order k if $(x - c)^k \mid A$ and $(x - c)^{k+1} \nmid A$.

H. If A has a multiple zero, then $(A, \delta(A)) > 1$.

3 *Finite fields.* Let $\mathscr{F}$ be a finite field. By Proposition 15, we have $|\mathscr{F}| = p^n$, where $n \geq 1$, $p = \text{char } \mathscr{F}$. Let $\mathscr{F}_0$ be the prime field of $\mathscr{F}$. Prove:

A. $x^{p^n} - x = \prod_{c \in \mathscr{F}} (x - c)$. Hence $\mathscr{F}$ is a splitting field of $x^{p^n} - x$ over $\mathscr{F}_0$.
B. The multiplicative group of $\mathscr{F}$ is cyclic of order $p^n - 1$. *Hint:* Assume the multiplicative group is not cyclic. Use the decomposition theorem for abelian groups (Theorem 11, Chap. 3) and obtain a contradiction, thus proving

OPOSITION 70 *The multiplicative group of a finite field is a cyclic group.*

4 Prove:

A. The polynomial $x^{p^n} - x$ has no multiple zeros in $\mathbf{Z}_p{}^c$, the algebraic closure of $\mathbf{Z}_p$.
B. If $\mathscr{K}_n = \{\alpha \in \mathbf{Z}_p{}^c \mid \alpha^{p^n} = \alpha\}$, then $|\mathscr{K}_n| = p^n$.
C. If $n \mid m$, then $\mathscr{K}_n \subset \mathscr{K}_m$.
D. $\mathscr{K}_n$ is the splitting field over $\mathbf{Z}_p$ of $x^{p^n} - x$.
E. Two finite fields of the same order are isomorphic.
F. To each $n \in \mathbf{Z}^+$ there is a unique subfield $\mathscr{K}_n$ in $\mathbf{Z}_p{}^c$.

14 LINEARLY ORDERED RINGS

If we once again reflect on the set of integers $\mathbf{Z}$, we recall that, in addition to satisfying the axioms for an integral domain, $\mathbf{Z}$ also satisfied the axioms concerning the existence of a positive cone. Extending these

† In this definition of derivative nothing is said about limits. We wish to apply this to discrete as well as topological rings.

ideas we shall say that a ring $\mathscr{R}$ is *linearly ordered* provided there exists a subset $\mathscr{P}$ of $\mathscr{R}$ such that (A) $0 \notin \mathscr{P}$, (B) $0 \neq a \in \mathscr{R}$ implies one and only one of a and $-a$ lies in $\mathscr{P}$, (C) $\mathscr{P}$ is closed under addition and multiplication. The set $\mathscr{P}$ is called a *positive cone* of $\mathscr{R}$.

PROPOSITION 71 *A linearly ordered ring has no zero divisors.*

PROOF. Suppose a and b are nonzero elements of a linearly ordered ring such that $ab = 0$. Then one of a and $-a$ and one of b and $-b$ lies in the positive cone. Consequently at least one of ab, $(-a)b$, $a(-b)$, $(-a)(-b)$ lies in the cone. But $ab = 0$ implies that all these expressions are 0 and hence cannot lie in the cone, giving us a contradiction.

The reader can easily prove

PROPOSITION 72 *If $\mathscr{R}$ is a linearly ordered ring, then the additive order of each nonzero element is infinite. Hence the characteristic of a linearly ordered integral domain is* 0.

EXERCISES 1 Prove: The cartesian sum of rings cannot be linearly ordered.

2 Let $\mathscr{R} = \{2n/3^u \mid u, n \in \mathbf{Z}, u \geq 0\}$:

A. Show that $\mathscr{R}$ is a linearly ordered commutative ring without unity.

B. Show that there is an extension $\mathscr{R}'$ of $\mathscr{R}$, containing a unity, such that $\mathscr{R}'$ is linearly ordered and the positive cone of $\mathscr{R}'$ contains the positive cone of $\mathscr{R}$.

C. Show that the set $\mathscr{R}_* = \{(r, n) \mid r \in \mathscr{R}, n \in \mathbf{Z}\}$ with $(r, n) + (s, m) = (r + s, n + m)$, $(r, n)(s, m) = (rs + ns + mr, mn)$ cannot be linearly ordered.

In a linearly ordered ring $\mathscr{R}$ with positive cone $\mathscr{P}$ we define the relation of "less than" just as we did for $\mathbf{Z}$; namely, $a < b$ exactly when $b - a \in \mathscr{P}$. The reader should prove

PROPOSITION 73 *In a linearly ordered ring $\mathscr{R}$ if a, b, $c \in \mathscr{R}$ we have:*

A. *$a < b$ and $b < c$ implies $a < c$.*

B. *$a < b$ implies $a + c < b + c$ and $a - c < b - c$.*

C. *$a < b$ and $0 < c$ implies $ac < bc$.*

D. *$a < b$ and $c < 0$ implies $ac > bc$.*

E. *If a, b are positive, then $a^n < b^n$ (n is a positive integer) if and only if $a < b$.*

F. *If $a \neq 0$, then $a^2 > 0$.*

G. *If $\mathscr{R}$ has a unity, then this unity is positive.*

In a linearly ordered field we have:

H. *If $0 < a < b$, then $a^{-1} > b^{-1} > 0$.*

I. *If $a < b < 0$, then $b^{-1} < a^{-1} < 0$.*

J. *The positive cone of a linearly ordered field is a multiplicative group.*

It is possible that a given ring may have several different subsets satisfying the definition of a positive cone, and so the ring has several different linear orderings. We shall see later that $\mathbf{Q}[\sqrt{2}]$ is one such field. Other examples of this phenomena are given in Exercise 3.

EXERCISE 3 Prove:

A. The set $\mathscr{P}$ of polynomials in $\mathbf{Z}[x]$ with positive leading coefficient is a positive cone for $\mathbf{Z}[x]$.

B. Let $\mathscr{P}^* = \{A \in \mathbf{Z}[x] \mid A = x^r A', x \nmid A', A'(0) > 0\}$. $\mathscr{P}^*$ is a positive cone for $\mathbf{Z}[x]$.

C. $\mathscr{P} \neq \mathscr{P}^*$.

D. Let $\mathscr{P}' = \{A \in \mathbf{Z}[x] \mid A = a_n(-x)^n + \cdots + a_1(-x) + a_0, a_n > 0\}$. Then $\mathscr{P}'$ is a positive cone for $\mathbf{Z}[x]$. How are $\mathscr{P}$, $\mathscr{P}^*$, $\mathscr{P}'$ related?

E. If $\mathscr{D}$ is a linearly ordered domain, then $\mathscr{D}[x]$ has at least four distinct linear orderings.

These examples raise the question of how many different linear orderings can be placed on a ring. We shall prove

PROPOSITION 74 *The ring* $\mathbf{Z}$ *has exactly one linear ordering.*

PROOF. We saw already in Chap. 1 that $\mathbf{Z}$ has at least one linear ordering. Let $\mathscr{P}$ be a positive cone for the ring $\mathbf{Z}$. By Proposition 73G, $1 \in \mathscr{P}$, and hence by the additive closure of $\mathscr{P}$ we have $\mathbf{Z}^+ \subset \mathscr{P}$. It follows that $\mathbf{Z}^- \cap \mathscr{P} = \varnothing$. Hence $\mathbf{Z}^+ = \mathscr{P}$, and thus there is but the one positive cone in $\mathbf{Z}$.

If $\mathscr{R}$ is a ring with a linear ordering and if $\mathscr{R}_1$ is a subring of $\mathscr{R}$, then $\mathscr{R}_1$ inherits an ordering from $\mathscr{R}$, namely, the one where we take the positive cone of $\mathscr{R}_1$ to be $\mathscr{R}_1 \cap \mathscr{P}(\mathscr{R})$. Different linear orderings on $\mathscr{R}$ may induce the same linear ordering on $\mathscr{R}_1$, e.g., $\mathbf{Z}$ can be considered as a subring of $\mathbf{Q}[\sqrt{2}]$, and the linear orderings on $\mathbf{Q}[\sqrt{2}]$ necessarily induce the same ordering on $\mathbf{Z}$.

Let $\mathscr{Q}$ be the quotient field of an integral domain $\mathscr{D}$. As noted above, any linear ordering on $\mathscr{Q}$ induces a linear ordering on $\mathscr{D}$. Now let $\mathscr{P}$ be a positive cone for $\mathscr{D}$; then the set of elements of $\mathscr{Q}$ that can be expressed as the quotient of two elements from $\mathscr{P}$ constitutes a positive cone $\mathscr{P}^*$ for $\mathscr{Q}$. Furthermore, $\mathscr{P}^* \cap \mathscr{D} = \mathscr{P}$. The reader can now show

PROPOSITION 75 *There is a one-to-one correspondence between the linear orderings on an integral domain and the linear orderings on a quotient field of that domain.*

As a consequence of the last two propositions, we have

PROPOSITION 76 *There is exactly one linear ordering on the field of rational numbers.*

We shall denote the positive cone of $\mathbf{Q}$ by $\mathbf{Q}^+$.

If $\mathscr{F}$ is a linearly ordered field, then $\mathscr{F}$ is of characteristic 0, and $\mathscr{F}$ contains a field $\mathscr{Q}_0$ that is the quotient field of the integral domain $\mathscr{D}_0$ generated by the unity of $\mathscr{F}$. Then $\mathscr{Q}_0 = \{\alpha \in \mathscr{F} \mid \alpha = \mathbf{m1}/\mathbf{n1}, \mathbf{m}, \mathbf{n} \neq 0 \in \mathbf{Z}\}$, and $\mathscr{Q}_0$ is isomorphic to $\mathbf{Q}$. If $\mathscr{P}$ is the positive cone of $\mathscr{F}$, let $\mathscr{P}_0 = \mathscr{P} \cap \mathscr{Q}_0$. Then $\mathscr{P}_0 \supset \{(\mathbf{n1})^{-1} \mid \mathbf{n} \in \mathbf{Z}^+\}$, and hence $\mathscr{P}_0 \supset \mathscr{S} = \{\alpha \in \mathscr{F} \mid \alpha = \mathbf{m1}/\mathbf{n1}, \mathbf{m}, \mathbf{n} \in \mathbf{Z}^+\}$. Since $0 \notin \mathscr{P}_0$ and $\mathscr{P}_0 \cap (-1)\mathscr{S}$ is empty, we see that $\mathscr{P}_0 = \mathscr{S}$.

Next, we observe that the mapping $\mathbf{m}/\mathbf{n} \to \mathbf{m1}/\mathbf{n1}$ of $\mathbf{Q}$ onto $\mathscr{Q}$ maps $\mathbf{Q}^+$ onto $\mathscr{P}_0$. A homomorphism φ of a linearly ordered ring $\mathscr{R}_1$ into a linearly ordered ring $\mathscr{R}_2$ is said to be an *order-preserving homomorphism* if $\mathscr{P}_1{}^{\varphi} \subset \mathscr{P}_2$. We have proved

PROPOSITION 77 *Every linearly ordered field contains an order-preserving isomorphic image of the rational field* $\mathbf{Q}$.

Combining this proposition with Proposition 7, we obtain

COROLLARY 1 *To each linearly ordered field $\mathscr{F}$ there is a linearly ordered field $\mathscr{F}'$ containing $\mathbf{Q}$ as a subfield and an order-preserving isomorphism of $\mathscr{F}$ onto $\mathscr{F}'$.*

Hence, when we study linearly ordered fields, we can, if we so desire, assume that the field contains $\mathbf{Q}$ as a subfield.

Suppose we are given a ring $\mathscr{R}$, a particular linear ordering on $\mathscr{R}$ and a subset $\mathscr{S}$ of $\mathscr{R}$. We say that a is a *lower bound* in $\mathscr{R}$ for the set $\mathscr{S}$, relative to the given ordering, provided $a \in \mathscr{R}$ and $a \leq s$ for all $s \in \mathscr{S}$. We say a is the *greatest lower bound* in $\mathscr{R}$ for the set $\mathscr{S}$, relative to the given linear ordering, provided a is a lower bound in $\mathscr{R}$ for $\mathscr{S}$ and a is not less than any other lower bound for $\mathscr{S}$. We say that a is a *minimum* for the set $\mathscr{S}$, relative to the given linear ordering, provided $a \in \mathscr{S}$ and, relative to the given linear ordering, a is a lower bound for $\mathscr{S}$.

In an entirely analogous way we can define an upper bound, a maximum element, and a least upper bound for a subset of an ordered ring.

Having fixed the ring and a linear ordering on it, we note that a set can have at most one minimum element and at most one greatest lower bound. Furthermore, if a set has a minimum, that minimum is also its greatest lower bound. We have seen that every subset of $\mathbf{Z}$ that has a greatest lower bound has a minimum. However there are numerous examples of sets that have a greatest lower bound but no minimum.

We saw in Chap. 1 that there did not exist $z \in \mathbf{Z}$ such that $0 < z < 1$. However, when we come to a linearly ordered field $\mathscr{F}$, we see that, if $x < y$, then $(x + y)/2 \in \mathscr{F}$ (*note:* here we use char $\mathscr{F} \neq 2$), and $x < (x + y)/2 < y$. In fact there are infinitely many different $z \in \mathscr{F}$ such that $x < z < y$. Similarly, if x is in the positive cone of $\mathscr{F}$, so is $x/2$. Hence the positive cone of an ordered field has no minimum.

On the other hand, 0 is clearly the greatest lower bound of the positive cone.

There are linearly ordered rings that contain subsets having lower bounds but no greatest lower bound. Consider the set

$$\mathcal{S} = \{x \in \mathbf{Q} \mid x > 0, x^2 > 2\}. \tag{3}$$

Clearly 1 is a lower bound for $\mathcal{S}$. If $s \in \mathcal{S}$, put $t = (s^2 - 2)/2s$. Then $(s - t)^2 > 2$, and $s > s - t > 1$. Thus $\mathcal{S}$ has no least element. By Proposition 73E we see that a positive b is a lower bound of $\mathcal{S}$ if and only if $b^2 \leq 2$. Now suppose $b \geq 1$ and $b^2 < 2$. Put $r = (2 - b^2)/4b$; then $b < b + r$, and $(b + r)^2 < 2$. Hence $\mathcal{S}$ has lower bounds in $\mathbf{Q}$ but no greatest lower bound in $\mathbf{Q}$.

A set $\mathcal{S}$ is said to be *simply ordered* if there is a binary relation $\leq$ defined on $\mathcal{S}$ such that (A) $a \leq a$ for all $a \in \mathcal{S}$; (B) if $a \leq b$ and $b \leq a$, then $a = b$; (C) if $a \leq b$ and $b \leq c$, then $a \leq c$. Clearly, every linear ordering is a simple ordering. However, the converse is not true. Put $\lfloor a \rfloor \leq \lfloor b \rfloor$ when $0 \leq a \leq b \leq p - 1$. Then $\leq$ is a simple ordering on the field $\mathbf{Z}_p$. On the other hand, as we saw in Proposition 72, finite fields cannot be linearly ordered.

If $\mathcal{S}$ is a simply ordered set, then a subset T of $\mathcal{S}$ is said to have a least element, relative to that ordering, provided there is an $m \in T$ such that $m \leq t$ for all $t \in T$. A set has at most one least element for any simple ordering. A simply ordered set $\mathcal{S}$ is said to be *well ordered* provided every subset of $\mathcal{S}$ has a least element. The reason why certain results hold in $\mathbf{Z}$ and do not hold for arbitrarily linearly ordered rings is that the linear ordering on $\mathbf{Z}$ is well ordered. Since the positive cone of a linearly ordered field has no least element, no field can be linearly well ordered. However, it can be shown that a set $\mathcal{S}$ can be well ordered if and only if there is a choice function on the subsets of $\mathcal{S}$. Thus, if we accept the axiom of choice, then every set (including fields) can be simply well ordered.

We shall say that a ring $\mathcal{R}$ is *complete relative to a linear ordering* provided every subset of the positive cone (for this ordering) has a greatest lower bound in $\mathcal{R}$. When no confusion can arise as to which ordering is being considered, we shall use the simpler phrase *complete ring*. From the example defined in (3) above, we see that $\mathbf{Q}$ is not complete relative to its only linear ordering. We shall show (Theorem 3) that there are complete fields. Hence being "complete" is a less stringent condition than being "linearly well ordered."

XERCISES 4 Prove: Let $\mathcal{F}$ be a field with a given linear ordering. $\mathcal{F}$ is complete (relative to that ordering) if and only if every subset of $\mathcal{F}$ that has a lower bound in $\mathcal{F}$ has a greatest lower bound in $\mathcal{F}$. $\mathcal{F}$ is complete if and only if every subset of $\mathscr{F}$ that has an upper bound in $\mathscr{F}$ has a least upper bound in $\mathscr{F}$.

5 Are any of the linear orderings on $\mathbf{Z}[x]$ complete?

6 Prove: If $0 \neq \alpha, \beta \in \mathbf{Q}$, then there is an $\mathbf{n} \in \mathbf{Z}$ such that $\mathbf{n}\alpha > \beta$.

7 Prove: If $\alpha, \beta \in \mathbf{Q}$, such that $1 < \alpha < \beta$, then there is an $n \in \mathbf{Z}^+$ such that $\alpha^n > \beta$.

A linearly ordered ring $\mathscr{R}$ is said to possess the *archimedean principle* if to each ordered pair α, β of elements in the positive cone of $\mathscr{R}$ there is an integer $\mathbf{n} \in \mathbf{Z}^+$ such that $\mathbf{n}\alpha > \beta$. A linearly ordered ring possessing this principle is called an *archimedean-ordered ring.* It follows from Exercise 6 that $\mathbf{Q}$ is an archimedean-ordered field.

Suppose $\mathscr{D}$ is a complete integral domain and that α is an element of its positive cone. Then the set $\mathscr{S} = \{\mathbf{n}\alpha \mid \mathbf{n} \in \mathbf{Z}^+\}$ has no upper bound in $\mathscr{D}$. Suppose it did; then since $\mathscr{D}$ is complete, $\mathscr{S}$ has a least upper bound, say γ. Then $\mathbf{n}\alpha \leq \gamma$ for all $\mathbf{n} \in \mathbf{Z}$, whence $(\mathbf{n} - 1)\alpha = \mathbf{n}\alpha - \alpha \leq \gamma - \alpha < \gamma$. But then $\mathbf{n}\alpha \leq \gamma - \alpha < \gamma$ for all $\mathbf{n} \in \mathbf{Z}^+$, contrary to γ being the least upper bound for $\mathscr{S}$. It follows that for any β in the positive cone of $\mathscr{D}$ there is an $\mathbf{n} \in \mathbf{Z}^+$ so that $\mathbf{n}\alpha > \beta$. We have proved

PROPOSITION 78 *A complete integral domain possesses the archimedean principle.*

The reader should now prove

PROPOSITION 79 *If $\mathscr{F}$ is an archimedean-ordered field with $\alpha, \beta \in \mathscr{F}$, $\alpha < \beta$, then there are integers $\mathbf{m}, \mathbf{n} \neq 0 \in \mathbf{Z}$ such that $\alpha < \mathbf{m}1/\mathbf{n}1 < \beta$.*

Thus we have

COROLLARY *If $\mathscr{F}$ is an archimedean-ordered field containing $\mathbf{Q}$ then between any two distinct elements of $\mathscr{F}$ there is a rational number.*

A subset V of $\mathbf{Q}^+$ will be called a *segment* of $\mathbf{Q}$ if (A) V has no minimum in $\mathbf{Q}$; (B) if $x < y$ and $x \in V$, then $y \in V$. If $\mathscr{F}$ is an ordered field and $\alpha \in \mathscr{F}$, then the set

$$S_\alpha = \{\mathbf{x} \in \mathbf{Q}^+ \mid \alpha < \mathbf{x}1\}$$

is a segment of $\mathbf{Q}$. We let $\mathfrak{W}$ be the collection of segments of $\mathbf{Q}$ and let $\mathfrak{W}^+ = \{V \in \mathfrak{W} \mid V \neq \mathbf{Q}^+\}$. The reader can easily prove

PROPOSITION 80 *If $\mathscr{F}$ is an archimedean-ordered field, then the mapping $\alpha \to S_\alpha$ is an injection of the positive cone of $\mathscr{F}$ into $\mathfrak{W}^+$. If $\mathscr{F}$ is a complete field the map is bijective.*

EXERCISES 8 Prove: A subring of an archimedean-ordered ring is archimedean.

9 Prove: Under set addition, $S_{\alpha+\beta} = S_\alpha + S_\beta$ for all α, β in the positive cone.

10 Prove: If $\mathscr{D}$ is a complete integral domain that is not isomorphic to $\mathbf{Z}$, then there is an element $d \in \mathscr{D}$ such that $0 < d < 1$.

11 Prove: The ring $\mathbf{Z}[x]$ is not archimedean relative to any of the linear orderings defined in Exercise 3.

12 Prove: If $V, W \in \mathfrak{W}$, then either $V \subset W$ or $W \subset V$.

So far we have not exhibited a field that is complete. Since complete fields are archimedean, our last proposition suggests how we might construct a complete field. We shall outline this construction, leaving the proofs to the reader.

LEMMA 1 *If $V, W \in \mathfrak{W}$ and $W + V$ is the set obtained by set addition, then the set $W + V$ is a segment, i.e., $W + V \in \mathfrak{W}$.*

LEMMA 2 *The operation of set addition is a commutative, associative binary operation on $\mathfrak{W}$. Furthermore, $V + \mathbf{Q}^+ = V$, for all $V \in \mathfrak{W}$.*

Suppose $V, W \in \mathfrak{W}$ and $W \subset V$. Let

$$X^* = \{x \in \mathbf{Q}^+ \mid x + V \subset W\} = \bigcap_{v \in V} (W - v),$$

and put

$$X = \begin{cases} X^* & \text{if } X^* \text{ has no minimum,} \\ X^* - \min X^* & \text{if } X^* \text{ has a minimum.} \end{cases}$$

Then $X \in \mathfrak{W}$ and

$$\begin{aligned} X + V &= \bigcup_{v \in V} X + v = \bigcup_{v \in V} \Big(\bigcap_{u \in V} (W - u) + v\Big) \\ &= \bigcup_{v \in V} \bigcap_{\substack{u \in V \\ u \le v}} (W - u + v) \\ &= \bigcup_{v \in V} \bigcap_{t \in \mathbf{Q}^+ \cap (v - V)} (W + t) = \bigcup_{v \in V} W = W. \end{aligned}$$

We have proved

LEMMA 3 *If $V, W \in \mathfrak{W}$ and $V \supset W$,* let X be defined as above. *Then $X \in \mathfrak{W}$ and $V + X = W$.*

The set X of Lemma 3 is called the difference between W and V, and we write $X = W - V$. Note that $W - V$ is not set subtraction and that $W - V$ is defined only when $W \subset V$.

LEMMA 4 *The operation of set multiplication is a commutative associative binary operation on $\mathfrak{W}$.*

Suppose that $x \in V \in \mathfrak{W}$. Since V has no least element, there is an element $y \in V$ such that $0 < y < x$, whence $y(x/y) = x$ and $x/y \in S_1$. Thus we have that $VS_1 \supset V$. On the other hand, if $z \in S_1$ and $x \in V$, then $x < xz$, and so $xz \in V$; i.e., $VS_1 \subset V$. Thus we have proved the first line of the following lemma:

LEMMA 5

$$VS_1 = V, \qquad \textit{for all } V \in \mathfrak{W}.$$
$$V\mathbf{Q}^+ = \mathbf{Q}^+, \qquad \textit{for all } V \in \mathfrak{W}.$$

If $V \in \mathfrak{W}^+$, let $Y = \bigcap S_{x^{-1}}$ $(x \in V)$. Then $V' = Y - \min Y \in \mathfrak{W}$. A positive rational number w is a lower bound of V if and only if $w^{-1} \in V'$. If $y \in V'$, then $yx > 1$ for all $x \in V$, and hence $V'V \subset S_1$. We now show that $V'V = S_1$. Let $a > 1$, and let $y \in V'$. Then y^{-1} is a lower bound of V, and there is a positive integer n such that $a^n y^{-1}$ is not a lower bound for V. Choose n to be minimal. Then there exists an $x \in V$ such that $a^{n-1}y^{-1} \leq x < a^n y^{-1}$. If $a^{n-1}y^{-1} = x$, then V would have a greatest lower bound, contrary to the definition of a segment. Thus we have

$$1 < (y/a^{n-1})x < a.$$

By the choice of n, $a^{n-1}y^{-1}$ is a lower bound for V, and hence $z = y/a^{n-1} \in V'$. Thus we have shown that to each $a \in S_1$ there are $x \in V$ and $z \in V'$ such that $1 < zx < a$. But VV' is a segment, and consequently $a \in VV'$, and hence $VV' = S_1$. We have proved

LEMMA 6 *If* $V \in \mathfrak{W}^+$, *then* $VV' = S_1$.

Now Lemmas 4, 5, and 6 imply

LEMMA 7 *The set* $\mathfrak{W}^+ = \{V \in \mathfrak{W} \mid V \neq \mathbf{Q}^+\}$ *is an abelian group under set multiplication.*

Finally to each $V \in \mathfrak{W}^+$ we form a second symbol $(-V)$. Let $\mathfrak{W}^-$ be the collection of symbols $(-V)$, and put $\mathfrak{R} = \mathfrak{W} \cup \mathfrak{W}$. On $\mathfrak{R}$ define

$$W + (-V) = (-V) + W = \begin{cases} W - V & \text{if } V \supset W, \\ (-[V - W]) & \text{if } W \supset V;^{\dagger} \end{cases}$$

$$(-V) + (-W) = (-W) + (-V) = (-[V + W]);$$

$$V(-W) = (-W)(V) = (-VW);$$

$$(-V)(-W) = (-W)(-V) = VW.$$

Using these definitions together with the previously developed properties of $\mathfrak{W}$ we can show

PROPOSITION 81 $\mathfrak{R}$ *is a linearly ordered field with* $\mathfrak{W}^+$ *as its positive cone.*

If $\mathbf{Q}'$ is the prime field of $\mathfrak{R}$, then the positive cone of $\mathbf{Q}'$ is the collection of subsets of $\mathfrak{W}^+$ that have a greatest lower bound in $\mathbf{Q}$. The map $a \to S_a$ is a map of $\mathbf{Q}^+$ into $\mathbf{Q}'$.

Given a subset $\mathfrak{B}$ of $\mathfrak{W}$, define

$$V^* = \bigcup_{V \in \mathfrak{B}} V.$$

† If $V, W \in \mathfrak{W}^+$, then either $V \subset W$ or $W \subset V$ so that this rule covers all cases.

Then $V^* \in \mathfrak{W}$, and V^* contains all $V \in \mathfrak{B}$; hence $V - V^* \in \mathfrak{W}$. It follows that V^* is a lower bound for the set $\mathfrak{B}$.

Now suppose that X is a lower bound in $\mathfrak{R}$ for the set $\mathfrak{B}$; then $V - X \in \mathfrak{W}$, for all $X \neq V \in \mathfrak{B}$. Consequently X contains each V in $\mathfrak{B}$ and hence $X \supset V^*$. Thus every lower bound of $\mathfrak{B}$ is necessarily smaller than V^*, and hence V^* is indeed the greatest lower bound for the set $\mathfrak{B}$. We have proved

THEOREM 3 *The field $\mathfrak{R}$ is a complete linearly ordered field.*

Finally we should like to prove

THEOREM 4 *To each complete linearly ordered field $\mathscr{F}$ there is an order-preserving isomorphism of $\mathscr{F}$ onto $\mathfrak{R}$.*

PROOF. We can assume that $\mathscr{F}$ contains $\mathbf{Q}$ as a subfield. Let $\mathscr{P}$ denote the positive cone of $\mathscr{F}$. By Proposition 80 the map $\alpha \xrightarrow{\varphi} S_\alpha$ is an injective map of $\mathscr{P}$ into $\mathfrak{W}^+$. Since $\mathscr{F}$ is complete, φ is surjective. It is easily shown that

$$S_{\alpha+\beta} = S_\alpha + S_\beta, \qquad S_{\alpha\beta} = S_\alpha S_\beta, \qquad \text{for } \alpha, \beta \in \mathscr{P}.$$

Finally, define

$$0^\varphi = \mathbf{Q}^+, \qquad (-\gamma)^\varphi = -(\gamma^\varphi), \qquad \text{for } \gamma \in \mathscr{P}.$$

One can now show that φ is indeed an order-preserving isomorphism of $\mathscr{F}$ onto $\mathfrak{R}$.

Theorem 4 tells us that to within an order-preserving isomorphism there is but one complete linearly ordered field. We shall let $\mathbf{R}$ denote a complete linearly ordered field that contains $\mathbf{Q}$ as a subset. $\mathbf{R}$ is called the *field of real numbers*. We denote the positive cone of $\mathbf{R}$ by $\mathbf{R}^+$.

The reader should prove

ROPOSITION 82 *If $\gamma \in \mathbf{R}^+$ and $n \in \mathbf{Z}$, then there is a unique $\delta \in \mathbf{R}^+$ such that $\delta^n = \gamma$.*

XERCISES 13 Prove: If $\mathscr{F}$ is an ordered field with positive cone $\mathscr{P}$, then $\mathscr{P}$ is a multiplicative group and $\mathscr{F}^\times$, the multiplicative group of $\mathscr{F}$, is isomorphic to the cartesian product $\mathbf{Z}_2 \times \mathscr{P}$.

14 Prove: Let $n \in \mathbf{Z}$ and $\gamma \in \mathbf{R}$. If $2 \mid n$ and $\gamma > 0$, there are exactly two distinct elements δ of $\mathbf{R}$ such that $\delta^n = \gamma$. If $2 \mid n$ and $\gamma < 0$, there is no δ in $\mathbf{R}$ such that $\delta^n = \gamma$. If $2 \nmid n$, there is exactly one δ in $\mathbf{R}$ such that $\delta^n = \gamma$.

15 Prove:

A. $\mathbf{R}$ splits $x^2 - 2$.

B. $\mathbf{P} = \mathbf{R}^+ \cap \mathbf{Q}[\sqrt{2}]$ is a positive cone for $\mathbf{Q}[\sqrt{2}]$.

C. There is an automorphism φ of $\mathbf{Q}[\sqrt{2}]$ such that $(\sqrt{2})^\varphi = -\sqrt{2}$, $a^\varphi = a$ for all $a \in \mathbf{Q}$.

D. $\mathbf{P}^\varphi$ is a positive cone for $\mathbf{Q}[\sqrt{2}]$.

E. $P^{\varphi} \neq P$. Hence $\mathbf{Q}[\sqrt{2}]$ has at least two linear orderings.
F. $\mathbf{Q}[\sqrt{2}]$ is not complete under either of these linear orderings.

Suppose in addition to the usual linear ordering on $\mathbf{R}$ there is a second linear ordering with positive cone $\mathscr{P}$. Clearly the nonzero squares of $\mathbf{R}$ lie in $\mathscr{P}$. But $\mathbf{R}^+$ is exactly the set of all nonzero squares. Hence $\mathbf{R}^+ \subset \mathscr{P}$. But then $\mathbf{R}^- \subset \mathscr{P}^-$, and we have $\mathbf{R}^+ = \mathscr{P}$. We have proved

PROPOSITION 83 *The field* $\mathbf{R}$ *has exactly one linear ordering.*

If $\delta, \gamma \in \mathbf{R}^+$ such that $\delta^n = \gamma$, we write $\delta = \gamma^{1/n}$ and say that δ is the *nth root* of γ. If $m, n \in \mathbf{Z}^+$, then $(\gamma^m)^{1/n} = (\gamma^{1/n})^m$. Also if $m, n, p, q \in \mathbf{Z}^+$ and $m/n = p/q$, then $(\gamma^m)^{1/n} = (\gamma^p)^{1/q}$. Hence for $a \in \mathbf{Q}^+ (a = m/n)$ we can define γ^a to be $(\gamma^m)^{1/n}$, and this definition is independent of the representative of a. If $\alpha \in \mathbf{R}^+$, we define

$$\gamma^\alpha = \text{greatest lower bound } \{\gamma^a \mid a \in \mathbf{Q}, a > \alpha\},$$

$$\gamma^{-\alpha} = (\gamma^{-1})^\alpha.$$

As usual we set $\gamma^0 = 1$.

EXERCISES 16 Prove: If $\gamma \in \mathbf{R}^+$, $\alpha, \beta \in \mathbf{R}$, then

$$\gamma^{\alpha+\beta} = \gamma^\alpha \gamma^\beta, \qquad \gamma^{\alpha\beta} = (\gamma^\alpha)^\beta.$$

17 Let $a \in \mathbf{R}$ such that $a > 1$. Prove:
A. $a^x > 1$ if $x > 0$.
B. $x > y$ implies $a^x > a^y$; hence $a \to a^x$ is monotone increasing.
C. $\text{glb}\{a^x | x \in \mathbf{R}\} = 0$.
D. Given $b \in \mathbf{R}^+$, let $S = \{x \in \mathbf{R}^+ \mid b < a^x\}$. S has a greatest lower bound β and $b = a^\beta$.
E. The map $x \xrightarrow{\varphi} a^x$ is a surjective map of $\mathbf{R}$ onto $\mathbf{R}^+$.
F. The map φ is injective.
G. There is an isomorphism of the additive group of $\mathbf{R}$ onto the multiplicative group $\mathbf{R}^+$.
H. The multiplicative group $\mathbf{R}^+$ has uncountably many automorphisms. The additive group $\mathbf{R}$ has uncountably many automorphisms.

Summarizing the results in Exercise 17, we have

PROPOSITION 84 *If* $1 < a \in \mathbf{R}$, *the map* $x \to a^x$ *is a monotonic increasing bijective isomorphism of the additive group* $\mathbf{R}$ *onto the multiplicative group* $\mathbf{R}^+$.

We denote the inverse map of $x \to a^x$ by $y \to \log_a y$. We have

PROPOSITION 85 *If* $1 < a \in \mathbf{R}$, *the map* $y \to \log_a y$ *is a monotonic increasing bijective isomorphism of* $\mathbf{R}^+$ *onto* $\mathbf{R}$.

ERCISES 18 Show that the additive group **Q** and the multiplicative group $\mathbf{Q}^+$ are not isomorphic.

19 Prove:

A. The only field automorphism of the field **Q** is the identity map.

B. The only field automorphism of **R** is the identity map.

20 Let $\mathscr{D}$ be a complete integral domain that is not isomorphic to **Z**. Then there exist $d \in \mathscr{D}$ such that $0 < d < 1$. For such d we have $d(2-d) \leq 1$ while $2 - d > 1$. Prove:

A. $T_d = \{x \in \mathscr{D} \mid xd \leq 1\}$ has a least upper bound d' and $dd' = 1$.

B. Each element of $\mathscr{D}^+$ has a multiplicative inverse in $\mathscr{D}$.

C. $\mathscr{D}$ is isomorphic to **R**.

Exercise 20 is an outline of a proof for

THEOREM 5 *A complete integral domain is isomorphic either to* **Z** *or to* **R**.

15 METRIC PROPERTIES OF THE REAL FIELD

In a linearly ordered field $\mathscr{F}$, we can define the absolute value of an element $a \in \mathscr{F}$ as $|a| = \max\{a, -a\}$. Let $\mathscr{F}^+$ denote the positive cone of $\mathscr{F}$. The map $a \to |a|$ is a map of $\mathscr{F}$ onto $\mathscr{F}^+ \cup 0$. It is easily verified that this map is a homomorphism of the multiplicative group $\mathscr{F}^\times$ onto $\mathscr{F}^+$; in fact

$$|ab| = |a|\,|b|, \qquad \text{for all } a, b \in \mathscr{F}.$$

Obviously $$-|a| \leq a \leq |a|, \qquad \text{for all } a \in \mathscr{F},$$

and hence $$|a + b| \leq |a| + |b|, \qquad \text{for all } a, b \in \mathscr{F}.$$

Also $$|a - b| < e \qquad \text{if and only if} \qquad a - e < b < a + e,$$

and $$|\,|a| - |b|\,| \leq |a - b| \leq |a| + |b|, \qquad \text{for all } a, b \in \mathscr{F}.$$

The reader can prove the following lemmas:

LEMMA 1 *If a is an element of a linearly ordered field $\mathscr{F}$ and $|a| < e$ for all $e \in \mathscr{F}^+$, then $a = 0$.*

LEMMA 2 *If a is in an archimedean-ordered field $\mathscr{F}$, and if $c, d \in \mathscr{F}^+$ such that $c < 1$ and $|a| < dc^n$, for all $n \in \mathbf{Z}^+$, then $a = 0$.*

A sequence $\{a_n\}$ of elements from a linearly ordered field will be said to have a *limit* a in $\mathscr{F}$ if there is a function $e \to N(e)$ from $\mathscr{F}^+$ to $\mathbf{Z}^+$ such that $|a - a_n| < e$ for all $n > N(e)$. In that event, we write $\lim a_n = a$.

LEMMA 3 *If a sequence from a linearly ordered field $\mathscr{F}$ has a limit in $\mathscr{F}$, that limit is unique.*

PROOF. Suppose $a \neq b$ are limits of the sequence $\{a_n\}$. Let $N(e)$ be the function such that $|a - a_n| < e$ for all $n > N(e)$, and let $M(e)$ be the function such that $|b - a_n| < e$ for $n > M(e)$. Suppose $b > a$ and put $e' = (b - a)/3$; then for $n > \max\{N(e'), M(e')\}$ we have

$$a - e' < a_n < a + e', \qquad b - e' < a_n < b + e'.$$

But $a + e' < b - e'$, and hence we have $a_n < a_n$, a contradiction.

Not every sequence of $\mathscr{F}$ need have a limit in $\mathscr{F}$; e.g., $\{1, 0, 1, 0, \ldots\}$ is a sequence without a limit. The sequence $\{1, 2, 3, \ldots\}$ has no limit if the ordering is archimedean.

A sequence $\{a_n\}$ from a linearly ordered field $\mathscr{F}$ is said to be *bounded* if there is an element $c \in \mathscr{F}^+$ such that $|a_n| < c$ for all $n \in \mathbf{Z}^+$. A sequence $\{a_n\}$ is *monotonic increasing* if $a_n \leq a_{n+1}$ for all $n \in \mathbf{Z}^+$ and is *monotonic decreasing* if $a_n \geq a_{n+1}$ for all $n \in \mathbf{Z}^+$. The reader should prove

LEMMA 4 *If a monotonic increasing sequence $\{a_n\}$ has a limit in the field, that limit is the least upper bound of the set $\{a_n\}$. If a monotonic decreasing sequence $\{a_n\}$ has a limit in the field, that limit is the greatest lower bound of the set $\{a_n\}$.*

PROPOSITION 86 *A linearly ordered field $\mathscr{F}$ is complete if and only if every bounded monotonic sequence of $\mathscr{F}$ has a limit in $\mathscr{F}$.*

PROOF. Suppose $\{a_n\}$ is a bounded monotonic increasing sequence of a complete field $\mathscr{F}$. The set $A = \{a_1, a_2, \ldots\}$, being bounded, has a least upper bound in $\mathscr{F}$. Let a denote this least upper bound. To each $e \in \mathscr{F}^+$ let $U_e = \{x \in \mathscr{F} \mid a - e < x \leq a\}$. If $A \cap U_e$ is empty, then $a - e$ is an upper bound for the set A, contrary to a being the least upper bound of A. Hence there is an integer $N(e)$ such that $a_{N(e)} \in U_e$. Since the sequence is monotonic increasing, we have

$$0 \leq a - a_n < e, \qquad \text{for } n \geq N(e).$$

It follows that $a = \lim a_n$. An analogous proof holds if the sequence is monotonic decreasing.

Conversely, suppose that every bounded monotonic sequence of $\mathscr{F}$ has a limit in $\mathscr{F}$. We wish to show that each subset A of $\mathscr{F}^+$ has a greatest lower bound in $\mathscr{F}$. Let

$$A^* = \bigcup_{a \in A} S_a, \qquad \text{where } S_a = \{x \in \mathscr{F} \mid x \geq a\}.$$

Clearly the sets A and A^* have the same greatest lower bound in $\mathscr{F}$. Each $x \in \mathscr{F}$ is either in A^* or is a lower bound for A^*. Let c be an element of A^*. If $c/2 \in A^*$, set $a_1 = c/2$ and $b_1 = 0$, and if $c/2 \notin A^*$, set $a_1 = c$ and $b_1 = c/2$. In both instances we have $a_1 \in A^*$, b_1 is a lower bound of A^*, and $a_1 - b_1 = c/2$. We now define two sequences inductively. Suppose we are given $a_1 \geq a_2 \geq \cdots \geq a_n$ and $b_1 \leq b_2 \leq \cdots \leq b_n$

of James G. Birney, soon to appear u
fessor Dumond. Birney — lawyer, c
ery agent, and Liberty Party candi
1840 and 1844 — maintained a larg
active in moral and political reform a
ly discovered, become an invaluab

such that $a_i \in A^*$, the b_i are lower bounds of A^*, and $a_i - b_i = c/2^i$. If $(a_n + b_n)/2 \in A^*$, put $a_{n+1} = (a_n + b_n)/2$ and $b_{n+1} = b_n$, but if $(a_n + b_n)/2 \notin A^*$, put $a_{n+1} = a_n$ and $b_{n+1} = (a_n + b_n)/2$. Then $a_n \geq a_{n+1}$, $b_n \leq b_{n+1}$ and $a_{n+1} - b_{n+1} = c/2^{n+1}$. By construction, the sequences $\{a_n\}$ and $\{b_n\}$ are bounded monotonic sequences, and hence, by hypothesis, they have limits in $\mathscr{F}$, say a and b respectively. The element a is the greatest lower bound of $\{a_n\}$, and b is the least upper bound of $\{b_n\}$. Thus

$$b_n \leq b \text{ and } a \leq a_n, \qquad \text{for all } n \in \mathbf{Z}^+.$$

Consequently, we have

$$a \leq a_n \leq b_n + c/2^n \leq b + c/2^n,$$

and therefore $\quad |b - a| \leq c/2^n, \qquad$ for all $n \in \mathbf{Z}^+$.

As we noted in Lemma 2, this implies that $a = b$. Now b is a lower bound of A^*, for if there is an $x \in A^*$ such that $x < b$, then there is an n such that $x < (x + b)/2 \leq b_n \leq b$, contrary to the definition of b_n. Since a is the greatest lower bound of $\{a_n\} \in A^*$, no element larger than b can be a lower bound for A. It follows that $a = b$ is the greatest lower bound for the set A^* and hence for the set A.

A sequence $\{a_n\}$ from an ordered field $\mathscr{F}$ is said to be a *cauchy sequence* provided there is a function $e \to M(e)$ of $\mathscr{F}^+$ into $\mathbf{Z}^+$ such that $|a_n - a_m| < e$ whenever $m, n > M(e)$.

A sequence $\{a_n\}$ is said to be a *null sequence* if it has 0 as its limit.

The reader should prove

LEMMA 5 *A bounded monotonic sequence is a cauchy sequence. Every cauchy sequence is bounded.*

LEMMA 6 *Every null sequence is a cauchy sequence.*

We now prove a fundamental property of the real field.

THEOREM 6 *A sequence from* **R** *has a limit in* **R** *if and only if it is a cauchy sequence.*

PROOF. Suppose the sequence $\{a_n\}$ has a limit a in **R**. Let $N(e)$ be the function such that $|a - a_n| < e$ for $n > N(e)$. Then

$$|a_n - a_m| = |a_n - a + a - a_m| \leq |a_n - a| + |a - a_m| < e,$$

provided $n, m > N(e/2)$. On taking $M(e) = N(e/2)$, we see that $\{a_n\}$ is a cauchy sequence.

Conversely, suppose $\{a_n\}$ is a cauchy sequence. Let $A_s = \{a_s, a_{s+1}, \ldots\}$. The sets A_s are bounded subsets of **R**, and since **R** is a complete field, these sets have a least upper bound u_s in **R** and a greatest lower bound v_s in **R**. We have

$$v_s \leq a_n \leq u_s, \qquad \text{for } n \geq s.$$

The sequence $\{v_s\}$ is a bounded monotonic increasing sequence, and it follows from Proposition 86 that $\{v_s\}$ has a limit v in $\mathbf{R}$. Let $N_1(e)$ be the function such that

$$v - e \le v_s \le a_n, \qquad \text{for } n \ge s > N_1(e). \tag{4}$$

Similarly $\{u_s\}$ has a limit u in $\mathbf{R}$. Let $N_2(e)$ be the function such that

$$a_n \le u_s \le u + e, \qquad \text{for } n \ge s > N_2(e). \tag{5}$$

Since $\{a_n\}$ is a cauchy sequence, there is a function $M(e)$ such that

$$a_m - e < a_n < a_m + e, \qquad \text{for } m, n > M(e).$$

If $m > M(e)$, then $a_m - e$ is a lower bound for A_s with $s > M(e)$. Thus we have

$$a_m - e \le v_s, \qquad \text{for } s, m > M(e).$$

Similarly $$u_s \le a_m + e, \qquad \text{for } s, m > M(e).$$

Hence $$0 \le u_s - v_s < 2e, \qquad \text{if } s > M(e),$$

and $$|u - v| \le |u - u_s| + |v - v_s| + |u_s - v_s| < 4e,$$

provided $s > \max\,\{M(e), N_1(e), N_2(e)\}$. It follows from Lemma 1 that $u = v$. In that case from (4) and (5) we obtain

$$u - e \le a_n \le u + e, \qquad \text{for } n > \max\,\{N_1(e), N_2(e)\},$$

and hence u is the limit of the sequence $\{a_n\}$.

EXERCISES 1 Prove: If $\{a_n\}$, $\{b_n\}$ are cauchy sequences of $\mathbf{R}$, then $\{-a_n\}$, $\{|a_n|\}$, $\{a_n + b_n\}$, and $\{a_n b_n\}$ are cauchy sequences and $\lim -a_n = -\lim a_n$, $\lim |a_n| \ge \lim a_n$, $\lim\ a_n + b_n = \lim a_n + \lim b_n$, $\lim a_n b_n = (\lim\ a_n)(\lim b_n)$.

2 Prove: If $x \in \mathbf{R}^+$, then x is the limit of a monotonic increasing sequence of national numbers.

By an infinite decimal we shall mean a map $n \to a_n$ of $\mathbf{Z}$ into the set $\{0, 1, \ldots, 9\}$ such that $a_n = 0$ if n is sufficiently large. As usual, we can denote an infinite decimal by the sequence

$$\mathbf{a} = \cdots a_3 a_2 a_1 a_0 \cdot a_{-1} a_{-2} \cdots.$$

We define the order of an infinite decimal $\mathbf{a}$ to be

$$N(\mathbf{a}) = \min\,\{n \in \mathbf{Z} \mid a_\nu = 0 \text{ for all } \nu > n\}.$$

To each infinite decimal we can associate the sequence of rational numbers

$$b_\nu = a_{N(\mathbf{a})} 10^{N(\mathbf{a})} + \cdots + a_{-\nu} 10^{-\nu}, \qquad \nu = 1, 2, \ldots.$$

The sequence $\{b_\nu\}$ is a bounded monotonic increasing sequence of nonnegative rational numbers and hence has a limit, say α, in $\mathbf{R}$. Thus we have defined a map $\mathbf{a} \xrightarrow{\lambda} \alpha$ from the set I, of all infinite decimals, into $\mathbf{R}^+ \cup 0$. This mapping is not injective, since 0.9999... and 1.0000... map into the same real number.

It is relatively easy to show that two infinite decimals $\mathbf{a}$ and $\mathbf{a}'$ determine the same real numbers if and only if there is an integer m such that

$$a_\nu = a'_\nu, \qquad \text{for } \nu > m;$$

$$a_\nu = a'_\nu + 1, \qquad \text{for } \nu = m;$$

$$a_\nu = 0, \quad a'_\nu = 9, \qquad \text{for } \nu < m.$$

Let I_0 be the set of infinite decimals that do not end with a chain of 0's. Then λ is an injective map of I_0 into $\mathbf{R}^+$.

In the opposite direction, suppose $\alpha \in \mathbf{R}^+$; then there is a largest integer $A < \alpha$ and $A = a_0 + a_1 10 + a_2 10^2 + \cdots + a_N 10^N + \ldots$, where $a_n = 0, 1, \ldots, 9$ and $a_n = 0$ for n sufficiently large. We use these a_n's for the values of an infinite decimal on the nonnegative integers and proceed to define the a_{-n} inductively. We let a_{-1} be the largest integer less than $10(\alpha - A)$. Clearly $0 \leq a_1 \leq 9$. Put $A_1 = A + a_{-1}10^{-1}$, and define a_{-2} to be the largest integer less than $100(\alpha - A_2)$. The process continues inductively. We then obtain an infinite decimal $\mathbf{a}$ that does not end in a chain of 0's and for which $\mathbf{a}^\lambda = \alpha$, thus obtaining

POSITION 87 *There is a one-to-one correspondence between I_0 and $\mathbf{R}^+$.*

Once we have this correspondence, we can define an addition and a multiplication on the elements of I_0; namely,

$$\mathbf{a} + \mathbf{b} = (\mathbf{a}^\lambda + \mathbf{b}^\lambda)^{\lambda^{-1}},$$

$$\mathbf{ab} = (\mathbf{a}^\lambda \mathbf{b}^\lambda)^{\lambda^{-1}}.$$

One could then enlarge I_0 by adjoining the symbols 0 and $-\mathbf{a}$. Call this enlarged set I^*. We can then define an addition and a multiplication on I^* so that I^* is a field isomorphic to $\mathbf{R}$. Actually there is an order-preserving operation of I^* onto $\mathbf{R}$ with I_0 serving as the positive cone for I^*. Thus we can, if we wish, consider the real field to be the set of infinite decimals. If we do so, the prime field consists of those decimals $\mathbf{a}$ such that

$$a_{n+s} = a_s, \qquad \text{for some } n \text{ and all sufficiently negative } s.$$

Such decimals are called *repeating decimals*.

It follows directly from Proposition 87 and Proposition 14, Chap. 2, and its corollary that

POSITION 88 $\mathbf{R}$ *is an uncountable set.*

The reader should prove

PROPOSITION 89 *The real field* $\mathbf{R}$ *contains an element that is transcendental over the field of rational numbers.*

PROPOSITION 90 *If* α *is transcendental over a field* $\mathscr{F}$, *then the minimal field containing* $\mathscr{F}$ *and* α *is isomorphic to the field* $\mathscr{F}(x)$, *where* x *is an indeterminate over* $\mathscr{F}$.

COROLLARY *If* $\alpha_1, \ldots, \alpha_m$ *are transcendental elements over* $\mathbf{Q}$ *and are a set of algebraically independent indeterminates over* $\mathbf{Q}$, *then the minimal field containing* $\mathbf{Q}$ *and* $\{\alpha_1, \ldots, \alpha_m\}$ *is denumerable.*

PROPOSITION 91 *The real field* $\mathbf{R}$ *contains an uncountable set of algebraically independent indeterminates over* $\mathbf{Q}$.

EXERCISES 3 Prove: If $\alpha < \beta$ are real numbers, then $S = \{x \in \mathbf{R} \mid \alpha < x < \beta\}$ is an uncountable set.

4 Prove:

A. $\mathbf{R}/\mathbf{Z}$ is an uncountable additive abelian group.

B. If $\lfloor \alpha \rfloor \in \mathbf{R}/\mathbf{Z}$ and $\mathbf{n} \in \mathbf{Z}^+$, then there is a $\lfloor \beta \rfloor \in \mathbf{R}/\mathbf{Z}$ such that $\mathbf{n}\lfloor \beta \rfloor = \lfloor \alpha \rfloor$.

5 Prove:

A. $\mathbf{Q}/\mathbf{Z}$ is a countable additive abelian subgroup of $\mathbf{R}/\mathbf{Z}$.

B. If $\lfloor \alpha \rfloor \in \mathbf{Q}/\mathbf{Z}$ and $\mathbf{n} \in \mathbf{Z}^+$, then there is a $\lfloor \beta \rfloor \in \mathbf{Q}/\mathbf{Z}$ such that $\mathbf{n}\lfloor \beta \rfloor = \lfloor \alpha \rfloor$.

C. $\mathbf{Q}/\mathbf{Z}$ is the torsion subgroup of $\mathbf{R}/\mathbf{Z}$.

6 Prove:

A. If $\mathscr{D}$ is a linearly ordered integral domain with positive cone $\mathscr{P}$ and if φ is a monomorphism of $\mathscr{D}'$ into $\mathscr{D}$, then $\mathscr{P}^{\varphi^{-1}}$ is a positive cone for $\mathscr{D}$.

B. Let α be the transcendental real number over $\mathbf{Q}$; then $\mathscr{P} = \{A \in \mathbf{Z}[x] \mid A(\alpha) > 0\}$ is a positive cone for $\mathbf{Z}[x]$. Relative to this ordering $\mathbf{Z}[x]$ is an archimedean domain.

16 VALUATIONS

In this section we extend the idea of the absolute value. We shall not study the most general situation, but we shall study the most important example.

A *valuation on a field* $\mathscr{K}$ is a mapping $a \to \|a\|$ of a field $\mathscr{K}$ into $\mathbf{R}^+ \cup 0$ such that

A. $\|a\| = 0$ if and only if $a = 0$,

B. $\|ab\| = \|a\| \cdot \|b\|$, for all $a, b \in \mathscr{K}$,

C. there is a $\gamma \in \mathbf{R}^+$ such that $\|1 + a\| \leq \gamma$ whenever $\|a\| \leq 1$.

Typical examples of a valuation on a field is the absolute value on **Q** and on **R**. In these cases $\gamma = 2$. There is at least one valuation on every field $\mathcal{K}$; namely, $\|a\| = 1$ for $0 \neq a \in \mathcal{K}$. For this valuation $\gamma = 1$. We refer to this valuation as the *trivial valuation* on $\mathcal{K}$. We cannot completely disregard the trivial valuation, since if $\mathcal{F}$ is a subfield of $\mathcal{K}$ and $\mathcal{K}$ has a nontrivial valuation, the restriction of that valuation to the subfield $\mathcal{F}$ may be the trivial valuation on $\mathcal{F}$.

Condition (B) implies that $\|1\| = 1$, whence $\|-1\| = 1$. Thus we have $\|a\| = \|-a\|$ for all $a \in \mathcal{K}$. On taking $a = 0$ in (C), we see that $\gamma \geq 1$. If $a^n = 1$, for some $n \in \mathbf{Z}^+$, then $\|a\|^n = 1$. It then follows from Proposition 82 that $\|a\| = 1$. Since $a^{p-1} = 1$ for all $0 \neq a \in \mathbf{Z}_p$, we have

POSITION 92 *The only valuation on* $\mathbf{Z}_p$ *is the trivial valuation.*

The field **Q** has nontrivial valuations besides the ordinary absolute value. Let p be a fixed rational prime. Each $a \neq 0$ in **Q** can be expressed uniquely as $a = p^\alpha \cdot m/n$ where $n > 0$, $(p, m) = (p, n) = (m, n) = 1$. Then the map

$$a \to \|a\|_p = p^{-\alpha}$$

is a valuation on **Q** with $\gamma = 1$. This valuation is called the *p-adic valuation* on **Q**.

If $\| \quad \|$ is a valuation on $\mathcal{K}$, so is $\| \quad \|^\lambda$, for any $\lambda \in \mathbf{R}^+$. Two such valuations are related in the sense that $\|a\| < 1$ exactly when $\|a\|^\lambda < 1$. Two valuations $\| \quad \|_1$ and $\| \quad \|_2$ on the same field are said to be *equivalent* if $\|a\|_1 < 1$ exactly when $\|a\|_2 < 1$. The reader can quickly check that this is indeed an equivalence relation on the set of all valuations on $\mathcal{K}$. We have just observed that a valuation is always equivalent to any positive real power of itself.

ERCISES 1 Prove: If $\| \quad \|_1$ and $\| \quad \|_2$ are equivalent valuations on $\mathcal{K}$, then $\|a\|_1 > 1$ exactly when $\|a\|_2 > 1$; $\|a\|_1 = 1$ exactly when $\|a\|_2 = 1$; $\|a\|_1 < \|b\|_1$ if and only if $\|a\|_2 < \|b\|_2$.

2 Prove: If $\| \quad \|_1$ is not the trivial valuation of $\mathcal{K}$ and $\| \quad \|_2$ is a valuation on $\mathcal{K}$ such that $\|a\|_1 < 1$ implies $\|a\|_2 < 1$, then $\| \quad \|_1$ and $\| \quad \|_2$ are equivalent valuations on $\mathcal{K}$.

3 Prove: The trivial valuation is equivalent only to itself.

4 Prove: If p, q are distinct primes, then $\| \quad \|_p$ and $\| \quad \|_q$ are not equivalent valuations on **Q**.

Suppose $\| \quad \|_1$ and $\| \quad \|_2$ are nontrivial equivalent valuations on $\mathcal{K}$. Then there is an element $c \in \mathcal{K}$ such that $\|c\|_1 > 1$. By Proposition 84, to each nonzero a in $\mathcal{K}$ there is a positive real number α such that $\|a\|_1 = \|c\|_1^\alpha$. Each positive real number is the least upper bound of a monotonic sequence of rationals. Say α is the least upper bound of the sequence $m_1/n_1 < m_2/n_2 < \ldots$; then $\|a^{n_s}\|_1 > \|c^{m_s}\|_1$, and therefore $\|a^{n_s}\|_2 > \|c^{m_s}\|_2$. Thus $\|a\|_2 > \|c\|_2^{m_s/n_s}$, for $s = 1, 2, \ldots$. It follows that $\|a\|_2 \geq \|c\|_2^{\alpha}$.

If $\|a\|_2 \neq \|c\|_2^{\alpha}$, there is a $\beta > \alpha$ such that $\|a\|_2 = \|c\|_2^{\beta}$. Now, using the same argument, we would find that

$$\|c\|_1^{\alpha} = \|a\|_1 \geq \|c\|_1^{\beta}, \qquad \text{with } \alpha < \beta;$$

but this is contrary to Proposition 84. Hence $\|a\|_1 = \|c\|_1^{\alpha}$ implies $\|a\|_2 = \|c\|_2^{\alpha}$. Then

$$\alpha = \frac{\log_2 \|a\|_1}{\log_2 \|c\|_1} = \frac{\log_2 \|a\|_2}{\log_2 \|c\|_2}.$$

If $\|a\|_1 \neq 0$ or 1, we see that

$$\frac{\log_2 \|a\|_2}{\log_2 \|a\|_1} = \frac{\log_2 \|c\|_1}{\log_2 \|c\|_2} = \delta,$$

whence

$$\|a\|_2 = \|a\|_1^{\delta},$$

where δ is a positive real number that depends only on c and not on the varying a. This last relation continues to hold if $\|a\|_1 = 0$ or 1. We have proved

PROPOSITION 93 *Two valuations on a field are equivalent if and only if one is a positive real power of the other.*

Given a valuation $\| \quad \|$ on $\mathcal{K}$, let m be the least upper bound of the bounded set of real numbers $\{\|1 + a\| \mid a \in \mathcal{K}, \|a\| \leq 1\}$. If $m > 2$, by Proposition 84, there is a $\lambda \in \mathbf{R}^+$ such that $m^{\lambda} = 2$. Now, by Proposition 93, we obtain

COROLLARY 1 *Every valuation on a field is equivalent to a valuation with $\gamma \leq 2$.*

We next show

PROPOSITION 94 *A valuation with $\gamma \leq 2$ satisfies the triangle inequality:*

$$\|a + b\| \leq \|a\| + \|b\|, \qquad a, b \in \mathcal{K}.$$

PROOF. If $\gamma \leq 2$, we can replace γ by 2, and condition (C) remains valid. Hence we assume

$$\|1 + a\| \leq 2, \qquad \text{whenever } \|a\| \leq 1.$$

Suppose b, c are two nonzero elements of $\mathcal{K}$ such that $\|b\| \leq \|c\|$. Then

$$\|b + c\| = \|c\| \cdot \|(b/c) + 1\| \leq 2\|c\|.$$

Consequently we have

$$\|b + c\| \leq 2 \max\{\|b\|, \|c\|\} \leq 2\{\|b\| + \|c\|\}. \tag{6}$$

Inspection shows that (6) holds for all $b, c \in \mathscr{K}$.

On repeating the argument, we obtain

$$\left\| \sum_{i=1}^{4} a_i \right\| \leq 2^2 \max \{\|a_i\|\},$$

and more generally

$$\left\| \sum_{1}^{2^m} a_i \right\| \leq 2^m \max_i \{\|a_i\|\}, \qquad m = 1, 2, \ldots.$$

If $n \in \mathbf{Z}^+$, there is a nonnegative integer m such that $2^{m-1} \leq n < 2^m \leq 2n$. Given $a_1, \ldots, a_n$, put $a_{n+1} = \cdots = a_{2^m} = 0$, to obtain

$$\left\| \sum_{i=1}^{n} a_i \right\| \leq 2^m \max_i \{\|a_i\|\} \leq 2n \sum_{i=1}^{n} \|a_i\|. \tag{7}$$

As a particular case of (7) we have

$$\|\mathbf{n1}\| \leq 2\mathbf{n}, \qquad \mathbf{n} \in \mathbf{Z}$$

If $a, b \in \mathscr{K}$, for each positive integer n, we have

$$\begin{aligned} \|a + b\|^n = \|(a + b)^n\| &= \left\| \sum_{\nu=0}^{n} \binom{n}{\nu} a^{n-\nu} b^\nu \right\| \\ &\leq 2(n + 1) \sum \left\| \binom{n}{\nu} \right\| \|a\|^{n-\nu} \|b\|^\nu \\ &\leq 4(n + 1) \sum \binom{n}{\nu} \|a\|^{n-\nu} \|b\|^\nu \\ &= 4(n + 1)(\|a\| + \|b\|)^n, \end{aligned}$$

and therefore

$$\|a + b\| \leq \sqrt[n]{4(n + 1)}\{\|a\| + \|b\|\}, \qquad n = 1, 2, \ldots.$$

The sequence $\sqrt[n]{4(n + 1)}$ is a monotonic decreasing sequence of real numbers with limit 1, and so

$$\|a + b\| \leq \|a\| + \|b\|.$$

This proves Proposition 94.

Valuations for which we may take $\gamma = 1$ are called *nonarchimedean valuations*; all others are called *archimedean*. The ordinary absolute value is an archimedean valuation on $\mathbf{Q}$, and the p-adic valuations are nonarchimedean valuations. The trivial valuation is nonarchimedean. Two equivalent valuations are either both nonarchimedean or both archimedean. For a nonarchimedean valuation one has $\|\mathbf{n1}\| \leq 1$, for all $\mathbf{n} \in \mathbf{Z}$.

Suppose we are given a valuation $\| \quad \|$ on a field $\mathscr{K}$ and that there is an integer $\mathbf{m} \geq 2$ such that $\|\mathbf{m}1\| \leq 1$. Each $\mathbf{n} \in \mathbf{Z}^+$ can be expressed uniquely as a finite sum

$$\mathbf{n} = \sum_{i=0}^{N} \mathbf{a}_i \mathbf{m}^i,$$

with $0 \leq \mathbf{a}_i < \mathbf{m}$ and $\mathbf{a}_N \neq 0$. Then $\mathbf{m}^N \leq \mathbf{n} < \mathbf{m}^{N+1}$ and $N \leq \log_{\mathbf{m}} \mathbf{n}$. If *the valuation satisfies the triangle inequality*, then $\|\mathbf{a}\| \leq |\mathbf{a}|$ and we obtain

$$\|\mathbf{n}1\| \leq \sum |\mathbf{a}_i| \leq (\mathbf{m} - 1)[1 + \log_{\mathbf{m}} \mathbf{n}],$$

and $\qquad \|\mathbf{n}1\|^{\mathbf{k}} = \|\mathbf{n}^{\mathbf{k}}\| \leq (\mathbf{m} - 1)[1 + \mathbf{k} \cdot \log_{\mathbf{m}} \mathbf{n}], \qquad \mathbf{k} = 1, 2, \ldots .$

Thus $\qquad \|\mathbf{n}1\| \leq \sqrt[\mathbf{k}]{(\mathbf{m} - 1)(1 + \mathbf{k} \log_{\mathbf{m}} \mathbf{n})}, \qquad \mathbf{k} = 1, 2, \ldots,$

and hence $\qquad \|\mathbf{n}1\| \leq 1, \qquad$ for all $\mathbf{n} \in \mathbf{Z}^+$,

and thus $\qquad \|\mathbf{n}1\| \leq 1, \qquad$ for $\mathbf{n} \in \mathbf{Z}$.

If $a, b \in \mathscr{K}$ and $\mathbf{n} \in \mathbf{Z}^+$, we have

$$\|a + b\|^{\mathbf{n}} \leq \sum \left\| \binom{\mathbf{n}}{\mathbf{s}} 1 \right\| \cdot \|a\|^{\mathbf{n}-\mathbf{s}} \|b\|^{\mathbf{s}} \leq (\mathbf{n} + 1) \max \{\|a\|^{\mathbf{n}}, \|b\|^{\mathbf{n}}\},$$

whence $\qquad \|a + b\| \leq \sqrt[\mathbf{n}]{\mathbf{n} + 1} \max \{\|a\|, \|b\|\},$

and hence $\quad \|a + b\| \leq \max \{\|a\|, \|b\|\}, \qquad$ for all $a, b \in \mathscr{K}$.

In particular, we have $\|1 + a\| \leq 1$ if $\|a\| \leq 1$. Since every valuation is equivalent to one satisfying the triangle inequality, we have proved

PROPOSITION 95 *A valuation is archimedean if and only if*

$$\|\mathbf{n}1\| > 1, \qquad \textit{for all integers } \mathbf{n} \geq 2.$$

The reader can prove

COROLLARY *There are no archimedean valuations on a field of characteristic $p \neq 0$.*

We shall prove

PROPOSITION 96 *Each archimedean valuation on* **Q** *is equivalent to the ordinary absolute value.*

PROOF. In proving this proposition, we can always replace the given valuation by an equivalent valuation. Hence we may suppose we have a valuation, $\|\quad\|$, which is an archimedean valuation on **Q** and which satisfies the triangle law. In that case, $1 < \|n\| \leq n$, for all integers $n > 1$. If m, n are integers greater than 1, we have

$$n = \sum_{i=0}^{N} a_i m^i,$$

where $0 \leq a_i < m$, $m^N \leq n < m^{N+1}$. But then

$$\|n\| \leq m(1 + (\log_2 n)/(\log_2 m)) \|m\|^{(\log_2 n)/(\log_2 m)}.$$

Hence, for all $k \in \mathbf{Z}^+$,

$$\|n^k\| \leq m(1 + k(\log_2 n)/(\log_2 m))\|m\|^{k(\log_2 n)/(\log_2 m)}.$$

It follows that

$$\|n\| \leq \|m\|^{(\log_2 n)/(\log_2 m)},$$

or

$$\|n\|^{1/\log_2 n} \leq \|m\|^{1/\log_2 m}.$$

But we could interchange the role of m and n, and hence we obtain

$$\|n\|^{1/\log_2 n} = \|m\|^{1/\log_2 m} = 2^\alpha, \qquad \text{for } m, n > 1.$$

Since $\|m\| > 1$, α must be a positive real number. Thus

$$\|n\| = 2^{\alpha \log_2 n} = n^\alpha, \qquad \text{for } n > 1.$$

As $\|n\| = \|-n\|$ and $\|1\| = 1$, we see that

$$\|n\| = |n|^\alpha \qquad \text{for all } n \in \mathbf{Z}.$$

Since $\mathbf{Q}$ is the quotient field of $\mathbf{Z}$ and $\| \quad \|$ is multiplicative, we obtain

$$\|a\| = |a|^\alpha, \qquad \text{for all } a \in \mathbf{Q}.$$

This proves the proposition.

ERCISES 5 Given a subset $A \subset \mathbf{R}$, we say $a \in \mathbf{R}$ is an *accumulation point* of A provided that for each $e \in \mathbf{R}^+$ the set $U_e = \{x \in \mathbf{R} \mid a - e < x < a + e\}$ has a nonempty intersection with A. Prove: Given an archimedean valuation $\| \quad \|$ on $\mathscr{K}$, the set $\Gamma = \{x \in \mathbf{R}^+ \mid x = \|a\| \text{ for some } a \in \mathscr{K}\}$ has an accumulation point different from 0, Γ is a multiplicative subgroup of $\mathbf{R}^+$ and is called the *group of values* or *the value group* for $\| \quad \|$.

6 Prove: If $\| \quad \|$ is a nonarchimedean valuation and $\|a\| \neq \|b\|$, then $\|a + b\| = \max\{\|a\|, \|b\|\}$.

We now determine a few properties of nonarchimedean valuations. Let $\| \quad \|$ be such a nonarchimedean valuation on $\mathscr{K}$. Define

$$\mathfrak{o} = \{\alpha \in \mathscr{K} \mid \|a\| \leq 1\}, \qquad \mathfrak{p} = \{a \in \mathscr{K} \mid \|a\| < 1\}.$$

The reader can easily show that

POSITION 97 *$\mathfrak{o}$ is an integral domain having $\mathscr{K}$ as quotient field. $\mathfrak{p}$ is a prime ideal of $\mathfrak{o}$.*

As a Corollary to Proposition 94, we have

COROLLARY *If $\| \quad \|$ is a nonarchimedean valuation on $\mathbf{Q}$, then $\mathbf{Z} \subset \mathfrak{o}$.*

We next prove

POSITION 98 *Every nontrivial nonarchimedean valuation on $\mathbf{Q}$ is equivalent to one of the p-adic valuations.*

PROOF. Let $\| \quad \|$ be a nontrivial nonarchimedean valuation on $\mathbf{Q}$. Then $\mathbf{Z} \subset \mathfrak{o}$. The reader can easily check that $\mathfrak{p} \cap \mathbf{Z}$ is a prime ideal of $\mathbf{Z}$. It cannot be all of $\mathbf{Z}$, else $\|1\| < 1$. If $\mathfrak{p} \cap \mathbf{Z} = (0)$, then $\|n\| = 1$ for all $n \in \mathbf{Z}$, and hence $\| \quad \|$ would be the trivial valuation. Therefore $\mathfrak{p} \cap \mathbf{Z} = p\mathbf{Z}$, for some prime $p \in \mathbf{Z}$. But then $m \in \mathbf{Z}$ has value less than 1 if and only if $p \mid m$.

Given $a \in \mathbf{Q}$, $a \neq 0$, we can write

$$a = p^{\alpha} m/n, \qquad \text{where } (p, m) = (p, n) = (m, n) = 1, \qquad \alpha \in \mathbf{Z}.$$

Hence $\|a\| = \|p^{\alpha}\| \cdot \|m\| \cdot \|n\|^{-1} = \|p\|^{\alpha}$. Let λ be the positive real number such that $\|p\| = p^{-\lambda}$. Then $\|a\| = \|a\|_p^{\lambda}$. This proves the proposition.

EXERCISES

7 Prove: If $\| \quad \|$ is a nonarchimedean valuation on $\mathbf{Q}$, the value group Γ for the valuation $\| \quad \|$, has no accumulation point other than 0. Γ is a group isomorphic to $\mathbf{Z}$. Γ is the cyclic multiplicative group generated by the largest element of Γ less than 1.

8 Prove: If $\| \quad \|$ is a nonarchimedean valuation on $\mathscr{K}$, the set $\mathscr{U} = \mathfrak{o} - \mathfrak{p}$ is a multiplicative group and is the group of units in the integral domain $\mathfrak{o}$. The group Γ, of Exercise 7, is isomorphic to $\mathscr{K}^{\times}/\mathscr{U}$.

9 Prove: Let $\| \quad \|_{\nu}$ $(\nu = 1, 2)$ be nonarchimedean valuations on $\mathscr{K}$. Let $\mathfrak{o}_{\nu}$, $\mathfrak{p}_{\nu}$ be the associated integral domains and prime ideals. Then $\| \quad \|_1$ and $\| \quad \|_2$ are equivalent if and only if $\mathfrak{o}_1 = \mathfrak{o}_2$, $\mathfrak{p}_1 = \mathfrak{p}_2$.

10 Determine $\mathfrak{o}$ and $\mathfrak{p}$ for a p-adic valuation on $\mathbf{Q}$.

An integral domain $\mathscr{D}$ is said to be maximal in a field provided $\mathscr{D} \subsetneq \mathscr{K}$ and no subdomain $\mathscr{D}'$ of $\mathscr{K}$ is such that $\mathscr{D} \subsetneq \mathscr{D}' \subsetneq \mathscr{K}$.

EXERCISES

11 Determine the maximal integral domains of $\mathbf{Q}$.

12 Prove: The integral domain $\mathfrak{o}$ associated with a nonarchimedean valuation on $\mathbf{Q}$ is a maximal domain of $\mathbf{Q}$.

It follows from the exercises above and Proposition 97 that there is a one-to-one correspondence between the set of maximal integral domains of $\mathbf{Q}$ and the set of equivalence classes of nonarchimedean valuations on $\mathbf{Q}$. If we extend the idea of valuations a bit, to a map of a field into a linearly ordered group, it can be shown that this is the situation for any field $\mathscr{K}$.

EXERCISES

13 Prove: $\mathfrak{o}/\mathfrak{p}$ is a field and in the case of a p-adic valuation on $\mathbf{Q}$, $\mathfrak{o}/\mathfrak{p}$ is isomorphic to $\mathbf{Z}_p$. For a p-adic valuation, $\mathfrak{p}$ is a principal ideal generated by p, and the ideals of $\mathfrak{o}$ are all principal ideals, each being generated by a power of p.

14 Prove: If $\mathcal{D}$ is an integral domain and $\mathcal{Q}$ is a quotient field of $\mathcal{D}$ and if $\| \quad \|$ is a valuation of $\mathcal{D}$, then we can extend $\| \quad \|$ to be a valuation on $\mathcal{Q}$ by defining the value of a ratio as the ratio of the values.

15 Let x be an indeterminate over a field $\mathcal{F}$. Let $\mathcal{K} = \mathcal{F}(x)$.
Prove:

A. If P is an irreducible polynomial over $\mathcal{F}$, the map $A \to \|A\|_P = 2^{-m}$, where $P^m \mid A$ and $P^{m+1} \nmid A$, defines a nontrivial nonarchimedean valuation on $\mathcal{K}$ that is the trivial valuation on $\mathcal{F}$.

B. The map $A \to \|A\|_\infty = 2^{-\deg A}$ is a nontrivial valuation on $\mathcal{K}$ that is the trivial valuation on $\mathcal{F}$.

C. Each valuation on $\mathcal{K}$ that is trivial on $\mathcal{F}$ is a nonarchimedean valuation and is equivalent to one of the valuations listed in (A) or (B), and $\mathfrak{o}/\mathfrak{p}$ contains a field isomorphic to $\mathcal{F}$.

D. Let $\mathcal{E} \supset \mathcal{F}$ be a field with a nontrivial valuation $\| \quad \|$, and suppose that $\mathcal{E}$ contains a transcendental over $\mathcal{F}$, say α. The map $A \to |||A||| = \|A(\alpha)\|$, $A \in \mathcal{F}(x)$, determines a valuation on $\mathcal{F}(x)$. Is it nontrivial on $\mathcal{F}$? Could $||| \quad |||$ be archimedean?

17 METRIC PROPERTIES OF VALUATED FIELDS

Let $\mathcal{K}$ be a field with a valuation $\| \quad \|$. Let $\{a_m\}$ be a sequence from $\mathcal{K}$. We say that the sequence $\{a_m\}$ is *bounded with respect to the valuation* provided there is a $\beta \in \mathbf{R}^+$ such that $\|a_m\| \le \beta$ for $m = 1, 2, \ldots$. The sequence $\{a_m\}$ is a *cauchy sequence with respect to the valuation* provided there is a map, $e \to M(e)$, from $\mathbf{R}^+$ to $\mathbf{Z}^+$ such that $\|a_m - a_n\| < e$ whenever $m, n > M(e)$. The sequence $\{a_m\}$ is a *null sequence with respect to the valuation* provided there is a map, $e \to N(e)$, from $\mathbf{R}^+$ into $\mathbf{Z}^+$ such that $\|a_n\| < e$ whenever $n > N(e)$.

We shall now investigate properties of such sequences. All results should be interpreted as being relative to a given fixed valuation even when, for the sake of simplicity of language, we neglect to specify that fact. Throughout, we shall assume the valuation satisfies the triangle inequality. This assumption is not necessary but it simplifies a few arguments. Most of the lemmas are easily verified, and the reader should give proofs wherever they are omitted.

Let $\mathcal{B}$, $\mathcal{C}$, and $\mathcal{N}$ be, respectively, the set of all bounded sequences, the set of all cauchy sequences, and the set of all null sequences of $\mathcal{K}$ with respect to the given valuation.

LEMMA 1 $\mathcal{N} \subset \mathcal{C} \subset \mathcal{B}$.

LEMMA 2 *If $\{a_n\}$ is a cauchy sequence containing a subsequence that is a null sequence, then $\{a_n\}$ is a null sequence.*

PROOF. Let $\{a_{n_s}\}$ be the subsequence that is a null sequence. Let $N(e)$ be the function such that $\|a_{n_s}\| < e$ whenever $s > N(e)$. Let $M(e)$

be the function such that $\|a_m - a_n\| < e$ whenever $m, n > M(e)$. Now, if $m > M(e/2)$, choose s such that $s > N(e/2)$, *and* $n_s > M(e/2)$; then $\|a_m\| < \|a_{n_s}\| + e/2 < e$. This proves the lemma.

LEMMA 3 *If $\{a_n\}$ is a nonnull cauchy sequence, then there is an $S \in \mathbf{Z}^+$ and a positive real number δ such that $\|a_m\| > \delta$ whenever $m > S$.*

LEMMA 4 *If $\{a_n\}$, $\{b_n\} \subset \mathscr{C}$, then the sequences $\{-a_n\}$ and $\{a_n + b_n\}$ are in $\mathscr{C}$.*

If $\{a_n\}$ and $\{b_n\} \in \mathscr{C}$, let $M(e)$ and $M'(e)$ be the functions such that $\|a_m - a_n\| < e$ when $m, n > M(e)$ and $\|b_m - b_n\| < e$ when $m, n > M'(e)$. By Lemma 1, $\{a_n\}$ and $\{b_n\}$ are bounded sequences. Let $\alpha, \beta \in \mathbf{R}^+$ such that $\|a_n\| \le \alpha$, $\|b_n\| \le \beta$ for all $n \in \mathbf{Z}^+$. Let $\alpha^* = \max\{\alpha, 1\}$ $\beta^* = \max\{\beta, 1\}$. We observe

$$\begin{aligned}\|a_m b_m - a_n b_n\| &\le \|a_n b_n - a_n b_m\| + \|a_n b_m - a_m b_m\| \\ &\le \alpha\|b_n - b_m\| + \beta\|a_n - a_m\| < e\end{aligned}$$

provided $m, n > \max\{M(e/2\alpha^*), M'(e/2\beta^*)\}$. We have proved

LEMMA 5 *If $\{a_n\}$, $\{b_n\} \in \mathscr{C}$, then $\{a_n b_n\} \in \mathscr{C}$.*

If $a \in \mathscr{K}$, let a^* denote the sequence having each entry equal to a. Clearly, the sequences a^* lie in $\mathscr{C}$. Hence there is an embedding of $\mathscr{K}$ into $\mathscr{C}$.

In view of Lemmas 4 and 5, we now define two binary operations on the elements of $\mathscr{C}$, namely,

$$\{a_n\} + \{b_n\} = \{a_n + b_n\},$$
$$\{a_n\} \cdot \{b_n\} = \{a_n b_n\}.$$

LEMMA 6 *Under the binary operations above, $\mathscr{C}$ is a commutative ring, with 1^* as its unity.*

LEMMA 7 *If $\{a_n\}$, $\{b_n\} \in \mathscr{N}$, then $\{-a_n\}$ and $\{a_n + b_n\} \in \mathscr{N}$.*

LEMMA 8 *If $\{a_n\} \in \mathscr{C}$ and $\{b_n\} \in \mathscr{N}$, then $\{a_n b_n\} \in \mathscr{N}$.*

As a consequence of Lemma 3, we have

LEMMA 9 *If $\{a_n\}$, $\{b_n\} \in \mathscr{C}$ and $\{a_n b_n\} \in \mathscr{N}$, then at least one of $\{a_n\}$ and $\{b_n\}$ is in $\mathscr{N}$.*

Lemmas 7, 8, and 9 tell us that

LEMMA 10 *$\mathscr{N}$ is a prime ideal of $\mathscr{C}$.*

It follows from Lemma 10 and Proposition 60 that $\mathscr{C}/\mathscr{N}$ is an integral domain. Actually, more is true. We shall prove

LEMMA 11 *$\mathscr{C}/\mathscr{N}$ is a field.*

PROOF. Let $\{a_n\}$ be a nonnull cauchy sequence. We need to show the existence of a cauchy sequence $\{b_n\}$ such that $(a_n + \mathcal{N})(b_n + \mathcal{N}) = 1^* + \mathcal{N}$. This is equivalent to showing the existence of a cauchy sequence $\{b_n\}$ such that $\{a_n b_n - 1\}$ is a null sequence.

By Lemma 3 there is an $S \in \mathbf{Z}^+$ and a $\delta \in \mathbf{R}^+$ such that $\|a_n\| > \delta$ if $n > S$. Hence $a_n \neq 0$ if $n > S$. Put

$$b_n = \begin{cases} 0 \quad , & \text{if } n \leq S, \\ a_n^{-1}, & \text{if } n > S. \end{cases}$$

Let $M(e)$ be the function such that $\|a_n - a_m\| < e$ when $m, n > M(e)$. Then

$$\|b_n - b_m\| \leq \|a_n a_m\|^{-1} \|a_m - a_n\| \leq \delta^{-2} \|a_m - a_n\| < e,$$

provided $$m, n > \max \{S, M(e\delta^2)\}.$$

Thus we have shown that $\{b_n\}$ is indeed a cauchy sequence. As our construction was such that $\{a_n b_n - 1\}$ is a null sequence, our proof is completed.

Since $a^* \in \mathcal{N}$ if and only if $a = 0$, it is easily seen that

LEMMA 12 *The map $a \to a^* + \mathcal{N}$ of $\mathcal{K}$ into the field $\mathcal{C}/\mathcal{N}$ is a monomorphism.*

We let $\mathcal{K}^*$ denote the isomorphic image of $\mathcal{K}$ under the map $a \to a^* + \mathcal{N}$. Since

$$\|a\| = \|a - b + b\| \leq \|a - b\| + \|b\|,$$

we see that

$$|\ \|a\| - \|b\|\ | \leq \|a - b\|,$$

for any $a, b \in \mathcal{K}$. We can therefore show

LEMMA 13 *If $\{a_n\} \in \mathcal{C}$, then $\{\|a_n\|\}$ is a cauchy sequence of* $\mathbf{R}$ *with respect to ordinary absolute value.*

It follows from Lemma 13 and Theorem 6 that, if $\{a_n\} \in \mathcal{C}$, then the sequence $\{\|a_n\|\}$ has a limit in $\mathbf{R}$.

LEMMA 14 *Suppose $\{a_n\} \in \mathcal{C}$; then $\{a_n\} \in \mathcal{N}$ if and only if* $\lim \|a_n\| = 0$.

Furthermore, we have

LEMMA 15 *If $\{a_n\}$, $\{b_n\} \in \mathcal{C}$ and if $\{a_n - b_n\} \in \mathcal{N}$, then* $\lim \|a_n\| = \lim \|b_n\|$.

LEMMA 16 *If $\{a_n\}$, $\{b_n\} \in \mathcal{C}$, then*

$$\lim \|a_n b_n\| = (\lim \|a_n\|)(\lim \|b_n\|),$$

and $$\lim \|a_n + b_n\| \leq (\lim \|a_n\|) + (\lim \|b_n\|).$$

It follows that, if $\{a_n\} + \mathcal{N} = \{b_n\} + \mathcal{N}$, then $\{a_n - b_n\} \in \mathcal{N}$, and hence $\lim \|a_n\| = \lim \|b_n\|$. Thus the map

$$\{a_n\} + \mathcal{N} \to \lim \|a_n\|$$

is a well-defined map of $\mathscr{C}/\mathscr{N}$ into **R**. Since $\|a_n\| \geq 0$, it follows that $\lim \|a_n\| \geq 0$, and hence this is a map of $\mathscr{C}/\mathscr{N}$ into $\mathbf{R}^+ \cup 0$. Lemmas 14 and 16 tell us

LEMMA 17 *The map*

$$\{a_n\} + \mathscr{N} \to \|\{a_n\} + \mathscr{N}\| = \lim \|a_n\|$$

is a valuation on $\mathscr{C}/\mathscr{N}$.

The valuation $\|\ \ \|$ is such that

$$\|a^* + \mathscr{N}\| = \|a\|, \qquad \text{for all } a \in \mathscr{K}.$$

Hence, $\|(\mathbf{n1})^* + \mathscr{N}\| = \|\mathbf{n1}\|$ for all $n \in \mathbf{Z}$. Proposition 95 now tells us that $\|\ \ \|$ and $\|\ \ \|$ are both archimedean or are both nonarchimedean.

If a field $\mathscr{K}$ has a valuation, we say that a sequence $\{a_n\}$ of $\mathscr{K}$ has the element $a \in \mathscr{K}$ as a *limit with respect to the valuation* provided $\{a_n - a\}$ is a null sequence relative to the given valuation.

EXERCISES 1 Prove: A sequence of $\mathscr{K}$ has at most one limit in $\mathscr{K}$.

2 Prove: If relative to a valuation the sequence $\{a_n\}$ has a as its limit and the sequence $\{b_n\}$ has b as its limit, then the sequences $\{-a_n\}$, $\{a_n + b_n\}$, and $\{a_n b_n\}$ have $-a$, $a + b$, and ab as their respective limits.

3 Prove: If relative to a valuation $\{a_n\}$ has a limit in $\mathscr{K}$, then the sequence $\{a_n\}$ is a cauchy sequence with respect to the valuation.

4 Prove or disprove: If $\{\|a_n\|\}$ is a cauchy sequence of **R**, then $\{a_n\}$ is a cauchy sequence relative to the valuation $\|\ \ \|$.

LEMMA 18 *If $\{a_v\}$ is a cauchy sequence of $\mathscr{K}$ with respect to $\|\ \ \|$, then $\{a_v^* + \mathscr{N}\}$ is a cauchy sequence of $\mathscr{C}/\mathscr{N}$ with respect to $\|\ \ \|$. Furthermore $\{a_v\} + \mathscr{N}$ is the limit of the sequence $\{a_v^* + \mathscr{N}\}$ relative to $\|\ \ \|$.*

LEMMA 19 *Each element of $\mathscr{C}/\mathscr{N}$ is the limit relative to $\|\ \ \|$ of a cauchy sequence of elements from $\mathscr{K}^*$.*

A field with a valuation is said to be *complete with respect to the valuation* provided each cauchy sequence with respect to the valuation has a limit in the field. It follows from Theorem 6 that the field of real numbers **R** is complete with respect to ordinary absolute value.

It should be noted that we have defined "complete relative to a linear ordering" and "complete relative to a valuation." These are not the same. It is a rare phenomena that the field **R** is complete in both senses. There are many fields with a nontrivial valuation that cannot be linearly ordered.

We now complete our sequence of lemmas, proving

PROPOSITION 99 *The field $\mathscr{C}/\mathscr{N}$ is complete with respect to the valuation $\|\ \ \|$.*

PROOF. Let $\{a_\nu^{(1)}\} + \mathcal{N}, \{a_\nu^{(2)}\} + \mathcal{N}, \ldots, \{a_\nu^{(n)}\} + \mathcal{N}, \ldots$ be a cauchy sequence of $\mathcal{C}/\mathcal{N}$ relative to $\| \ \|$. Let $M_*(e)$ be the function such that

$$\|\{a_\nu^{(n)}\} - \{a_\nu^{(m)}\} + \mathcal{N}\| < e, \qquad \text{when } n, m > M_*(e).$$

Since the sequence $\{a_\nu^{(n)}\}$ are cauchy sequences of $\mathcal{K}$ relative to $\| \ \|$, there are functions $M_n(e)$ such that

$$\|a_r^{(n)} - a_s^{(n)}\| < e, \qquad \text{when } r, s > M_n(e).$$

For each n, let $N(n)$ be a fixed integer greater than $M_n(1/n)$, and let $a_{(n)} = a^{(n)}_{N(n)}$. Then for each n there is an element $a_{(n)} \in \mathcal{K}$ such that

$$\|a_r^{(n)} - a_{(n)}\| < \frac{1}{n}, \qquad \text{when } r > M_n(1/n).$$

Consequently $\|\{a_\nu^{(n)}\} - a^*_{(n)} + \mathcal{N}\| = \lim\limits_{\nu \to \infty} \|a_\nu^{(n)} - a_{(n)}\| \leq \dfrac{1}{n}$.

We then have

$$\begin{aligned}\|a_{(n)} - a_{(m)}\| &= \|a^*_{(n)} - a^*_{(m)} + \mathcal{N}\|\\ &\leq \|a^*_{(n)} - \{a_\nu^{(n)}\} + \mathcal{N}\| + \|a^*_m - \{a_\nu^{(m)}\} + \mathcal{N}\|\\ &+ \|\{a_\nu^{(m)}\} - \{a_\nu^{(n)}\} + \mathcal{N}\| \leq \frac{1}{n} + \frac{1}{m} + \frac{e}{2} < e,\end{aligned}$$

provided $m, n > \max\{4e^{-1}, M_*(e/2)\} = J(e)$. Thus, we have shown that the sequence $\{a_{(n)}\}$ is a cauchy sequence relative to $\| \ \|$. In particular $\{a_{(n)}\} + \mathcal{N}$ is an element of the field $\mathcal{C}/\mathcal{N}$.

We have also shown that

$$\|\{a_{(\nu)}\} - a^*_{(n)} + \mathcal{N}\| = \lim_\nu \|a_{(\nu)} - a_{(n)}\| < e,$$

when $n > J(e)$. Finally, we observe that

$$\begin{aligned}&\|\{a_{(\nu)}\} - \{a_\nu^{(n)}\} + \mathcal{N}\|\\ &\leq \|\{a_{(\nu)}\} - a^*_{(n)} + \mathcal{N}\| + \|a^*_{(n)} - \{a_\nu^{(n)}\} + \mathcal{N}\|\\ &\leq \lim \|a_{(\nu)} - a_{(n)}\| + \frac{1}{n} \leq e,\end{aligned}$$

provided $n > \max\{2/e, J(e/2)\}$.

This completes the proof, for we have shown that the cauchy sequence $\{\{a_\nu^{(n)}\} + \mathcal{N}\}$ has $\{a_{(n)}\} + \mathcal{N}$ as its limit.

If $\mathcal{K}_1, \mathcal{K}_2$ are fields with valuations $\| \ \|_1$ and $\| \ \|_2$ respectively, such that $\mathcal{K}_1 \subset \mathcal{K}_2$ and $\|a\|_1 = \|a\|_2$ for all $a \in \mathcal{K}_1$, we say that $\| \ \|_2$ is an *extension* of $\| \ \|_1$ to the field $\mathcal{K}_2$.

An isomorphism τ of a field $\mathcal{K}_1$ with valuation $\| \ \|_1$ onto a field

$\mathcal{K}_2$ with valuation $\| \quad \|_2$ is said to be a *continuous isomorphism* provided the valuations

$$a \to \|a^\tau\|_2, \qquad a \to \|a\|_1$$

are equivalent valuations on $\mathcal{K}_1$.

We also have

PROPOSITION 100 *If $\mathcal{K}_1$ is a field that contains $\mathcal{K}$ and if $\mathcal{K}_1$ is complete relative to a valuation that extends a valuation $\| \quad \|$ on $\mathcal{K}$, then $\mathcal{K}_1$ contains an isomorphic replica of $\mathcal{C}/\mathcal{N}$ where $\mathcal{C}$ and $\mathcal{N}$ are respectively the cauchy sequences and the null sequences of $\mathcal{K}$ relative to $\| \quad \|$.*

The proof consists in showing that the map

$$\{a_n\} + \mathcal{N} \to \lim a_n \text{ (relative to valuation on } \mathcal{K}_1)$$

of $\mathcal{C}/\mathcal{N}$ into $\mathcal{K}_1$ is a monomorphism.

COROLLARY *Let $\mathcal{K}$ be a field with valuation $\| \quad \|$. If $\mathcal{K}_1 \supset \mathcal{K}$ and if no proper subfield of $\mathcal{K}_1$ is complete with respect to a valuation extending $\| \quad \|$ and $\mathcal{K}_1$ is complete, then $\mathcal{K}_1$ and $\mathcal{C}/\mathcal{N}$ are continuously isomorphic.*

Combining Propositions 7 and 99, we see that there is a field $\overline{\mathcal{K}}$ such that (A) $\mathcal{K} \subset \overline{\mathcal{K}}$, (B) there is an isomorphism σ of $\overline{\mathcal{K}}$ onto $\mathcal{C}/\mathcal{N}$, (C) $a^\sigma = a^* + \mathcal{N}$ for all $a \in \mathcal{K}$. The map $a \to \overline{\|\alpha\|} = \| \alpha^\sigma \|$ is a valuation on $\overline{\mathcal{K}}$ that extends the valuation $\| \quad \|$. A sequence $\{\alpha_n\}$ in $\overline{\mathcal{K}}$ is cauchy relative to $\overline{\| \quad \|}$ if and only if the sequence $\{\alpha_n{}^\sigma\}$ in $\mathcal{C}/\mathcal{N}$ is a cauchy sequence with respect to $\| \quad \|$. Hence $\overline{\mathcal{K}}$ is complete with respect to $\overline{\| \quad \|}$. Furthermore, from Lemma 19, we see that each element of $\overline{\mathcal{K}}$ is a limit, relative to $\overline{\| \quad \|}$, of a cauchy sequence from $\mathcal{K}$.

Summarizing, we have proved

THEOREM 7 *To each field $\mathcal{K}$ with a valuation $\| \quad \|$ there exists (to within a c isomorphism) a unique minimal extension $\overline{\mathcal{K}}$ of $\mathcal{K}$ such that $\overline{\mathcal{K}}$ has a valuation that extends $\| \quad \|$ and $\overline{\mathcal{K}}$ is complete with respect to that valuation. There is a continuous isomorphism of $\overline{\mathcal{K}}$ onto $\mathcal{C}/\mathcal{N}$.*

A field $\overline{\mathcal{K}}$ satisfying the conditions of Theorem 7 is called a *completion of $\mathcal{K}$ with respect to the valuation $\| \quad \|$.*

Since each real number is the limit of a bounded monotonic increasing sequence of rational numbers, each real number is the limit of a cauchy sequence of rational numbers relative to the ordinary absolute value. Hence we have

PROPOSITION 101 **R** *is the completion of* **Q** *with respect to ordinary absolute value.*

If $\{a_n\}$ is a cauchy sequence (null sequence) relative to a valuation $\| \quad \|_1$ and if $\| \quad \|_1$ and $\| \quad \|_2$ are equivalent valuations, then $\{a_n\}$ is a cauchy sequence (null sequence) relative to $\| \quad \|_2$. Thus we have

PROPOSITION 102 *If $\overline{\mathscr{K}}$ is the completion of $\mathscr{K}$ with respect to $\| \ \|_1$ and if $\| \ \|_1$ and $\| \ \|_2$ are valuations on $\overline{\mathscr{K}}$ equivalent* on $\mathscr{K}$, *then $\overline{\mathscr{K}}$ is complete with respect to $\| \ \|_2$.*

Up to now we have only been able to speak of finite sums. However in fields, complete with respect to a valuation, one can give meaning to certain infinite sums. Given a sequence $\{a_n\}$, we define the sequence of partial sums

$$s_n = a_1 + a_2 + \cdots + a_n, \qquad n = 1, 2, \ldots.$$

If the sequence $\{s_n\}$ is a cauchy sequence and hence has a limit in the field, say s, we define

$$\sum_{\nu=1}^{\infty} a_\nu = s,$$

and we say that $\sum_{\nu=1}^{\infty} a_\nu$ *converges to* s. Clearly, if $\sum a_\nu$ converges, then the sequence $\{a_n\}$ is a null sequence. However, if $\{a_n\}$ is a null sequence, the sum $\sum a_\nu$ need not converge. For example $\{1/n\}$ is a null sequence in **R** relative to absolute value, but $\sum_{\nu=1}^{\infty} 1/n$ does not converge in **R**. Thus it may seem a bit surprising to find

PROPOSITION 103 *If $\mathscr{K}$ is complete with respect to a nonarchimedean valuation, then $\sum a_\nu$ converges in $\mathscr{K}$ exactly when $\{a_n\}$ is a null sequence relative to the valuation.*

The proof makes use of Exercise 6 of Sec. 16.

PROPOSITION 104 *Every infinite decimal defines a convergent series in* **R**.

The proof is left to the reader.

EXERCISES 5 Let $\mathbf{Q}_p$ denote the completion of $\mathbf{Q}$ relative to the p-adic valuation. Prove:

A. Every series of the form $\sum_{\nu=0}^{\infty} a_\nu p^\nu$, $0 \leq a_\nu \leq p-1$, converges in $\mathbf{Q}_p$.

B. If $a \in \mathbf{Q}$, then there are integers s, n, m such that

$$a = \sum_{\nu=m}^{\infty} a_\nu p^\nu, \qquad 0 \leq a_\nu \leq p - 1,$$

and

$$a_{n+j} = a_j, \qquad \text{if } j \geq s.$$

C. In $\mathbf{Q}_2$ the series $1 + 2 + 4 + \cdots + 2^n + \cdots$ converges to -1.

D. $\mathbf{Q}$ is not complete relative to any of its nontrivial valuations.

E. Let

$$\Gamma_p = \{x \in \mathbf{R}^+ \mid \|a\|_p = x \text{ for some } a \in \mathbf{Q}\},$$

$$\Gamma_p^* = \{x \in \mathbf{R}^+ \mid \overline{\|\alpha\|}_p = x \text{ for some } \alpha \in \mathbf{Q}_p\};$$

then $\Gamma_p = \Gamma_p^*$.

F. Let $\mathfrak{o}$, $\mathfrak{p}$ be the integral domain in $\mathbf{Q}$ and the prime ideal associated with $\| \;\; \|_p$. Let $\mathfrak{o}_*$, $\mathfrak{p}_*$ be the integral domain in $\mathbf{Q}_p$ and the prime ideal associated with $\overline{\| \;\; \|}_p$. Then $\mathfrak{o}_* \supset \mathfrak{o}$, and $\mathfrak{p}_* \supset \mathfrak{p}$. To each $\alpha \in \mathfrak{o}_*$ there is an $a \in \mathfrak{o}$ such that $\alpha - a \in \mathfrak{p}_*$. The fields $\mathfrak{o}_*/\mathfrak{p}_*$ and $\mathfrak{o}/\mathfrak{p}$ are isomorphic.

G. To each $\alpha \in \mathbf{Q}_p$, $\alpha \neq 0$, there is an $n \in \mathbf{Z}$ and $\beta \in \mathfrak{o}_* - \mathfrak{p}_*$ such that $\alpha = p^n\beta$.

H. Each $\beta \in \mathfrak{o}_* - \mathfrak{p}_*$ is the limit of a convergent series $\sum_{\nu=0}^{\infty} a_\nu p^\nu$ where $a_0 \neq 0$, $0 \leq a_\nu \leq p - 1$.

I. $\mathbf{Q}_p$ is an uncountable set and contains transcendentals over $\mathbf{Q}$.

6 A. Let p be an odd prime and let m be a positive integer. Prove: If $a, b \in \mathbf{Z}$ such that $a \equiv b^2 \pmod{p^m}$, then there is an integer c such that $a \equiv (b + cp^m)^2 \pmod{p^{m+1}}$.

B. Prove: If p is an odd prime and $a, b \in \mathbf{Z}$ such that $a \equiv b^2 \pmod{p}$, then there is an $\alpha \in \mathbf{Q}_p$ such that $\alpha^2 = a$.

C. Prove: $\mathbf{Q}_p$ is not algebraically closed.

7 Prove: If a, b are odd integers such that $a \equiv b^2 \pmod{8}$, then there is an $\alpha \in \mathbf{Q}_2$ such that $a = \alpha^2$.

8 Prove: Every field is complete with respect to the trivial valuation.

9 Prove: If $x \in \mathbf{Q}$ is such that $\|x\|_p \leq 1$ for all primes p, then $x \in \mathbf{Z}$.

Let x be an indeterminate over a field $\mathscr{F}$. For $A \in \mathscr{F}[x]$, put $\|A\|_0 = 2^{-m}$ if $x^m \mid A$, $x^{m+1} \nmid A$. Then the map

$$\frac{A}{B} \to \|A\|_0/\|B\|_0$$

is a well-defined valuation on $\mathscr{K} = \mathscr{F}(x)$. Let $\mathfrak{o}$ be the integral ideal associated with $\| \;\; \|_0$. Then

$$\mathfrak{o} = \left\{\frac{A}{B} \,\middle|\, A, B \in \mathscr{F}\,[x],\, x \nmid B\right\}.$$

The ideal associated with $\| \;\; \|_0$ is

$$\mathfrak{p} = \{xA/B \mid A, B \in \mathscr{F}[x], x \nmid B\}.$$

Clearly $\mathfrak{o}/\mathfrak{p}$ is isomorphic to $\mathscr{F}$. The value group Γ of $\mathscr{K}$ for $\| \;\; \|_0$ is the set of powers of 2.

Let $\mathscr{K}_*$ be the completion of $\mathscr{K}$ relative to the valuation $\| \;\; \|_0$. Let $\| \;\; \|$ be the valuation on $\mathscr{K}_*$ that extends $\| \;\; \|_0$. Let $\mathfrak{o}_*$, $\mathfrak{p}_*$, Γ_* be the associated integral domain, prime ideal, and value group for $\mathscr{K}_*$ relative to $\| \;\; \|$. Then $\Gamma = \Gamma_*$. Consequently, to each $\alpha \in \mathscr{K}_*$ there is an $a \in \mathscr{K}$ such that $\|\alpha\| = \|a\|_0$; i.e., $\alpha - a \in \mathfrak{p}_*$. Thus each coset $\alpha + \mathfrak{p}_*$ contains an element of $\mathscr{K}$, and so we have $\mathfrak{o}_*/\mathfrak{p}_* \cong \mathfrak{o}/\mathfrak{p}$. Also

$\mathfrak{p}_* = x\mathfrak{o}_*$. If $0 \neq \beta \in \mathscr{K}_*$, then there is an integer m such that

$$\beta = x^m\alpha, \qquad \alpha \in \mathfrak{o}_* - \mathfrak{p}_*.$$

If $\alpha \in \mathfrak{o}_*$, then $\alpha = a_0 + x\alpha_1$, where a_0 is a unique element of $\mathscr{F}$ and $\alpha_1 \in \mathfrak{o}_*$. But then $\alpha_1 = a_1 + x\alpha_2$, etc. Thus for each $k \in \mathbf{Z}^+$ we find

$$\alpha = a_0 + a_1x + a_2x^2 + \cdots + a_kx^k + x^{k+1}\alpha_{k+1},$$

where $a_0, a_1, \ldots, a_k$ are uniquely determined elements of $\mathscr{F}$ and $\alpha_{k+1} \in \mathfrak{o}_*$. The partial sums

$$s_k = a_0 + \cdots + a_kx^k$$

form a cauchy sequence having α as its limit. Hence the series $a_0 + a_1x + \cdots$ converges to α. Conversely each such sequence converges to an element in $\mathfrak{o}_*$. Hence

$$\mathfrak{o}_* = \left\{\sum_{\nu=0}^{\infty} a_\nu x^\nu \mid a_\nu \in \mathscr{F}\right\},$$

and therefore $$\mathscr{K}_* = \left\{x^{-m} \sum_{\nu=0}^{\infty} a_\nu x^\nu \mid a_\nu \in \mathscr{F},\, m \in \mathbf{Z}\right\}.$$

The field $\mathscr{K}_*$ is usually called the *field of formal power series over* $\mathscr{F}$.

Let $\mathscr{E}$ be the set of all maps of $\mathbf{Z}$ into $\mathscr{F}$ that map sufficiently negative integers into 0;

$$\mathscr{E} = \{\sigma \in \mathscr{T}(\mathbf{Z}, \mathscr{F}) \mid \sigma(m) = 0 \text{ if } m \text{ sufficiently negative}\}.$$

$\mathscr{E}$ is an additive group with $(\sigma + \tau)(m) = \sigma(m) + \tau(m)$, for all $m \in Z$. If $\sigma, \tau \in \mathscr{E}$, define $\sigma\tau$ as

$$m \xrightarrow{\sigma\tau} \sum_{\nu=-\infty}^{\infty} \sigma(m-\nu)\tau(\nu).$$

The right-hand side of the latter has meaning, since $\sigma(s) = 0$ if $s < -S$ and $\tau(t) = 0$ if $t < -T$. Hence the sum is really over $-\mathscr{T} \leq \nu \leq S + m$. It is easily shown that under these operations $\mathscr{E}$ *is a field isomorphic to* $\mathscr{K}_*$.

Suppose we denote $\mathscr{K}_*$ by $\mathscr{F}\langle x\rangle$. Then $\mathscr{F}\langle x^{1/k}\rangle \supset \mathscr{F}\langle x\rangle$, for each $k \in \mathbf{Z}^+$. Put

$$\mathscr{F}\langle\langle x\rangle\rangle = \bigcup_{\nu=1}^{\infty} \mathscr{F}\left\langle x^{\frac{1}{p_1\cdots p_\nu}}\right\rangle,$$

where $p_1 = 2$, $p_2 = 3, \ldots, p_\nu = \nu$th prime. Then $\mathscr{F}\langle\langle x\rangle\rangle$ is a field containing all roots of x. One can prove that if $\mathscr{F}$ *is algebraically closed, then* $\mathscr{F}\langle\langle x\rangle\rangle$ *is algebraically closed.* The interested reader should see R. J. Walker, *Algebraic Curves*, Princeton, 1950; or J. G. Semple and G. T. Kneebone, *Algebraic Curves*, Oxford, 1959.

18 THE FIELD OF COMPLEX NUMBERS

We recall that **R** is a linearly ordered field; hence there is no element of **R** whose square is -1. Then $x^2 + 1$ is irreducible over **R**. This polynomial does have a zero in the splitting field for $x^2 + 1$; call this zero i. Then $i^2 = -1$. Let

$$\mathbf{C} = \{a + bi \mid a, b \in \mathbf{R}\} = \mathbf{R}[i].$$

C is a field containing **R**. Specifically we have

$$(a + bi) = 0, \qquad \text{if and only if } a = b;$$

$$(a + bi) + (c + di) = (a + c) + (b + d)i;$$

$$(a + bi)(c + di) = (ac - bd) + (bc + ad)i.$$

$$\text{If } (a + bi) \neq 0, \text{ then } (a + bi)^{-1} = a/(a^2 + b^2) - bi/(a^2 + b^2).$$

One can easily check that **C** is isomorphic to $\mathbf{R}|-1|$. **C** is called the *field of complex numbers.*

The reader should verify

LEMMA 1 *The map* $a + bi \to \sqrt{a^2 + b^2}$ *is a valuation on* **C** *that extends the ordinary absolute value on* **R**.

It is customary to call $\sqrt{a^2 + b^2}$ the absolute value of the complex number $a + bi$ and to write $|a + bi| = \sqrt{a^2 + b^2}$. We observe $|a + bi| = |a - bi|$. Since the ordinary absolute valuation on **R** is an archimedean valuation on **R**, the valuation $|a+bi|$ is an archimedean valuation on **C**. (Why?)

We next show

LEMMA 2 *The only valuation on* **C** *that extends the ordinary absolute value on* **R** *is the valuation* $a + bi \to |a + bi|$.

PROOF. Let $\| \;\|$ be a valuation on **C** that extends on **R**. We have

$$\|(a + bi)(a - bi)\| = \|a^2 + b^2\| = |a^2 + b^2| = a^2 + b^2.$$

Suppose $\|a + bi\| \neq \sqrt{a^2 + b^2}$, say $\|a + bi\| < \sqrt{a^2 + b^2}$. Then $\sqrt{a^2 + b^2} < \|a - bi\|$, also $b \neq 0$; for if $b = 0$, then $\|a + 0i\| = \|a\| = |a| = \sqrt{a^2 + 0^2}$. Let

$$\gamma_n = \frac{(a + bi)^{n+1} + (a - bi)^{n+1}}{(a + bi)^n + (a - bi)^n}, \qquad n = 1, 2, \ldots.$$

Then

$$\gamma_n = (a - bi)\left(\frac{\beta^{n+1} + 1}{\beta^n + 1}\right),$$

where $\beta = (a + bi)(a - bi)^{-1}$.

Because of our assumption we have $\|\beta\| < 1$. Hence $\{\beta^n\}$ is a null sequence with respect to the valuation $\| \quad \|$, and therefore $\{\gamma_n\}$ has $a - bi$ as its limit relative to $\| \quad \|$. Since $\{\gamma_n\}$ has a limit it is a cauchy sequence relative to $\| \quad \|$. But

$$(a + bi)^n + (a - bi)^n = 2 \sum_{m=0}^{\infty} \binom{n}{2m} a^{n-2m} b^{2m} \in \mathbf{R},$$

and hence $\{\gamma_n\}$ is a sequence of elements from **R**. Consequently $\{\gamma_n\}$ is a cauchy sequence of **R** (relative to the absolute value). Since **R** is complete relative to the absolute value, the sequence $\{\gamma_n\}$ must have a limit in **R**. Since a sequence can have at most one limit, we see that $a - bi \in \mathbf{R}$, and hence $b = 0$. But this contradicts the fact that $b \neq 0$. Hence $\|a + bi\| \geq \sqrt{a^2 + b^2}$. In an entirely analogous way we can show that $\|a + bi\|$ cannot be larger than $\sqrt{a^2 + b^2}$. Thus $\|a + bi\| = \sqrt{a^2 + b^2}$, and this completes the proof of the lemma.

Since any archimedean valuation on **C** induces one on **R**, we see that

POSITION 105 *Each archimedean valuation on* **C** *is equivalent to the valuation*

$$a + bi \to |a + bi| = \sqrt{a^2 + b^2}.$$

The reader should prove

LEMMA 3 *The sequence $\{a_n + b_n i\}$ is a cauchy sequence of* **C** *if and only if both $\{a_n\}$ and $\{b_n\}$ are cauchy sequences of* **R**.

POSITION 106 **C** *is complete relative to its archimedean valuations.*

XERCISES 1 Let $\mathscr{K}$ be a field complete with respect to a valuation $\| \quad \|$. Let $m \in \mathscr{K}$ such that there is no element in $\mathscr{K}$ whose square is m. Form $\mathscr{K}|m|$. Prove:

A. $\mathscr{K}|m|$ is a field.

B. The map $[a, b] \to |||[a, b]||| = \|a^2 - b^2 m\|^{1/2}$ is a valuation on $\mathscr{K}|m|$ such that $|||[a, 0]||| = \|a\|$.

C. The valuation $|||[a, b]|||$ is the only valuation on $\mathscr{K}|m|$ such that $|||[a, 0]||| = \|a\|$ for all $a \in \mathscr{K}$.

D. $\mathscr{K}|m|$ is complete relative to the valuation $|||[a, b]|||$.

2 Prove: It is impossible to define a linear ordering on **C**.

We now prove an interesting result concerning complex numbers:

POSITION 107 *There is an isomorphism of the multiplicative group* $\mathbf{C}^\times$ *onto the group* $\mathbf{R}^+ \times \mathbf{R}/\mathbf{Z}$.

Note: $\mathbf{R}^+$, $\mathbf{C}^\times$ are multiplicative groups, and $\mathbf{R}/\mathbf{Z}$ is an additive group.

PROOF. The reader will recall from trigonometry that, if $a, b \in \mathbf{R}$ such that $a^2 + b^2 \neq 0$, then there is a unique real number θ such that $0 \leq \theta < 1$, $a = (a^2 + b^2)^{1/2} \cos 2\pi\theta$, $b = (a^2 + b^2)^{1/2} \sin 2\pi\theta$. Thus the map

$$a + bi = \sqrt{(a^2 + b^2)}\{\cos 2\pi\theta + i \sin 2\pi\theta\} \to (|a + bi|, \theta)$$

is an injective map of $\mathbf{C}^\times$ into $\mathbf{R}^+ \times \mathbf{R}/\mathbf{Z}$. Clearly, it is also surjective. Now

$$(\cos 2\pi\theta)(\cos 2\pi\varphi) - (\sin 2\pi\theta)(\sin 2\pi\varphi) = \cos 2\pi(\theta + \varphi),$$

$$(\sin 2\pi\theta)(\cos 2\pi\varphi) + (\sin 2\pi\varphi)(\cos 2\pi\theta) = \sin 2\pi(\theta + \varphi),$$

and since $|(a + bi)(c + di)| = |a + bi|\,|c + di|$, we see that the map is indeed an isomorphism.

The set $\mathbf{C}_1 = \{\alpha \in \mathbf{C} \mid |\alpha| = 1\}$ is clearly a multiplicative group. The group $\mathbf{C}_1$ is isomorphic to the group $\mathbf{R}/\mathbf{Z}$. There is a one-to-one correspondence between $\mathbf{C}_1$ and the points on a circle, and consequently $\mathbf{C}_1$ is called the *circle group*.

If $n \in \mathbf{Z}^+$ and $\zeta \in \mathbf{C}$ such that $\zeta^n = 1$, we say that ζ is an *nth root of unity*. We note that 1 is an nth root of unity for every positive integer n. An element of $\mathbf{C}$ is an nth root of unity if and only if its multiplicative order is a divisor of n. All nth roots of unity lie in $\mathbf{C}_1$. An nth root of unity is said to be a *primitive nth root of unity* if it is not an mth root for some positive integer $m < n$.

EXERCISES

3 Prove: The complex number $\cos 2\pi\theta + i \sin 2\pi\theta$ has finite multiplicative order if and only if $\theta \in \mathbf{Q}$.

4 Let U_n be the set of all nth roots of unity. Prove:
A. U_n is a cyclic group of order n.
B. The primitive nth roots of unity are exactly the generators of U_n.

5 Prove:
A. $\mathbf{C}_1$ has the property that, if $\alpha \in \mathbf{C}_1$ and $n \in \mathbf{Z}^+$, then there exist n distinct elements $\beta_1, \ldots, \beta_n \in \mathbf{C}$, such that $\beta_\nu{}^n = \alpha$, $(\nu = 1, 2, \ldots, n)$.
B. $\mathbf{C}$ has the property that, if $0 \neq \alpha \in \mathbf{C}$, then there are exactly n distinct elements $\beta_1, \ldots, \beta_n \in \mathbf{C}$ such that $\beta_\nu{}^n = \alpha$, $(\nu = 1, 2, \ldots, n)$.

6 Let $U = \bigcup_{n=1}^{\infty} U_n$. Prove:
A. U is a group.
B. U is isomorphic to $\mathbf{Q}/\mathbf{Z}$.
C. If $\alpha \in U$ and $n \in \mathbf{Z}^+$, then there exist n distinct elements $\beta_1, \ldots, \beta_n$ in U such that $\beta_\nu{}^n = \alpha$.
D. U is an infinite group such that each element of U is of finite order.
E. Every proper subgroup of U is a finite cyclic group.
F. U is not a cyclic group.

We have indicated that every field has an algebraic closure, although we proved this only for countable fields. Accepting the unproved assertion, we would know that **R** has an algebraic closure $\mathbf{R}^c$. Clearly $\mathbf{R}^c$ must contain an isomorphic copy of **C**, and so we could find $\mathbf{R}^c$ by finding $\mathbf{C}^c$. Now there is a remarkable theorem that asserts **C** *is algebraically closed.* There have been many proofs of this result. The shorter ones all depend on additional topological properties of **C** that we have not developed. There are proofs based more or less on the metric theory that we have developed. However, these proofs are exceedingly long. (See L. Weisner, *Theory of Equations*, Wiley, 1938.) We have therefore decided to omit all proofs of this fact. The interested reader can look into elementary complex variable texts or elementary topology texts to find the shorter proofs. Since $\mathbf{C} \subset \mathbf{R}^c \subset \mathbf{C}^c = \mathbf{C}$ we see that $\mathbf{R}^c = \mathbf{C}$; i.e., **C** *is the algebraic closure of* **R**.

EXERCISE 7 Prove:

A. If $A \in \mathbf{R}[x]$ and $A(a + bi) = 0$, $b \neq 0$, then $x^2 - 2ax + a^2 + b^2$ is a divisor of A in $\mathbf{R}[x]$.

B. Assuming that **C** is algebraically closed, show that the irreducible polynomials over **R** are either linear or of the form $ax^2 + bx + c$ where $b^2 - 4ac < 0$.

CHAPTER FIVE

VECTOR SPACES

1 INTRODUCTION

In this chapter we shall study vector spaces. Vector spaces possess some of the properties of several different algebraic structures, and we are able to prove many powerful theorems concerning them. This is very provident, for vector spaces appear very naturally throughout other parts of mathematics.

A vector space consists of an additive abelian group together with the action of a field upon that group. To emphasize the role of the field, we speak of a vector space over a field. A *vector space* $\mathscr{V}$ *over the field* $\mathscr{F}$ is an additive abelian group $\mathscr{V}$ such that

A. If $a \in \mathscr{F}$, $\alpha \in \mathscr{V}$, then $a\alpha$ is a uniquely defined element of $\mathscr{V}$.

B. If $a, b \in \mathscr{F}$, $\alpha, \beta \in \mathscr{V}$, then:

1. $(a + b)\alpha = a\alpha + b\alpha$,
2. $a(\alpha + \beta) = a\alpha + a\beta$,
3. $(ab)\alpha = a(b\alpha)$,
4. If 1 is the unity of $\mathscr{F}$, then $1\alpha = \alpha$.

Sometimes, elements of $\mathscr{V}$ are called vectors and elements of $\mathscr{F}$ are called scalars. In this case, the "product" $a\alpha$ is referred to as the "scalar product." As a shorthand notation, we shall let $\mathscr{V}/\mathscr{F}$ stand for "$\mathscr{V}$ is a vector space over the field $\mathscr{F}$."

We shall usually denote elements of $\mathscr{V}$ by the early letters of the Greek alphabet or by lower-case boldface roman letters, e.g., **x**, **y**, etc. It is customary to denote both the additive identity of $\mathscr{V}$ and the additive identity of $\mathscr{F}$ by the same symbol 0. This causes little confusion, since one can usually tell from the context of the equation whether 0 denotes a vector or a field element. However, to avoid confusion we denote the zero vector by $\mathbf{0}$.

The reader will observe that any skewfield $\mathscr{S}$, containing the field $\mathscr{F}$, is a vector space over $\mathscr{F}$. In particular $\mathscr{F}$ is always a vector space over $\mathscr{F}$. The field $\mathbf{C}$ is a vector space over the field $\mathbf{Q}$, over the field $\mathbf{R}$, and over the field $\mathbf{C}$. This example illustrates the importance of specifying the field when speaking of a vector space.

If x is an indeterminate over a field $\mathscr{F}$, then $\mathscr{F}[x]$ is a vector space over $\mathscr{F}$. More generally, if a ring $\mathscr{R}$ with unity contained a field $\mathscr{F}$ such that the unity of $\mathscr{F}$ is the unity of $\mathscr{R}$, then $\mathscr{R}$ would be a vector space over $\mathscr{F}$. In this case, properties 1 and 2 follow from the distributive laws for $\mathscr{R}$, property 3 follows from the associative law for multiplication in $\mathscr{R}$, and property 4 is a property of the unity of $\mathscr{F}$ being the unity of $\mathscr{R}$.

We next give several other examples of vector spaces. We shall define the sum $\alpha + \beta$ and the product $a\alpha$ and leave the reader to verify that they are vector spaces over the appropriate field:

a. If $\mathscr{F}$ is a field, then the cartesian sum of $\mathscr{F}$ by itself n times, denoted by $\mathscr{F}^{(n)}$, is a vector space over $\mathscr{F}$, where

$$(a_1, \ldots, a_n) + (b_1, \ldots, b_n) = (a_1 + b_1, \ldots, a_n + b_n),$$

$$a(b_1, \ldots, b_n) = (ab_1, \ldots, ab_n).$$

b. More generally let $\mathscr{T}(X, \mathscr{F})$ be the set of all functions of a set X into a field $\mathscr{F}$. If $a \in \mathscr{F}, f, g \in \mathscr{T}$, define

$$x \xrightarrow{f+g} f(x) + g(x), \qquad x \xrightarrow{af} af(x).$$

Then $\mathscr{T}(X, \mathscr{F})$ is a vector space over $\mathscr{F}$.

c. Let $\mathscr{V}$ be an additive group whose nonidentity elements have order 2. If $\alpha \in \mathscr{V}$, $\lfloor a \rfloor \in \mathbf{Z}_2$ define

$$\lfloor a \rfloor \alpha = \begin{cases} \mathbf{0} \text{ if } \lfloor a \rfloor = \lfloor 0 \rfloor, \\ \alpha \text{ if } \lfloor a \rfloor = \lfloor 1 \rfloor. \end{cases}$$

More generally, if $\mathscr{V}$ is an additive abelian group whose nonidentity elements have order p (p a prime), then $\mathscr{V}$ is a vector space over $\mathbf{Z}_p$, where

$$\lfloor a \rfloor \alpha = a\alpha.$$

d. Let $\mathscr{V}$ be the additive abelian group $\mathbf{R}/\mathbf{Q}$. To each pair $0 < n, m \in \mathbf{Z}$ and $\alpha \in \mathscr{V}$ there is a unique $\beta \in \mathscr{V}$ such that $n\beta = m\alpha$. If $0 < q, p \in \mathbf{Z}$ and $\delta \in \mathscr{V}$ such that $mq = pn$ and $q\delta = p\alpha$, then

$$nq\beta = mq\alpha = pn\alpha = nq\delta,$$

whence

$$\beta = \delta.$$

We now define $(m/n)\alpha$ to be β. Then $(m/n)\alpha = (p/q)\alpha$, whenever $m/n = p/q$. Consequently, for each $a \in \mathbf{Q}$ and $\alpha \in \mathscr{V}$, $a\alpha$ is a well-defined element of $\mathscr{V}$. $\mathscr{V}$ is a vector space over $\mathbf{Q}$.

e. If $\mathscr{V}_o$ is the trivial group consisting of the additive identity $\mathbf{0}$ alone and $\mathscr{F}$ is any field, then $\mathscr{V}_o$ is a vector space over $\mathscr{F}$, where $a\mathbf{0} = \mathbf{0}$ for all $a \in \mathscr{F}$. $\mathscr{V}_o$ is usually called the *zero space*. We shall often write $\mathscr{O}$ for $\mathscr{V}_o$.

f. Let $\mathscr{V}_\lambda$ $(\lambda \in \Lambda)$ be a collection of vector spaces over the same field $\mathscr{F}$. We have defined the cartesian sum, $\sum \mathscr{V}_\lambda$, of the additive groups $\mathscr{V}_\lambda$. The group $\sum \mathscr{V}_\lambda$ consisted of all the possible arrays

$$(\ldots, \alpha_\lambda, \ldots), \qquad \text{where } \alpha_\lambda \in \mathscr{V}_\lambda.$$

Two arrays were the same element in $\sum \mathscr{V}_\lambda$ if and only if they agreed at each $\lambda \in \Lambda$. Addition was defined by

$$(\dots, \alpha_\lambda, \dots) + (\dots, \beta_\lambda, \dots) = (\dots, \alpha_\lambda + \beta_\lambda, \dots).$$

If we now define

$$a(\dots, \alpha_\lambda, \dots) = (\dots, a\alpha_\lambda, \dots),$$

then $\sum \mathscr{V}_\lambda$ is a vector space over $\mathscr{F}$. We will call $\sum \mathscr{V}_\lambda$ the *cartesian sum of the spaces* $\mathscr{V}_\lambda$. One can also show that the restricted cartesian sum $r\sum \mathscr{V}_\lambda$ is also a vector space over $\mathscr{F}$.

There are a number of simple consequences of the definition of a vector space, which we list in the next proposition and leave to the reader to prove.

ROPOSITION 1 *Let* $\mathscr{V}$ *be a vector space over* $\mathscr{F}$. *If* $a \in \mathscr{F}$, $\alpha \in \mathscr{V}$, *then:*
A. $a\mathbf{0} = \mathbf{0}$.
B. $0\alpha = \mathbf{0}$.
C. $a\alpha = \mathbf{0}$ if and only if $a = 0$ or $\alpha = \mathbf{0}$.
D. $(-a)\alpha = -(a\alpha)$.

Let $\mathscr{V}$ be a nonzero vector space over a field $\mathscr{F}$. Consider the ring of endomorphism $\mathscr{E}(\mathscr{V})$ of the additive abelian group $\mathscr{V}$. If $a \in \mathscr{F}$, the map

$$\alpha \xrightarrow{\rho_a} a\alpha$$

is in $\mathscr{E}(\mathscr{V})$. Furthermore, by Proposition 1C, ρ_a is the zero map if and only if $a = 0$. Thus the mapping

$$a \to \rho_a$$

of $\mathscr{F}$ into $\mathscr{E}(\mathscr{V})$ is an injection. Since

$$\alpha^{\rho_{a+b}} = (a+b)\alpha = a\alpha + b\alpha = \alpha^{\rho_a} + \alpha^{\rho_b} = \alpha^{\rho_a + \rho_b}, \qquad \alpha \in \mathscr{V},$$

$$\alpha^{\rho_{ab}} = (ab)\alpha = (ba)\alpha = b(a\alpha) = b(\alpha^{\rho_a}) = \alpha^{\rho_a\rho_b}, \qquad \alpha \in \mathscr{V},$$

we have

$$\rho_{a+b} = \rho_a + \rho_b, \qquad \rho_{ab} = \rho_a\rho_b,$$

and hence the injection is an operation-preserving map of $\mathscr{F}$ into $\mathscr{E}(\mathscr{V})$. Thus the map $a \to \rho_a$ is an isomorphism of $\mathscr{F}$ into $\mathscr{E}(\mathscr{V})$.

Conversely, suppose there is a monomorphism φ of a field $\mathscr{F}$ into the ring of endomorphisms $\mathscr{E}(\mathscr{V})$ of an additive abelian group $\mathscr{V}$. Then for each $a \in \mathscr{F}$, $\alpha \in \mathscr{V}$ we can define

$$a\alpha = (\alpha)^{a\varphi}.$$

Clearly, this product is defined for all $a \in \mathscr{F}$, $\alpha \in \mathscr{V}$.
Furthermore,

$$(a + b)\alpha = \alpha^{(a+b)\varphi} = \alpha^{(a\varphi + b\varphi)} = \alpha^{(a\varphi)} + \alpha^{(b\varphi)} = a\alpha + b\alpha.$$

$$a(\alpha + \beta) = (\alpha + \beta)^{(a\varphi)} = \alpha^{(a\varphi)} + \beta^{(a\varphi)} = a\alpha + a\beta.$$

$$(ab)\alpha = (ba)\alpha = \alpha^{(ab)\varphi} = \alpha^{(a\varphi b\varphi)} = (a\alpha)^{b\varphi} = b(a\alpha).$$

$$1\alpha = \alpha^{1\varphi} = \alpha^{\iota} = \alpha.$$

Now, by assumption, $\mathscr{V}$ is an additive abelian group, and hence $\mathscr{V}$ is a vector space over $\mathscr{F}$. We have proved

PROPOSITION 2 *An additive abelian group $\mathscr{V}$ is a vector space over $\mathscr{F}$ if and only if there is a monomorphism of $\mathscr{F}$ into the group of endomorphisms of $\mathscr{V}$.*

We may rephrase Proposition 2 to read as follows: *An additive abelian group $\mathscr{V}$ is a vector space over a field $\mathscr{F}$ if and only if the ring of endomorphisms of $\mathscr{V}$ contains a subring that is isomorphic to $\mathscr{F}$.* Now for each abelian group $\mathscr{G}$ there is an operation-preserving map of $\mathbf{Z}$ into $\mathscr{E}(\mathscr{G})$, say $n \to n^{\varphi}$, where

$$\alpha^{n\varphi} = \underbrace{\alpha + \cdots + \alpha}_{n \text{ times}}, \qquad \text{and} \qquad \alpha^{(-n\varphi)} = (-\alpha)^{n\varphi}, \text{ if } n \in \mathbf{Z}^+.$$

However, this map is often not injective, and there is usually no way to extend this action of $\mathbf{Z}$ on $\mathscr{G}$ to action by elements of $\mathbf{Q}$ on $\mathscr{G}$. Thus, we see that vector spaces are a special subclass in the class of all abelian groups. In Chap. 3, we saw that it was possible to obtain a structure theorem for finite abelian groups. We shall soon see that the structure theorems for vector spaces over fields are very simple. The action of the field on the space will replace the finiteness assumptions. Because the structure is so simple, we can state many explicit results on the rings of endomorphisms of vector spaces, etc.

The reader should prove the following corollaries of Proposition 2:

COROLLARY 1 *If $\mathscr{V}$ is a vector space over $\mathscr{F}$ and there is a monomorphism of a field $\mathscr{F}_1$ into the field $\mathscr{F}$, then $\mathscr{V}$ is vector space over $\mathscr{F}_1$.*

COROLLARY 2 *If $\mathscr{F}_1$ is a subfield of $\mathscr{F}$ and $\mathscr{V}$ is a vector space over $\mathscr{F}$, then $\mathscr{V}$ is a vector space over $\mathscr{F}_1$.*

OROLLARY 3 *If $\mathscr{V}$ is a vector space over $\mathscr{F}$ and there is an isomorphism of an additive abelian group $\mathscr{W}$ onto $\mathscr{V}$, then $\mathscr{W}$ is a vector space over $\mathscr{F}$.*

PROOF. Let λ be the isomorphism and define

$$a\omega = (a\omega^{\lambda})^{\lambda^{-1}}, \qquad a \in \mathscr{F}, \omega \in \mathscr{W}.$$

Corollary 3 is not valid if we have an isomorphism of $\mathscr{W}$ into $\mathscr{V}$ that is not onto. For example, there is an injection of the additive group of **Z** into the additive group of **Q**, but **Z** is not a vector space over the field **Q**.

An additive subgroup of a vector space $\mathscr{V}$ over $\mathscr{F}$, which is itself a vector space over $\mathscr{F}$, is called a *subspace* of $\mathscr{V}$ over $\mathscr{F}$. When speaking of subspaces, one must be careful with regard to the field. **Q** is a subspace of **C**/**Q** but it is not a subspace of **C**/**R**.

XERCISES 1 As noted above, if $\mathscr{F}$ is a field, then $\mathscr{F}^{(n)}$ is a vector space over $\mathscr{F}$. Which of the following are subspaces of $\mathscr{F}^{(n)}$ over $\mathscr{F}$?

A. $\mathscr{V}_1 = \{(a_1, \ldots, a_n) \mid a_2 = 0\}$.
B. $\mathscr{V}_2 = \{(a_1, \ldots, a_n) \mid a_1 = 1\}$.
C. $\mathscr{V}_3 = \{(a_1, \ldots, a_n) \mid a_1 = a_2\}$.
D. $\mathscr{V}_4 = \{(a_1, \ldots, a_n) \mid a_1 + a_2 + a_3 = 0 \text{ and } a_2 - a_3 + a_4 = 0\}$.

2 Let x be an indeterminate over a field $\mathscr{F}$. Which of the following are subspaces of $\mathscr{F}[x]$ over $\mathscr{F}$?

A. All monic polynomials of degree at most 5.
B. All polynomials of degree at least 10.
C. All polynomials having a and b as zeros.
D. All polynomials having a as a multiple zero.
E. All polynomials divisible by x.
F. All polynomials A such that $A(b) = A(c)$.
G. All polynomials A such that $2A(0) = A(1)$.

3 Let $\mathscr{V}$ be the set of all functions from the real interval $I = \{x \in \mathbf{R} \mid -1 \leq x \leq 1\}$ to **R**. Then $\mathscr{V}$ is a vector space over **R**. Which of the following are subspaces of over **R**?

A. $\mathscr{V}_1 = \{f \in \mathscr{V} \mid f(0) = 0\}$.
B. $\mathscr{V}_2 = \{f \in \mathscr{V} \mid f(1) = f(-1)\}$.
C. $\mathscr{V}_3 = \{f \in \mathscr{V} \mid f(x) = 0 \text{ if } x < 0\}$.
D. $\mathscr{V}_4 = \{f \in \mathscr{V} \mid f \text{ is continuous at } x = a\}$.
E. $\mathscr{V}_5 = \{f \in \mathscr{V} \mid f \text{ is continuous on } I\}$.
F. $\mathscr{V}_6 = \{f \in \mathscr{V} \mid f(x) = f(-x) \text{ for all } x \in I\}$.
G. $\mathscr{V}_7 = \{f \in \mathscr{V} \mid f(x) \leq f(y) \text{ if } x < y\}$.
H. $\mathscr{V}_8 = \{f \in \mathscr{V} \mid f \text{ is integrable and } \int_{-1}^{1} f = 0\}$.

Let $\mathfrak{A}$ be a subset of $\mathscr{V}/\mathscr{F}$. A finite sum of the form

$$a_1\alpha_1 + \cdots + a_n\alpha_n, \qquad a_i \in \mathscr{F}, \alpha_i \in \mathfrak{A}, n \in \mathbf{Z}^+,$$

is called a *linear combination* of elements from $\mathfrak{A}$ with coefficients from $\mathscr{F}$. If in the linear combination $\sum a_\nu \alpha_\nu$, some $a_\nu \neq 0$, we say the linear combination is *nontrivial.* We let $\langle \mathfrak{A} \rangle = \langle \mathfrak{A} \rangle_{\mathscr{F}}$ denote the set of all linear combinations from $\mathfrak{A}$ over $\mathscr{F}$. The reader can prove

PROPOSITION 3 *If $\mathfrak{A} \subset \mathscr{V}/\mathscr{F}$, then $\langle \mathfrak{A} \rangle$ is a subspace of $\mathscr{V}/\mathscr{F}$ and $\langle \mathfrak{A} \rangle$ is the smallest subspace of $\mathscr{V}$ that contains $\mathfrak{A}$.*

COROLLARY *If $\mathscr{W}$ is a subspace of $\mathscr{V}/\mathscr{F}$, then $\mathscr{W} = \langle \mathscr{W} \rangle_{\mathscr{F}}$.*

We say that the set $\mathfrak{A}$ *spans* the subspace $\mathscr{W}$ over $\mathscr{F}$ if $\mathscr{W} = \langle \mathfrak{A} \rangle_{\mathscr{F}}$. The reader should compare the concept of "spans" with the concept of "generates a subgroup."

EXERCISE 4 A. If $\mathfrak{A} = \{(1, 1, 1), (0, 2, 0)\}$ is a subset of $\mathbf{Z}_3^{(3)}$, determine $\langle \mathfrak{A} \rangle$.
B. Determine the spaces spanned by the sets in Exercises 1 to 3.

PROPOSITION 4 *If $\mathscr{W}_\nu$ are subspaces of $\mathscr{V}/\mathscr{F}$, then $\bigcap_\nu \mathscr{W}_\nu$ is a subspace of $\mathscr{V}/\mathscr{F}$. It is the maximum subspace common to all of the $\mathscr{W}_\nu$.*

The proof is straightforward and is left to the reader.

If $\mathscr{W}_1$ and $\mathscr{W}_2$ are subspaces of $\mathscr{V}/\mathscr{F}$, then the set $\mathscr{W}_1 \cup \mathscr{W}_2$ is usually not a subspace. As we did for groups, we define the sum of $\mathscr{W}_1$ and $\mathscr{W}_2$ to be

$$\mathscr{W}_1 + \mathscr{W}_2 = \langle \mathscr{W}_1 \cup \mathscr{W}_2 \rangle_{\mathscr{F}}.$$

The reader can prove

PROPOSITION 5 *If $\mathscr{W}_1$ and $\mathscr{W}_2$ are subspaces $\mathscr{V}/\mathscr{F}$, then $\mathscr{W}_1 + \mathscr{W}_2$ is the smallest subspace of $\mathscr{V}/\mathscr{F}$ that contains both $\mathscr{W}_1$ and $\mathscr{W}_2$.*

Let $\mathfrak{A}$ be a subset of $\mathscr{V}/\mathscr{F}$. If the zero vector $\mathbf{0}$ is a nontrivial linear combination of element of $\mathfrak{A}$ over $\mathscr{F}$, we say that the set is a *linearly dependent set over $\mathscr{F}$*. A set that is not linearly dependent over $\mathscr{F}$ is said to be *linearly independent over $\mathscr{F}$*. A set that contains the zero vector is always linearly dependent, since $1\mathbf{0} = \mathbf{0}$. A set that consists of a single nonzero vector is always a linearly independent set (see Proposition 1).

EXERCISE 5 Prove:

A. If x is an indeterminate over $\mathscr{F}$, then $\mathfrak{A} = \{1, x, \ldots, x^m, \ldots\}$ is a linearly independent set over $\mathscr{F}$. Show that $\mathfrak{A}$ spans $\mathscr{F}[x]$.

B. Let $\mathscr{V}$ be as in Exercise 3. Let $\mathfrak{A} = \{f_c \mid c \in I, f_c(c) = 1, f_c(x) = 0$ if $x \neq c\}$. Then $\mathfrak{A}$ is a linearly independent set over $\mathbf{R}$. Show that $\mathfrak{A}$ does not span $\mathscr{V}$.

The reader should prove

OPOSITION 6 *Let $\mathfrak{B} \subset \mathfrak{A} \subset \mathscr{V}/\mathscr{F}$. If $\mathfrak{A}$ is a linearly independent set over $\mathscr{F}$, so is $\mathfrak{B}$. If $\mathfrak{B}$ is a linearly dependent set over $\mathscr{F}$, so is $\mathfrak{A}$.*

OPOSITION 7 *If α is expressible as a linear combination over $\mathscr{F}$ of elements from a set $\mathfrak{A}$, then $\{\mathfrak{A}, \alpha\}$ is a linearly dependent set over $\mathscr{F}$. Conversely, if $\mathfrak{A}$ is a linearly dependent set over $\mathscr{F}$, then one of the $\alpha \in \mathfrak{A}$ is expressible as a linear combination over $\mathscr{F}$ of elements from the set $\mathfrak{A} - \{\alpha\}$.*

OROLLARY 1 *If $\mathfrak{B} \subsetneq \mathfrak{A} \subset \mathscr{V}/\mathscr{F}$ and $\langle\mathfrak{B}\rangle_{\mathscr{F}} = \langle\mathfrak{A}\rangle_{\mathscr{F}}$, then $\mathfrak{A}$ is a linearly dependent set over $\mathscr{F}$.*

OROLLARY 2 *If $\mathfrak{B} \subsetneq \mathfrak{A} \subset \mathscr{V}/\mathscr{F}$ and $\mathfrak{A}$ is a linearly independent set over $\mathscr{F}$, then $\langle\mathfrak{B}\rangle_{\mathscr{F}} \neq \langle\mathfrak{A}\rangle_{\mathscr{F}}$.*

OROLLARY 3 *Suppose $\mathfrak{A} \subset \mathscr{V}/\mathscr{F}$. If $\mathfrak{A}$ is a linearly independent set over $\mathscr{F}$, then no subset of $\mathfrak{A}$ spans $\langle\mathfrak{A}\rangle_{\mathscr{F}}$. Conversely, if no proper subset of $\mathfrak{A}$ spans $\langle\mathfrak{A}\rangle_{\mathscr{F}}$, then $\mathfrak{A}$ is a linearly independent set over $\mathscr{F}$.*

OPOSITION 8 *Let $\mathfrak{A}$ be a countable set that spans $\mathscr{V}/\mathscr{F}$. Let $\mathfrak{B}_0$ be a countable linearly independent set of elements of $\mathscr{V}/\mathscr{F}$. Then there exists a linearly independent countable set $\mathfrak{B}$ which spans $\mathscr{V}$ and which contains $\mathfrak{B}_0$.*

PROOF. Let $\mathfrak{A} = \{\alpha_1, \alpha_2, \ldots\}$. Put $\mathfrak{B}_k = \mathfrak{B}_0 \cup \{\alpha_1, \ldots, \alpha_k\}$ and $\mathscr{V}_k = \langle\mathfrak{B}_k\rangle$, for $k = 1, 2, \ldots$. Then

$$\mathscr{V}_1 \subseteq \mathscr{V}_2 \subseteq \ldots .$$

Let $m_1 < m_2 < \ldots$ be exactly those integers such that $\mathscr{V}_{m-1} \neq \mathscr{V}_m$. For such m, α_m is not a linear combination of elements from $\mathfrak{B}_{m-1}$. Set $\mathfrak{B} = \mathfrak{B}_0 \cup \{\alpha_{m_1}, \alpha_{m_2}, \ldots\}$. Since $\mathfrak{B}$ is the union of two countable sets, $\mathfrak{B}$ itself is countable. Clearly each $\alpha \in \mathfrak{A}$ is a linear combination of elements from $\mathfrak{B}$. Hence $\mathscr{V} = \langle\mathfrak{A}\rangle = \langle\mathfrak{B}\rangle$. If $\mathfrak{B}$ were a linearly dependent set over $\mathscr{F}$, there would be an integer N such that α_{m_N} was a linear combination of elements from $\mathfrak{B}_0 \cup \{\alpha_{m_1}, \ldots, \alpha_{m_{N-1}}\}$. But then $\alpha_{m_N} \in \mathscr{V}_{m_N - 1}$, contrary to the definition of m_N. This proves the proposition.

A linearly independent set (over $\mathscr{F}$) of vectors from $\mathscr{V}|\mathscr{F}$ that spans $\mathscr{V}$ is called a *basis* of $\mathscr{V}$ over $\mathscr{F}$. A space may have several different bases.

The reader can prove the following

COROLLARY *If a space $\mathscr{V}|\mathscr{F}$ is spanned (over $\mathscr{F}$) by a countable set, then $\mathscr{V}$ has a countable basis over $\mathscr{F}$.*

PROPOSITION 9 *A subset $\mathfrak{A}$ is a basis for a vector space $\mathscr{V}$ over $\mathscr{F}$ if either:*
A. *$\mathfrak{A}$ is a maximal linearly independent set (over $\mathscr{F}$) in $\mathscr{V}$, or*
B. *$\mathfrak{A}$ is a minimal spanning set (over $\mathscr{F}$) of the space $\mathscr{V}$.*

The proof follows easily from Proposition 6.

PROPOSITION 10 *If $\mathfrak{A}$ is a basis for $\mathscr{V}$ over $\mathscr{F}$, then each $\alpha \in \mathscr{V}$ is expressible as a linear combination of elements from $\mathfrak{A}$ in exactly one way.*

PROOF. If α can be expressed as two different linear combinations of elements from $\mathfrak{A}$, then the difference of these two expressions would be a nontrivial linear combination that is the zero vector. But then $\mathfrak{A}$ would be a linearly dependent set, contrary to the hypothesis.

COROLLARY 1 *If $\mathfrak{A}$ is a basis of $\mathscr{V}|\mathscr{F}$, then each element of $\mathscr{V}$ can be expressed uniquely as*

$$\sum_{\alpha \in \mathfrak{A}} a_\alpha \alpha, \qquad a_\alpha \in \mathscr{F},$$

where $a_\alpha = 0$ for all but finitely many α. Furthermore

$$\left(\sum_{\alpha \in \mathfrak{A}} a_\alpha \alpha\right) + \left(\sum_{\alpha \in \mathfrak{A}} b_\alpha \alpha\right) = \sum_{\alpha \in \mathfrak{A}} (a_\alpha + b_\alpha)\alpha,$$

$$a\left(\sum_{\alpha \in \mathfrak{A}} a_\alpha \alpha\right) = \sum_{\alpha \in \mathfrak{A}} (a a_\alpha)\alpha.$$

The proof is left to the reader.

PROPOSITION 11 *If $\mathscr{V}$ has a countable basis over $\mathscr{F}$, then every basis for $\mathscr{V}$ over $\mathscr{F}$ is countable.*

PROOF. Let $\mathfrak{B}$ be a basis for $\mathscr{V}$ over $\mathscr{F}$, and let $\mathfrak{A}$ be a countable base for $\mathscr{V}$ over $\mathscr{F}$. Then each $\alpha_j \in \mathfrak{A}$ is expressible as a linear combination of elements from a finite subset $\mathfrak{B}_j$ of $\mathfrak{B}$. But then $\bigcup \mathfrak{B}_j$ is a countable subset of $\mathfrak{B}$ that spans $\langle \mathfrak{A} \rangle$ and hence spans $\mathscr{V}$. Since $\mathfrak{B}$ is a basis and hence a minimal spanning set, we have $\mathfrak{B} = \bigcup \mathfrak{B}_j$; i.e., $\mathfrak{B}$ is countable.

COROLLARY 1 *If $\mathscr{V}$ has a countable basis over $\mathscr{F}$, then each subspace $\mathscr{W}$ of $\mathscr{V}$ (over $\mathscr{F}$) has a countable basis.*

PROOF. Let $\mathfrak{B}_0$ be a basis of $\mathscr{W}/\mathscr{F}$. By Proposition 8 there is a basis $\mathfrak{B}$ of $\mathscr{V}/\mathscr{F}$ that contains $\mathfrak{B}_0$. If $\mathfrak{B}_0$ is uncountable, then $\mathfrak{B}$ is also uncountable, and we would have contradicted Proposition 11.

COROLLARY 2 *If a space $\mathscr{V}/\mathscr{F}$ is spanned (over $\mathscr{F}$) by a countable set and if $\mathfrak{B}_0$ is a linearly independent set (over $\mathscr{F}$), then there is a basis of $\mathscr{V}/\mathscr{F}$ that contains $\mathfrak{B}_0$.*

The proof is left to the reader.

If we assume there is a choice map defined on $\mathscr{V}$, then we can show $\mathscr{V}$ has a basis over $\mathscr{F}$ without the assumption that $\mathscr{V}$ has a countable spanning set. Similarly, if there is a choice map defined on $\mathscr{V}$, then the hypothesis that $\mathscr{V}/\mathscr{F}$ is spanned by a countable set may be dropped from Corollary 2. We shall not give a proof of these two facts here.

We next prove a number of analogous but more specific results for spaces with finite bases.

LEMMA *If $\{\alpha_1, \ldots, \alpha_n\}$ is a finite linearly independent set over $\mathscr{F}$ and if $a_1, \ldots, a_{n-1} \in \mathscr{F}$, then $\{\alpha_1 - a_1\alpha_n, \ldots, \alpha_{n-1} - a_{n-1}\alpha_n\}$ is a linearly independent set over $\mathscr{F}$.*

The proof is left to the reader.

OPOSITION 12 *Let $\{\alpha_1, \ldots, \alpha_n\}$ be a finite linearly independent set over $\mathscr{F}$. Let $\mathscr{W} = \langle\alpha_1, \ldots, \alpha_n\rangle_{\mathscr{F}}$. If $\{\beta_1, \ldots, \beta_m\} \in \mathscr{W}$ is a linearly independent set over $\mathscr{F}$, then $m \leq n$.*

PROOF. The proof is by induction on n. Since $\beta_\nu \in \mathscr{W}$, there are $a_{\nu\mu} \in \mathscr{F}$ such that

$$\beta_\nu = \sum_{\mu=1}^{n} a_{\nu\mu}\alpha_\mu, \qquad \nu = 1, \ldots, m.$$

If $n = 1$, then clearly any two β_ν are linearly dependent over $\mathscr{F}$, and hence $m \leq n$ for the case $n = 1$.

We next suppose that the proposition is true for linearly independent sets of order less than n and prove it is true for sets of order n. If $a_{1n} = \cdots = a_{mn} = 0$, then the β_ν all lie in $\{\alpha_1, \ldots, \alpha_{n-1}\}$. It then follows from the induction hypothesis that $m \leq n - 1 < n$. If, on the other hand, some $a_{\nu n} \neq 0$, say $a_{mn} \neq 0$, put

$$\gamma_\nu = \beta_\nu - a_{\nu n}a_{mn}{}^{-1}\beta_m, \qquad \nu = 1, \ldots, m - 1.$$

Then $\gamma_\nu \in \langle\alpha_1, \ldots, \alpha_{n-1}\rangle$. By the preceding lemma $\{\gamma_1, \ldots, \gamma_{m-1}\}$ is a linearly independent set (over $\mathscr{F}$). It follows from the induction hypothesis that $m - 1 \leq n - 1$, and hence $m \leq n$. This proves the proposition.

The reader should prove

COROLLARY 1 *If $\mathfrak{A}$ and $\mathfrak{B}$ are linearly independent sets (over $\mathscr{F}$) and $\langle\mathfrak{A}\rangle = \langle\mathfrak{B}\rangle$, then $|\mathfrak{A}| = |\mathfrak{B}|$.*

COROLLARY 2 *The order of a maximal set of linearly independent elements (over $\mathscr{F}$) from $\mathscr{V}|\mathscr{F}$ is uniquely determined by $\mathscr{V}|\mathscr{F}$.*

COROLLARY 3 *Different bases of $\mathscr{V}$ over $\mathscr{F}$ have the same order.*

We now define the *dimension* of a vector space $\mathscr{V}$ over $\mathscr{F}$ to be the order of any one of the bases of $\mathscr{V}$ over $\mathscr{F}$. $\mathscr{V}_0 = \mathscr{O}$ is said to have dimension 0. In view of Corollary 3, this is a well-defined map of $\mathscr{V}$ into $\mathbf{Z} \cup \{\infty\}$. We denote the dimension of $\mathscr{V}$ over $\mathscr{F}$ by $\dim_{\mathscr{F}} \mathscr{V}$. The reader can quickly verify that $\dim_{\mathbf{Q}} \mathbf{C} = \infty$, $\dim_{\mathbf{R}} \mathbf{C} = 2$, $\dim_{\mathbf{C}} \mathbf{C} = 1$. Thus the dimension depends on the field as well as on the additive group. We write $\dim \mathscr{V}$ if no confusion will arise.

The reader can prove

COROLLARY 4 *If $\mathscr{V}$ is a finite dimensional space over $\mathscr{F}$ and $\mathscr{W}$ is a subspace of $\mathscr{V}$, then*

$$\dim_{\mathscr{F}} \mathscr{W} \le \dim_{\mathscr{F}} \mathscr{V},$$

and *$\mathscr{W}$ is a proper subspace of $\mathscr{V}$ if and only if*

$$0 < \dim_{\mathscr{F}} \mathscr{W} < \dim_{\mathscr{F}} \mathscr{V}.$$

EXERCISES 6 Prove:

A. $\dim_{\mathscr{F}} \mathscr{F}^{(n)} = n$. If x is an indeterminate over $\mathscr{F}$, then $\dim_{\mathscr{F}} \mathscr{F}[x] = \infty$.

B. If α is a root of a polynomial A, which is irreducible over $\mathscr{F}$, then $\mathscr{F}[\alpha]$ is a vector space over $\mathscr{F}$ of dimension $\deg A$.

C. Corollary 4 is false if $\dim_{\mathscr{F}} \mathscr{V} = \infty$.

7 Determine the dimension of each of the spaces spanned by the sets specified in Exercises 1 to 3.

8 Prove:

A. If $\mathscr{F}$ is a countable field and if $\mathscr{V}|\mathscr{F}$ is a vector space with countable basis over $\mathscr{F}$, then $\mathscr{V}$ is a countable set.

B. $\mathbf{R}$ does not have a countable basis over $\mathbf{Q}$.

C. $\mathscr{T}(\mathbf{Z}, \mathbf{Q})$ does not have a countable basis over $\mathbf{Q}$.

9 Prove: If $\mathscr{W}$ is a subspace of a finite dimensional space $\mathscr{V}|\mathscr{F}$ such that $\dim \mathscr{W} = \dim \mathscr{V}$, then $\mathscr{W} = \mathscr{V}$. Show that this result no longer holds true in case $\mathscr{V}$ is an infinite dimensional space over $\mathscr{F}$.

10 Prove: If $\mathscr{V}_1, \mathscr{V}_2$ are vector spaces over $\mathscr{F}$ and $\mathscr{V}_1 + \mathscr{V}_2$ is their cartesian sum, then

$$\dim_{\mathscr{F}} (\mathscr{V}_1 + \mathscr{V}_2) = \dim_{\mathscr{F}} \mathscr{V}_1 + \dim_{\mathscr{F}} \mathscr{V}_2.$$

11 Prove: If $\mathscr{V}_1, \mathscr{V}_2$ are finite dimensional subspaces of $\mathscr{V}/\mathscr{F}$, then

$$\dim_{\mathscr{F}}(\mathscr{V}_1 + \mathscr{V}_2) + \dim_{\mathscr{F}}(\mathscr{V}_1 \cap \mathscr{V}_2) = \dim_{\mathscr{F}} \mathscr{V}_1 + \dim_{\mathscr{F}} \mathscr{V}_2.$$

Let $\mathscr{V}$ and $\mathscr{W}$ be vector spaces over the same field $\mathscr{F}$. A map φ of $\mathscr{V}$ into $\mathscr{W}$ such that

$$(\alpha + \beta)^{\varphi} = \alpha^{\varphi} + \beta^{\varphi}, \qquad (a\alpha)^{\varphi} = a(\alpha^{\varphi}),$$

when $\alpha, \beta \in \mathscr{V}$ and $a \in \mathscr{F}$, is called an *operation-preserving map* of the vector space $\mathscr{V}$ into the vector space $\mathscr{W}$. It is also called a *morphism* of $\mathscr{V}$ into $\mathscr{W}$. More traditionally such a map is called a *linear transformation* of $\mathscr{V}$ into $\mathscr{W}$. We shall use all three expressions. When using the terminology of linear transformations, we shall usually denote the image of α under the map φ by $\alpha\varphi$. As in previous situations, we have

POSITION 13 *If φ is a linear transformation from $\mathscr{V}/\mathscr{F}$ into $\mathscr{W}/\mathscr{F}$, then the kernel of φ is a subspace of $\mathscr{V}/\mathscr{F}$, and the image set $\mathscr{V}\varphi$ is a subspace of $\mathscr{W}/\mathscr{F}$.*

As usual, we have monomorphisms (injective morphisms), surjective morphisms, and isomorphisms (bijective morphisms). We also have the concepts of morphisms of a vector space into itself (endomorphisms and automorphisms).

The significance of the dimension lies in the following two results:

POSITION 14 *If $\dim_{\mathscr{F}} \mathscr{V} = n \in \mathbf{Z}^+$, then $\mathscr{V}/\mathscr{F}$ is isomorphic to the vector space $\mathscr{F}^{(n)}$.*

PROOF. Let $\{\alpha_1, \ldots, \alpha_n\}$ be a basis of $\mathscr{V}/\mathscr{F}$. By Proposition 10 each $\alpha \in \mathscr{V}$ can be expressed in a unique way as a linear combination of $\alpha_1, \ldots, \alpha_n$ over $\mathscr{F}$. If $\alpha = a_1\alpha_1 + \cdots + a_n\alpha_n$, the map $\alpha \to (a_1, \ldots, a_n)$ is clearly a morphism of $\mathscr{V}$ into $\mathscr{F}^{(n)}$. One easily checks that it is an isomorphism.

POSITION 15 *If $\mathscr{V}/\mathscr{F}$ is spanned by a countable set and $\dim_{\mathscr{F}} \mathscr{V} = \infty$, then $\mathscr{V}$ is isomorphic to $\mathscr{F}[x]$, where x is an indeterminate over $\mathscr{F}$.*

PROOF. By the Corollary to Proposition 8, $\mathscr{V}$ has a countable basis over $\mathscr{F}$; say $\{\alpha_1, \alpha_2, \ldots\}$ is such a base. Then each α can be expressed uniquely as a linear combination of finitely many α_i. Then we can write

$$\alpha = \sum_{i=1}^{\infty} a_i\alpha_i, \qquad \text{where } a_i = 0 \text{ for all but finitely many } i.$$

The map $\alpha \to \sum_{i=1}^{\infty} a_i x^i$ is the desired map, as the reader can show.

COROLLARY *Two vector spaces over the same field $\mathscr{F}$ each with a countable basis are isomorphic if and only if they have the same dimension.*

The proof is a direct consequence of the fact that "being isomorphic" is an equivalence relation on the collection of vector spaces over $\mathscr{F}$. The last two propositions are structure theorems for vector spaces that are analogous to the decomposition theorem for abelian groups.

The reader should prove

PROPOSITION 16 *If $\mathfrak{A}$ is a basis of a vector space $\mathscr{V}$ over $\mathscr{F}$, then $\mathscr{V}$ is isomorphic to $r\sum_{\alpha \in \mathfrak{A}} \mathscr{F}_\alpha$, where $\mathscr{F}_\alpha = \mathscr{F}$. There is a monomorphism φ of $\mathscr{V}$ into $\sum_\alpha \mathscr{F}_\alpha$, where $\mathscr{F}_\alpha = \mathscr{F}$. The morphism φ is bijective if and only if $|\mathfrak{A}|$ is finite.*

PROPOSITION 17 *If φ is a monomorphism of $\mathscr{V}|\mathscr{F}$ into $\mathscr{W}|\mathscr{F}$ and $\mathfrak{A}$ is a linearly independent set (over $\mathscr{F}$) of $\mathscr{V}$, then $\mathfrak{A}\varphi$ is a linearly independent set of $\mathscr{W}$.*

COROLLARY *If φ is a monomorphism of $\mathscr{V}|\mathscr{F}$ into $\mathscr{W}|\mathscr{F}$, then* $\dim_{\mathscr{F}} \mathscr{V} \le \dim_{\mathscr{F}} \mathscr{W}$.

EXERCISES 12 Show that, if $\dim_{\mathbf{Q}} \mathscr{V} = n > 1$, then there are many maps of $\mathscr{V}$ into $\mathbf{Q}^{(n)}$.

13 Prove: $\{1, x, \ldots, x^{p-1}\}$ and $\{1 - x^{p-1}, \ldots, 1 - (x - p + 1)^{p-1}\}$ are two distinct bases for the set of maps of $\mathbf{Z}_p$ into $\mathbf{Z}_p$.

14 Let $\delta_{ij} = \begin{cases} 0 \text{ if } i \ne j \\ 1 \text{ if } i = j \end{cases}$, $i, j \in \mathbf{Z}$. Put $\mathbf{e}_i = (\delta_{i1}, \ldots, \delta_{in})$. Show that $\{\mathbf{e}_1, \ldots, \mathbf{e}_n\}$ is a basis of $\mathscr{F}^{(n)}$ over $\mathscr{F}$.

15 Prove: If $\{\alpha, \beta, \gamma\}$ is a linearly independent set over $\mathscr{F}$ and char $\mathscr{F} \ne 2$, then $\{\alpha + \beta, \beta + \gamma, \gamma + \alpha\}$ is a linearly independent set over $\mathscr{F}$.

16 Prove: If $|X| = n$, then the vector space $\mathscr{T}(X, \mathscr{F})$ is isomorphic to $\mathscr{F}^{(n)}$.

17 If $\mathscr{W}$ is a finite dimensional space over a field $\mathscr{K}$, and $\mathscr{K}$ is a finite dimensional space over $\mathscr{F}$, then $\mathscr{W}$ is a finite dimensional space over $\mathscr{F}$.

If $\mathscr{V}_1, \mathscr{V}_2$ are subspaces of $\mathscr{V}$ such that $\mathscr{V}_1 \cap \mathscr{V}_2 = \mathbf{0}, \mathscr{V}_1 + \mathscr{V}_2 = \mathscr{V}$, we say that $\mathscr{V}$ is the *direct sum* of $\mathscr{V}_1$ and $\mathscr{V}_2$. In this case, we shall write $\mathscr{V} = \mathscr{V}_1 + \mathscr{V}_2$ (direct). As with groups we can talk of the direct sum of many subspaces.

If $\mathscr{W}, \mathscr{W}'$ are subspaces of $\mathscr{V}|\mathscr{F}$ such that $\mathscr{V} = \mathscr{W} + \mathscr{W}'$ (direct), we say that $\mathscr{W}'$ is a space *complimentary* to $\mathscr{W}$ in $\mathscr{V}$. A space can have several complimentary spaces; e.g., $\langle(0, 1)\rangle$ and $\langle(1, 1)\rangle$ are both complimentary spaces for $\langle(1, 0)\rangle$ in $\mathscr{F}^{(2)}$.

Corollary 2 of Proposition 11 allows us to state

PROPOSITION 18 *If $\mathscr{V}|\mathscr{F}$ has a countable base over $\mathscr{F}$ and $\mathscr{W}$ is a subspace of $\mathscr{V}$, then $\mathscr{W}$ has a complimentary space in $\mathscr{V}$.*

PROOF. Let $\mathfrak{B}_0$ be a basis of $\mathscr{W}$ over $\mathscr{F}$. Let $\mathfrak{B}$ be a basis of $\mathscr{V}$ that contains $\mathfrak{B}_0$. By Corollary 2 of Proposition 11, such a set $\mathfrak{B}$ exists. Then $\langle \mathfrak{B} - \mathfrak{B}_0 \rangle$ is complimentary to $\mathscr{W}$.

2 LINEAR FUNCTIONALS

Let $\mathscr{V}$ be a vector space over $\mathscr{F}$. A linear transformation f of $\mathscr{V}$ into $\mathscr{F}$ is called a *linear functional* on $\mathscr{V}$. We shall denote the image of the vector α under the linear functional f by αf. Then

$$(\alpha + \beta)f = \alpha f + \beta f, \qquad (a\alpha)f = a(\alpha f) \qquad \text{for } \alpha, \beta \in \mathscr{V}, a \in \mathscr{F}.$$

If $\mathfrak{A}$ is a basis of $\mathscr{V}$ over $\mathscr{F}$ and if for each $\alpha \in \mathfrak{A}$ there is a $c_\alpha \in \mathscr{F}$, then

$$\beta = \sum_{\alpha \in \mathfrak{A}} a_\alpha \alpha \to \sum_{\alpha \in \mathfrak{A}} a_\alpha c_\alpha$$

is a linear functional on $\mathscr{V}$. Note that the right-hand side of this equation is defined, since all but finitely many of the a_α are 0. As we shall see, every linear functional on a finite dimensional space $\mathscr{V}$ is of this type.

ERCISES 1 Which of the following are linear functionals on $\mathscr{F}^{(n)}$?
A. $(a_1, \ldots, a_n)f = a_2^2 - a_1^2$.
B. $(a_1, \ldots, a_n)f = 0$.
C. $(a_1, \ldots, a_n)f = 1$.

2 Show: If $\mathscr{V}$ is the set of continuous functions from

$$I = \{x \in \mathbf{R} | -1 \leq x \leq 1\}$$

into $\mathbf{R}$, then $\alpha f = \int_{-1}^{1} \alpha \, dx$ is a linear functional on $\mathscr{V}$. Also, if $g \in \mathscr{V}$ then $\alpha g^* = \int_{-1}^{1} \alpha(x)g(x)\, dx$ is a linear functional on $\mathscr{V}$.

Under the usual operations

$$\alpha(f + g) = \alpha f + \alpha g, \ \alpha(af) = a(\alpha f), \ \alpha(fg) = (\alpha f)(\alpha g), \text{ for all } \alpha \in \mathscr{V},$$

the set of all maps of $\mathscr{V}$ into $\mathscr{F}$ is both a ring and a vector space over $\mathscr{F}$. This suggests we investigate the algebraic structure of $\mathscr{V}^*$, the set of all linear functionals on $\mathscr{V}$. It is immediately clear that $\mathscr{V}^*$ is an additive abelian group, with

$$\alpha \xrightarrow{f+g} \alpha(f + g) = \alpha f + \alpha g.$$

On the other hand it is difficult to see how to define a multiplication so that $\mathscr{V}^*$ would be a ring. We can, however, view $\mathscr{V}^*$ as a vector space over $\mathscr{F}$ by defining

$$\alpha \xrightarrow{fa} \alpha(fa) = (\alpha f)a.$$

We adopt the custom of writing fa, rather than af, to indicate scalar multiplication in $\mathscr{V}^*$. The reader should verify

PROPOSITION 19 *If $\mathscr{V}$ is a vector space over $\mathscr{F}$, then $\mathscr{V}^*$, the set of all linear functionals on $\mathscr{V}$, is a vector space over $\mathscr{F}$.*

Let $\mathfrak{A}$ be a basis of a vector space $\mathscr{V}$ over $\mathscr{F}$. If $f \in \mathscr{V}^*$, then $\text{res}_{\mathfrak{A}} f$ is an element of $\mathscr{T}(\mathfrak{A}, \mathscr{F})$. Conversely, if $g \in \mathscr{T}(\mathfrak{A}, \mathscr{F})$, then the map

$$\beta = \sum_{\alpha \in \mathfrak{A}} b_\alpha \alpha \to \sum_{\alpha \in \mathfrak{A}} b_\alpha(\alpha g), \qquad \beta \in \mathscr{V},$$

is a linear functional on $\mathscr{V}$ whose restriction to $\mathfrak{A}$ is the map g. Furthermore, different maps of $\mathfrak{A}$ into $\mathscr{F}$ induce different linear functionals on $\mathscr{V}$. We have thus shown that the restriction map is a bijective map of $\mathscr{V}^*$ onto $\mathscr{T}(\mathfrak{A}, \mathscr{F})$. Since

$$\text{res}_{\mathfrak{A}}\ (g+g_1) = \text{res}_{\mathfrak{A}}\ g + \text{res}_{\mathfrak{A}}\ g_1$$

and

$$\text{res}_{\mathfrak{A}}\ ga = (\text{res}_{\mathfrak{A}}\ g)a$$

for all $g, g_1 \in \mathscr{V}$ and $a \in \mathscr{F}$, we have proved

PROPOSITION 20 *If $\mathfrak{A}$ is a basis of a vector space $\mathscr{V}$ over $\mathscr{F}$, then $\mathscr{V}^*$ is isomorphic to the vector space $\mathscr{T}(\mathfrak{A}, \mathscr{F})$.*

As a consequence of Proposition 20 and Exercise 16, Sec. 1, we have

PROPOSITION 21 *If $\mathscr{V}$ is a finite dimensional space over $\mathscr{F}$, then $\mathscr{V}$ and $\mathscr{V}^*$ are isomorphic vector spaces over $\mathscr{F}$.*

On the other hand, from Propositions 16 and 20 we obtain

PROPOSITION 22 *If $\mathscr{V}$ is an infinite dimensional space over $\mathscr{F}$, then $\mathscr{V}$ and $\mathscr{V}^*$ are not isomorphic spaces over $\mathscr{F}$.*

The reader can prove

PROPOSITION 23 *If $\alpha_1, \dots, \alpha_n$ is a basis of $\mathscr{V}$ over $\mathscr{F}$, let $f_1, \dots, f_n$ be the linear functionals on $\mathscr{V}$ such that*

$$\alpha_\nu f_\mu = \begin{cases} 1 \text{ if } \nu = \mu, \\ 0 \text{ if } \nu \neq \mu; \end{cases}$$

then $\{f_1, \dots, f_n\}$ is a basis of $\mathscr{V}^*$ over $\mathscr{F}$.

PROOF. Suppose $f_1 c_1 + \cdots + f_n c_n = 0$; then $0 = \alpha_j(f_1 c_1 + \cdots + f_n c_n) = c_j\ (j = 1, \dots, n)$, and consequently $\{f_1, \dots, f_n\}$ is a linearly independent set. If $f \in \mathscr{V}^*$, let $\alpha_j f = b_j$, $(j = 1, \dots, n)$; then $f_1 b_1 + \cdots + f_n b_n$ and f are linear functionals having the same value on $\alpha_1, \dots, \alpha_n$, and hence they are the same linear functional. It follows that the set $\{f_1, \dots, f_n\}$ span $\mathscr{V}^*$ and therefore $\{f_1, \dots, f_n\}$ is a basis of $\mathscr{V}^*$.

Now given a basis $\{\alpha_1, \dots, \alpha_n\}$ of $\mathscr{V}/\mathscr{F}$, each $\alpha \in \mathscr{V}$ can be expressed uniquely as $\sum_{\nu=1}^{n} a_\nu \alpha_\nu$. If f_μ are as in Proposition 23, then each $f \in \mathscr{V}^*$ can be expressed uniquely as $\sum_{\mu=1}^{n} f_\mu b_\mu$. In that case

$$\alpha f = (\sum a_\nu \alpha_\nu)(\sum f_\mu b_\mu) = \sum a_\nu b_\nu.$$

Thus relative to the basis $\{\alpha_1, \ldots, \alpha_n\}$ of $\mathscr{V}$, we see that αf is expressible as a homogeneous linear polynomial in the variables $a_1, \ldots, a_n$. Such polynomials are called *linear forms*. Thus we have a map

$$f = \sum_{\mu=1}^{n} f_\mu b_\mu \xrightarrow{\delta} \sum_{\mu=1}^{n} a_\mu b_\mu = \mathbf{L}(a_1, \ldots, a_n)$$

of $\mathscr{V}^*$ into $\mathbf{L}^{(n)}$, the set of all linear forms in n variables, the coefficient of a_μ being $\alpha_\mu f$. As the reader can show, the map δ is bijective.

POSITION 24 *If $\mathscr{V}$ has a countable basis over $\mathscr{F}$ and $\alpha \neq \mathbf{0}$, then there is at least one linear functional f on $\mathscr{V}$ for which $\alpha f \neq 0$.*

PROOF. Since $\mathscr{V}$ has a countable basis over $\mathscr{F}$, by Proposition 11, Corollary 2, there is a basis $\mathfrak{A}$ of $\mathscr{V}$ such that $\alpha \in \mathfrak{A}$. Let f be the linear functional on $\mathscr{V}$ such that the restriction of f to $\mathfrak{A}$ maps α into 1 and all other elements of $\mathfrak{A}$ into 0. The linear functional f is the desired map.

POSITION 25 *If $\mathscr{V}$ has a countable basis over $\mathscr{F}$ and if $\mathscr{V}^{**}$ is the set of all linear functionals on $\mathscr{V}^*$, then $\mathscr{V}$ is naturally isomorphic to a subspace (over $\mathscr{F}$) of $\mathscr{V}^{**}$.*

PROOF. If $\alpha, \beta \in \mathscr{V}$ and $f, g \in \mathscr{V}^*$, then

$$(\alpha + \beta)f = \alpha f + \beta f, \qquad (a\alpha)f = a(\alpha f),$$
$$\alpha(f + g) = \alpha f + \alpha g, \qquad \alpha(fa) = (\alpha f)a.$$

The last line tells us that each $\alpha \in \mathscr{V}$ defines in a natural way a linear functional on $\mathscr{V}^*$. If $\alpha \neq \beta$, then by Proposition 24 there is an $f \in \mathscr{V}^*$ such that $(\alpha - \beta)f \neq 0$; i.e., $\alpha f \neq \beta f$. Consequently distinct elements of $\mathscr{V}$ define distinct linear functionals on $\mathscr{V}^*$; i.e., there is an embedding of $\mathscr{V}$ into $\mathscr{V}^{**}$. The first set of equations tells us that the addition and scalar multiplication in $\mathscr{V}$ agrees with the addition and scalar multiplication in $\mathscr{V}^{**}$ of elements of $\mathscr{V}$. Therefore the image of $\mathscr{V}$ under this natural map is a subspace of $\mathscr{V}^{**}$. Henceforth we shall view $\mathscr{V}$ as a subspace of $\mathscr{V}^{**}$.

It follows from Propositions 21 and 25 that

COROLLARY *If $\mathscr{V}$ is a finite dimensional vector space over $\mathscr{F}$, then $\mathscr{V} = \mathscr{V}^{**}$.*

Let $\mathscr{X}$ be a subset of $\mathscr{V}/\mathscr{F}$. Put

$$\mathfrak{A}^*(\mathscr{X}) = \{f \in \mathscr{V}^* \mid \alpha f = 0, \text{ for all } \alpha \in \mathscr{X}\}.$$

The set $\mathfrak{A}^*(\mathscr{X})$ is called the *annihilating set of* $\mathscr{X}$. The reader can prove

PROPOSITION 26 A. *$\mathfrak{A}^*(\mathscr{X})$ is a subspace of $\mathscr{V}^*$ over $\mathscr{F}$.*
B. $\mathfrak{A}^*(\mathscr{O}) = \mathscr{V}^*$, $\mathfrak{A}^*(\mathscr{V}) = \mathscr{O}^*$.
C. *If $\mathscr{X} \subset \mathscr{Y} \subset \mathscr{V}$, then $\mathfrak{A}^*(\mathscr{X}) \supset \mathfrak{A}^*(\mathscr{Y})$.*
D. $\mathfrak{A}^*(\mathscr{X}) = \mathfrak{A}^*(\langle\mathscr{X}\rangle)$.
E. $\mathfrak{A}^*(\mathscr{X} \cup \mathscr{Y}) = \mathfrak{A}^*(\mathscr{X}) \cap \mathfrak{A}^*(\mathscr{Y})$.
F. *If $\mathscr{V}$ has a countable basis and if $\langle\mathscr{X}\rangle \neq \langle\mathscr{Y}\rangle$,* then $\mathfrak{A}^*(\mathscr{X}) \neq \mathfrak{A}^*(\mathscr{Y})$.

PROPOSITION 27 *If $\mathscr{V}$ is a finite dimensional space over $\mathscr{F}$ and if $\mathscr{X}$ is a subset of $\mathscr{V}$, then*

$$\dim_{\mathscr{F}} \mathfrak{A}^*(\mathscr{X}) = \dim_{\mathscr{F}} \mathscr{V} - \dim_{\mathscr{F}} \langle\mathscr{X}\rangle_{\mathscr{F}}.$$

PROOF. Suppose $\dim_{\mathscr{F}} \mathscr{V} = n$. Let $\{\alpha_1, \ldots, \alpha_m\}$ be a maximal set of linearly independent vectors chosen from the set $\mathscr{X}$. Then $\langle\alpha_1, \ldots, \alpha_m\rangle = \langle\mathscr{X}\rangle$. By Proposition 8 there are $\alpha_{m+1} \ldots, \alpha_n$ such that $\{\alpha_1, \ldots, \alpha_n\}$ is a basis of $\mathscr{V}$ over $\mathscr{F}$. Let f_μ be as defined in Proposition 23. Since each $\alpha \in \mathscr{X}$ is a linear combination of $\alpha_1, \ldots, \alpha_m$, we clearly have $f_{m+1}, \ldots, f_n \in \mathfrak{A}^*(\mathscr{X})$. If $f \in \mathfrak{A}^*(\mathscr{X})$, then $f = \sum_{\mu=1}^{n} f_\mu c_\mu$ and $0 = \alpha_\nu f = c_\nu$, for $\nu = 1, \ldots, m$. Consequently $\{f_{m+1}, \ldots, f_n\}$ is a linearly independent spanning set of $\mathfrak{A}^*(\mathscr{X})$. Hence $\dim \mathfrak{A}^*(\mathscr{X}) = n - m = \dim \mathscr{V} - \dim \langle\mathscr{X}\rangle$, as was to be proved.

When $\mathscr{V}$ is a finite dimensional space over $\mathscr{F}$, we have seen that $\mathscr{V} = \mathscr{V}^{**}$. Hence the annihilating set of a subset $\mathscr{X}^*$ of $\mathscr{V}^*$ is a subspace of $\mathscr{V}$; we denote it by $\mathfrak{A}(\mathscr{X}^*)$. Results similar to Propositions 26 and 27 hold for the annihilator $\mathfrak{A}$. The reader can prove

PROPOSITION 28 *If $\mathscr{V}$ is finite dimensional over $\mathscr{F}$, then:*
A. $\mathfrak{A}^*\mathfrak{A}(\mathscr{X}^*) = \langle\mathscr{X}^*\rangle$.
B. $\mathfrak{A}\,\mathfrak{A}^*(\mathscr{X}) = \langle\mathscr{X}\rangle$.
C. $\mathfrak{A}^*(\mathscr{X} \cap \mathscr{Y}) = \mathfrak{A}^*(\mathscr{X}) + \mathfrak{A}^*(\mathscr{Y})$.
D. *If $\mathscr{W}'$ is a space complimentary to the subspace $\mathscr{W}$ in $\mathscr{V}$, then $\mathfrak{A}^*(\mathscr{W}')$ is complimentary to $\mathfrak{A}^*(\mathscr{W})$ in $\mathscr{V}^*$.*

This sequence of three propositions may be summarized as follows:

PROPOSITION 29 *If $\mathscr{V}$ is a finite dimensional vector space over $\mathscr{F}$, then the map $\mathscr{W} \to \mathfrak{A}^*(\mathscr{W})$ is a bijective map of subspaces of $\mathscr{V}$ onto subspaces of $\mathscr{V}^*$ that inverts inclusion and interchanges intersection and sum.*

EXERCISE 3 Let $\mathscr{V} = \mathscr{W}_1 + \mathscr{W}_2$(direct). Prove:
A. There are monomorphisms σ_ν of $\mathscr{W}_\nu^*$ into $\mathscr{V}^*$, ($\nu = 1, 2$).
B. $\sigma_1(\mathscr{W}_1^*) \cap \sigma_2(\mathscr{W}_2^*) = \mathscr{O}^*$.
C. $\mathscr{V}^*$ is isomorphic to the cartesian sum $\mathscr{W}_1^* + \mathscr{W}_2^*$.

Let $\mathscr{V} \times \mathscr{V}^* = \{(\alpha, f) \mid \alpha \in \mathscr{V}, f \in \mathscr{V}^*\}$; i.e., $\mathscr{V} \times \mathscr{V}^*$ is the set of ordered pairs, the first from $\mathscr{V}$, the second from $\mathscr{V}^*$. Then

$$(\alpha, f) \xrightarrow{M} \alpha f = (\alpha, f)M$$

is a map from the set $\mathscr{V} \times \mathscr{V}^*$ into $\mathscr{F}$ such that, if $\alpha, \beta \in \mathscr{V}, f, g \in \mathscr{V}^*$, and $a, b \in \mathscr{F}$, then

$$(a\alpha + b\beta, f)M = a(\alpha, f)M + b(\beta, f)M$$

$$(\alpha, fa + gb)M = a(\alpha, f)M + b(\beta, g)M.$$

We now generalize this idea. Let $\mathscr{V}_1, \ldots, \mathscr{V}_k$ be vector spaces over $\mathscr{F}$, and let $\mathscr{V}_1 \times \cdots \times \mathscr{V}_k = \{(\alpha_1, \ldots, \alpha_k) \mid \alpha_\nu \in \mathscr{V}_\nu, \nu = 1, \ldots, k\}$. A map M of $\mathscr{V}_1 \times \cdots \times \mathscr{V}_k$ into $\mathscr{F}$ such that for each s

$$(\alpha_1, \ldots, \alpha_{s-1}, a\alpha_s + b\beta_s, \alpha_{s+1}, \ldots, \alpha_n)M$$
$$= a(\alpha_1, \ldots, \alpha_s, \ldots, \alpha_n)M + b(\alpha_1, \ldots, \beta_s, \ldots, \alpha_s)M,$$

for all $a, b \in \mathscr{F}$ and $\alpha_\nu, \beta_\nu \in \mathscr{V}_\nu$, is called a *multilinear functional on* $\mathscr{V}_1 \times \cdots \times \mathscr{V}_k$. When $k = 2$, M is called a *bilinear functional.*

The reader should prove

ROPOSITION 30 *If M is a multilinear functional on $\mathscr{V}_1 \times \cdots \times \mathscr{V}_k$ and one of $\alpha_1 \ldots, \alpha_k$ is the* **0** *vector, then $(\alpha_1, \ldots, \alpha_k)M = 0$.*

ROPOSITION 31 *If $\mathscr{V}_1, \ldots, \mathscr{V}_k$ are vector spaces over $\mathscr{F}$, then the set of all multilinear functionals on $\mathscr{V}_1 \times \cdots \times \mathscr{V}_k$ is a vector space over $\mathscr{F}$.*

ROPOSITION 32 *Let $\{\alpha_1, \ldots, \alpha_n\}$ be a basis of $\mathscr{V}_1$ over $\mathscr{F}$, and let $\{\beta_1, \ldots, \beta_m\}$ be a basis of $\mathscr{V}_2$ over $\mathscr{F}$. Let M be a bilinear functional on $\mathscr{V}_1 \times \mathscr{V}_2$. Then there exist $c_{ij} \in \mathscr{F}$ $(1 \le i \le n, 1 \le j \le m)$ such that*

$$\left(\sum_{s=1}^{n} a_s\alpha_s, \sum_{t=1}^{m} b_t\beta_t\right)M = \sum_{i=1}^{n} \sum_{j=1}^{m} a_i c_{ij} b_j.$$

Conversely, each such map is a bilinear functional on $\mathscr{V}_1 \times \mathscr{V}_2$.

COROLLARY *If $\dim_{\mathscr{F}} \mathscr{V}_1 = n$, $\dim_{\mathscr{F}} \mathscr{V}_2 = m$, then the space of bilinear functionals on $\mathscr{V}_1 \times \mathscr{V}_2$ is of dimension mn.*

EXERCISES 4 Generalize Proposition 32 and its corollary to multilinear functionals on $\mathscr{V}_1 \times \cdots \times \mathscr{V}_k$ with $k > 2$.

5 Prove: A function f from $\mathscr{V}_1 \times \cdots \times \mathscr{V}_k$ to $\mathscr{F}$ is a multilinear functional if and only if on fixing any $k - 1$ of the arguments the resulting function is a linear functional.

Let M be a bilinear functional on $\mathscr{V}_1 \times \mathscr{V}_2$. For a fixed $\beta \in \mathscr{V}_2$, the map $\alpha \to (\alpha, \beta)M$ is a linear functional on $\mathscr{V}_1$, which we shall denote by $M_{1\beta}$. Similarly, for a fixed $\alpha \in \mathscr{V}_2$ the map $\beta \to (\alpha, \beta)M$ is a linear functional on $\mathscr{V}_2$, which we denote by $M_{2\alpha}$. Put

$$\mathscr{C}_1(M) = \bigcap_{\beta \in \mathscr{V}_2} \mathfrak{A}(M_{1\beta}), \qquad \mathscr{C}_2(M) = \bigcap_{\alpha \in \mathscr{V}_1} \mathfrak{A}(M_{2\alpha}).$$

We say that M is a *nonsingular bilinear functional* on $\mathscr{V}_1 \times \mathscr{V}_2$, provided $\mathscr{C}_1(M) = \mathscr{O}$ and $\mathscr{C}_2(M) = \mathscr{O}$. Thus M is a nonsingular bilinear functional on $\mathscr{V}_1 \times \mathscr{V}_2$ if and only if to each nonzero $\alpha \in \mathscr{V}_1$ there is a $\beta \in \mathscr{V}_2$ such that $(\alpha, \beta)M \neq 0$ and to each nonzero $\beta \in \mathscr{V}_2$ there is a $\alpha \in \mathscr{V}_1$ such that $(\alpha, \beta)M \neq 0$. If $\mathscr{V}$ has a countable basis, the map $(\alpha, f) \to \alpha f$ is a nonsingular bilinear functional on $\mathscr{V} \times \mathscr{V}^*$.

PROPOSITION 33 *Let $\mathscr{V}_1$ and $\mathscr{V}_2$ be finite dimensional vector spaces over $\mathscr{F}$. There is a nonsingular bilinear functional on $\mathscr{V}_1 \times \mathscr{V}_2$ if and only if $\dim \mathscr{V}_1 = \dim \mathscr{V}_2$.*

PROOF. Suppose $\dim \mathscr{V}_1 = n \geq \dim \mathscr{V}_2 = m$. Let $\{\beta_1, \dots, \beta_m\}$ be a basis of $\mathscr{V}_2$. Let M be a linear functional on $\mathscr{V}_1 \times \mathscr{V}_2$. By Proposition 26D we have

$$\mathscr{C}_1(M) = \bigcap_{\nu=1}^{m} \mathfrak{A}(M_{1\beta_\nu}).$$

By Proposition 27, $\dim \mathfrak{A}(M_{1\beta}) = n - 1$. But then by Exercise 11, Sec. 1,

$$\dim \bigcap_{1}^{m} \mathfrak{A}(M_{1\beta_\nu}) \geq n - m.$$

Hence if $n > m$, then M is a singular bilinear functional. Thus we have proved that, if there is a nonsingular linear functional on $\mathscr{V}_1 \times \mathscr{V}_2$, then $m = n$.

In the other direction, if $m = n$, put

$$c_{ij} = \begin{cases} 1 \text{ if } i = j, \\ 0 \text{ if } i \neq j. \end{cases}$$

Then the bilinear functional specified in Proposition 32 is a nonsingular.

3 LINEAR FORMS

Throughout this section, $\mathscr{V}$ will be a finite dimensional vector space over a field $\mathscr{F}$, say $\dim \mathscr{V} = n$. Let $\mathscr{V}^{(k)}$ denote the set of ordered k-tuples of elements from $\mathscr{V}$. A multilinear functional on $\mathscr{V}^{(k)}$ is called a *linear form of order k* on the space $\mathscr{V}$. Let $\mathscr{L}_k$ be the set of all linear forms of order k on $\mathscr{V}$. Then $\mathscr{L}_k$ is a vector space of dimension n^k over the field $\mathscr{F}$. $\mathscr{L}_1$ is the set of linear functionals on $\mathscr{V}$ and is not the zero space unless $\mathscr{V}$ is the zero space.

Let G be a linear form of order s on $\mathscr{V}$, and let H be a linear form of order t on $\mathscr{V}$. Then, because of the distributive and associative laws on $\mathscr{F}$, the map

$$(\alpha_1, \ldots, \alpha_{s+t}) \to [(\alpha_1, \ldots, \alpha_s)G][(\alpha_{s+1}, \ldots, \alpha_{s+t})H]$$

is a linear form of order $s + t$ on $\mathscr{V}$. We shall denote this map by $G \times H$. Clearly if G and H are nonzero linear forms, then $G \times H$ is also nonzero. Since there are nonzero linear forms of order 1 on $\mathscr{V}$, namely, the linear functionals on $\mathscr{V}$, it follows by induction that for each positive integer k there are nonzero linear forms of order k on $\mathscr{V}$.

Each $\sigma \in \Pi_k$ induces a map

$$F \to F^\sigma$$

of $\mathscr{L}_k$ into itself, where

$$(\alpha_1, \ldots, \alpha_k)F^\sigma = (\alpha_{1\sigma}, \ldots, \alpha_{k\sigma})F.$$

The reader can quickly check to see that

$$(F^\sigma)^\tau = F^{\sigma\tau}, \qquad \text{if } \sigma, \tau \in \Pi_k;$$

$$F^\iota = F, \qquad \text{where } \iota \text{ is the identity of } \Pi_k;$$

$$(Fa)^\sigma = F^\sigma a, \qquad \text{for } F \in \mathscr{L}_k,\ a \in \mathscr{F};$$

$$(F + G)^\sigma = F^\sigma + G^\sigma, \qquad \text{if } F, G \in \mathscr{L}_k.$$

Since the maps $F \to F^\sigma$, $F \to F^{\sigma^{-1}}$ of $\mathscr{L}_k$ into itself are inverses of one another, they must be bijective maps. We then have

POSITION 34 *If $\sigma \in \Pi_k$, the map $F \to F^\sigma$ of $\mathscr{L}_k$ into itself is an automorphism of the vector space $\mathscr{L}_k$.*

XERCISES 1 Show that in general $G \times H \neq H \times G$.

2 Prove:

A. If F and G are linear forms of the same order, then $(F + G) \times H = (F \times H) + (G \times H)$. And $H \times (F + G) = (H \times F) + (H \times G)$.

B. $(F \times G) \times H = F \times (G \times H)$.

3 Prove: Given $\sigma \in \Pi_k$, $(k \geq 2)$, there is an $F \in \mathscr{L}_k$ such that $F^\sigma \neq F$.

If F is a linear form of order k, then

$$G = \sum_{\tau \in \Pi_k} F^\tau$$

is a linear form of order k such that $G^\sigma = G$, for all $\sigma \in \Pi_k$. We say that a linear form F of order k on $\mathscr{V}$ *is symmetric* if $F^\sigma = F$, for all $\sigma \in \Pi_k$. Trivially, every linear form of order 1 is symmetric. If F is a nonzero symmetric linear form of order h on $\mathscr{V}$ and if g is a nonzero linear functional on $\mathscr{V}$, then the map G defined by

$$(\alpha_1, \ldots, \alpha_{h+1})G = [(\alpha_1, \ldots, \alpha_h)F][\alpha_{h+1}g] \\ + [(\alpha_1, \ldots, \alpha_{h-1}, \alpha_{h+1})F][\alpha_h g] + \cdots + [(\alpha_{h+1}, \alpha_2, \ldots, \alpha_h)F][\alpha_1 g]$$

is a nonzero symmetric linear form of order $h + 1$. The proof follows easily from Exercise 4 below.

We let ${}^s\mathscr{L}_k$ denote the set of all symmetric linear forms of order k on $\mathscr{V}$. The reader can check that ${}^s\mathscr{L}_k$ is a vector space over $\mathscr{F}$. Hence we have

PROPOSITION 35 *The set ${}^s\mathscr{L}_k$ is a nonzero subspace of $\mathscr{L}_k$.*

Recall that an element $\sigma \in \Pi_k$ can always be expressed as a product of finitely many transpositions. Although the product was not unique, it was true that σ could nct be expressed both as a product of an even number of transpositions and as a product of an odd number of transpositions. Thus we can define a homomorphism of Π_k into the multiplicative group $\{1, -1\}$ as follows:

$$\operatorname{sgn}(\sigma) = \begin{cases} -1, & \text{if } \sigma \text{ is an odd product of transpositions,} \\ 1, & \text{if } \sigma \text{ is an even product of transpositions.} \end{cases}$$

A linear form F of order k is said to be *skewsymmetric* provided $F^\sigma = F(\operatorname{sgn} \sigma)$, for all $\sigma \in \Pi_k$. If F is a linear form of order k, then

$$G = \sum_{\tau \in \Pi_k} F^\tau (\operatorname{sgn} \tau)$$

is a skewsymmetric linear form. Since $\operatorname{sgn} \iota = 1$ and $\Pi_1 = \langle \iota \rangle$, we see that every linear form of order 1 is a skewsymmetric linear form. We let ${}^{ss}\mathscr{L}_k$ denote the set of all skewsymmetric linear forms of order k on $\mathscr{V}$.

A linear form F is said to be an *alternating form* if $(\alpha_1, \ldots, \alpha_n)F = 0$ whenever two of the α_v are equal. Again, trivially all forms of order 1 are alternating forms. The set of all alternating forms of order k on $\mathscr{V}$ will be denoted by ${}^a\mathscr{L}_k$. The reader can prove

PROPOSITION 36 *${}^{ss}\mathscr{L}_k$ and ${}^a\mathscr{L}_k$ are subspaces of $\mathscr{L}_k$.*

EXERCISES 4 Prove: $F \in {}^{ss}\mathscr{L}_k$ if and only if $F^\sigma = -F$ for all transpositions σ in Π_k. $F \in {}^s\mathscr{L}_k$ if and only if $F^\sigma = F$ for all transpositions σ in Π_k.

5 Prove: If $k \geq 2$, then ${}^s\mathscr{L}_k \cap {}^a\mathscr{L}_k = \mathscr{O}$.

The reader should prove

PROPOSITION 37 *If char $\mathscr{F} \neq 2$, then ${}^{ss}\mathscr{L}_k \subset {}^a\mathscr{L}_k$. For all fields $\mathscr{F}$, ${}^a\mathscr{L}_k \subset {}^{ss}\mathscr{L}_k$.*

COROLLARY *If char $\mathscr{F} \neq 2$, then ${}^{ss}\mathscr{L}_k = {}^{a}\mathscr{L}_k$.*

EXERCISES 6 Show that there are k such that ${}^{ss}\mathscr{L}_k \neq {}^{a}\mathscr{L}_k$ when char $\mathscr{F} = 2$.

7 Prove: If char $\mathscr{F} \neq 2$, show that every linear form of order 2 is the sum of a symmetric and a skewsymmetric linear form. Does this result hold for linear forms of higher order?

The reader should prove

OPOSITION 38 *If $F \in {}^{a}\mathscr{L}_k$, and $s \neq t$, then*

$$(\alpha_1, \ldots, \alpha_{s-1}, \alpha_s + b\alpha_t, \alpha_{s+1}, \ldots, \alpha_k)F = (\alpha_1, \ldots, \alpha_s, \ldots, \alpha_k)F.$$

LEMMA *If $O \neq F \in {}^{a}\mathscr{L}_k$ and $(\gamma_1, \ldots, \gamma_k)F \neq 0$, then $\{\gamma_1, \ldots, \gamma_k\}$ is a linearly independent set.*

OPOSITION 39 *If $k > n = \dim \mathscr{V}$, then there is no nonzero alternating form of order k on $\mathscr{V}$.*

On the other hand, we have

OPOSITION 40 *If $1 \leq k \leq n$, then there are nonzero alternating forms of order k on $\mathscr{V}$.*

PROOF. The proof will be by induction. We know there are nonzero alternating forms of order 1. Suppose $1 \leq h < n$ and there is a nonzero alternating form F of order h on $\mathscr{V}$. By Lemma 1 to Proposition 39, there is a linearly independent set $\{\gamma_1, \ldots, \gamma_h\}$ such that $(\gamma_1, \ldots, \gamma_h)F \neq 0$. Since $h < n$, there is a vector $\gamma_{h+1} \in \mathscr{V}$ such that $\{\gamma_1, \ldots, \gamma_h, \gamma_{h+1}\}$ is a linearly independent set. Consequently there is a linear functional (see Proposition 23) g on $\mathscr{V}$ such that $\gamma_\nu g = 0$, $(\nu = 1, 2, \ldots, h)$, and $\gamma_{h+1}g \neq 0$. Consider the map

$$\begin{aligned}(\alpha_1, \ldots, \alpha_{h+1})G &= [(\alpha_{h+1}, \alpha_2, \ldots, \alpha_h)F][\alpha_1 g] \\ &\quad + [(\alpha_1, \alpha_{h+1}, \alpha_3, \ldots, \alpha_h)F][\alpha_2 g] + \cdots + [(\alpha_1, \ldots, \alpha_{h-1}, \alpha_{h+1})F][\alpha_h g] \\ &\quad - [(\alpha_1, \ldots, \alpha_h)F][\alpha_{h+1} g].\end{aligned}$$

The reader can easily check that G is a nonzero alternating form of order $h + 1$ on $\mathscr{V}$.

POSITION 41 *If $n = \dim \mathscr{V}$ and $O \neq F \in {}^{a}\mathscr{L}_n$, then $(\gamma_1, \ldots, \gamma_n)F \neq 0$ if and only if $\{\gamma_1, \ldots, \gamma_n\}$ is a linearly independent set.*

PROOF. By the Lemma to Proposition 39, if $(\gamma_1, \ldots, \gamma_n)F \neq 0$, then $\{\gamma_1, \ldots, \gamma_n\}$ is a linearly independent set.

To prove the converse, we note that, if $F \neq O$, then there is a set $\{\gamma_1, \ldots, \gamma_n\}$ such that $(\gamma_1, \ldots, \gamma_n)F \neq 0$. Let $\{\alpha_1, \ldots, \alpha_n\}$ be another linearly independent set, then $\{\alpha_1, \ldots, \alpha_n\}$ spans $\mathscr{V}$, and we have

$$\gamma_i = \sum_{j=1}^{n} a_{ij}\alpha_j, \qquad i = 1, \ldots, n.$$

Then

$$(\gamma_1, \ldots, \gamma_n)F = \left[\sum_{\sigma \in \Pi_n} (\text{sgn } \sigma) a_{11\sigma} a_{22\sigma} \cdots a_{nn\sigma}\right][(\alpha_1, \ldots, \alpha_n)F].$$

Since the left-hand side is nonzero, we must have $(\alpha_1, \ldots, \alpha_n)F \neq 0$. This proves the lemma.

PROPOSITION 42 *If $n = \dim \mathscr{V}$, then $\dim {}^a\mathscr{L}_n = 1$.*

PROOF. By Proposition 41, we see that, if F and G are nonzero alternating forms of order n and if $\{\gamma_1, \ldots, \gamma_n\}$ is a linearly independent set in $\mathscr{V}$, then

$$(\gamma_1, \ldots, \gamma_n)F = (\gamma_1, \ldots, \gamma_n)Ga,$$

where a is a nonzero element from $\mathscr{F}$. Then

$$(\gamma_1, \ldots, \gamma_n)(F - Ga) = 0.$$

Since ${}^a\mathscr{L}_k$ is a vector space, $F - Ga \in {}^a\mathscr{L}_k$. It now follows from Proposition 41 that $F - Ga$ is the 0 form. Thus two alternating forms of order n are linearly dependent, and this proves the proposition.

EXERCISES

8 If $\dim \mathscr{V} = n$, determine the dimensions of $\mathscr{L}_k$, ${}^s\mathscr{L}_k$, ${}^a\mathscr{L}_k$.

9 Let $\dim \mathscr{V} = n < \infty$, clearly there are alternating linear forms F of order 1 such that $\alpha_1 F = 0$ and $\{\alpha_1\}$ is a linearly independent set. Is it true that for $1 \leq k < n$ there are $F \in {}^a\mathscr{L}_k$ such that $(\alpha_1, \ldots, \alpha_k)F = 0$ for some linearly independent set $\{\alpha_1, \ldots, \alpha_k\}$?

4 LINEAR TRANSFORMATIONS

Let $\mathscr{V}$, $\mathscr{W}$ be vector spaces over the same field $\mathscr{F}$. We have defined a *linear transformation* from $\mathscr{V}$ to $\mathscr{W}$ to be a map θ of $\mathscr{V}$ into $\mathscr{W}$ such that

$$(\alpha + \beta)\theta = \alpha\theta + \beta\theta, \qquad (a\alpha)\theta = a(\alpha\theta), \qquad \text{for } \alpha, \beta \in \mathscr{V}, a \in \mathscr{F}.$$

Thus a linear transformation is a homomorphism of the space $\mathscr{V}$ into the space $\mathscr{W}$.

The kernel of θ, denoted by $\mathscr{V}_\theta$, is the set

$$\mathscr{V}_\theta = \{\alpha \in \mathscr{V} \mid \alpha\theta = 0\}.$$

The image of the set $\mathscr{V}$ under θ shall be denoted by $\mathscr{V}\theta$. In Proposition 13 we proved that, *if θ is a linear transformation of $\mathscr{V}$ into $\mathscr{W}$, then $\mathscr{V}_\theta$ is a subspace of $\mathscr{V}$ and $\mathscr{V}\theta$ is a subspace of $\mathscr{W}$.*

The reader can further prove

POSITION 43 *If $\mathscr{V}'_\theta$ is a space complimentary to $\mathscr{V}_\theta$ in $\mathscr{V}$, then the restriction map ${}_{\mathscr{V}'_\theta}\theta$ is an isomorphism of $\mathscr{V}'_\theta$ onto $\mathscr{V}\theta$.*

XERCISES 1 Let θ, θ_1 be linear transformations of $\mathscr{V}_1$ into $\mathscr{V}_2$, let φ be a linear transformation of $\mathscr{V}_2$ into $\mathscr{V}_3$, and let χ be a linear transformation of $\mathscr{V}_3$ into $\mathscr{V}_4$. Prove:

A. $\theta\varphi$ is a linear transformation of $\mathscr{V}_1$ into $\mathscr{V}_3$.

B. $(\theta\varphi)\chi = \theta(\varphi\chi)$.

C. $(\theta a + \theta_1 b)\varphi = (\theta\varphi)a + (\theta_1\varphi)b$, where $a, b \in \mathscr{F}$.

2 A. Show that the map $(a_1, \ldots, a_{2k})\theta = (a_1, a_3, \ldots, a_{2k-1})$ is a linear transformation of $\mathscr{F}^{(2k)}$ onto $\mathscr{F}^{(k)}$.

B. Show that the map $A \to \delta A$, where δ is the derivative, is a linear transformation of $\mathscr{F}[x]$ onto $\mathscr{F}[x]$.

C. Let $\{\alpha_1, \ldots, \alpha_s\}$ be a finite set of vectors from $\mathscr{V}$; let $f_1, \ldots, f_s \in \mathscr{V}^*$ and define

$$\beta\theta = (\beta f_1)\alpha_1 + \cdots + (\beta f_s)\alpha_s.$$

Show that θ is a linear transformation of $\mathscr{V}$ onto $\langle\alpha_1, \ldots, \alpha_s\rangle$.

If θ is a linear transformation of $\mathscr{V}$ into $\mathscr{W}$, then the dimension of $\mathscr{V}\theta$ is called the *rank* of θ, and the dimension of the kernel $\mathscr{V}_\theta$ is called the *nullity* of θ.

If $\alpha_1, \ldots, \alpha_r$ are vectors from $\mathscr{V}$ such that $\{\alpha_1\theta, \ldots, \alpha_r\theta\}$ is a linearly independent set, then $\{\alpha_1, \ldots, \alpha_r\}$ is a linearly independent set. For if $\sum_{i=1}^{r} a_i\alpha_i = \mathbf{0}$, then

$$\mathbf{0} = \left(\sum_{i=1}^{r} a_i\alpha_i\right)\theta = \sum_{i=1}^{r} a_i(\alpha_i\theta),$$

and hence each $a_i = 0$. Consequently, we see that a basis of $\mathscr{V}\theta$ must be the image set of a linearly independent set of vectors from $\mathscr{V}$. Suppose $\mathscr{V}$ and $\mathscr{W}$ have countable bases. Then rank $\theta \leq \dim \mathscr{V}$, and since $\mathscr{V}\theta \subset \mathscr{W}$, we also have rank $\theta \leq \dim \mathscr{W}$, thus proving

)POSITION 44 *If $\mathscr{V}$, $\mathscr{W}$ have countable bases and if θ is a linear transformation of $\mathscr{V}$ into $\mathscr{W}$, then rank $\theta \leq \min\{\dim \mathscr{V}, \dim \mathscr{W}\}$.*

As an immediate consequence of Proposition 43 we have

LEMMA *If $\mathscr{V}'_\theta$ is a complimentary space to $\mathscr{V}_\theta$ in $\mathscr{V}$, then rank $\theta = \dim \mathscr{V}'_\theta$.*

Combining this lemma with Exercise 10, Sec. 1, we obtain

POSITION 45 *If θ is a linear transformation of $\mathscr{V}$ into $\mathscr{W}$ and if $\mathscr{V}$ is finite dimensional, then*

$$\textit{rank } \theta + \textit{nullity } \theta = \dim \mathscr{V}.$$

As with linear functionals, a linear transformation θ from $\mathscr{V}$ to $\mathscr{W}$ is completely determined by its values on a basis of $\mathscr{V}$, since

$$(\sum a_\nu \alpha_\nu)\theta = \sum (a_\nu \alpha_\nu)\theta = \sum a_\nu(\alpha_\nu \theta).$$

Therefore, in the future we shall often only describe a linear transformation by stating its values on some basis of $\mathscr{V}$. As our remarks indicate, if $\mathfrak{A}$ is a basis of $\mathscr{V}$, then $\mathscr{V}\theta = \langle \mathfrak{A}\theta \rangle$. Thus we have

PROPOSITION 46 *If θ is a linear transformation of $\mathscr{V}$ into $\mathscr{W}$ and if $\mathfrak{A}$ is a basis of $\mathscr{V}$, then rank θ is the order of the maximal set of linearly independent vectors from the set $\mathfrak{A}\theta$.*

The reader can now deduce

PROPOSITION 47 *If θ, φ are linear transformations, then*

$$\text{rank } \theta\varphi \leq \min\{\text{rank } \theta, \text{ rank } \varphi\}.$$

EXERCISES 3 Determine the rank and nullity of each of the linear transformations in Exercise 2.

4 A. A linear transformation θ is injective if and only if nullity $\theta = 0$.
B. If $\mathscr{V}$ is finite dimensional, then a linear transformation θ is injective if and only if rank $\theta = \dim \mathscr{V}$. Show that this statement is false if $\mathscr{V}$ is infinite dimensional.

As usual, we define the sum of two linear transformations θ, φ from $\mathscr{V}$ to $\mathscr{W}$ as the map

$$\alpha \xrightarrow{\theta+\varphi} \alpha\theta + \alpha\varphi, \qquad \text{for all } \alpha \in \mathscr{V},$$

and the scalar multiplication of a linear transformation by

$$\alpha \xrightarrow{\theta a} a(\alpha\theta), \qquad \text{for all } \alpha \in \mathscr{V}.$$

We let $\mathscr{L}(\mathscr{V}, \mathscr{W})$ denote the set of all linear transformations of $\mathscr{V}$ into $\mathscr{W}$ together with the operations just defined. Then in a straightforward fashion we obtain

PROPOSITION 48 *$\mathscr{L}(\mathscr{V}, \mathscr{W})$ is a vector space over $\mathscr{F}$.*

Let $\mathfrak{A}$ be a basis of $\mathscr{V}$, and let $\mathfrak{B}$ be a basis of $\mathscr{W}$. Consider the linear transformations $\theta_{\alpha\beta}$, $(\alpha \in \mathfrak{A}, \beta \in \mathfrak{B})$, from $\mathscr{V}$ into $\mathscr{W}$, where

$$\alpha'\theta_{\alpha\beta} = \delta(\alpha', \alpha)\beta, \qquad \alpha' \in \mathfrak{A},$$

and

$$\delta(\alpha', \alpha) = \begin{cases} 1 \text{ if } \alpha' = \alpha, \\ 0 \text{ if } \alpha' \neq \alpha. \end{cases}$$

LEMMA $\{\theta_{\alpha\beta} \mid \alpha \in \mathfrak{A}, \beta \in \mathfrak{B}\}$ *is a linearly independent set of linear transformations from* $\mathscr{V}$ *to* $\mathscr{W}$.

PROOF. Suppose $\sum_{\alpha \in \mathfrak{A}\, \beta \in \mathfrak{B}} \theta_{\alpha\beta} a_{\alpha\beta} = 0$, where $a_{\alpha\beta} \in \mathscr{F}$ and all but finitely many of the $a_{\alpha\beta} = 0$. For each $\alpha' \in \mathfrak{A}$ we have

$$\mathbf{0} = \alpha'\left(\sum_{\alpha,\beta} \theta_{\alpha\beta} a_{\alpha\beta}\right) = \sum_{\beta \in \mathfrak{B}} a_{\alpha'\beta}\beta.$$

But $\mathfrak{B}$ is a linearly independent set, and hence

$$a_{\alpha'\beta} = 0, \qquad \text{for all } \beta \in \mathfrak{B}.$$

As this is true for all $\alpha' \in \mathfrak{A}$, we have shown that all $a_{\alpha\beta} = 0$. This proves the lemma.

OPOSITION 49 *If* $\mathscr{V}$ *is a finite dimensional space, then* $\{\theta_{\alpha\beta} \mid \alpha \in \mathfrak{A}, \beta \in \mathfrak{B}\}$ *is a basis for* $\mathscr{L}(\mathscr{V}, \mathscr{W})$.

PROOF. Because of the lemma, we need only show that the set $\{\theta_{\alpha\beta}\}$ spans $\mathscr{L}(\mathscr{V}, \mathscr{W})$. Let $\theta \in \mathscr{L}(\mathscr{V}, \mathscr{W})$; then, for each $\alpha \in \mathfrak{A}$,

$$\alpha\theta = \sum_{\beta \in \mathfrak{B}} a_{\alpha\beta}\beta,$$

where $a_{\alpha\beta} \in \mathscr{F}$, and only finitely many of the $a_{\alpha\beta}$ are not 0. Since $\mathfrak{A}$ is a finite set, the expression

$$\sum_{\alpha \in \mathfrak{A}} \sum_{\beta \in \mathfrak{B}} \theta_{\alpha\beta} a_{\alpha\beta}$$

has only finitely many nonzero scalars and hence lies in the space $\langle\{\theta_{\alpha\beta} \mid \alpha \in \mathfrak{A}, \beta \in \mathfrak{B}\}\rangle$. But

$$\alpha\left(\sum_{\alpha,\beta} \theta_{\alpha\beta} a_{\alpha\beta}\right) = \alpha\theta,$$

for all $\alpha \in \mathfrak{A}$, and therefore

$$\theta = \sum_{\alpha,\beta} \theta_{\alpha\beta} a_{\alpha\beta}.$$

This proves the proposition.

If $\dim \mathscr{W} = 1$, then $\mathscr{L}(\mathscr{V}, \mathscr{W})$ and $\mathscr{V}^*$ are isomorphic. Earlier (Propositions 16, 20, and 22) we saw that, when $\mathscr{V}$ is of infinite dimension, then $\mathscr{V}^*$ was not spanned by $\{f_\alpha \mid \alpha \in \mathfrak{A}\}$. It therefore follows that the conclusion of Proposition 49 is false if $\dim \mathscr{V} = \infty$.

We let $\mathscr{E}(\mathscr{V})$ be the set $\mathscr{L}(\mathscr{V}, \mathscr{V})$. By Proposition 48, $\mathscr{E}(\mathscr{V})$ is a vector space. By Exercise 1, $\mathscr{E}(\mathscr{V})$ is a ring. If ι is the identity map, then

$$a \to \iota a$$

is an isomorphism of $\mathscr{F}$ into $\mathscr{E}(\mathscr{V})$. We let $\mathscr{F}' = \{\iota a \mid a \in \mathscr{F}\}$. Then

$$\theta(\iota a) = \theta a = (\iota a)\theta, \qquad \text{for all } \theta \in \mathscr{E}(\mathscr{V}).^{\dagger}$$

In particular $\iota a + \iota b = \iota(a+b)$, $(\iota a)(\iota b) = \iota(ab)$, and $\iota a = 0$ if and only if $a = 0$. Hence the map $a \to \iota a$ is an isomorphism of $\mathscr{F}$ onto $\mathscr{F}'$, and $\mathscr{F}'$ is a field. Thus we have proved

PROPOSITION 50 *If $\mathscr{V}$ is a vector space over a field $\mathscr{F}$, then $\mathscr{E}(\mathscr{V})$ is a ring containing a field $\mathscr{F}'$ that is isomorphic to $\mathscr{F}$, and $\mathscr{E}(\mathscr{V})$ is a vector space over $\mathscr{F}'$.*

Since $\theta_{\alpha\alpha'}\theta_{\alpha\alpha'} = \delta(\alpha,\alpha')\theta_{\alpha\alpha}$ and this is zero when $\alpha = \alpha'$, we see that $\mathscr{E}(\mathscr{V})$ has divisors of zero provided $\dim \mathscr{V} \geq 2$. As

$$\theta_{\alpha\alpha'}\theta_{\alpha'\alpha} = \theta_{\alpha\alpha} \qquad \theta_{\alpha'\alpha}\theta_{\alpha\alpha'} = \theta_{\alpha'\alpha'},$$

we see that $\mathscr{E}(\mathscr{V})$ is not commutative if $\dim \mathscr{V} \geq 2$.

A ring $\mathscr{A}$ which contains a field $\mathscr{K}$ in its center and which is a finitely dimensional vector space over $\mathscr{K}$ is called a (*linear*) *algebra over* $\mathscr{K}$. If $\dim \mathscr{V} = n < \infty$, then $\dim \mathscr{E}(\mathscr{V}) = n^2$, and consequently $\mathscr{E}(\mathscr{V})$ is a (linear) algebra over $\mathscr{F}'$.†

$\mathscr{E}(\mathscr{V})$ is the set of vector space endomorphisms of $\mathscr{V}$. Thus, from our knowledge of rings of endomorphisms of abelian groups, we expect

PROPOSITION 51 *$\theta \in \mathscr{E}(\mathscr{V})$ is a unit of $\mathscr{E}(\mathscr{V})$ if and only if θ is bijective: i.e., θ is a vector space automorphism of $\mathscr{V}$.*

The proof is left to the reader.

A bijective linear transformation of $\mathscr{V}$ into itself is called a *nonsingular* linear transformation.

EXERCISES 5 Prove: If $\dim \mathscr{V} < \infty$, then $\theta \in \mathscr{E}(\mathscr{V})$ is nonsingular if and only if $\operatorname{rank} \theta = \dim \mathscr{V}$.

6 Prove: If θ is a nonsingular linear transformation, then $\operatorname{rank} \theta\varphi = \operatorname{rank} \varphi$, $\operatorname{rank} (\chi\theta) = \operatorname{rank} \chi$.

7 Let θ be a one-to-one linear transformation of $\mathscr{V}$ into itself. Prove:

A. If $\dim \mathscr{V} = \infty$, then θ has a right inverse but need not have a left inverse.

B. If $\dim \mathscr{V} < \infty$, then θ is nonsingular.

C. If $\dim \mathscr{V} = \infty$ and θ is not surjective, show that there are $\varphi \in \mathscr{E}(\mathscr{V})$ such that $\operatorname{rank} \theta\varphi \neq \operatorname{rank} \varphi$.

D. If $\dim \mathscr{V} = \infty$, the $\operatorname{rank} \chi\theta = \operatorname{rank} \chi$ for all $\chi \in \mathscr{E}(\mathscr{V})$.

8 Let θ be a fixed element of $\mathscr{E}(\mathscr{V})$. Let $\mathfrak{A}(\theta) = \{\varphi \in \mathscr{E}(\mathscr{V}) \mid \varphi\theta = 0\}$. Show that $\mathfrak{A}(\theta)$ is a subspace of $\mathscr{E}(\mathscr{V})$. Clearly $\mathfrak{A}(0) = \mathscr{E}(\mathscr{V})$, $\mathfrak{A}(\iota) = \mathscr{O}$. If $1 \leq k < \dim \mathscr{E}(\mathscr{V})$, is there a θ such that $\dim \mathfrak{A}(\theta) = k$? If $\mathscr{E}'$ is a

† Since $\theta_a = \theta(\iota_a) = (\iota_a)\theta$, henceforth we let $a\theta = \theta_a$ for all $a \in \mathscr{F}$ and all $\theta \in \mathscr{E}(\mathscr{V})$.

subspace of $\mathscr{E}(\mathscr{V})$, is there a $\theta \in \mathscr{E}(\mathscr{V})$ such that $\mathfrak{A}(\theta) = \mathscr{E}'$? Show that $\mathscr{E}(\mathscr{V})\mathfrak{A}(\theta) \subset \mathfrak{A}(\theta)$.

Let $\mathscr{V}$ be a finitely dimensional vector space over a field $\mathscr{F}$, say $\dim \mathscr{V} = n$. Let F be a fixed nonzero alternating form of order n on $\mathscr{V}$. By Proposition 42, there is such a form F, and each such form is a scalar multiple of F. Let $\theta \in \mathscr{E}(\mathscr{V})$, and consider the map

$$(\alpha_1, \ldots, \alpha_n) \xrightarrow{\theta F} (\alpha_1\theta, \ldots, \alpha_n\theta)F$$

from $\mathscr{V}^{(n)}$ to $\mathscr{F}$. Clearly θF is a nonzero alternating form of order n on $\mathscr{V}$. Hence

$$\theta F = F\Delta(\theta),$$

where $\Delta(\theta) \in \mathscr{F}$. The reader should check that $\theta(Fa) = (\theta F)a$. If G is another nonzero alternating form of order n, then $G = Fg$, for some $g \in \mathscr{F}$. We have

$$\theta G = \theta(Fg) = (\theta F)g = F\Delta(\theta)g = Fg\Delta(\theta) = G\Delta(\theta).$$

Hence $\Delta(\theta)$ depends only on θ and not on any particular alternating form. $\Delta(\theta)$ is called the *determinant* of the linear transformation θ. The reader should prove

POSITION 52 A. $\Delta(\iota) = 1$.
B. $\Delta(\theta a) = \Delta(\theta)a^n$.
C. $\Delta(\theta\varphi) = \Delta(\theta)\Delta(\varphi)$.
D. $\Delta(\theta) = 0$ *if and only if* θ *is singular.*

5 MATRICES

Let $\mathscr{R}$ be a ring. A rectangular array

$$\mathbf{A} = \begin{pmatrix} a_{11} & \cdots & a_{1m} \\ \vdots & & \vdots \\ a_{n1} & \cdots & a_{nm} \end{pmatrix}, \qquad a_{ij} \in \mathscr{R},$$

is called an *n by m matrix over* $\mathscr{R}$ or an n by m matrix with entries from $\mathscr{R}$. We let $\mathfrak{M}_{n,m}(\mathscr{R})$ be the set of all n by m matrices over $\mathscr{R}$. Eventually we shall define an addition and scalar multiplication for elements of $\mathfrak{M}_{n,m}(\mathscr{R})$.

We begin by considering $\mathfrak{M}_{n,m}(\mathscr{F}) = \mathfrak{M}_{n,m}$, where $\mathscr{F}$ is a field. Each matrix $\mathbf{A} \in \mathfrak{M}_{n,m}$ can be viewed as a map of the set of ordered pairs $X = \{(1, 1), \ldots, (1, m), \ldots, (n, m)\}$ into $\mathscr{R}$, namely,

$$(i, j) \to a_{ij}.$$

If we view the elements of $\mathfrak{M}_{n,m}$ in this way, then $\mathfrak{M}_{n,m}$ is a vector space $\mathscr{T}(X, \mathscr{F})$ over $\mathscr{F}$, (see example b, page 234) where

$$\begin{pmatrix} a_{11} & \cdots & a_{1m} \\ \vdots & & \vdots \\ a_{n1} & \cdots & a_{nm} \end{pmatrix} + \begin{pmatrix} b_{11} & \cdots & b_{1m} \\ \vdots & & \vdots \\ b_{n1} & \cdots & b_{nm} \end{pmatrix} = \begin{pmatrix} a_{11} + b_{11} & \dots & a_{1m} + b_{1m} \\ \vdots & & \vdots \\ a_{n1} + b_{n1} & \dots & a_{nm} + b_{nm} \end{pmatrix}, \tag{1}$$

$$\begin{pmatrix} a_{11} & \dots & a_{1m} \\ \vdots & & \vdots \\ a_{n1} & \cdots & a_{nm} \end{pmatrix} a = \begin{pmatrix} a_{11}a & \cdots & a_{1m}a \\ \vdots & & \vdots \\ a_{n1}a & \dots & a_{nm}a \end{pmatrix}. \tag{2}$$

It should be noted that we only define addition of matrices provided they have the same height and width.

By an *ordered basis* of a vector space $\mathscr{V}$ over $\mathscr{F}$, we mean a countable basis with a prescribed arrangement $\alpha_1, \alpha_2, \dots$. Let $\mathfrak{A} = \{\alpha_1, \dots, \alpha_n\}$ be an ordered basis of $\mathscr{V}$, and let $\mathfrak{B} = \{\beta_1, \dots, \beta_m\}$ be an ordered basis of $\mathscr{W}$. Let $\theta_{ij} = \theta_{\alpha_i\beta_j}$. There is a map

$$\theta = \sum_{i=1}^{n} \sum_{j=1}^{m} \theta_{ij}a_{ij} \to \begin{pmatrix} a_{11} & \cdots & a_{1m} \\ \vdots & & \vdots \\ a_{n1} & \cdots & a_{nm} \end{pmatrix} = \mathbf{M}(\theta)$$

of $\mathscr{L}(\mathscr{V}, \mathscr{W})$ into $\mathfrak{M}_{n,m}$. Since $\{\theta_{11}, \dots, \theta_{nm}\}$ is a basis of $\mathscr{L}(\mathscr{V}, \mathscr{W})$, this map is defined, and the reader should verify that it is an isomorphism of $\mathscr{L}(\mathscr{V}, \mathscr{W})$ onto $\mathfrak{M}_{n,m}(\mathscr{F})$.

The matrix $\mathbf{M}(\theta)$ is called a *matrix representation of* θ. It should be noted that $\mathbf{M}(\theta)$ actually depends on the ordered bases $\mathfrak{A}$ and $\mathfrak{B}$ as well as on θ. If we changed either of them, $\mathbf{M}(\theta)$ would change. When necessary, we shall indicate this dependence by writing $\mathbf{M}(\theta; \mathfrak{A}, \mathfrak{B})$.

We now specialize. Let $\mathscr{V} = \mathscr{F}^{(n)}$ and $\mathscr{W} = \mathscr{F}^{(m)}$. Then

$$\mathbf{e}_1 = (\delta_{11}, \dots, \delta_{1n}), \dots, \mathbf{e}_n = (\delta_{n1}, \dots, \delta_{nn}),$$

is an ordered basis for $\mathscr{F}^{(n)}$, and

$$\mathbf{e}_1' = (\delta_{11}, \dots, \delta_{1m}), \dots, \mathbf{e}_m' = (\delta_{m1}, \dots, \delta_{mm})$$

is an ordered basis for $\mathscr{F}^{(m)}$. By Proposition 49, the linear transformations θ_{ij} $(1 \le i \le n, 1 \le j \le m)$, where

$$\mathbf{e}_i\theta_{jk} = \delta_{ij}\mathbf{e}_k'$$

are a basis for $\mathscr{L}(\mathscr{F}^{(n)}, \mathscr{F}^{(m)})$. If $\theta \in \mathscr{L}(\mathscr{F}^{(n)}, \mathscr{F}^{(m)})$, then $\theta = \sum_{ij} \theta_{ij}a_{ij}$ and

$$(x_1, \dots, x_n)\theta = \left(\sum_{i=1}^{n} x_i a_{i1}, \dots, \sum_{i=1}^{n} x_i a_{im}\right).$$

We now define

$$(x_1, \dots, x_n)\begin{pmatrix} a_{11} & \cdots & a_{1m} \\ \vdots & & \vdots \\ a_{n1} & \dots & a_{nm} \end{pmatrix} = \left(\sum_i x_i a_{i1}, \dots, \sum_i x_i a_{im}\right). \tag{3}$$

With this definition, we obtain

$$[(x_1, \ldots, x_n) + (y_1, \ldots, y_n)](a_{ij}) = (x_1, \ldots, x_n)(a_{ij}) + (y_1, \ldots, y_n)(a_{ij}),$$
$$[a(x_1, \ldots, x_n)](a_{ij}) = a[(x_1, \ldots, x_n)(a_{ij})].$$

Thus we may view the matrix (a_{ij}) as a linear transformation from $\mathscr{F}^{(n)}$ into $\mathscr{F}^{(m)}$. Furthermore, to each $\theta \in \mathscr{L}(\mathscr{F}^{(n)}, \mathscr{F}^{(m)})$ there is a unique matrix $(a_{ij}) \in \mathfrak{M}_{n,m}$ such that

$$(x_1, \ldots, x_n)\theta = (x_1, \ldots, x_n)(a_{ij}),$$

for all $(x_1, \ldots, x_n) \in \mathscr{F}^{(n)}$. Thus we have

POSITION 53 $\mathfrak{M}_{n,m}(\mathscr{F}) = \mathscr{L}(\mathscr{F}^{(n)}, \mathscr{F}^{(m)})$.

Since a matrix over a field is a linear transformation, we can speak of the *rank* of a matrix, the *nullity* of a matrix, the *kernel* of a matrix, etc.

XERCISES 1 A. Determine a matrix representation of the linear transformation $\frac{d}{dx}$ on the space of polynomials of degree less than n.

B. A linear transformation from $\mathscr{F}^{(2)}$ to $\mathscr{F}^{(3)}$ takes (1, 1) into (2, 1, 3) and takes (1, −1) into (0, 5, 2); find the matrix of this transformation.

2 Prove:

A. The image of $\mathscr{F}^{(n)}$ under the linear transformation (a_{ij}) is the space spanned by the *row vectors* $(a_{11}, \ldots, a_{1m}), \ldots, (a_{n1}, \ldots, a_{nm})$ of the matrix (a_{ij}).

B. The rank of the linear transformation (a_{ij}) is the maximal number of linearly independent row vectors in the matrix (a_{ij}).

3 Prove: A n by m matrix (a_{ij}) is of rank 1 if and only if there exist $u_1, \ldots, u_n$ (not all 0) and $v_1, \ldots, v_m$ (not all 0) in the field $\mathscr{F}$ such that $a_{ij} = u_i v_j$, $1 \leq i \leq n$, $1 \leq j \leq m$.

Now suppose $(a_{ij}) \in \mathfrak{M}_{n,m}$, $(b_{jk}) \in \mathfrak{M}_{m,q}$; then the map

$$(x_1, \ldots, x_n) \xrightarrow{\theta} (x_1, \ldots, x_n)(a_{ij})(b_{jk})$$

is a linear transformation from $\mathscr{F}^{(n)}$ into $\mathscr{F}^{(q)}$. Thus the map θ is a matrix $(c_{ik}) \in \mathfrak{M}_{n,q}$, where

$$(x_1, \ldots, x_n)(c_{ik}) = (x_1, \ldots, x_n)(a_{ij})(b_{jk}),$$

for all $(x_1, \ldots, x_n) \in \mathscr{F}^{(n)}$. Now

$$\mathbf{e}_i(c_{ik}) = \sum_{k=1}^{q} c_{ik}\mathbf{e}_k'',$$

and
$$\mathbf{e}_i(a_{ij})(b_{jk}) = \left[\sum_{j=1}^{m} a_{ij}\mathbf{e}_j'\right](b_{jk}) = \sum_{k=1}^{q}\left[\sum_{j=1}^{m} a_{ij}b_{jk}\right]\mathbf{e}_k''.$$

Hence $$c_{ik} = \sum_{j=1}^{m} a_{ij} b_{jk}.$$

This suggests that we make the following definition:

$$\begin{pmatrix} a_{11} & \cdots & a_{1m} \\ \vdots & & \vdots \\ a_{n1} & \cdots & a_{nm} \end{pmatrix} \begin{pmatrix} b_{11} & \cdots & b_{1q} \\ \vdots & & \vdots \\ b_{m1} & \cdots & b_{mq} \end{pmatrix} = \begin{pmatrix} \sum_{j=1}^{m} a_{1j} b_{j1} & \cdots & \sum_{j=1}^{m} a_{1j} b_{jq} \\ \vdots & & \vdots \\ \sum_{j} a_{nj} b_{j1} & \cdots & \sum_{j} a_{nj} b_{jq} \end{pmatrix}. \tag{4}$$

We note that this product is such that Eq. 3 is the special case where $n = 1$. We only define products of matrices when they fit as indicated in Eq. 4. Thus the product $(a_{ij})(b_{jk})$ may be defined while the product $(b_{ij})(a_{jk})$ is not defined.

Now $\mathfrak{M}_{n,n}(\mathscr{F})$ is exactly the set of endomorphisms of $\mathscr{F}^{(n)}$; i.e., $\mathfrak{M}_{n,n}(\mathscr{F}) = \mathscr{E}(\mathscr{F}^{(n)})$. Hence $\mathfrak{M}_{n,n}(\mathscr{F})$ is a ring, the ring of n by n matrices. We let $\mathbf{I}_n$ be the n by n matrix with 1 on the main diagonal and 0 elsewhere. Then $\mathscr{F}' = \{\mathbf{I}_n a \mid a \in \mathscr{F}\}$ is a field isomorphic to $\mathscr{F}$, and therefore $\mathfrak{M}_{n,n}(\mathscr{F})$ is an algebra over $\mathscr{F}'$.

EXERCISES 4 A. Let $\mathbf{A} = \begin{pmatrix} 1 & 2 & 3 \\ 0 & 6 & -1 \\ 7 & 0 & 2 \end{pmatrix}$, $\mathbf{B} = \begin{pmatrix} 0 & 1 & 2 \\ 0 & 0 & 3 \\ 0 & 0 & 0 \end{pmatrix}$, $\mathbf{C} = \begin{pmatrix} 0 & 1 \\ 2 & -5 \\ 6 & 0 \end{pmatrix}$.

Compute $\mathbf{A}^2$, $\mathbf{B}^2$, $\mathbf{A}^3$, $\mathbf{A}^2 + 2\mathbf{AB} - \mathbf{B}^2$, $\mathbf{A} - 3\mathbf{B}^2$, $\mathbf{A}^2\mathbf{C}$.

B. Suppose $(a_{ij}) = \mathbf{A}$, $\mathbf{E}_{st} \in \mathfrak{M}_{n,n}$, where $\mathbf{E}_{st}$ has 1 in the s,t position and 0 elsewhere. Compute $\mathbf{AE}_{st}$ and $\mathbf{E}_{st}\mathbf{A}$.

5 Prove:

A. If $\mathbf{A}$ is a n by p matrix and $\mathbf{B}$ is a p by m matrix, then nullity $(\mathbf{AB}) \le$ nullity $\mathbf{A}$ + nullity $\mathbf{B}$.

B. If $\mathbf{A}$,$\mathbf{B}$ are n by n matrices, then rank $(\mathbf{AB}) \ge$ rank $\mathbf{A}$ + rank $\mathbf{B} - n$.

By Proposition 42 there is a unique alternating linear form of order n on $\mathscr{F}^{(n)}$ such that

$$(\mathbf{e}_1, \ldots, \mathbf{e}_n)F = 1.$$

Let $\mathbf{A} = (a_{ij}) \in \mathfrak{M}_{n,n}(\mathscr{F})$; then

$$\begin{aligned}(\mathbf{e}_1, \ldots, \mathbf{e}_n)\mathbf{A}F &= (\mathbf{e}_1\mathbf{A}, \ldots, \mathbf{e}_n\mathbf{A})F \\ &= (a_{11}\mathbf{e}_1 + \cdots + a_{1n}\mathbf{e}_n, \ldots, a_{n1}\mathbf{e}_1 + \ldots + a_{nn}\mathbf{e}_n)F \\ &= \left(\sum_{\sigma \in \Pi_n} (\operatorname{sgn} \sigma) a_{11\sigma} a_{22\sigma} \cdots a_{nn\sigma}\right)(\mathbf{e}_1, \ldots, \mathbf{e}_n)F \\ &= \sum_{\sigma \in \Pi_n} (\operatorname{sgn} \sigma) a_{11\sigma} \cdots a_{nn\sigma}.\end{aligned}$$

But $$(\mathbf{e}_1, \ldots, \mathbf{e}_n)\mathbf{A}F = (\mathbf{e}_1, \ldots, \mathbf{e}_n)F\Delta(\mathbf{A}) = \Delta(\mathbf{A}).$$

Thus we have

$$\Delta(\mathbf{A}) = \sum_{\sigma \in \Pi_n} (\operatorname{sgn} \sigma) a_{11^\sigma} \cdots a_{nn^\sigma}, \tag{5}$$

where $\Delta(\mathbf{A})$ is the *determinant* of $\mathbf{A}$. One often sees $\Delta(\mathbf{A})$ written as det $\mathbf{A}$, and we shall occasionally follow this practice. It follows from Proposition 52 that $\det(\mathbf{I}_n a) = a^n$, $\det(\mathbf{AB}) = \det \mathbf{A} \det \mathbf{B}$, and $\det \mathbf{A} = 0$ if $\mathbf{A}$ is a singular matrix. Note that we define only the determinant of square matrices.

We now return to the more general problem of considering matrices over a ring $\mathscr{R}$. We define addition of such matrices as in Eq. 1 and multiplication as in Eq. 4. The reader can prove

OPOSITION 54 *If $\mathscr{R}$ is a ring, then $\mathfrak{M}_{n,n}(\mathscr{R})$ is a ring. The map*

$$a \xrightarrow{\lambda} \begin{pmatrix} a & 0 \ldots 0 \\ 0 & a \cdots 0 \\ 0 & \cdots \cdots a \end{pmatrix}$$

is an injection of $\mathscr{R}$ into $\mathfrak{M}_{n,n}(\mathscr{R})$. The ring $\mathfrak{M}_{n,n}(\mathscr{R})$ has a unity if and only if $\mathscr{R}$ has a unity.

OPOSITION 55 *If $n \geq 2$ and $\mathscr{R}$ is not the zero ring, then $\mathfrak{M}_{n,n}(\mathscr{R})$ is not commutative and has divisors of zero. More specifically there exist $\mathbf{O} \neq \mathbf{A} \in \mathfrak{M}_{n,n}(\mathscr{R})$ such that a power of $\mathbf{A}$ is $\mathbf{O}$. $\mathfrak{Z}(\mathfrak{M}_{n,n}(\mathscr{R})) = \mathfrak{Z}(\mathscr{R})^\lambda$.*

If $\mathbf{A} = (a_{ij})$ is a square matrix over a commutative ring $\mathscr{R}$, we define the determinant of $\mathbf{A}$ as in Eq. 5. We have the following results:

OPOSITION 56 *Let $\mathbf{A}, \mathbf{B} \in \mathfrak{M}_{n,n}(\mathscr{R})$, where $\mathscr{R}$ is a commutative ring:*

A. *If $\mathbf{A}$ has two rows alike, then det $(\mathbf{A}) = 0$.*

B. *If $\mathbf{A}$ has a row of zeros, then det $(\mathbf{A}) = 0$.*

C. *If $\mathbf{B}$ is obtained from $\mathbf{A}$ by multiplying one row of $\mathbf{A}$ by a scalar c, then det $\mathbf{B} = c$ det $\mathbf{A}$.*

D. *If $\mathbf{B}$ is obtained from $\mathbf{A}$ by interchanging two rows of $\mathbf{A}$, then det $\mathbf{B} = -$ det $\mathbf{A}$.*

E. *If $\mathbf{B}$ is obtained from $\mathbf{A}$ by adding a scalar multiple of one row of $\mathbf{A}$ to another row of $\mathbf{A}$, then det $\mathbf{B} =$ det $\mathbf{A}$.*

F. *det $(\mathbf{AB}) =$ (det $\mathbf{A}$)(det $\mathbf{B}$).*

PROOF. Suppose first that $\mathscr{R}$ has no zero divisors; then there is a field $\mathscr{F}$ that contains $\mathscr{R}$, and consequently $\mathfrak{M}_{n,n}(\mathscr{F}) \supset \mathfrak{M}_{n,n}(\mathscr{R})$. For such rings, Proposition 56 follows from Propositions 37, 38, 52, and the following:

LEMMA *Let F be the unique alternating linear form of order n on $\mathscr{F}^{(n)}$ such that*

$(\mathbf{e}_1, \ldots, \mathbf{e}_n)F = 1$. *If* $\mathbf{A} \in \mathfrak{M}_{n,n}(\mathscr{F})$, *then* $det(\mathbf{A})$ *is the value of* F *on the row vectors of* $\mathbf{A}$.

PROOF. Let $\alpha_i = (a_{i1}, \ldots, a_{in})$, $(i = 1, \ldots, n)$, be the row vectors of $\mathbf{A}$; then

$$(\alpha_1, \ldots, \alpha_n)F = (\mathbf{e}_1, \ldots, \mathbf{e}_n)\mathbf{A}F = (\mathbf{e}_1, \ldots, \mathbf{e}_n)F \det \mathbf{A} = \det \mathbf{A}.$$

However, Proposition 56 holds for all commutative rings, and these results can be derived directly from the definition (5). This is easily done for parts A to E, and the reader should do so. Part F is more difficult. One must show that

$$\det(\mathbf{AB}) = \sum_{\sigma,\lambda \in \Pi_n} (\operatorname{sgn} \sigma\lambda) a_{11\sigma} \cdots a_{nn\sigma} b_{11\sigma\lambda} \cdots b_{nn\sigma\lambda}$$

$$= \sum_{\sigma \in \Pi_n} (\operatorname{sgn} \sigma) \left(\sum_{s=1}^{n} a_{1s} b_{s1\sigma} \right) \cdots \left(\sum_{t=1}^{n} a_{nt} b_{tn\sigma} \right).$$

This is a tedious task, and we shall not carry it out here.

Given any n by m matrix $\mathbf{A}$, if we strike out the i_1th, i_2th, ..., i_sth rows and the j_1th, ..., j_tth columns, we have a $n - s$ by $m - t$ matrix remaining. We denote it by $\mathbf{A}_{i_1, \ldots, i_s;\, j_1, \ldots, j_t}$. Each such matrix is called a *minor* of $\mathbf{A}$.

If $\mathbf{A}$ is a square matrix, we call $\mathscr{A}_{ij} = (-1)^{i+j}$ *det* $\mathbf{A}_{i;j}$ the *(i, j)th cofactor of* $\mathbf{A}$. On examining Eq. 5, we see that

$$\det \mathbf{A} = \sum_{i=1}^{n} a_{ij} \mathscr{A}_{ij}, \qquad j = 1, 2, \ldots, n. \tag{6}$$

PROPOSITION 57 *If* $\mathbf{A} \in \mathfrak{M}_{n,n}(\mathscr{R})$, *then*

$$\sum_{i=1}^{n} a_{ij} \mathscr{A}_{ik} = \delta_{jk} \det(\mathbf{A}). \tag{7}$$

PROOF. The proof follows from Eq. 6 and the first property of Proposition 56.

If $\mathbf{A} = \begin{pmatrix} a_{11} & \cdots & a_{1m} \\ \vdots & & \vdots \\ a_{n1} & \cdots & a_{nm} \end{pmatrix}$, we call the matrix $\mathbf{A}^t = \begin{pmatrix} a_{11} & \cdots & a_{n1} \\ \vdots & & \vdots \\ a_{1m} & \cdots & a_{nm} \end{pmatrix}$ the *transpose* of the matrix $\mathbf{A}$.

The reader can prove

PROPOSITION 58 *If* $\mathscr{R}$ *is a commutative ring with unity, then:*

A. *The map* $\mathbf{A} \to \mathbf{A}^t$ *is a bijective map of* $\mathfrak{M}_{n,m}(\mathscr{R})$ *into* $\mathfrak{M}_{m,n}(\mathscr{R})$.

B. $(\mathbf{A}^t)^t = \mathbf{A}$.

C. $(\mathbf{A}c)^t = \mathbf{A}^t c$.

D. $(\mathbf{A} + \mathbf{B})^t = \mathbf{A}^t + \mathbf{B}^t$.

E. *If* $\mathbf{AB}$ *is defined, then* $(\mathbf{AB})^t = \mathbf{B}^t \mathbf{A}^t$.

As an immediate consequence of Eq. 7 we have

POSITION 59 *If $\mathscr{R}$ is a commutative ring with unity and* $\mathbf{A} \in \mathfrak{M}_{n,n}(\mathscr{R})$, *put* $\mathbf{B} = (\mathscr{A}_{ij})^t$*; then*

$$\mathbf{AB} = \mathbf{BA} = \mathbf{I}_n \det(\mathbf{A}).$$

The matrix **B** is called the *adjoint* of **A** and is denoted by adj **A**. From this we obtain

POSITION 60 *If $\mathscr{R}$ is a commutative ring with unity, then* $\mathbf{A} \in \mathfrak{M}_{n,n}(\mathscr{R})$ *is a unit in* $\mathfrak{M}_{n,n}(\mathscr{R})$ *if and only if det* **A** *is a unit of* $\mathscr{R}$. *If* **A** *is a unit in* $\mathfrak{M}_{n,n}(\mathscr{R})$, *then its reciprocal is* $(adj\ \mathbf{A})(det\ \mathbf{A})^{-1}$.

PROOF. If **A** is a unit, it follows directly from part F of proposition 56 that det **A** is a unit. The second part follows from Proposition 59. Finally it follows from the second part that, if det **A** is a unit, then $(\text{adj } \mathbf{A})(\det \mathbf{A})^{-1} = \mathbf{B}$ is in $\mathfrak{M}_{n,n}(\mathscr{R})$ and $\mathbf{AB} = \mathbf{I}_n$; i.e., **A** is a unit of $\mathfrak{M}_{n,n}(\mathscr{R})$.

If $\mathbf{A} \in \mathfrak{M}_{n,n}(\mathscr{R})$ is a unit in that ring, we call **A** a *unimodular matrix over* $\mathscr{R}$.

If $\sigma, \varphi \in \Pi_n$, then

$$a_{11\sigma} \cdots a_{nn\sigma} = a_{1\varphi 1\varphi\sigma} \cdots a_{n\varphi n\varphi\sigma}.$$

Let $\varphi = \sigma^{-1}$; then

$$a_{11\sigma} \cdots a_{nn\sigma} = a_{1\varphi 1} \cdots a_{n\varphi n}.$$

But $\text{sgn } \sigma = \text{sgn } \sigma^{-1} = \text{sgn } \varphi$, and as σ ranges over Π_n, so does $\varphi = \sigma^{-1}$. We therefore have

$$\det \mathbf{A} = \sum_{\sigma \in \Pi_n} (\text{sgn } \sigma) a_{11\sigma} \cdots a_{nn\sigma}$$
$$= \sum_{\varphi \in \Pi_n} (\text{sgn } \varphi) a_{1\varphi 1} \cdots a_{n\varphi n}.$$

We have thus shown

POSITION 61 *det* $\mathbf{A} =$ *det* $\mathbf{A}^t$.

COROLLARY *If* **A** *is nonsingular, so is* $\mathbf{A}^t$.

We then obtain, from Proposition 61,

POSITION 62 *The properties listed in Proposition* 56 *hold if we replace "row" by "column."*

The results of Propositions 56 and 62 together with Eq. 6 enable one to compute the determinant of a matrix **A** with considerably less effort than if one uses the definition directly. Specifically, we use the various properties of determinants to obtain matrices having the same determinant but having 0 in many entries, and consequently their determinant is more easily determined; e.g.,

$$\det\begin{pmatrix} a_{11} & a_{12} \cdots a_{1n} \\ 0 & a_{22} \cdots a_{2}{}^{n} \\ \vdots & \vdots \\ 0 & 0 \ \cdots a_{nn} \end{pmatrix} = a_{11}a_{22} \cdots a_{nn},$$

and

$$\det\begin{pmatrix} a_{11} & a_{12} \cdots a_{1n} \\ 0 & a_{22} \cdots a_{2n} \\ \vdots & \vdots \\ 0 & a_{2n} \cdots a_{nn} \end{pmatrix} = a_{11}\mathscr{A}_{11}.$$

The following is an example of such a reduction:

$$\det\begin{pmatrix} 2 & 7 & 9 & 6 \\ 3 & -1 & 5 & 2 \\ 4 & 8 & 7 & 9 \\ 2 & 0 & 4 & 6 \end{pmatrix} = 2\det\begin{pmatrix} 2 & 7 & 9 & 6 \\ 3 & -1 & 5 & 2 \\ 4 & 8 & 7 & 9 \\ 1 & 0 & 2 & 3 \end{pmatrix}$$

$$= 2\det\begin{pmatrix} 0 & 7 & 5 & 0 \\ 0 & -1 & -1 & -7 \\ 0 & 8 & -1 & -3 \\ 1 & 0 & 2 & 3 \end{pmatrix}$$

$$= -2\det\begin{pmatrix} 7 & 5 & 0 \\ -1 & -1 & -7 \\ 8 & -1 & -3 \end{pmatrix} = 2\det\begin{pmatrix} 7 & 5 & 0 \\ 1 & 1 & 7 \\ 8 & -1 & -3 \end{pmatrix}$$

$$= 2\det\begin{pmatrix} 7 & -2 & -49 \\ 1 & 0 & 0 \\ 8 & -9 & -59 \end{pmatrix} = -2\det\begin{pmatrix} -2 & -49 \\ -9 & -59 \end{pmatrix} = 646.$$

The reader should determine which properties of determinants were used at each stage in the above reduction.

Although these methods do save time, they can be quite tedious if the matrix is large. For quicker mechanical methods one should investigate books on numerical analysis. This is especially so when one needs to determine the inverse of a large nonsingular matrix.

EXERCISES 6 Evaluate:

$$\det\begin{pmatrix} 1 & 2 & 7 & 5 \\ 0 & 4 & 8 & 6 \\ 9 & 3 & 2 & 1 \\ 8 & -7 & 0 & 1 \end{pmatrix}, \qquad \det\begin{pmatrix} x & 1 & x & 1 \\ x+1 & 0 & 0 & 2 \\ x+1 & 1-x & 3 & x \\ x^2 & x & 1 & 0 \end{pmatrix}.$$

7 Determine the reciprocal matrix to each of the following:

$$\begin{pmatrix} 1 & 2 & 7 \\ 8 & 0 & 6 \\ 0 & 0 & 3 \end{pmatrix}, \qquad \begin{pmatrix} 1 & 0 & 0 & 1 \\ 0 & 1 & 1 & 0 \\ 1 & 0 & 1 & 0 \\ 1 & 1 & 0 & 1 \end{pmatrix}.$$

8 Prove:

A.

$$\det\begin{pmatrix} a_{11} \cdots a_{1r} & b_{11} \cdots b_{1s} \\ \vdots \quad\quad \vdots & \vdots \quad\quad \vdots \\ a_{r1} \cdots a_{rr} & b_{r1} \cdots b_{rs} \\ 0 \cdots 0 & c_{11} \cdots c_{1s} \\ \vdots \quad\quad \vdots & \vdots \quad\quad \vdots \\ 0 \cdots 0 & c_{s1} \cdots c_{ss} \end{pmatrix} = \det(a_{ij})\det(c_{ij}).$$

B. If $\begin{pmatrix} \mathbf{A} & \mathbf{B} \\ \mathbf{O} & \mathbf{C} \end{pmatrix}$, where **A**, **C** are square matrices, is nonsingular, then **A** and **C** are nonsingular.

9 Prove: A square matrix **A** over a field is nonsingular if and only if its row vectors are a linearly independent set and its column vectors are a linearly independent set.

10 Prove: If **A** is a rectangular matrix over a field $\mathscr{F}$, then rank **A** is max $\{s \in \mathbf{Z} |$ there is an s by s minor of **A** with nonzero determinant$\}$.

11 Prove: If **A** is a rectangular matrix over $\mathscr{F}$, then the order of the maximal set of linearly independent row vectors of **A** and the order of the maximal set of linearly independent column vectors of **A** both equal the rank of **A**.

12 Prove: If **A** is a n by n matrix, then:

A. det (adj **A**) = (det **A**)$^{n-1}$.

B. adj (adj **A**) = (det **A**)$^{n-2}$ **A**.

C. If rank **A** = n, then rank **A** = rank (adj **A**).

D. If rank **A** = $n - 1$, then rank (adj **A**) = 1.

E. If rank **A** < $n - 1$, then rank (adj **A**) = 0.

13 Prove:

A. If $a, b \in \mathbf{Z}$ and $(a, b) = 1$, then there are $u, v \in \mathbf{Z}$ such that $\begin{pmatrix} a & b \\ u & v \end{pmatrix}$ is unimodular.

B. If $a, b, c \in \mathbf{Z}$ and $(a, b, c) = 1$, then there are $u_2, v_2, u_3, v_3, w_3 \in \mathbf{Z}$ so that

$$\begin{pmatrix} a & b & c \\ u_2 & v_2 & 0 \\ u_3 & v_3 & w_3 \end{pmatrix}$$

is unimodular.

C. If $a_1, a_2, \ldots, a_n \in \mathbf{Z}$ and $(a_1, a_2, \ldots, a_n) = 1$, then there is a unimodular matrix in $\mathfrak{M}_{n,n}(\mathbf{Z})$ having $a_1, \ldots, a_n$ as its first row.

D. The greatest common divisor of the elements of any row of a unimodular matrix with entries from **Z** is 1.

E. Let **A** be a unimodular n by n matrix over **Z**; then the set $\{\det \mathbf{A}_{3,\ldots,n;\, i_1,\ldots,i_{n-2}} \mid 1 \le i_1 < \cdots < i_{n-2} \le n$ has greatest common divisor 1.

F. More generally, if **A** is a n by n unimodular matrix over **Z**, then for each s, the set

$$\{\det \mathbf{A}_{1,2,\ldots,s;\, i_1,\ldots,i_s} | 1 \le i_1 < i_2 < \cdots < i_s \le n\}$$

has greatest common divisor 1.

G. If $a_{11}, \ldots, a_{1n}, a_{21}, \ldots, a_{2n} \in \mathbf{Z}$ are such that the greatest common divisor of the integers $\{c_{ij} = a_{1i}a_{2j} - a_{1j}a_{2i} \mid 1 \le i < j \le n\}$ is 1, then there is a unimodular matrix over $\mathbf{Z}$ with $(a_{11}, \ldots, a_{1n})$ and $(a_{21}, \ldots, a_{2n})$ as its first two rows.

H. Generalize G.

We now define several types of square matrices:

1. The matrix (a_{ij}) is said to be *diagonal* if $a_{ij} = 0$ when $i \ne j$.
2. A diagonal matrix is said to be a *scalar matrix* if $a_{11} = \cdots = a_{nn}$.
3. A matrix (a_{ij}) is said to be *upper triangular* if $a_{ij} = 0$ when $i < j$.
4. A matrix (a_{ij}) is said to be *strictly* (*upper*) *triangular* if $a_{ij} = 0$ when $i \le j$.
   Analogously we could define *lower triangular*.
5. A matrix (a_{ij}) is said to be a *permutation matrix* provided the row vectors are some arrangement of the vectors $\mathbf{e}_1, \ldots, \mathbf{e}_n$.
6. A matrix (a_{ij}) is said to be *nilpotent* if some power of it is $\mathbf{O}$.
7. A matrix (a_{ij}) is said to be *idempotent* if it is equal to its square.
8. A matrix (a_{ij}) is *symmetric* if $a_{ij} = a_{ji}$ for all i and j.
9. A matrix (a_{ij}) is *skew symmetric* if $a_{ij} = -a_{ji}$ for all i and j.
10. An n by n *elementary matrix* is one obtained from $\mathbf{I}_n$ by one of the following three processes: (A) multiplying a row of $\mathbf{I}_n$ by a scalar; (B) interchanging two rows of $\mathbf{I}_n$; (C) adding a scalar multiple of one row of $\mathbf{I}_n$ to another row.

EXERCISES 14 Prove each of the following are rings:

A. The set of all n by n matrices over a ring.

B. The set T_n of all n by n upper triangular matrices over a ring.

C. The set ${}^sT_n$ of all n by n strictly upper triangular matrices over a ring.

15 Prove:

A. A nilpotent matrix is singular.

B. A triangular matrix over an integral domain is nilpotent if and only if it is strictly triangular.

C. The determinant of a triangular matrix is the product of the terms on the diagonal.

D. ${}^sT_n$ is an ideal in T_n.

16 A. Prove: An elementary matrix is nonsingular and elementary matrices of type B and C are unimodular.

B. Find the inverse of the various elementary matrices.

17 A. If $n > 1$, show that there are idempotent singular n by n matrices over a field.

B. Prove: Over a field, $\mathbf{I}_n$ is the only nonsingular idempotent triangular matrix.

C. Determine all singular idempotent triangular matrices.

18 Prove:

A. A permutation matrix is unimodular.

B. The set $\mathscr{P}_n$ of all n by n permutation matrices forms a group under multiplication.

C. There is an isomorphism λ of $\mathscr{P}_n$ onto Π_n.

D. If $\mathbf{P}$ is a permutation matrix, then $\det \mathbf{P} = \operatorname{sgn}(\mathbf{P}^\lambda)$.

E. A permutation matrix is expressible as a finite product of elementary matrices of type B.

19 A. Determine necessary and sufficient conditions for a diagonal matrix $\mathbf{D} \in \mathfrak{M}_{n,n}(\mathscr{F})$ to commute with all matrices in $\mathfrak{M}_{n,n}(\mathscr{F})$.

B. Let $\mathscr{C}$ be the set of matrices of $\mathfrak{M}_{n,n}(\mathscr{F})$ that commute with all matrices of $\mathfrak{M}_{n,n}(\mathscr{F})$. Determine the elements in $\mathscr{C}$.

20 Prove:

A. A matrix $\mathbf{A}$ is symmetric if and only if $\mathbf{A}^t = \mathbf{A}$.

B. A matrix $\mathbf{A}$ is skew symmetric if and only if $\mathbf{A}^t = -\mathbf{A}$.

C. If char $\mathscr{F} \neq 2$, then the diagonal terms of a skew symmetric matrix over $\mathscr{F}$ are 0.

D. If char $\mathscr{F} \neq 2$, then a nonzero matrix over $\mathscr{F}$ cannot be both symmetric and skew symmetric.

E. If char $\mathscr{F} \neq 2$, then every matrix over $\mathscr{F}$ is the sum of a symmetric matrix and a skew symmetric matrix.

F. If $\mathbf{A}, \mathbf{B}$ are symmetric, so is $\mathbf{A}a + \mathbf{B}b$.

G. If $\mathbf{A}, \mathbf{B}$ are symmetric, then $\mathbf{AB}$ is symmetric if and only if $\mathbf{AB} = \mathbf{BA}$.

21 A. Describe the action of multiplying a matrix $\mathbf{A}$ on the left (on the right) by elementary matrices of each type.

B. Prove: If $\mathbf{A}$ is an n by m nonzero matrix over a field, then there is a n by n nonsingular matrix $\mathbf{U}$ and a m by m nonsingular matrix $\mathbf{V}$ such that

$$\mathbf{UAV} = \begin{pmatrix} 1 & 0 & \cdots & 0 \\ 0 & b_{22} & \cdots & b_{2m} \\ \vdots & \vdots & & \vdots \\ 0 & b_{n2} & \cdots & b_{nm} \end{pmatrix}.$$

Hint: The $\mathbf{U}$ and $\mathbf{V}$ are products of elementary matrices.

22 Prove: If a n by m matrix $\mathbf{A}$ is of the form

$\mathbf{A} = \begin{pmatrix} \mathbf{A}_1 & \mathbf{O} \\ \mathbf{O} & \mathbf{A}_2 \end{pmatrix}$, where $\mathbf{A}_1$ is s by t and $\mathbf{A}_2$ is $(n-s)$ by $(m-t)$,

and $\mathbf{B} = \begin{pmatrix} \mathbf{B}_1 & \mathbf{O} \\ \mathbf{O} & \mathbf{B}_2 \end{pmatrix}$, where $\mathbf{B}_1$ is t by r and $\mathbf{B}_2$ is $(m-t)$ by $(q-r)$,

then $\mathbf{AB} = \begin{pmatrix} \mathbf{A}_1\mathbf{B}_1 & \mathbf{O} \\ \mathbf{O} & \mathbf{A}_2\mathbf{B}_2 \end{pmatrix}$.

Using induction and the results in Exercise 21, the reader can prove

PROPOSITION 63 *Every nonsingular matrix over a field is a finite product of elementary matrices.*

Since the group of nonsingular matrices (for $n \geq 2$) is nonabelian, we do not expect to obtain a unique product in the proposition above. Using the results of Exercise 21 and Proposition 63, we obtain

PROPOSITION 64 *If* $\mathbf{A}$ *is a* n *by* m *matrix of rank* r *over a field, then* $\mathbf{A} = \mathbf{U}\mathbf{E}_r\mathbf{V}$, *where* $\mathbf{U}$ *and* $\mathbf{V}$ *are nonsingular and* $\mathbf{E}_r = (e_{ij})$ *is such that* $e_{11} = \cdots = e_{rr} = 1$, *and all other entries are* 0.

EXERCISE 23 Prove:

A. If $\mathbf{A}$ is an n by m matrix over $\mathbf{Z}$, then $\mathbf{A} = \mathbf{UDV}$, where $\mathbf{U}$, $\mathbf{V}$ are unimodular matrices over $\mathbf{Z}$ and $\mathbf{D} = (d_{ij})$ is such that $d_{ij} = 0$ if $i \neq j$, and $d_{ii} \mid d_{i+1,\, i+1}$. $\mathbf{D}$ is uniquely determined by $\mathbf{A}$.

B. The same theorem with $\mathbf{Z}$ replaced by $\mathscr{F}[x]$, the ring of polynomials over the field $\mathscr{F}$.

C. There are 2 by 2 matrices $\mathbf{A}$ over the ring $\mathscr{R}$ of functions of $\mathbf{Z}$ into $\mathbf{Z}$ such that $\mathbf{UAV}$ is not diagonal for any unimodular matrices $\mathbf{U}$,$\mathbf{V}$ in $\mathfrak{M}_{22}(\mathscr{R})$.

6 LINEAR EQUATIONS

We now examine questions concerning the solvability of systems of linear equations. Here we shall restrict our attention to the case where the coefficients lie in a field $\mathscr{F}$.

A system

$$\sum_{i=1}^{n} x_i a_{ij} = b_j, \qquad j = 1, \ldots, m, \tag{8}$$

of linear equations can be viewed as a single matrix equation:

$$(x_1, \ldots, x_n)\begin{pmatrix} a_{11} & \cdots & a_{1m} \\ \vdots & & \\ a_{n1} & & a_{nn} \end{pmatrix} = (b_1, \ldots, b_m),$$

which we shall write as

$$\mathbf{xA} = \mathbf{b}. \tag{9}$$

We say that the system of Eq. 8 is *homogeneous* provided $\mathbf{b} = \mathbf{0}$.

Let

$$\mathscr{N} = \{\mathbf{x} \in \mathscr{F}^{(n)} \mid \mathbf{xA} = \mathbf{0}\}.$$

Then $\mathscr{N}$ is exactly the kernel of the linear transformation $\mathbf{A}$. It follows from Propositions 13 and 45 that

LEMMA *$\mathcal{N}$ is a subspace of $\mathcal{F}^{(n)}$ of dimension n − rank* **A**.

If Eq. 9 has a solution, then **b** is in the subspace $\mathcal{F}^{(n)}\mathbf{A}$, and consequently **b** is a linear combination of the row vectors of **A**. It follows that

$$\text{rank}\begin{pmatrix} a_{11} & \cdots & a_{1m} \\ \vdots & & \vdots \\ a_{n1} & \cdots & a_{nm} \\ b_1 & \cdots & b_m \end{pmatrix} = \text{rank}\begin{pmatrix} a_{11} & \cdots & a_{1m} \\ \vdots & & \vdots \\ a_{n1} & \cdots & a_{nm} \end{pmatrix}. \tag{10}$$

The converse also holds, and we have

OPOSITION 65 *Equation* 9 *has a solution for x if and only if Eq.* 10 *holds.*

If **x** and **y** are solutions of Eq. 9, then $(\mathbf{x}-\mathbf{y})\mathbf{A} = \mathbf{0}$ and hence $\mathbf{x}-\mathbf{y} \in \mathcal{N}$. Conversely if $\mathbf{x}-\mathbf{y} \in \mathcal{N}$, then $\mathbf{xA} = \mathbf{yA}$. Thus we have

OPOSITION 66 *If* **x** *is a solution of Eq.* 9, *then the set of all solutions of Eq.* 9 *is* $\{\mathbf{x}+\mathbf{z} \mid \mathbf{z} \in \mathcal{N}\} = \mathbf{x} + \mathcal{N}$.

EXERCISE 1 Prove:

A. If $n > m$, there are $\mathbf{x} \neq \mathbf{0}$ such that $\mathbf{xA} = \mathbf{0}$.
B. If $n < m$, then there are **b** such that $\mathbf{xA} = \mathbf{b}$ has no solution.
C. If rank $\mathbf{A} = n$, then Eq. 9 has at most one solution.
D. If **A** is a nonsingular matrix, then for each **b** there is exactly one **x** such that $\mathbf{xA} = \mathbf{b}$.

Although our theory tells us when systems of linear equations have solutions, it is not easily adaptable for finding solutions. We do note that, if **V** is a nonsingular m by m matrix, then the set of solutions of Eq. 9 is exactly the same as the set of solutions of

$$\mathbf{xAV} = \mathbf{bV} = \mathbf{b}'.$$

If $\mathbf{xA} = \mathbf{b}$ and **U** is a nonsingular n by n matrix, then

$$\mathcal{X} = \{\mathbf{x} \in \mathcal{F}^{(n)} \mid \mathbf{xA} = \mathbf{b}\} \quad \text{and} \quad \mathcal{Y} = \{\mathbf{x} \in \mathcal{F}^{(n)} \mid \mathbf{xUA} = \mathbf{b}\}$$

are such that $\mathcal{X} = \mathcal{Y}\mathbf{U}$. Hence if we can determine $\mathcal{Y}$, then we can determine $\mathcal{X}$.

We saw in Proposition 64 that there were nonsingular matrices **U**, **V** such that

$$\mathbf{UAV} = \mathbf{E}_r, \qquad r = \text{rank } \mathbf{A}.$$

The equation

$$\mathbf{xE}_r = \mathbf{bV} = \mathbf{b}'$$

has a solution if and only if $b'_{r+1} = \cdots = b'_m = 0$; and in that case

$$\begin{aligned}\mathscr{Z} &= \{\mathbf{x} \in \mathscr{F}^{(n)} \mid \mathbf{x}\mathbf{E}_r = \mathbf{b}'\} \\ &= \{\mathbf{b}' + t_1\mathbf{e}_{r+1} + \cdots + t_{m-r}\mathbf{e}_m \mid t_1, \ldots, t_{m-r} \in \mathscr{F}\} \\ &= \{\mathbf{x} \in \mathscr{F}^{(n)} \mid \mathbf{x}\mathbf{U}\mathbf{A}\mathbf{V} = \mathbf{b}\mathbf{V}\} \\ &= \{\mathbf{x} \in \mathscr{F}^{(n)} \mid \mathbf{x}\mathbf{U}\mathbf{A} = \mathbf{b}\}.\end{aligned}$$

But then $\mathscr{X} = \{\mathbf{x} \in \mathscr{F}^{(n)} \mid \mathbf{x}\mathbf{A} = \mathbf{b}\} = \mathscr{Z}\mathbf{U}$.

Thus, if we know $\mathbf{U}$, $\mathbf{V}$ such that $\mathbf{UAV} = \mathbf{E}_r$, then $\mathscr{X}$ is easily found.

Now suppose $\mathbf{A}$ is a nonsingular matrix over a field $\mathscr{F}$. Then $\mathbf{xA} = \mathbf{b}$ implies that $\mathbf{x} = \mathbf{b}\mathbf{A}^{-1} = \mathbf{b}(\operatorname{adj} \mathbf{A})/\det \mathbf{A}$; i.e.,

$$x_j = \frac{\sum_{i=1}^{n} b_i \mathscr{A}_{ij}}{\det \mathbf{A}} = \frac{\det \mathbf{A}^{(j)}}{\det \mathbf{A}},$$

where $\mathbf{A}^{(j)}$ differs from $\mathbf{A}$ in having $(b_1 \ldots, b_n)$ as its jth row. Thus, when $\mathbf{A}$ is nonsingular, we can express the coordinates of the solution in terms of ratios of the determinants of n by n minors of the *augmented matrix* $\begin{pmatrix}\mathbf{A}\\ \mathbf{b}\end{pmatrix} = \tilde{\mathbf{A}}$.

A similar phenomena holds even when $\mathbf{A}$ is not a square matrix. Suppose that $\mathbf{A}$ is an n by m matrix of rank r. After rearranging the order of the equations and relabeling the variables, we may assume that

$$\mathbf{A}^* = \begin{pmatrix} a_{11} & \cdots & a_{1r} \\ \vdots & & \vdots \\ a_{r1} & \cdots & a_{rr}\end{pmatrix} = \mathbf{A}_{r+1, \ldots, n; r+1, \ldots, n}$$

is a nonsingular matrix. Then the first r columns of the matrix $\tilde{\mathbf{A}} = \begin{pmatrix}\mathbf{A}\\ \mathbf{b}\end{pmatrix}$ are linearly independent. By Proposition 65, if Eq. 9 has a solution, then any $r + 1$ columns of $\tilde{\mathbf{A}}$ must be linearly dependent; i.e., if there is a solution, then the last $m-r$ equations are expressible as linear combinations of the first r. Consequently any solution of the first r equations is necessarily a solution of the whole system. Thus we need to solve

$$\sum_{i=1}^{r} x_i a_{ij} = b_j - \sum_{i=r+1}^{n} x_i a_{ij}, \qquad j = 1, 2, \ldots, r.$$

Since $\mathbf{A}^*$ is nonsingular, we have just seen that for any choice of $x_{r+1}, \ldots, x_n$, we have $x_j \det \mathbf{A}^* = \det \mathbf{A}^{(j)}$, where $\mathbf{A}^{(j)}$ differs from $\mathbf{A}^*$ in having $(b_1 - \sum_{i=r+1}^{n} x_i a_{i1}, \ldots, b_r - \sum_{i=r+1}^{n} x_i a_{ir})$ as its jth row. But then

$$x_j \det \mathbf{A}^* = m_{j\,n+1} - x_{r+1} m_{j\,r+1} - \cdots - x_n m_{jn}, \qquad j = 1, \ldots, r, \quad (11)$$

where $\pm\, m_{jv}$ is the determinant of the minor $\mathbf{A}_{j, r+1, \ldots, v-1, v+1, \ldots m; r+1, \ldots, n}$ of the matrix $\tilde{\mathbf{A}}$. The effect of relabeling the variables was to simplify the notation. If we had not done so, we would still have found that the $m_{j\nu}$ were (to within sign) the determinants of certain r by r minors. Thus we have

POSITION 67 *The solution set of Eq.* 9 *is spanned by certain vectors whose coordinates are ratios of certain r by r minors of* $\tilde{\mathbf{A}}$, *where* $r = \text{rank}\ \mathbf{A}$.

Suppose we are given a system of linear equations, say (9), where the coefficients lie in a field $\mathcal{F}$, and suppose we are given a field $\mathcal{E}$ that contains $\mathcal{F}$. It is natural to inquire whether the system could have a solution in $\mathcal{E}$ and none in $\mathcal{F}$. The result just proved shows that this is impossible. All the minors of $\tilde{\mathbf{A}}$ necessarily lie in $\mathcal{F}$, and hence if there is a solution set in $\mathcal{E}$, it must be spanned by vectors that have coordinates in $\mathcal{F}$, and hence there must be a solution in $\mathcal{F}$. We have

COROLLARY *A system of linear equations with coefficients in a field* $\mathcal{F}$ *has a solution in an extended field* $\mathcal{E} \supset \mathcal{F}$ *if and only if the system has a solution in* $\mathcal{F}$.

If the system of linear equations (9) has its coefficients in an integral domain $\mathcal{D}$, we might reasonably ask that the coordinates of the solutions lie in $\mathcal{D}$. We see from Eq. 11 that we have such a solution provided det $\mathbf{A}^*$ divides (in $\mathcal{D}$) each of $m_{1\ n+1}, \ldots, m_{r\ n+1}$. For in that case we can take the $x_{r+1}, \ldots, x_n$ to be multiples of det $\mathbf{A}^*$. However, it may occur that det $\mathbf{A}^*$ does not divide each of $m_{1\ n+1}, \ldots, m_{r\ n+1}$ and still Eq. 9 has a solution in $\mathcal{D}$. In case $\mathcal{D}$ is a unique factorization domain, it can be shown that *a system of linear equations* (9) *with coefficients in* $\mathcal{D}$ *has a solution in* $\mathcal{D}$ *if and only if the greatest common divisor of the determinants of all the r by r minors of* $\mathbf{A}$ *is equal to the greatest common divisor of the determinants of all the r by r minors of* $\tilde{\mathbf{A}}$. The proof is relatively straightforward but tedious, and we shall not give it here.

When seeking integral solutions of linear equations with coefficients in $\mathbf{Z}$, it is useful to recall (Exercise 23) that every matrix over $\mathbf{Z}$ can be expressed as $\mathbf{A} = \mathbf{UDV}$, where $\mathbf{U},\mathbf{V}$ are unimodular matrices over $\mathbf{Z}$ and $\mathbf{D}$ is a diagonal matrix over $\mathbf{Z}$. Then $\mathbf{xA} = \mathbf{b}$ has a solution in $\mathbf{Z}$ exactly when $\mathbf{yD} = \mathbf{bV} = \mathbf{b}'$ has a solution, i.e., exactly when $d_{ii} \mid b'_i$, $(i = 1, \ldots, m)$.

ERCISES 2

A. Determine the solution sets with coordinates in $\mathbf{Q}$, if any, of the following:

$$\begin{cases} x_1 - x_2 + x_4 = 0 \\ x_2 - x_3 = 0 \\ x_3 - x_4 = 0, \end{cases} \quad \begin{cases} x_1 - x_2 + 3x_3 = 4 \\ 3x_1 + 4x_2 - 2x_3 = 1 \\ 17x_1 + 18x_2 - 4x_3 = 0, \end{cases} \quad \begin{cases} x_1 - x_2 + 3x_3 = 4 \\ 2x_1 + 4x_2 - 3x_3 = 2 \\ 3x_1 + 2x_2 = -3. \end{cases}$$

B. Determine the solution sets with coordinates in $\mathbf{Z}$, if any, of each of the above systems of linear equations.

3 Prove:

A. If a system of linear equations over $\mathbf{Z}$ has a solution in $\mathbf{Z}$, then for each j, $(j = 1, \ldots, m)$, the greatest common divisor of $a_{1j}, \ldots, a_{nj}$ must divide b_j.

B. If a system of linear equations over $\mathbf{Z}$ has a solution in $\mathbf{Q}^{(n)}$ and if for each j, $(j = 1, \ldots, m)$, the greatest common divisor of $a_{1j}, \ldots, a_{nj}$ divides b_j, then the system has a solution with the $x \in \mathbf{Z}$.

4 If $\mathbf{U} = (u_{ij})$ is a nonsingular matrix and if $\{\alpha_1, \ldots, \alpha_n\}$ is a basis of an n-dimensional vector space $\mathscr{V}$, put $\alpha_i^* = \sum_{j=1}^{n} u_{ij}\alpha_j$, $(i = 1, \ldots, n)$. Prove: $\{\alpha_1^*, \ldots, \alpha_n^*\}$ is a basis of $\mathscr{V}$.

5 Prove: If $\{\alpha_1, \ldots, \alpha_n\}$, $\{\alpha_1^*, \ldots, \alpha_n^*\}$ are two bases of a vector space $\mathscr{V}$ and if $\alpha_i^* = \sum_{j=1}^{n} u_{ij}\,\alpha_j$, $(i = 1, \ldots, n)$, then (u_{ij}) is a nonsingular matrix.

7 EQUIVALENCE OF MATRICES

Let $\mathscr{V}$ and $\mathscr{W}$ be finitely dimensional spaces over a field $\mathscr{F}$. We saw at the start of Sec. 5 that, for each pair of ordered bases, $\mathfrak{A} = \{\alpha_1, \ldots, \alpha_n\}$ of $\mathscr{V}$ and $\mathfrak{B} = \{\beta_1, \ldots, \beta_m\}$ of $\mathscr{W}$, there is an isomorphism of $\mathscr{L}(\mathscr{V}, \mathscr{W})$ onto $\mathfrak{M}_{n,m}(\mathscr{F})$. This isomorphism was the map

$$\theta = \sum_{i=1}^{n}\sum_{j=1}^{m}\theta_{ij}a_{ij} \to \begin{pmatrix} a_{11} & \cdots & a_{1m} \\ \vdots & & \\ a_{n1} & & a_{nm} \end{pmatrix} = \mathbf{M}(\theta) = \mathbf{M}(\theta; \mathfrak{A}, \mathfrak{B}),$$

where $\alpha_i\theta_{st} = \delta_{is}\beta_t$.

Let $\varphi \in \mathscr{L}(\mathscr{V}, \mathscr{F}^{(n)})$ be such that $\alpha_i\varphi = \mathbf{e}_i$, $(i = 1, \ldots, n)$. Let $\psi \in \mathscr{L}(\mathscr{W}, \mathscr{F}^{(m)})$ be such that $\beta_j\psi = \mathbf{e}'_j$, $(j = 1, \ldots, m)$. The maps φ, ψ are bijective and hence have inverses. Now

$$\alpha_i\theta = \sum_{j=1}^{m} a_{ij}\beta_j, \qquad i = 1, \ldots, n,$$

and

$$\alpha_i\varphi\mathbf{M}(\theta)\psi^{-1} = \mathbf{e}_i\mathbf{M}(\theta)\psi^{-1} = \left(\sum_{j=1}^{m} a_{ij}\mathbf{e}'_j\right)\psi^{-1} = \sum_{j=1}^{m} a_{ij}\beta_j, \qquad i = 1, \ldots, n.$$

Since the linear maps θ and $\varphi\mathbf{M}(\theta)\psi^{-1}$ agree on a basis of $\mathscr{V}$, they are the same map on $\mathscr{V}$; i.e.,

$$\theta = \varphi\mathbf{M}(\theta)\psi^{-1}.$$

Since rank $\varphi = n$, rank $\psi^{-1} = m$, we have

PROPOSITION 68 *rank* $\theta =$ *rank* $\mathbf{M}(\theta)$.

We next investigate the effect a change of ordered bases of $\mathscr{V}$ or of $\mathscr{W}$ has on the matrix representation of θ. Let $\mathfrak{A}^* = \{\alpha_1^*, \ldots, \alpha_n^*\}$ be an ordered basis of $\mathscr{V}$, and let $\mathfrak{B}^* = \{\beta_1^*, \ldots, \beta_m^*\}$ be an ordered basis of $\mathscr{W}$. We have the bijective linear transformations $\varphi^* \in \mathscr{L}(\mathscr{V}, \mathscr{F}^{(n)})$ such that $\alpha_i^*\varphi^* = \mathbf{e}_i$, $(i = 1, \ldots, n)$, and $\psi^* \in \mathscr{L}(\mathscr{W}, \mathscr{F}^{(m)})$ such that $\beta_i^*\psi^* = \mathbf{e}_i'$, $(i = 1, \ldots, m)$. We also have the nonsingular linear transformations $\sigma \in \mathscr{L}(\mathscr{V}, \mathscr{V})$ given by $\alpha_i\sigma = \alpha_i^*$, $(i = 1, \ldots, n)$, and $\tau \in \mathscr{L}(\mathscr{W}, \mathscr{W})$ given by $\beta_j\tau = \beta_j^*$, $(j = 1, \ldots, m)$. Then we have the matrix representations $\mathbf{M}(\sigma; \mathfrak{A}, \mathfrak{A}^*)$ and $\mathbf{M}(\tau; \mathfrak{B}, \mathfrak{B}^*)$. By Proposition 68, these two matrices are nonsingular, and hence their inverses exist and are nonsingular.

The following relations hold:

$$\sigma\varphi^* = \varphi\mathbf{M}(\sigma) = \varphi\mathbf{M}(\sigma; \mathfrak{A}, \mathfrak{A}^*),$$

$$\tau\psi^* = \psi\mathbf{M}(\tau) = \psi\mathbf{M}(\tau; \mathfrak{B}, \mathfrak{B}^*),$$

$$\theta\tau\psi^* = \sigma\varphi^*\mathbf{M}^*(\theta) = \sigma\varphi^*\mathbf{M}(\theta; \mathfrak{A}^*, \mathfrak{B}^*).$$

Hence $$\theta\psi\mathbf{M}(\tau) = \theta\tau\psi^* = \sigma\varphi^*\mathbf{M}^*(\theta) = \varphi\mathbf{M}(\sigma)\mathbf{M}^*(\theta),$$

and $$\mathbf{M}(\theta) = \varphi^{-1}\theta\psi = \mathbf{M}(\sigma)\mathbf{M}^*(\theta)\mathbf{M}(\tau)^{-1}.$$

Thus we have

$$\mathbf{M}(\theta) = \mathbf{M}(\sigma)\mathbf{M}^*(\theta)\mathbf{M}(\tau)^{-1}.$$

We have proved

OPOSITION 69 *If* $\mathbf{M}$ *and* $\mathbf{M}^*$ *are matrix representations of the same linear transformation, then there exist nonsingular matrices* $\mathbf{U}, \mathbf{V}$ *such that* $\mathbf{M} = \mathbf{U}\mathbf{M}^*\mathbf{V}$.

We next prove the converse of Proposition 69, namely,

OPOSITION 70 *If* $\mathbf{M}$ *and* $\mathbf{M}^*$ *are matrices such that there are nonsingular matrices* $\mathbf{U}, \mathbf{V}$ *for which* $\mathbf{M} = \mathbf{U}\mathbf{M}^*\mathbf{V}$ *and if* $\mathbf{M}$ *is a matrix representation for some* $\theta \in \mathscr{L}(\mathscr{V}, \mathscr{W})$, *then* $\mathbf{M}^*$ *is also a matrix representation for* θ.

PROOF. By hypothesis there are ordered bases $\mathfrak{A} = \{\alpha_1, \ldots, \alpha_n\}$ of $\mathscr{V}$ and $\mathfrak{B} = \{\beta_1, \ldots, \beta_m)$ of $\mathscr{W}$ such that $\mathbf{M} = \mathbf{M}(\theta; \mathfrak{A}, \mathfrak{B}) = (m_{ij})$. If $\mathbf{U} = (u_{ij})$, put $\alpha_i^* = \sum_{j=1}^{n} u_{ij}\alpha_j$, $(i = 1, \ldots, n)$. Then $\{\alpha_1^*, \ldots, \alpha_n^*\}$ is a basis of $\mathscr{V}$. (See Exercise 4, Sec. 6.) Let $\mathbf{W} = \mathbf{V}^{-1}$, and put $\beta_j^* = \sum_{k=1}^{m} w_{jk}\beta_k$, $(j = 1, \ldots, m)$. Then $\{\beta_1^*, \ldots, \beta_m^*\}$ is a basis of $\mathscr{W}$. We then have

$$\alpha_i^*\theta = \left(\sum_j u_{ij}\alpha_j\right)\theta = \sum_{j=1}^{n} u_{ij} \sum_{k=1}^{m} m_{jk}\beta_k$$

$$= \sum_{j=1}^{n} u_{ij} \sum_{k=1}^{m} m_{jk} \sum_{t=1}^{m} v_{kt}\beta_t^*$$

$$= \sum_{t=1}^{m} \left(\sum_{j=1}^{n} \sum_{k=1}^{m} u_{ij}m_{jk}v_{kt} \right) \beta_t^*;$$

whence $$\mathbf{M}(\theta; \mathfrak{A}^*, \mathfrak{B}^*) = \mathbf{UMV} = \mathbf{M}^*.$$

We shall say that two rectangular matrices over a field are *equivalent* if they represent the same linear transformation. Clearly this is an equivalence relation on $\mathfrak{M}_{n,m}(\mathscr{F})$. Equivalent matrices obviously have the same height and width. It follows from Propositions 69 and 70 that *two matrices* $\mathbf{M}, \mathbf{M}^*$ *are equivalent if and only if there are nonsingular matrices* $\mathbf{U}$ *and* $\mathbf{V}$ *such that* $\mathbf{M}^* = \mathbf{UMV}$. It follows from Proposition 68 that equivalent matrices have the same rank. And it follows from Proposition 64 that each n by m matrix of rank r is equivalent to $\mathbf{E}_r$. Consequently matrices of the same rank are equivalent.

The proof of Proposition 64 involves some tedious computations with elementary matrices and consequently is not a very elegant argument. For aesthetic reasons one would prefer not to use Proposition 64. We now show that Proposition 64 is not necessary to prove that all n by m matrices of rank r are equivalent to $\mathbf{E}_r$. Let $\mathbf{A}$ be an n by m matrix of rank r. There is a permutation matrix $\mathbf{U}$ such that the first r row vectors of $\mathbf{UA}$ are a linearly independent set. Let $\beta_1, \ldots, \beta_r$ be these row vectors; then $\mathbf{e}_i\mathbf{UA} = \beta_i$, $(i = 1, \ldots, r)$. Choose $\beta_{r+1}, \ldots, \beta_m$ so that $\{\beta_1, \ldots, \beta_m\}$ is a basis of $\mathscr{F}^{(m)}$. Let $\mathbf{V}$ be the linear transformation on $\mathscr{F}^{(m)}$ such that $\beta_i\mathbf{V} = \mathbf{e}'_i$, $(i = 1, \ldots, m)$. Then

$$\mathbf{UAV} = \begin{pmatrix} \mathbf{I}_r & \mathbf{O} \\ \mathbf{A} & \mathbf{O} \end{pmatrix},$$

but

$$\begin{pmatrix} \mathbf{I}_r & \mathbf{O} \\ -\mathbf{A} & \mathbf{I}_{n-r} \end{pmatrix}\begin{pmatrix} \mathbf{I}_r & \mathbf{O} \\ \mathbf{A} & \mathbf{O} \end{pmatrix} = \begin{pmatrix} \mathbf{I}_r & \mathbf{O} \\ \mathbf{O} & \mathbf{O} \end{pmatrix} = \mathbf{E}_r,$$

and hence $\mathbf{A}$ is equivalent to $\mathbf{E}_r$. We have proved

PROPOSITION 71 *Two rectangular matrices over a field* $\mathscr{F}$ *are equivalent exactly when they have the same height, width, and rank.*

COROLLARY *If* $s = \min(n, m)$, *then there are exactly* $s + 1$ *classes of equivalent matrices in* $\mathfrak{M}_{n,m}(\mathscr{F})$.

Consider the map

$$\mathbf{A} \xrightarrow{\Lambda} \mathbf{UAV}$$

of $\mathfrak{M}_{n,m}$ into itself, where $\mathbf{U}$ is a n by n nonsingular matrix and $\mathbf{V}$ is a m by m nonsingular matrix. Since Λ and the map $\mathbf{A} \to \mathbf{U}^{-1}\mathbf{AV}^{-1}$ are inverses, Λ must be bijective. Clearly $(\mathbf{A} + \mathbf{B})\Lambda = \mathbf{A}\Lambda + \mathbf{B}\Lambda$, $(\mathbf{A}c)\Lambda = (\mathbf{A}\Lambda)c$, and rank $(\mathbf{A}\Lambda) =$ rank $\mathbf{A}$. Hence Λ is a rank-preserving automorphism of the vector space $\mathfrak{M}_{n,m}$. Is the converse true; i.e., is every rank-preserving automorphism of $\mathfrak{M}_{n,m}$ of the type $\mathbf{A} \to \mathbf{UAV}$, where $\mathbf{U}$ and $\mathbf{V}$ are nonsingular? In general the answer is no. The map

$$\mathbf{A} \xrightarrow{\Psi} \mathbf{A}^t$$

is an automorphism of the vector space $\mathfrak{M}_{n,n}$ into itself which preserves rank. However, there do not exist nonsingular matrices $\mathbf{U},\mathbf{V}$ so that

$\mathbf{A}^t = \mathbf{UAV}$, for all $\mathbf{A} \in \mathfrak{M}_{n,n}$. This can be seen quite easily for the case $n = 2$. The relations

$$\mathbf{UE}_{12}\mathbf{V} = \mathbf{E}_{21}, \ \mathbf{UE}_{21}\mathbf{V} = \mathbf{E}_{12} \text{ imply that } \mathbf{U} = \begin{pmatrix} 0 & a \\ b & 0 \end{pmatrix}, \ \mathbf{V} = \begin{pmatrix} 0 & a^{-1} \\ b^{-1} & 0 \end{pmatrix},$$

with $ab \neq 0$. But then $\mathbf{UE}_{11}\mathbf{V} = ba^{-1}\mathbf{E}_{22} \neq \mathbf{E}_{11}{}^t = \mathbf{E}_{11}$.

To answer this question completely we need several tools that are developed in the exercises below.

XERCISES 1 Prove:

A. If $\mathbf{A}$ and $\mathbf{B}$ are equivalent matrices, so are $\mathbf{A}^t$, $\mathbf{B}^t$.

B. If $\mathbf{A}$ is a square matrix, then $\mathbf{A}$ and $\mathbf{A}^t$ are equivalent.

C. If $n \geq 2$, there do not exist nonsingular matrices $\mathbf{U}$ and $\mathbf{V}$ such that $\mathbf{A}^t = \mathbf{UAV}$ for all $\mathbf{A} \in \mathfrak{M}_{n,n}$.

D. Explain the difference between B and C.

2 Prove: A n by m matrix of rank r is the sum of r matrices of rank 1.

3 Prove: If $\mathbf{A} \in \mathfrak{M}_{n,m}$ is of rank 1, then there is a nonzero $\mathbf{B} \in \mathfrak{M}_{n,1}$ and a nonzero $\mathbf{C} \in \mathfrak{M}_{1,m}$ such that $\mathbf{A} = \mathbf{BC}$. (*Note:* This is Exercise 3, Sec. 5.)

4 Prove: If $\mathbf{A} \in \mathfrak{M}_{n,m}$ is of rank r if and only if $\mathbf{A} = \mathbf{B}_1\mathbf{C}_1 + \cdots + \mathbf{B}_r\mathbf{C}_r$, where $\mathbf{O} \neq \mathbf{B}_j \in \mathfrak{M}_{n,1}$, $\mathbf{O} \neq \mathbf{C}_j \in \mathfrak{M}_{1,m}$ and the sets $\{\mathbf{B}_1, \ldots, \mathbf{B}_r\}$, $\{\mathbf{C}_1, \ldots, \mathbf{C}_r\}$ are linearly independent. (*Hint:* $\mathbf{A}$ is equivalent to $\mathbf{E}_r$ if and only if rank $\mathbf{A} = r$.)

5 Prove: If $\mathbf{A} = \mathbf{B}_1\mathbf{C}_1 + \cdots + \mathbf{B}_t\mathbf{C}_t$, where $\mathbf{B}_j \in \mathfrak{M}_{n,1}$, $\mathbf{C}_j \in \mathfrak{M}_{1,m}$, then rank $\mathbf{A} = \min\{\dim\langle\mathbf{B}_1, \ldots, \mathbf{B}_t\rangle, \dim\langle\mathbf{C}_1, \ldots, \mathbf{C}_t\rangle\}$.

6 Prove: If $\mathbf{A}$ is a square matrix of rank 1 over a field $\mathscr{F}$, then there is a $c \in \mathscr{F}$ such that $\mathbf{A}^2 = c\mathbf{A}$. $\mathbf{I} - \mathbf{A}$ is nonsingular if and only if $c \neq 1$.

7 Let Φ be a rank-preserving automorphism of $\mathfrak{M}_{n,m}$. Prove:

A. The map $\mathbf{A} \to (\mathbf{A}^t\Phi)^t = \mathbf{A}\Psi\Phi\Psi$ is a rank-preserving automorphism of the vector space $\mathfrak{M}_{m,n}$.

B. If $m = n$, the map $\Phi\Psi$ is a rank-preserving automorphism of the vector space $\mathfrak{M}_{n,n}$.

We now prove

THEOREM 1 *Let Φ be a rank-preserving automorphism of the vector space $\mathfrak{M}_{n,m}(\mathscr{F})$. If $m \neq n$, then $\mathbf{X}\Phi = \mathbf{UXV}$, where $\mathbf{U}$ and $\mathbf{V}$ are nonsingular matrices. If $m = n$, then either $\mathbf{X}\Phi = \mathbf{UXV}$ or $\mathbf{X}\Phi = \mathbf{UX}^t\mathbf{V}$, where $\mathbf{U}$ and $\mathbf{V}$ are nonsingular matrices.*

PROOF. Suppose $n \leq m$. Since $\mathbf{E}_{st}$ is of rank 1, by Exercise 3, we have

$$\mathbf{E}_{st}\Phi = \mathbf{U}_{st}\mathbf{V}_{st}, \qquad s = 1, \ldots, n; t = 1, \ldots, m,$$

where $\mathbf{O} \neq \mathbf{U}_{st} \in \mathfrak{M}_{n,1}$, $\mathbf{O} \neq \mathbf{V}_{st} \in \mathfrak{M}_{1,m}$. If $\sigma \in \Pi_n$, then $\mathbf{E}_{1\sigma(1)} + \cdots + \mathbf{E}_{k\sigma(k)}$, $(k \leq n)$, is of rank k, and hence the matrix $\mathbf{U}_{1\sigma(1)}\mathbf{V}_{1\sigma(1)}$

$+ \cdots + \mathbf{U}_{k\sigma(k)}\mathbf{V}_{k\sigma(k)}$ has rank k. It follows from Exercise 4 that each of the sets $\{\mathbf{U}_{1\sigma(1)}, \ldots, \mathbf{U}_{k\sigma(k)}\}$, $\{\mathbf{V}_{1\sigma(1)}, \ldots, \mathbf{V}_{k\sigma(k)}\}$, with $k \le n$, is a linearly independent set of matrices. On the other hand, for each $s = 1, \ldots, n$, the matrix $\mathbf{E}_{s1} + \cdots + \mathbf{E}_{sm}$ has rank 1. Hence, by Exercise 5, for a given s either $\dim \langle \mathbf{U}_{s1}, \ldots, \mathbf{U}_{sm} \rangle = 1$ or $\dim \langle \mathbf{V}_{s1}, \ldots, \mathbf{V}_{sm} \rangle = 1$. Similarly, because $\mathbf{E}_{1t} + \cdots \mathbf{E}_{nt}$ has rank 1, for each t, either $\dim \langle \mathbf{U}_{1t}, \ldots, \mathbf{U}_{nt} \rangle = 1$ or $\dim \langle \mathbf{V}_{1t}, \ldots, \mathbf{V}_{nt} \rangle = 1$.

Suppose $\dim \langle \mathbf{U}_{11}, \ldots, \mathbf{U}_{1m} \rangle = 1$. If $s \ne 1$, then $\{\mathbf{U}_{1s}, \mathbf{U}_{s1}\}$ is a linearly independent set. But $\{\mathbf{U}_{11}, \mathbf{U}_{1s}\}$ is a linearly dependent set, and hence $\{\mathbf{U}_{11}, \mathbf{U}_{s1}\}$ is linearly independent. Consequently $\dim \langle \mathbf{U}_{11}, \ldots, \mathbf{U}_{n1} \rangle \ne 1$, and hence $\dim \langle \mathbf{V}_{11}, \ldots, \mathbf{V}_{n1} \rangle = 1$. If s and t differ from 1, then $\langle \mathbf{V}_{11}, \mathbf{V}_{st} \rangle$ is a linearly independent set. Since $\langle \mathbf{V}_{11}, \mathbf{V}_{s1} \rangle$ is a linearly dependent set, the set $\langle \mathbf{V}_{s1}, \mathbf{V}_{st} \rangle$ is linearly independent. Consequently, for $s = 2, \ldots, n$, we have $\dim \langle \mathbf{U}_{s1}, \ldots, \mathbf{U}_{sm} \rangle = 1$. Similarly it can be shown that for $t = 1, \ldots, m$ we have $\dim \langle \mathbf{V}_{1t}, \ldots, \mathbf{V}_{nt} \rangle = 1$. Therefore there are nonzero n by 1 matrices $\mathbf{U}_1, \ldots, \mathbf{U}_n$ and nonzero 1 by n matrices $\mathbf{V}_1, \ldots, \mathbf{V}_m$ and nonzero field elements $a(s,t)$, $b(s,t)$, such that $\mathbf{U}_{st} = a(s, t)\mathbf{U}_s$, $\mathbf{V}_{st} = b(s, t)\mathbf{V}_t$, $(s = 1, \ldots, n;\ t = 1, \ldots, m)$.

Let $\mathbf{U}$ be the n by n matrix having $\mathbf{U}_1, \ldots, \mathbf{U}_n$ as its column vectors, and let $\mathbf{V}$ be the m by m matrix having $\mathbf{V}_1, \ldots, \mathbf{V}_m$ as its row vectors. Since $\mathbf{E}_{11} + \cdots + \mathbf{E}_{nn}$ has rank n, we see that $\mathbf{U}$ is a nonsingular matrix.

Thus, assuming that $n \le m$ and $\dim \langle \mathbf{U}_{11}, \ldots, \mathbf{U}_{1m} \rangle = 1$, we have found that

$$\mathbf{X}\Phi = \left(\sum_{s=1}^{n} \sum_{t=1}^{m} \mathbf{E}_{st} x_{st} \right) \Phi = \sum_{s=1}^{n} \sum_{t=1}^{m} \mathbf{U}\mathbf{E}_{st}\mathbf{V} a(s, t) b(s, t) x_{st}.$$

If the rank of $\mathbf{V}$ were less than m, there would be a nonzero vector $\mathbf{y} \in \mathscr{F}^{(m)}$ such that $\mathbf{y}\mathbf{V} = \mathbf{0}$. Let $\mathbf{Y}$ be the n by m matrix with each row vector equal to $\mathbf{y}$, then $\mathbf{Y}\mathbf{V} = \mathbf{O}$. Let $\mathbf{W} = \mathbf{U}^{-1}\mathbf{Y}$, then rank $\mathbf{W} = 1$. Since $a(s, t)b(s, t) \ne 0$, there exist x_{st} such that $w_{st} = a(s, t)b(s, t)x_{st}$ for $s = 1, \ldots, n;\ t = 1, \ldots, m$. Then $\mathbf{X} = (x_{st})$ is a matrix of positive rank and

$$\mathbf{X}\Phi = \mathbf{U}\mathbf{W}\mathbf{V} = \mathbf{Y}\mathbf{V} = \mathbf{O},$$

contrary to the hypothesis on Φ. Hence $\mathbf{V}$ is nonsingular.

Let $\mathbf{T}$ be the n by m matrix having 1 in each position. Then rank $\mathbf{T} = 1$ and $\mathbf{S} = \mathbf{U}^{-1}\mathbf{T}\mathbf{V}^{-1}$ is a n by m matrix of rank 1. Now $\mathbf{S}\Phi = (a(s, t)b(s, t))$ must have rank 1, and therefore there exist nonzero field elements $p_1, \ldots, p_n$ such that the jth row of $\mathbf{S}\Phi$ is p_j times the first row. Let $q_j = a(1, j)b(1, j)$; then $q_j \ne 0$ and $p_i q_j = a(i, j)b(i, j)$, for $i = 1, \ldots, n$; $j = 1, \ldots m$. Let $\mathbf{P}$ be the m by m diagonal matrix with $p_{ii} = p_i$, and let $\mathbf{Q}$ be the n by n diagonal matrix with $q_{jj} = q_j$. We then have $\mathbf{X}\Phi = \mathbf{U}\mathbf{P}\mathbf{X}\mathbf{Q}\mathbf{V}$, where $\mathbf{U}\mathbf{P}$, $\mathbf{Q}\mathbf{V}$ are nonsingular matrices. Thus we have proved the proposition, assuming $n \le m$ and $\dim \langle \mathbf{U}_{11}, \ldots, \mathbf{U}_{1m} \rangle = 1$.

Now suppose $n \le m$ and $\dim \langle \mathbf{U}_{11}, \ldots, \mathbf{U}_{1m} \rangle \ne 1$. Then in an entirely analogous manner we could prove that there are nonzero matrices $\mathbf{U}_1, \ldots, \mathbf{U}_m, \in \mathfrak{M}_{n,1}$; nonzero matrices $\mathbf{V}_1, \ldots, \mathbf{V}_n \in \mathfrak{M}_{1,m}$; and nonzero field elements $a(s, t)$, $b(s, t)$ such that

$$\mathbf{U}_{st} = \mathbf{U}_t a(s, t), \qquad \mathbf{V}_{st} = \mathbf{V}_s b(s, t), \qquad s = 1, \ldots, n;\ t = 1, \ldots, m.$$

Since $\mathbf{E}_{11} + \cdots + \mathbf{E}_{nn}$ has rank n, we can conclude that $\dim \langle \mathbf{U}_1, \ldots, \mathbf{U}_n \rangle = n$.

If $n < m$, then $\mathbf{U}_m = \mathbf{U}_1 c_1 + \cdots + \mathbf{U}_n c_n$, since the $\mathbf{U}_j$ lie in an n-dimensional space. Choose x_j such that $x_j a(1, j) b(1, j) = a(1, m) b(1, m) c_j$, for $j = 1, \ldots, n$. Then rank $(x_1 \mathbf{E}_{11} + \cdots + x_n \mathbf{E}_{1n} - \mathbf{E}_{1m}) = 1$, and $(\mathbf{E}_{11} x_1 + \cdots + \mathbf{E}_{1n} x_n - \mathbf{E}_{1m})\Phi = \mathbf{O}$, which contradicts the assumption on Φ. Hence we have proved the proposition for the case $n < m$.

If $m = n$, then $\mathbf{E}_{st}\Phi = a(s, t) b(s, t) \mathbf{U}_t \mathbf{V}_s$, and therefore $\mathbf{E}_{st}\Phi\Psi = a(s, t) b(s, t) \mathbf{V}_s{}^t \mathbf{U}_t{}^t = a(s, t) b(s, t) \mathbf{U}_s^* \mathbf{V}_t^*$, where $\mathbf{U}_s^* = \mathbf{V}_s{}^t$, $\mathbf{V}_t^* = \mathbf{U}_t{}^t$, and $\dim \langle \mathbf{U}_1^*, \ldots, \mathbf{U}_n^* \rangle = n$, $\dim \langle \mathbf{V}_1^*, \ldots, \mathbf{V}_n^* \rangle = n$. The map $\Phi\Psi$ is a rank-preserving automorphism, and $\mathbf{E}_{st}\Phi\Psi$ is in the form we discussed in the first place. Thus we find that

$$\mathbf{X}\Phi\Psi = \mathbf{U}_2 \mathbf{X} \mathbf{V}_2.$$

where $\mathbf{U}_2$ and $\mathbf{V}_2$ are nonsingular. But then

$$\mathbf{X}\Phi = \mathbf{X}\Phi\Psi\Psi = (\mathbf{U}_2 \mathbf{X} \mathbf{V}_2)\Psi = \mathbf{V}_2{}^t \mathbf{X}^t \mathbf{U}_2{}^t = \mathbf{U}_3 \mathbf{X}^t \mathbf{V}_3.$$

This is the exceptional case that arises when $n = m$.

There remains the case $n > m$. We proved in Exercise 7 that the map $\Psi\Phi\Psi$ is a rank-preserving automorphism of $\mathfrak{M}_{m,n}$. Hence the map $\Psi\Phi\Psi$ is an instance for which we have already proved the proposition. Thus there exists nonsingular matrices $\mathbf{A}$ and $\mathbf{B}$ such that

$$\mathbf{X}\Psi\Phi\Psi = \mathbf{A}\mathbf{X}\mathbf{B}, \qquad \text{for all } \mathbf{X} \in \mathfrak{M}_{m,n}.$$

But then

$$(\mathbf{X}\Psi)\Psi\Phi\Psi = \mathbf{A}(\mathbf{X}\Psi)\mathbf{B}, \qquad \text{for all } \mathbf{X} \in \mathfrak{M}_{n,m};$$

that is, $\mathbf{X}\Phi = [\mathbf{A}(\mathbf{X}\Psi)\mathbf{B}]\Psi = \mathbf{B}^t \mathbf{X} \mathbf{A}^t$, for all $\mathbf{X} \in \mathfrak{M}_{n,m}$. Since $\mathbf{A}^t$, and $\mathbf{B}^t$ are nonsingular, this completes the proof of the proposition.

8 SIMILARITY, CANONICAL MATRICES

Let $\mathscr{V}$ be a finitely dimensional vector space over a field $\mathscr{F}$. Let $\mathfrak{A} = \{\alpha_1, \ldots, \alpha_n\}$ and $\mathfrak{B} = \{\beta_1, \ldots \beta_n\}$ be two ordered bases of $\mathscr{V}$. We have seen that there is a mapping of $\mathscr{E}(\mathscr{V})$ onto $\mathfrak{M}_{n,n}(\mathscr{F})$ given by

$$\theta \to \mathbf{M} = (m_{ij}), \tag{11}$$

where $\alpha_i \theta = \sum_{j=1}^{n} m_{ij} \beta_j$, $(i = 1, \ldots, n)$. This mapping is bijective and preserves addition and scalar multiplication. Consequently this map is an isomorphism of the vector space $\mathscr{E}(\mathscr{V})$ onto the vector spaces $\mathfrak{M}_{n,n}(\mathscr{F})$.

Now $\mathscr{E}(\mathscr{V})$ and $\mathfrak{M}_{n,n}(\mathscr{F})$ are also rings, and if we wish this map also to preserve ring multiplication, it is necessary to take $\mathfrak{A} = \mathfrak{B}$. If $\mathfrak{A} = \mathfrak{B}$ then the map (11) is indeed an isomorphism of the ring $\mathscr{E}(\mathscr{V})$ onto the ring $\mathfrak{M}_{n,n}(\mathscr{F})$; for if $\alpha_i\theta = \sum_{j=1}^{n} a_{ij}\alpha_j$ and $\alpha_i\varphi = \sum_{j=1}^{n} b_{ij}\alpha_j$, then

$$\alpha_i\theta\varphi = \left(\sum_{k=1}^{n} a_{ik}\alpha_k\right)\varphi = \sum_{k=1}^{n} a_{ik}\sum_{j=1}^{n} b_{kj}\alpha_j = \sum_{j=1}^{n}\left(\sum_{k=1}^{n} a_{il}\,b_{kj}\right)\alpha_j,$$

and hence
$$\theta\varphi \rightarrow \left(\sum_{k=1}^{n} a_{ik}b_{kj}\right) = (a_{ij})(b_{ij}).$$

If λ is the isomorphism of V onto $\mathscr{F}^{(n)}$ such that $\alpha_i\lambda = \mathbf{e}_i$, $(i = 1, \ldots, n)$, then

$$\theta = \lambda\mathbf{M}\lambda^{-1}. \tag{12}$$

In this case we say $\mathbf{M}$ is a *matrix ring representation of* θ.

The map

$$\theta \xrightarrow{\Lambda} \lambda\mathbf{M}\lambda^{-1}$$

has the property that $(\theta\varphi)\Lambda = (\theta\Lambda)(\varphi\Lambda)$, $(\theta a)\Lambda = (\theta\Lambda)a$, $(\theta + \varphi)\Lambda = \theta\Lambda + \varphi\Lambda$. Thus Λ is an isomorphism of the algebra $\mathscr{E}(\mathscr{V})$ onto $\mathfrak{M}_{n,n}$. Since λ is of rank n, Λ is a rank-preserving map.

If G is a nonzero alternating linear form of order n on $\mathscr{F}^{(n)}$, then

$$(\beta_1, \ldots, \beta_n)F = (\beta_1\lambda, \ldots, \beta_n\lambda)G$$

is clearly a nonzero alternating linear form on $\mathscr{V}$. If $\theta \in \mathscr{E}(\mathscr{V})$, we have defined the determinant of θ to be a field element $\Delta(\theta)$ such that

$$(\beta_1\theta, \ldots, \beta_n\theta)F = (\beta_1, \ldots, \beta_n)F \cdot \Delta(\theta).$$

Now let $(\gamma_1, \ldots, \gamma_n)G = \det \mathbf{C}$, where the ith row of the matrix $\mathbf{C}$ is γ_i, $(i = 1, \ldots, n)$. Then G is a nonzero alternating form on $\mathscr{F}^{(n)}$. We have

$$\begin{aligned}(\alpha_1, \ldots, \alpha_n)F\Delta(\theta) &= (\alpha_1\theta, \ldots, \alpha_n\theta)F\\ &= (\alpha_1\theta\lambda, \ldots, \alpha_n\theta\lambda)G.\end{aligned}$$

It follows from (12) that

$$\begin{aligned}(\alpha_1, \ldots, \alpha_n)F\Delta\theta = (\alpha_1\lambda\mathbf{M}, \ldots, \alpha_n\lambda\mathbf{M})G &= (\mathbf{e}_1\mathbf{M}, \ldots, \mathbf{e}_n\mathbf{M})G\\ &= \det \mathbf{M}.\end{aligned}$$

But $(\alpha_1, \ldots, \alpha_n)F = (\alpha_1\lambda, \ldots, \alpha_n\lambda)G = (\mathbf{e}_1, \ldots, \mathbf{e}_n)G = 1$. Hence we have

PROPOSITION 72 *If λ is a bijective linear transformation of a vector space $\mathscr{V}$ over $\mathscr{F}$ onto $\mathscr{F}^{(n)}$ and $\theta = \lambda\mathbf{M}\lambda^{-1} \in \mathscr{E}(\mathscr{V})$, then det θ = det* $\mathbf{M}$.

We shall say that two n by n matrices $\mathbf{A}$ and $\mathbf{B}$ over a field $\mathscr{F}$ are *similar* provided they are both matrix ring representations of the same $\theta \in \mathscr{E}(\mathscr{V})$, where $\mathscr{V}$ is some n-dimensional space over $\mathscr{F}$. Suppose Λ and

Γ are isomorphisms of the algebra $\mathscr{E}(\mathscr{V})$ onto $\mathfrak{M}_{n,n}$ such that $\theta\Lambda = \mathbf{A}$ and $\theta\Gamma = \mathbf{B}$. By Proposition 68, Λ and Γ are rank-preserving maps. Hence similar matrices have the same rank. Proposition 72 tells us that similar matrices have the same determinant. However, as we shall see, the converse of neither of these statements is valid; i.e., two matrices with the same rank and determinant need not be similar.

The map

$$\mathbf{X} \xrightarrow{\Phi} \mathbf{X}\Lambda^{-1}\Gamma$$

of $\mathfrak{M}_{n,n}$ into itself is a rank-preserving automorphism of the algebra $\mathfrak{M}_{n,n}$, which carries $\mathbf{A}$ into $\mathbf{B}$. Now suppose Ψ is a rank-preserving automorphism of the algebra $\mathfrak{M}_{n,n}$ such that $\mathbf{A}\Psi = \mathbf{B}$. Let Υ denote the identity map on $\mathfrak{M}_{n,n}$; then Υ is a rank-preserving automorphism of the algebra $\mathfrak{M}_{n,n}$ and $\mathbf{A}\Upsilon = \mathbf{A}$. Then $\mathbf{A}$ and $\mathbf{B}$ are matrix ring representations of the same linear transformation, namely, $\mathbf{A} \in \mathscr{E}(\mathscr{F}^{(n)}) = \mathfrak{M}_{n,n}$, and hence $\mathbf{A}$ and $\mathbf{B}$ are similar. We have proved

ROPOSITION 73 *Two matrices,* $\mathbf{A}, \mathbf{B} \in \mathfrak{M}_{n,n}(\mathscr{F})$ *are similar if and only if there is a rank-preserving automorphism* Φ *of the algebra* $\mathfrak{M}_{n,n}$ *for which* $\mathbf{A}\Phi = \mathbf{B}$.

It is easily checked that being similar is an equivalence relation on the algebra $\mathfrak{M}_{n,n}(\mathscr{F})$. Obviously, if two square matrices are similar, they are equivalent. Thus on the ring of square matrices, a similarity class is a subset of an equivalence class. We now prove several results for similarity that are analogous to our results for equivalence of matrices.

OPOSITION 74 Φ *is a rank-preserving automorphism of the algebra* $\mathfrak{M}_{n,n}(\mathscr{F})$ *if and only if there is a nonsingular matrix* $\mathbf{U}$ *such that* $\mathbf{X}\Phi = \mathbf{U}\mathbf{X}\mathbf{U}^{-1}$.

PROOF. Suppose $\mathbf{U}$ is a nonsingular matrix. The map $\mathbf{X}\Phi = \mathbf{U}\mathbf{X}\mathbf{U}^{-1}$ of $\mathfrak{M}_{n,n}(\mathscr{F})$ into itself is clearly such that $(\mathbf{X}+\mathbf{Y})\Phi = \mathbf{X}\Phi + \mathbf{Y}\Phi, (a\mathbf{X})\Phi = a(\mathbf{X}\Phi)$, $(\mathbf{X}\mathbf{Y})\Phi = (\mathbf{X}\Phi)(\mathbf{Y}\Phi)$, $(\mathbf{U}^{-1}\mathbf{X}\mathbf{U})\Phi = \mathbf{X}$ for all $\mathbf{X}, \mathbf{Y} \in \mathfrak{M}_{n,n}$. Since $\mathbf{U}$ is nonsingular, rank $\mathbf{X}$ = rank $\mathbf{U}\mathbf{X}\mathbf{U}^{-1}$ = rank $\mathbf{X}\Phi$. Finally, we note that, if $\mathbf{X}\Phi = \mathbf{Y}\Phi$, then $\mathbf{U}(\mathbf{X}-\mathbf{Y})\mathbf{U}^{-1} = \mathbf{O}$, and hence $\mathbf{X}-\mathbf{Y} = \mathbf{U}^{-1}\mathbf{O}\mathbf{U} = \mathbf{O}$. Thus we have shown that the map Φ preserves operations, preserves rank, and is bijective; i.e., Φ is a rank-preserving automorphism of $\mathfrak{M}_{n,n}$.

A rank-preserving automorphism Φ of the algebra $\mathfrak{M}_{n,n}$ is automatically a rank-preserving automorphism of the vector space $\mathfrak{M}_{n,n}$. Hence by Theorem 1 we see that either $\mathbf{X}\Phi = \mathbf{U}\mathbf{X}\mathbf{V}$ or $\mathbf{X}\Phi = \mathbf{U}\mathbf{X}'\mathbf{V}$, where $\mathbf{U}$ and $\mathbf{V}$ are nonsingular matrices. Since $\mathbf{X}\Phi = (\mathbf{X}\mathbf{I})\Phi = (\mathbf{X}\Phi)(\mathbf{I}\Phi)$ for all $\mathbf{X} \in \mathfrak{M}_{n,n}$ and since Φ is rank-preserving, we see that, when $\mathbf{X}$ is nonsingular, we must have

$$\mathbf{I} = (\mathbf{X}\Phi)^{-1}(\mathbf{X}\Phi)(\mathbf{I}\Phi) = \mathbf{I}\Phi.$$

Hence $\mathbf{I} = \mathbf{I}\Phi = \mathbf{U}\mathbf{V}$, and $\mathbf{V} = \mathbf{U}^{-1}$.

If $\mathbf{X}\Phi = \mathbf{U}\mathbf{X}^t\mathbf{U}^{-1}$, then

$$\mathbf{U}\mathbf{Y}^t\mathbf{X}^t\mathbf{U}^{-1} = \mathbf{U}(\mathbf{X}\mathbf{Y})^t\mathbf{U}^{-1} = (\mathbf{X}\mathbf{Y})\Phi = (\mathbf{X}\Phi)(\mathbf{Y}\Phi) = \mathbf{U}\mathbf{X}^t\mathbf{Y}^t\mathbf{U}^{-1},$$

for all $\mathbf{X}, \mathbf{Y} \in \mathfrak{M}_{n,n}$. Consequently we would have $\mathbf{X}^t\mathbf{Y}^t = \mathbf{Y}^t\mathbf{X}^t$ for all $\mathbf{X}, \mathbf{Y} \in \mathfrak{M}_{n,n}$. But this is false when $n \geq 2$, since $\mathbf{E}_{12}\mathbf{E}_{21} \neq \mathbf{E}_{21}\mathbf{E}_{12}$. It follows that $\mathbf{X}\Phi = \mathbf{U}\mathbf{X}\mathbf{U}^{-1}$ for some nonsingular matrix $\mathbf{U}$.

PROPOSITION 75 *Two matrices* $\mathbf{A}, \mathbf{B} \in \mathfrak{M}_{n,n}(\mathscr{F})$ *are similar if and only if there is a nonsingular* $\mathbf{U} \in \mathfrak{M}_{n,n}(\mathscr{F})$ *such that* $\mathbf{B} = \mathbf{U}\mathbf{A}\mathbf{U}^{-1}$.

PROOF. As noted in the proof of Proposition 74, the map $\mathbf{X} \to \mathbf{U}\mathbf{X}\mathbf{U}^{-1}$ is a rank-preserving automorphism of the algebra $\mathfrak{M}_{n,n}$. It follows from Proposition 73 that $\mathbf{A}$ and $\mathbf{B} = \mathbf{U}\mathbf{A}\mathbf{U}^{-1}$ are similar.

If $\mathbf{A}$ and $\mathbf{B}$ are similar, it follows from Proposition 73 that there is a rank-preserving automorphism Φ of $\mathfrak{M}_{n,n}$ such that $\mathbf{A}\Phi = \mathbf{B}$. It follows from Proposition 74 that $\mathbf{B} = \mathbf{A}\Phi = \mathbf{U}\mathbf{A}\mathbf{U}^{-1}$ for some nonsingular matrix $\mathbf{U}$.

It should be noted that Proposition 74 will not be valid if we only assume that Φ is a ring automorphism of $\mathfrak{M}_{n,n}$ and do not assume that $(a\mathbf{X})\Phi = a(\mathbf{X}\Phi)$ for all $a \in \mathscr{F}$ and $\mathbf{X} \in \mathfrak{M}_{n,n}$. The map

$$\mathbf{A} = \begin{pmatrix} a_{11} + {}_1b_1\sqrt{2} & a_{12} + b_{12}\sqrt{2} \\ a_{21} + b_{21}\sqrt{2} & a_{22} + b_{22}\sqrt{2} \end{pmatrix} \xrightarrow{\Phi}$$

$$\mathbf{B} = \begin{pmatrix} a_{11} - b_{11}\sqrt{2} & a_{12} - b_{12}\sqrt{2} \\ a_{21} - b_{21}\sqrt{2} & a_{22} - b_{22}\sqrt{2} \end{pmatrix}$$

is bijective on $\mathfrak{M}_{2,2}\,(\mathbf{Q}(\sqrt{2}))$ and is such that

$$(\mathbf{X} + \mathbf{Y})\Phi = \mathbf{X}\Phi + \mathbf{Y}\Phi, \quad (\mathbf{X}\mathbf{Y})\Phi = (\mathbf{X}\Phi)(\mathbf{Y}\Phi)$$

for all $\mathbf{X},\mathbf{Y} \in \mathfrak{M}_{2,2}$. However, there is no nonsingular matrix $\mathbf{U}$ such that $\mathbf{B} = \mathbf{U}\mathbf{A}\mathbf{U}^{-1}$.

As defined, similarity depends on the field $\mathscr{F}$, since $\mathbf{U} \in \mathfrak{M}_{n,n}(\mathscr{F})$. If $\mathbf{A}, \mathbf{B} \in \mathfrak{M}_{n,n}(\mathscr{F}) \subset \mathfrak{M}_{n,n}(\mathscr{K})$, where $\mathscr{F} \subset \mathscr{K}$, it would appear that $\mathbf{A}$ and $\mathbf{B}$ might be similar in $\mathfrak{M}_{n,n}(\mathscr{K})$ but not in $\mathfrak{M}_{n,n}(\mathscr{F})$. However if $\mathbf{B}\mathbf{U} = \mathbf{U}\mathbf{A}$, for some $\mathbf{U} \in \mathfrak{M}_{n,n}(\mathscr{K})$, then the n^2 entries u_{ij} of $\mathbf{U}$ satisfy a system of n^2 homogeneous equations with coefficients from $\mathscr{F}$. This system has a solution in $\mathscr{K}$ if and only if the matrix of coefficients is singular and if it is singular, we can already find $u_{ij} \in \mathscr{F}$ that satisfy $\mathbf{U}\mathbf{A} = \mathbf{B}\mathbf{U}$. (See the corollary to Proposition 67.) Thus we have

PROPOSITION 76 *Suppose* $\mathscr{F} \subset \mathscr{K}$. *If* $\mathbf{A}, \mathbf{B} \in \mathfrak{M}_{n,n}(\mathscr{F})$ *are similar as matrices in* $\mathfrak{M}_{n,n}(\mathscr{K})$, *then they are similar as matrices of* $\mathfrak{M}_{n,n}(\mathscr{F})$.

We shall say that $\varphi, \psi \in \mathscr{E}(\mathscr{V})$ are *similar* provided there is a nonsingular linear transformation $\chi \in \mathscr{E}(\mathscr{V})$ such that $\varphi = \chi\psi\chi^{-1}$, and we write $\varphi \simeq \psi$. The reader can easily verify

POSITION 77 *Being similar is an equivalence relation on $\mathscr{E}(\mathscr{V})$. If $\varphi, \psi \in \mathscr{E}(\mathscr{V})$ and $\varphi = \lambda \mathbf{A} \lambda^{-1}$, $\psi = \lambda \mathbf{B} \lambda^{-1}$, where $\mathbf{A}, \mathbf{B}$ are matrix ring representations of φ and ψ, then $\varphi \simeq \psi$ if and only if $\mathbf{A} \simeq \mathbf{B}$.*

When we considered the equivalence classes of matrices, we found that each class consisted of all matrices with the same height, width, and rank. These three numbers are called *invariants* of the equivalence class. We also saw that each class contained an easily identifiable matrix, namely, $\mathbf{E}_r$. Such a matrix is called a *canonical matrix* of the class. We saw in the exercises in Sec. 7 that it is often advantageous to use the canonical matrix in making certain calculations. We now seek to determine a set of invariants for similarity classes and to describe a canonical matrix in each such class. Later we shall show that such information can be useful in solving other problems.

The reader should verify

POSITION 78 *If $\mathbf{A} \simeq \mathbf{B}$, then rank $\mathbf{A}$ = rank $\mathbf{B}$ and det $\mathbf{A}$ = det $\mathbf{B}$. $\mathbf{A} \simeq \mathbf{I}$ if and only if $\mathbf{A} = \mathbf{I}$.*

It follows that $\begin{pmatrix} a & 0 \\ 0 & a^{-1} \end{pmatrix} = \mathbf{A}$, $a \neq 0$, is a matrix such that det $\mathbf{A}$ = det $\mathbf{I} = 1$, rank $\mathbf{A}$ = rank $\mathbf{I}$, and yet $\mathbf{A} \not\simeq \mathbf{I}$. Consequently, rank and determinant are invariants of a similarity class, but they do not determine a unique similarity class. Different similarity classes can have the same rank and determinant.

Given $\theta \in \mathscr{E}(\mathscr{V})$, we say that *$\mathscr{W}$ is a subspace of $\mathscr{V}$ invariant under θ*, if $\mathscr{W}\theta \subset \mathscr{W}$. Clearly $\mathscr{O}$ and $\mathscr{V}$ are invariant spaces (under θ). There are transformations $\theta \in \mathscr{E}(\mathscr{V})$ such that $\mathscr{O}$ and $\mathscr{V}$ are the only subspaces of $\mathscr{V}$ that are invariant under θ. For one such example, consider $\mathscr{V} = \mathbf{Q}^{(2)}$, $\mathbf{e}_1\theta = \mathbf{e}_2$, $\mathbf{e}_2\theta = 3\mathbf{e}_1$. A proper subspace of $\mathbf{Q}^{(2)}$ is one-dimensional. Say $\mathscr{W} = \langle \alpha \rangle$ is a proper subspace of $\mathbf{Q}^{(2)}$, which is invariant under θ; then $\alpha \neq \mathbf{0}$ and $\alpha\theta = c\alpha$, for some $c \in \mathbf{Q}$. But $\alpha = a\mathbf{e}_1 + b\mathbf{e}_2$, and so we would have

$$3b\mathbf{e}_1 + a\mathbf{e}_1 = ca\mathbf{e}_1 + cb\mathbf{e}_2;$$

whence $3b = ca$, $a = cb$, or $(3 - c^2)b = 0$. Since $c \in \mathbf{Q}$, $3 \neq c^2$ and consequently $b = 0$; but then $a = 0$ and $\alpha = \mathbf{0}$, a contradiction.

Invariant spaces will play a role here much like invariant sets and fixed points did in our study of the group Π_n.

ERCISES 1 Let $\mathscr{V} = \mathbf{Q}^{(3)}$, $\mathbf{e}_1\theta = \mathbf{e}_2$, $\mathbf{e}_2\theta = \mathbf{e}_3$, $\mathbf{e}_3\theta = 5\mathbf{e}_1$. Determine all invariant spaces of $\mathscr{V}$ under θ.

2 Prove: If $\mathscr{W}_1$, $\mathscr{W}_2$ are spaces invariant under θ, then $\mathscr{W}_1 \cap \mathscr{W}_2$ and $\mathscr{W}_1 + \mathscr{W}_2$ are invariant under θ.

If $\mathscr{V} = \mathscr{W}_1 + \mathscr{W}_2$ (direct) and $\varphi \in \mathscr{E}(\mathscr{V})$ such that $\alpha\varphi = \alpha$ for all $\alpha \in \mathscr{W}_1$ and $\mathscr{W}_2$ is the kernel of φ, then we say φ is a *projection of $\mathscr{V}$ onto $\mathscr{W}_1$ along $\mathscr{W}_2$*. The reader can prove

PROPOSITION 79 $\varphi \in \mathscr{E}(\mathscr{V})$ *is a projection if and only if* φ *is idempotent*; i.e., $\varphi^2 = \varphi$. $\varphi \in \mathscr{E}(\mathscr{V})$ *is a projection if and only if* $\iota - \varphi$ *is idempotent.*

If $\mathscr{V} = \mathscr{W}_1 + \cdots + \mathscr{W}_r$ (direct), where the $\mathscr{W}_\nu$ are invariant under θ, then $\theta = \theta_1 + \cdots + \theta_r$, where

$$\text{res}_{\mathscr{W}_\nu}\theta_\mu = \delta_{\mu\nu}\,\text{res}_{\mathscr{W}_\nu}\theta, \qquad \mu, \nu = 1, 2, \ldots, r.$$

In this case we say θ is *reduced* by the decomposition $\mathscr{V} = \mathscr{W}_1 + \cdots + \mathscr{W}_r$ (direct), and we say θ is the direct sum of $\theta_1, \ldots, \theta_r$. When θ is so reduced we shall write

$$\theta = \theta_1 + \cdots + \theta_r \text{ (direct)}.$$

When θ is such a direct sum, then θ has a matrix ring representation in the shape

$$\begin{pmatrix} \mathbf{M}_1 & \mathbf{O} & \cdots & \mathbf{O} \\ \mathbf{O} & \mathbf{M}_2 & \cdots & \mathbf{O} \\ \\ \mathbf{O} & \cdots & \mathbf{O} & \mathbf{M}_r \end{pmatrix},$$

where the $\mathbf{M}_j$ are square matrices of the appropriate size. Actually $\mathbf{M}_j$ is the matrix ring representation of the restriction of θ_j to $\mathscr{W}_j$. (*Note:* If $\theta = \theta_1 + \cdots + \theta_r$ (direct), the θ_i need not be projections.)

A linear transformation $\theta \in \mathscr{E}(\mathscr{V})$ may have a proper invariant space and yet not be reduced by any decomposition of $\mathscr{V}$. The simplest example is when $\mathscr{V}$ is $\mathscr{F}[x]$ and $\theta = \dfrac{d}{dx}$. Let $\mathscr{V}_k$ be the set of polynomials in $\mathscr{F}[x]$ of degree less than k. Then $\mathscr{V}_k$ is an invariant space for θ of dimension k. Also, every proper invariant subspace is a $\mathscr{V}_k$, for some k. Suppose $\mathscr{W}_k$ is a subspace of $\mathscr{V}$ such that $\mathscr{V} = \mathscr{V}_k + \mathscr{W}_k$ (direct). Then $\mathscr{W}_k$ must contain a polynomial of degree k, whence $\mathscr{W}_k\theta \cap \mathscr{V}_k \neq 0$. Thus $\mathscr{W}_k\theta \not\subseteq \mathscr{W}_k$; i.e., $\mathscr{W}_k$ is not invariant under θ.

EXERCISES 3 Prove: If a subspace $\mathscr{W}$ of a finitely dimensional space $\mathscr{V}$ is invariant under θ, then $\varphi\theta = \varphi\theta\varphi$ for every projection φ of $\mathscr{V}$ onto $\mathscr{W}$.

4 Prove: A necessary and sufficient condition that a linear transformation $\theta \in \mathscr{E}(\mathscr{V})$ be reduced by the decomposition $\mathscr{V} = \mathscr{W}_1 + \mathscr{W}_2$ (direct) is that $\varphi\theta = \theta\varphi$, where φ is the projection of $\mathscr{V}$ on $\mathscr{W}_1$ along $\mathscr{W}_2$.

If $\mathbf{0} \neq \alpha \in \mathscr{V}$ is such that $\langle\alpha\rangle$ is invariant under θ, we call α an *eigenvector* of θ.† If α is an eigenvector of θ, then there is a unique scalar c, depending on α and θ, so that

$$\alpha\theta = c\alpha.$$

† Note that the **0** vector is never an eigenvector.

This c is called the *eigenvalue* of θ associated with the eigenvector α. If c is an eigenvalue of θ, then there is a nonzero $\alpha \in \mathscr{V}$ such that $\alpha\theta = c\alpha$. If α is an eigenvector and $a \neq 0$, then $a\alpha$ is an eigenvector of θ having associated with it the same eigenvalue as did α. We put

$$\mathscr{W}(c, \theta) = \{\alpha \in \mathscr{V} \mid \alpha\theta = c\alpha\}.$$

$\mathscr{W}(c, \theta) \neq 0$ if and only if c is an eigenvalue of θ. The reader can prove

OSITION 80 *If $\theta \in \mathscr{E}(\mathscr{V})$, then, for each $c \in \mathscr{F}$, the set $\mathscr{W}(c, \theta)$ is a subspace of $\mathscr{V}$, invariant under θ.*

The set of all eigenvalues of θ is called the *spectrum of* θ. We denote this set by Sp (θ). Since $\mathscr{V}(0, \theta)$ is the kernel of θ, $0 \in$ Sp (θ) if and only if θ is a singular transformation.

ERCISES 5 A. If $\mathscr{V} = \mathscr{F}[x]$, $\theta = d/dx$, determine Sp (θ).

B. If $\mathscr{V} = \mathscr{F}^{(n)}$, and θ is a diagonal matrix, determine Sp (θ).

C. What is the spectrum of the identity map?

D. What is the spectrum of the O map?

E. If $\mathscr{V}$ is of finite dimension, with basis $\{\alpha_1, \ldots, \alpha_n\}$, determine the spectrum of the transformations θ_{ij}, where $\alpha_s\theta_{ij} = \delta_{si}\alpha_j$?

6 For each example in Exercise 5, determine the spaces $\mathscr{W}(c, \theta)$ for $c \in$ Sp (θ).

OSITION 81 *Let τ be an isomorphism of a vector space $\mathscr{V}|\mathscr{F}$ onto a vector space $\mathscr{V}'|\mathscr{F}$. If $\theta \in \mathscr{E}(\mathscr{V})$, then $\tau^{-1}\theta\tau \in \mathscr{E}(\mathscr{V}')$, and*

$$\text{Sp}\,(\theta) = \text{Sp}\,(\tau^{-1}\theta\tau).$$

PROOF. If $\alpha\theta = c\alpha$, then $(\alpha\tau)(\tau^{-1}\theta\tau) = \alpha\theta\tau = (c\alpha)\tau = c(\alpha\tau)$. Hence Sp $(\tau^{-1}\theta\tau) \supset$ Sp (θ). But then Sp $(\theta) =$ Sp $(\tau(\tau^{-1}\theta\tau)\tau^{-1}) \supset$ Sp $(\tau^{-1}\theta\tau)$; whence Sp $(\theta) =$ Sp $(\tau^{-1}\theta\tau)$.

OROLLARY 1 *If $\theta, \varphi \in \mathscr{E}(\mathscr{V})$ are similar, then* Sp $(\theta) =$ Sp (φ).

Thus the spectrum is an additional similarity class invariant. Note that $\mathbf{I}$ and $\begin{pmatrix} a & 0 \\ 0 & a^{-1} \end{pmatrix}$ have different spectrums. Thus the spectrum does differentiate between some similarity classes that have the same rank and determinant. However, the spectrum in itself will not be sufficient to distinguish similarity classes; e.g., $\begin{pmatrix} 1 & 0 \\ 0 & 1 \end{pmatrix}$ and $\begin{pmatrix} 1 & 1 \\ 0 & 1 \end{pmatrix}$ have the same spectrum but are not similar.

OROLLARY 2 *If $\mathbf{M}$ is a matrix ring representation of $\theta \in \mathscr{E}(\mathscr{V})$, then* Sp $(\theta) =$ Sp $(\mathbf{M})$.

The proof follows from Proposition 81 and Eq. 12.

PROPOSITION 82 A. *$c \in \text{Sp}(\theta)$ if and only if $\iota c - \theta$ is a singular transformation.*
B. *If A is a polynomial over $\mathcal{F}$ and $c \in \text{Sp}(\theta)$, then $A(c) \in \text{Sp}(A(\theta))$.*†
C. *If θ is nonsingular, then $\text{Sp}(\theta^{-1})$ is exactly the set of reciprocals of elements in $\text{Sp}(\theta)$.*

The proof is left to the reader.

Now suppose $\dim \mathcal{V} = n < \infty$. By Proposition 82, $c \in \text{Sp}(\theta)$ if and only if $\iota c - \theta$ is singular. By Proposition 52, $\iota c - \theta$ is singular exactly when $\det(\iota c - \theta) = 0$. If $\theta \to \mathbf{M}(\theta)$ is a matrix representation of $\mathcal{E}(\mathcal{V})$ onto $\mathfrak{M}_{n,n}$, then $\iota \to \mathbf{I}$ and $\iota c - \theta \to \mathbf{I}c - \mathbf{M}$. It follows from Proposition 72 that $\det(\iota c - \theta) = 0$ exactly when $\det(\mathbf{I}c - \mathbf{M}) = 0$. Let x be an indeterminate over $\mathcal{F}$; then $\det(\mathbf{I}x - \mathbf{M})$ is a monic polynomial of degree n in x. Thus we obtain

PROPOSITION 83 *If $\mathcal{V}$ is of finite dimension and if $\theta \to \mathbf{M}$ is a matrix representation of $\mathcal{E}(\mathcal{V})$ onto $\mathfrak{M}_{n,n}$, then $c \in \text{Sp}(\theta)$ if and only if c is a zero of the polynomial $\det(\mathbf{I}x - \mathbf{M})$.*

The polynomial $\det(\mathbf{I}x - \mathbf{M})$ is independent of the matrix ring representation $\mathbf{M}$ and depends on θ alone, since $\det(\mathbf{I}x - \mathbf{UMU}^{-1}) = \det(\mathbf{U}(\mathbf{I}x - \mathbf{M})\mathbf{U}^{-1}) = (\det \mathbf{U})\cdot\det(\mathbf{I}x - \mathbf{M})\cdot(\det \mathbf{U})^{-1} = \det(\mathbf{I}x - \mathbf{M})$. This polynomial is called the *characteristic polynomial of* θ and will be denoted by Γ_θ. As we saw in Chap. 4, Γ_θ has at most $n = \deg \Gamma_\theta$ zeros in $\mathcal{F}$, and hence

COROLLARY *If $\mathcal{V}$ is of finite dimension, then $|\text{Sp}(\theta)| \le \dim \mathcal{V}$.*

We note that the eigenvalues lie in the field $\mathcal{F}$. If $\mathcal{F}$ is not algebraically closed, it is possible that the characteristic polynomial has no zeros in $\mathcal{F}$ and so the spectrum can be empty. The following would be such an example. Let $\mathcal{V} = \mathbf{R}^{(2)}$, and let $\theta = \begin{pmatrix} 1 & -2 \\ 3 & 1 \end{pmatrix}$; then $\Gamma_\theta = (x-1)^2 + 6$, which has no zeros in $\mathbf{R}$.

EXERCISES 7 A. Prove: If $\mathbf{A}$ is a square matrix, then $\text{Sp}(\mathbf{A}) = \text{Sp}(\mathbf{A}^t)$.
B. Prove: If $\mathbf{A}$ is a triangular matrix, then $\text{Sp}(\mathbf{A}) = \{$the distinct elements on the diagonal of $\mathbf{A}\}$.

8 Determine the eigenvalues of:

$$\begin{pmatrix} a & b \\ c & d \end{pmatrix}, \quad \begin{pmatrix} 1 & 1 & 0 \\ 1 & 1 & 1 \\ 0 & 0 & 1 \end{pmatrix}, \quad \begin{pmatrix} 1 & 1 & 0 \\ 0 & 1 & 0 \\ 0 & 1 & 2 \end{pmatrix}.$$

9 Give examples to show that matrices with the same spectrum need not be similar.

† If $A = a_0x + \cdots + a_nx^n \in \mathcal{F}[x]$, $\theta \in \mathcal{E}(\mathcal{V})$, we define $A(\theta) = a_0\iota + \cdots + a_n\theta^n$.

POSITION 84 *If $c_1, \ldots, c_k$ are distinct elements of* Sp (θ), *then*

$$\mathscr{W} = \langle \mathscr{W}(c_1, \theta), \ldots, \mathscr{W}(c_k, \theta)\rangle = \mathscr{W}(c_1, \theta) + \cdots + \mathscr{W}(c_k, \theta) \text{ (direct)}.$$

PROOF. If $\delta \in \mathscr{W}$, then $\delta = \sum_{j=1}^{k} \delta_j$, where $\delta_j \in \mathscr{W}_j$. As with groups we show that the sum is direct by showing that $\sum_{j=1}^{k} \delta_j = \mathbf{0}$ if and only if each $\delta_j = \mathbf{0}$. The proof will be by induction on k. The conclusion holds trivially if $k = 1$. Suppose the proposition is true for sets of less than k eigenvalues. Suppose $\sum_{j=1}^{k} \delta_j = \mathbf{0}$. If some $\delta_j \neq \mathbf{0}$, we can, after relabeling, assume $\delta_k \neq \mathbf{0}$. Then $-\delta_k = \sum_{j=1}^{k-1} \delta_j$. But $\delta_j\theta = c_j\delta_j$, $\quad (j = 1, \ldots, k)$

and hence $\quad \mathbf{0} = -\delta_k(\theta - \iota c_k) = \sum_{j=1}^{k-1} \delta_j(\theta - \iota c_k) = \sum_{j=1}^{k-1} (c_j - c_k)\delta_j.$

By the induction hypothesis,

$$\langle \mathscr{W}(c_1, \theta), \ldots, \mathscr{W}(c_{k-1}, \theta)\rangle = \mathscr{W}(c_1, \theta) + \cdots + \mathscr{W}(c_{k-1}, \theta) \text{ (direct)}.$$

Hence $\qquad (c_j - c_k)\delta_j = \mathbf{0}, \qquad j = 1, \ldots, k-1.$

But $c_j \neq c_k$, and so

$$\delta_j = \mathbf{0}, \qquad j = 1, \ldots, k-1,$$

and therefore $\delta_k = \mathbf{0}$, This completes the proof of Proposition 84.

The reader should prove

COROLLARY *If* $|\text{Sp}\,\theta| = \dim \mathscr{V}$, *then* $\mathscr{V} = \mathscr{W}(c_1, \theta) + \cdots + \mathscr{W}(c_n, \theta)$ (direct) *and* θ *has a matrix ring representation that is diagonal.*

ERCISE 10 Give examples of diagonal matrices for which $|\text{Sp}\,(\theta)| \neq \dim \mathscr{V}$.

POSITION 85 *If dim* $\mathscr{V} = n < \infty$, $\theta \in \mathscr{E}(\mathscr{V})$ *and* $(x - c)^m | \Gamma_\theta$ *but* $(x - c)^{m+1} \nmid \Gamma_\theta$, *then dim* $\mathscr{W}(c, \theta) \leq m$.

PROOF. Let $\alpha_1, \ldots, \alpha_r$ be a basis of $\mathscr{W}(c, \theta)$. Then there are $\alpha_{r+1}, \ldots, \alpha_n \in \mathscr{V}$ such that $\{\alpha_1, \ldots, \alpha_n\}$ is a basis of $\mathscr{V}$. Let λ be the isomorphism of $\mathscr{V}$ into $\mathscr{F}^{(n)}$ such that $\alpha_i\lambda = \mathbf{e}_i$, $(i = 1, \ldots, n)$. We have $\theta = \lambda\mathbf{M}\lambda^{-1}$, where $\mathbf{M} = \begin{pmatrix} c\mathbf{I}_r & \mathbf{O} \\ \mathbf{S} & \mathbf{T} \end{pmatrix}$, $\mathbf{I}_r$ is an r by r diagonal matrix with 1's on the diagonal, $\mathbf{S}$ is an n-r by r matrix, and $\mathbf{T}$ is a n-r by n-r matrix. Then

$$\Gamma_\theta = \det(\mathbf{I}_r x - c\mathbf{I}_r) \det(\mathbf{I}_{n-r}x - \mathbf{T}) = (x - c)^r P(x),$$

and hence $r \leq m$.

The inequality $\dim \mathscr{W}(c, \theta) \leq m$ in Proposition 85 is necessary. For let $\mathscr{V}$ be the set of polynomials over $\mathscr{F}$ of degree at most $n - 1$. Then $\mathscr{V}$ is of dimension n and $1, x, \ldots, x^{n-1}$ is a basis for $\mathscr{V}$. Let θ be the derivative.

Then $\mathbf{M}(\theta) = \begin{pmatrix} 0 & 0 & & \cdots & 0 \\ 1 & 0 & & & 0 \\ \vdots & & & & \vdots \\ 0 & \cdots & 0 & n-1 & 0 \end{pmatrix}$ and $\Gamma_\theta = x^n$; yet $\mathscr{W}(0;\theta) = \langle 1 \rangle$.

If we need to distinguish between the multiplicity of the several zeros of Γ_θ, we shall denote the multiplicity of c by $m(c)$.

The reader should prove

LEMMA 1 *If $\mathscr{V}$ is a vector space over $\mathscr{F}$ and $\mathscr{W}$ is a subspace of $\mathscr{V}$, then the collection $\mathscr{V} - \mathscr{W}$ of cosets $\{\alpha + \mathscr{W}\}$ of $\mathscr{V}$ modulo $\mathscr{W}$ is a vector space over $\mathscr{F}$, and $\dim(\mathscr{V} - \mathscr{W}) = \dim \mathscr{V} - \dim \mathscr{W}$.*

If $\mathscr{W}$ is an invariant subspace relative to $\theta \in \mathscr{E}(\mathscr{V})$, then θ induces a linear transformation θ^* of $\mathscr{V} - \mathscr{W}$ into itself; namely,

$$(\alpha + \mathscr{W})\theta^* = \alpha\theta + \mathscr{W} = (\alpha + \mathscr{W})\theta.$$

The reader should verify that θ^* is indeed a linear transformation.

If $\{\beta_{n-m+1}, \ldots, \beta_n\}$ is a basis of $\mathscr{W}$, choose $\{\beta_1, \ldots, \beta_{n-m}\}$ such that $\{\beta_1, \ldots, \beta_n\}$ is a basis of $\mathscr{V}$. Then $\{\beta_1 + \mathscr{W}, \ldots, \beta_{n-m} + \mathscr{W}\}$ is a basis of $\mathscr{V} - \mathscr{W}$. Conversely, if $\{\alpha_1 + \mathscr{W}, \ldots, \alpha_{n-m} + \mathscr{W}\}$ is a basis of $\mathscr{V} - \mathscr{W}$, then $\{\alpha_1, \ldots, \alpha_{n-m}, \beta_{n-m+1}, \ldots, \beta_n\}$ is a basis of $\mathscr{V}$. On choosing a basis for $\mathscr{W}$ and for $\mathscr{V} - \mathscr{W}$, we obtain the following relation between the matrix ring representations of θ, θ^*, and $\operatorname{res}_{\mathscr{W}} \theta$:

$$\mathbf{M}(\theta) = \begin{pmatrix} \mathbf{M}(\theta^*) & \mathbf{A} \\ \mathbf{O} & \mathbf{M}(\operatorname{res}_{\mathscr{W}} \theta) \end{pmatrix}.$$

Thus we have

LEMMA 2 *If $\mathscr{W}$ is an invariant subspace of $\mathscr{V}$ relative to $\theta \in \mathscr{E}(\mathscr{V})$ and if $(\alpha + \mathscr{W})\theta^* = \alpha\theta + \mathscr{W}$ is the linear transformation on $\mathscr{V} - \mathscr{W}$ induced by θ, then*

$$\Gamma_\theta = \Gamma_{\theta^*}\Gamma_{res_{\mathscr{W}}\theta}.$$

PROPOSITION 86 *If $\mathscr{V}$ is a finite dimensional space over an algebraically closed field $\mathscr{F}$, then each $\theta \in \mathscr{E}(\mathscr{V})$ has a matrix representation* **M** *that is upper triangular. An element c appears as often on the diagonal of* **M** *as $x - c$ appears as a factor of Γ_θ.*

PROOF. Let $m(c) = \max\{m \in \mathbf{Z} \mid (x-c)^m \mid \Gamma_\theta\}$. The proof will be by induction on the dimension of $\mathscr{V}$. If $\dim \mathscr{V} = 1$, say $\mathscr{V} = \langle \alpha_1 \rangle$, then $\alpha_1\theta = c\alpha_1$; hence $\mathbf{M}(\theta) = (c)$ and $\Gamma_\theta = x - c$. Hence the proposition is true for spaces of dimension 1.

Suppose the proposition is true for vector spaces of dimension less than $n = \dim \mathscr{V}$. Since $\mathscr{F}$ is algebraically closed, Γ_θ has a zero, say c, in $\mathscr{F}$, and there is a nonzero vector $\alpha_n \in \mathscr{V}$ so that $\alpha_n\theta = c\alpha_n$. Let $\mathscr{W} = \langle \alpha_n \rangle$; then $\mathscr{W}$ is a subspace of $\mathscr{V}$ invariant relative to θ, $\Gamma_{\operatorname{res}_{\mathscr{W}}\theta} =$

$x - c$, and $\mathscr{V} - \mathscr{W}$ is a vector space of dimension $n - 1 < \dim \mathscr{V}$. Let $\{\alpha_1 + \mathscr{W}, \ldots, \alpha_{n-1} + \mathscr{W}\}$ be a basis of $\mathscr{V} - \mathscr{W}$. Then the matrix ring representation of θ relative to the basis $\alpha_1, \ldots, \alpha_n$ is

$$\mathbf{M}(\theta) = \begin{pmatrix} \mathbf{M}(\theta^*) & \mathbf{A} \\ \mathbf{O} & c \end{pmatrix},$$

where $\mathbf{M}(\theta^*)$ is the matrix ring representation of θ^* relative to the basis $\{\alpha_1 + \mathscr{W}, \ldots, \alpha_{n-1} + \mathscr{W}\}$. It follows from the induction hypothesis that there is a basis of $\mathscr{V} - \mathscr{W}$ such that $\mathbf{M}(\theta^*)$ is upper triangular, but then $\mathbf{M}(\theta)$ is upper triangular. Since $\mathbf{M}(\theta)$ is triangular, the elements on the diagonal of $\mathbf{M}(\theta)$ must be as specified. This completes the proof of the proposition.

The reader should show that $\begin{pmatrix} 1 & 0 & 0 \\ 0 & 2 & 1 \\ 0 & 0 & 3 \end{pmatrix}$ and $\begin{pmatrix} 1 & 2 & 2 \\ 0 & 2 & 1 \\ 0 & 0 & 3 \end{pmatrix}$ are similar over any field. Thus similar classes of matrices over algebraically closed fields always contain upper triangular matrices, but each class may contain many such matrices. Consequently upper triangular matrices are not canonical matrices for the similarity classes.

XERCISE 11 Show that the assumption of algebraic closure is needed in Proposition 86 by showing that $\begin{pmatrix} 1 & 1 \\ 2 & 3 \end{pmatrix}$ is not equivalent to an upper triangular matrix over $\mathbf{Q}$.

9 MINIMAL POLYNOMIAL OF A LINEAR TRANSFORMATION

To obtain better results, we need to introduce some additional concepts. If $\theta \in \mathscr{E}(\mathscr{V})$ and $B = b_0 + b_1 x + \cdots + b_q x^q \in \mathscr{F}[x]$, we let

$$B(\theta) = b_0 \iota + b_1 \theta + \cdots + b_q \theta^q \in \mathscr{E}(\mathscr{V}).$$

OSITION 87 *The map $B \to B(\theta)$ is a ring homomorphism of $\mathscr{F}[x]$ into $\mathscr{E}(\mathscr{V})$ with $a \to \iota a$, for $a \in \mathscr{F}$.*

The proof is left for the reader.

Suppose $\mathscr{V}$ is of finite dimension over $\mathscr{F}$. If $\dim \mathscr{V} = n$, then $\mathscr{E}(\mathscr{V})$ is of dimension n^2. It follows that $\{\iota, \theta, \ldots, \theta^{n^2}\}$ is a linearly dependent set. Consequently, there are a_v, not all 0, so that

$$a_0 \iota + \cdots + a_{n^2} \theta^{n^2} = O.$$

Put
$$\mathscr{I}_\theta = \{A \in \mathscr{F}[x] \mid A(\theta) = O\}.$$

We have just seen that $\mathscr{I}_\theta$ contains nonzero polynomials. Since $\mathscr{I}_\theta$ is the kernel of a ring homomorphism, $\mathscr{I}_\theta$ is an ideal in $\mathscr{F}[x]$, and so by

Proposition 44, Chap. 4, $\mathcal{I}_\theta$ is a principal ideal generated by a unique monic polynomial P_θ. No nonzero polynomial of degree less than P_θ vanishes at θ. For this reason P_θ is called the *minimal polynomial of* θ. The minimal polynomial of θ need not be irreducible; e.g., x^2 is the minimal polynomial for $\begin{pmatrix} 0 & 0 \\ 1 & 0 \end{pmatrix}$.

Given $\theta \in \mathscr{E}(\mathscr{V})$ and a subspace $\mathscr{W}$ of $\mathscr{V}$, put

$$\mathcal{I}_{\mathscr{W},\theta} = \{A \in \mathscr{F}[x] \mid \mathscr{W}A(\theta) = \mathscr{O}\}.$$

Again, the reader can verify that $\mathcal{I}_{\mathscr{W},\theta}$ is an ideal in $\mathscr{F}[x]$ and hence is generated by a monic polynomial that we denote by $P_{\mathscr{W},\theta}$. The reader should prove

PROPOSITION 88 *Let $\theta \in \mathscr{E}(\mathscr{V})$, where $\mathscr{V}$ is finite dimensional, then:*

A. $P_{\mathscr{W},\theta} = 1$ *if and only if* $\mathscr{W} = \mathscr{O}$.

B. $P_{\mathscr{V},\theta} = P_\theta$.

C. If $\mathscr{W}_1 \subset \mathscr{W}$, *then* $P_{\mathscr{W}_1,\theta}$ *is a divisor of* $P_{\mathscr{W},\theta}$.

D. $P_{\mathscr{W}_1+\mathscr{W}_2,\theta}$ *is the least common multiple of* $P_{\mathscr{W}_1,\theta}$ *and* $P_{\mathscr{W}_2,\theta}$.

E. *If* $\mathscr{W}_1$ *is a subspace of* $\mathscr{V}$ *and* θ_1 *is the restriction of* θ *to* $\mathscr{W}_1$, *then* $P_{\mathscr{W}_1,\theta_1} = P_{\mathscr{W}_1,\theta}$.

F. *If* $\theta \simeq \varphi$, *then* $P_\theta = P_\varphi$.

COROLLARY 1 *If $\mathscr{W}$ is a subspace of $\mathscr{V}$, then $P_{\mathscr{W},\theta}$ is a divisor of P_θ.*

COROLLARY 2 *$P_{\mathscr{W}_1 \cap \mathscr{W}_2,\theta}$ is a divisor of the greatest common divisor of $P_{\mathscr{W}_1,\theta}$ and $P_{\mathscr{W}_2,\theta}$.*

When speaking of $P_{\langle\alpha\rangle,\theta}$, we shall simplify the notation by writing $P_{\alpha,\theta}$.

COROLLARY 3 *If $\{\alpha_1, \ldots, \alpha_q\}$ is a basis of $\mathscr{W}$, then $P_{\mathscr{W},\theta}$ is the least common multiple of $P_{\alpha_1,\theta}, \ldots, P_{\alpha_q,\theta}$.*

COROLLARY 4 *If $\mathscr{W}_1$, $\mathscr{W}_2$ are subspaces of $\mathscr{V}$ such that $(P_{\mathscr{W}_1,\theta}, P_{\mathscr{W}_2,\theta}) = 1$, then $\mathscr{W}_1 \cap \mathscr{W}_2 = \mathscr{O}$ and $P_{\mathscr{W}_1+\mathscr{W}_2,\theta} = P_{\mathscr{W}_1,\theta} P_{\mathscr{W}_2,\theta}$*

LEMMA 1 *If G is a monic divisor of $P_{\alpha,\theta}$, then there is a $\beta \in \mathscr{V}$ such that $G = P_{\beta,\theta}$.*

PROOF. *Say* $GH = P_{\alpha,\theta}$. *Put* $\beta = \alpha H(\theta)$. *Then* $\beta G(\theta) = \alpha H(\theta)G(\theta) = \alpha P_{\alpha,\theta}(\theta) = \mathbf{0}$. Hence $P_{\beta,\theta} \mid G$. But $\mathbf{0} = \beta P_{\beta,\theta}(\theta) = \alpha H(\theta)P_{\beta,\theta}(\theta)$, and hence $P_{\alpha,\theta}$ divides $HP_{\beta,\theta}$, whence $G \mid P_{\beta,\theta}$. Since G and $P_{\beta,\theta}$ are both monic, it follows that $G = P_{\beta,\theta}$.

LEMMA 2 *Let Q be an irreducible factor in $\mathscr{F}[x]$ of P_θ. If $P_\theta = Q^m J$, where $(Q, J) = 1$, then there is a $\gamma \in \mathscr{V}$ such that $P_{\gamma,\theta} = Q^m$.*

PROOF. Let $\{\alpha_1, \ldots, \alpha_n\}$ be a basis of $\mathscr{V}$; then $P_{\alpha_i,\theta} = Q^{m_i} J_i$, where $(Q, J_i) = 1$. By Corollary 3, $m = \max\{m_1, \ldots, m_n\}$, say $m = m_j$. We apply Lemma 1 with $G = Q^m$, and $\alpha = \alpha_j$ to obtain the conclusion.

LEMMA 3 *If $(P_{\alpha,\theta}, P_{\beta,\theta}) = 1$, then $P_{\alpha+\beta,\theta} = P_{\alpha,\theta} P_{\beta,\theta}$.*

PROOF. Since $(\alpha+\beta)P_{\alpha,\theta}(\theta)P_{\beta,\theta}(\theta) = \alpha P_{\alpha,\theta}(\theta)P_{\beta,\theta}(\theta) + \beta P_{\alpha,\theta}(\theta)P_{\beta,\theta}(\theta) = \alpha P_{\alpha,\theta}(\theta)P_{\beta,\theta}(\theta) + \beta P_{\beta,\theta}(\theta)P_{\alpha,\theta}(\theta) = \mathbf{0}$, we have $P_{\alpha+\beta,\theta}|P_{\alpha,\theta}P_{\beta,\theta}$. But $\alpha = (\alpha+\beta)+(-\beta)$. Hence

$$\alpha P_{\alpha+\beta,\theta}(\theta)P_{\beta,\theta}(\theta) = \mathbf{0},$$

and so $P_{\alpha,\theta}|P_{\alpha+\beta,\theta}P_{\beta,\theta}$. But $(P_{\alpha,\theta}, P_{\beta,\theta}) = 1$, and consequently $P_{\alpha,\theta}|P_{\alpha+\beta,\theta}$. Similarly $P_{\beta,\theta}|P_{\alpha+\beta,\theta}$. As $(P_{\alpha,\theta}, P_{\beta,\theta}) = 1$, we must have $P_{\alpha,\theta}P_{\beta,\theta}|P_{\alpha+\beta,\theta}$. Since all the polynomials are monic, we have $P_{\alpha,\theta}P_{\beta,\theta} = P_{\alpha+\beta,\theta}$.

OPOSITION 89 *If $\mathscr{V}$ is of finite dimension over $\mathscr{F}$ and $\theta \in \mathscr{E}(\mathscr{V})$, then there is an $\alpha \in \mathscr{V}$ such that $P_{\alpha,\theta} = P_\theta$.*

PROOF. Let $P_\theta = Q_1^{m_1} \cdots Q_r^{m_r}$ where Q_i are irreducible polynomials over $\mathscr{F}$. By Lemma 2 there are γ_j such that $P_{\gamma_j,\theta} = Q_j^{m_j}$, and by Lemma 3, $P_{\gamma_1+\cdots+\gamma_r,\theta} = P_\theta$.

Given a monic polynomial $R \in \mathscr{F}[x]$, the kernel of the linear transformation $R(\theta)$ is a space $\mathscr{W}_R$ such that $P_{\mathscr{W}_R,\theta}$ is a factor of R. In most instances $P_{\mathscr{W}_R,\theta} \neq R$; however, there are polynomials R such that $P_{\mathscr{W}_R,\theta} = R$. For example, if $P_\theta = Q_1^{m_1} \cdots Q_s^{m_r}$, where Q_i are irreducible over $\mathscr{F}$, and if $R = Q_j^{m_j}$ then, by Lemma 2 above, $P_{\mathscr{W}_R,\theta} = R$. We shall prove

OPOSITION 90 *Let $\mathscr{V}$ be a finitely dimensional vector space over $\mathscr{F}$. If $\theta \in \mathscr{E}(\mathscr{V})$ and $P_\theta = Q_1^{m_1} \cdots Q_r^{m_r}$, where $Q_1, \ldots, Q_r$ are distinct irreducible polynomials over $\mathscr{F}$, let $\mathscr{W}_j$ be the kernel of $Q_j^{m_j}(\theta)$. Then the $\mathscr{W}_j$ are invariant under θ, and $\mathscr{V} = \mathscr{W}_1 + \cdots + \mathscr{W}_r$*(direct). *This decomposition of $\mathscr{V}$ reduces θ to a direct sum*

$$\theta = \theta_1 + \cdots + \theta_r \text{ (direct)},$$

where $P_{\theta_j} = Q_j^{m_j}$.

PROOF. Put $R_j = Q_j^{m_j}$, $R_jS_j = P_\theta$, $(j = 1, 2, \ldots, r)$. Then $(R_j, S_j) = 1$, and $(S_1, \ldots, S_r) = 1$. It follows from the Euclidean algorithm for polynomials that there are polynomials $T_1, \ldots, T_r$ so that

$$T_1S_1 + \cdots + T_rS_r = 1.$$

If $\alpha \in \mathscr{V}$, put $\alpha_j = \alpha T_j(\theta)\, S_j(\theta)$. Clearly $\alpha_j R_j(\theta) = \mathbf{0}$, and hence $\alpha_j \in \mathscr{W}_j$; furthermore $\alpha = \alpha_1 + \cdots + \alpha_r$. Thus $\mathscr{V} = \mathscr{W}_1 + \cdots + \mathscr{W}_r$.

Let $\beta_j \in \mathscr{W}_j (j = 1, \ldots, r)$, and suppose $\beta_1 + \cdots + \beta_r = \mathbf{0}$. Then

$$\mathbf{0} = \beta_1 S_j(\theta) + \cdots + \beta_r S_j(\theta), \qquad j = 1, \ldots, r.$$

But $\beta_i S_j(\theta) = \mathbf{0}$ if $i \neq j$. Hence

$$\beta_j S_j(\theta) = \mathbf{0}, \qquad j = 1, \ldots, r.$$

Thus we have $P_{\beta_j,\theta}|S_j$, $(j = 1, \ldots, r)$. On the other hand $\beta_j \in \mathscr{W}_j$, and hence $P_{\beta_j,\theta}|R_j$, $(j = 1, \ldots, r)$. But $(R_j, S_j) = 1$; hence $P_{\beta_j,\theta} = 1, (j = 1, \ldots, r)$, and by Proposition 88, $\beta_j = \mathbf{0}, (j = 1, \ldots, r)$. Thus we have proved that $\mathscr{V}$ is the direct sum of $\mathscr{W}_1, \ldots, \mathscr{W}_r$.

If $\alpha \in \mathscr{W}_j$, then

$$(\alpha\theta)R_j(\theta) = \alpha R_j(\theta)\theta = \mathbf{0}\theta = \mathbf{0},$$

Hence $\mathscr{W}_j\theta$ is in the kernel of $R_j(\theta)$; but then $\mathscr{W}_j\theta \subset \mathscr{W}_j$, and hence the $\mathscr{W}_j$ are invariant under θ.

Since $\mathscr{V} = \mathscr{W}_1 + \cdots + \mathscr{W}_r$ (direct), we have that $\theta = \theta_1 + \cdots + \theta_r$ (direct), where $\text{res}_{\mathscr{W}_j}\theta_i = \delta_{ij}\,\text{res}_{\mathscr{W}_j}\theta$. Thus θ_j is the restriction of θ to $\mathscr{W}_j$. But then Lemma 2 of Proposition 89 implies that $P_{\mathscr{W}_j,\theta} = R_j$. It follows from Proposition 88 that $P_{\theta_j} = R_j$. This completes the proof of Proposition 90.

If $\theta \in \mathscr{E}(\mathscr{V})$ is such that its minimal polynomial P_θ is a power of an irreducible polynomial, we shall call θ a *primary* linear transformation.

Suppose that $\theta = \varphi_1 + \cdots + \varphi_s$(direct) is a decomposition of θ into a direct sum of primary linear transformations having pairwise relatively prime minimal polynomials. Then $\mathscr{V} = \mathscr{U}_1 + \cdots + \mathscr{U}_s$(direct), $\text{res}_{\mathscr{U}_j}\,\theta = \varphi_j$ and $P_{\varphi_j} = P_{\mathscr{U}_j,\theta}$ are primary polynomials such that $P_\theta = P_{\varphi_1} \cdots P_{\varphi_s}$. But $P_\theta = R_1 \cdots R_r$, and so by the unique factorization theorem for polynomials we must have $r = s$, and after relabeling the subscripts, we have $P_{\varphi_j} = R_j$, $(j = 1, \ldots, r)$. But then $\mathscr{U}_j$ lies in the kernel of $R_j(\theta)$, which is $\mathscr{W}_j$. Consequently $\dim \mathscr{V} = \Sigma \dim \mathscr{U}_j \le \Sigma \dim \mathscr{W}_j = \dim \mathscr{V}$, and hence $\mathscr{U}_j = \mathscr{W}_j$, $(j = 1, 2, \ldots, r)$. As $\theta_j = \text{res}_{\mathscr{W}_j}\,\theta = \text{res}_{\mathscr{U}_j}\,\theta = \varphi_j$, we have proved

PROPOSITION 91 *The decomposition of θ into a direct sum of primary linear transformations $\theta = \theta_1 + \cdots + \theta_r$*(direct), *such that $(P_{\theta_j}, P_{\theta_i}) = 1$ when $i \neq j$, is unique to within order of addition.*

PROPOSITION 92 *Let θ, $\varphi \in \mathscr{E}(\mathscr{V})$ such that $\theta \simeq \varphi$. If $\theta = \theta_1 + \cdots + \theta_r$*(direct), *where the θ_i are primary transformations with relatively prime minimal polynomials, and if $\varphi = \varphi_1 + \cdots + \varphi_s$*(direct), *where the φ_i are primary transformations with relatively prime minimal polynomials, then $r = s$ and, after a rearrangement of the φ_i, $\theta_i \simeq \varphi_i$, $(i = 1, 2, \ldots, r)$.*

PROOF. Suppose $\theta = \lambda\varphi\lambda^{-1}$, where λ is a nonsingular element of $\mathscr{E}(\mathscr{V})$. Put $\theta_j' = \lambda\varphi_j\lambda^{-1}$, $(j = 1, \ldots, s)$. By Proposition 88F, $P_{\theta_j'} = P_{\varphi_j}$ and hence $\theta = \theta_1' + \cdots + \theta_s'$(direct) is a direct decomposition of θ into primary transformations having pairwise relatively prime minimal polynomials. By Proposition 91, $r = s$, and after a relabeling the θ_j', we have $\theta_j = \theta_j' = \lambda\varphi_j\lambda^{-1}$, $(j = 1, \ldots, r)$.

As a consequence of the last three propositions, we can determine canonical matrices for similarity classes provided we can determine canonical matrices for those similarity classes which have a primary minimal polynomial.

If $\beta \in \mathscr{V}$, $\theta \in \mathscr{E}(\mathscr{V})$, let

$$\langle \beta, \theta \rangle = \langle \beta, \beta\theta, \beta\theta^2, \dots \rangle.$$

The reader should prove

OPOSITION 93 A. *The subspace $\langle \beta, \theta \rangle$ is invariant under θ.*
B. $P_{\langle \beta, \theta \rangle, \theta} = P_{\beta, \theta}$.
C. $\dim_{\mathscr{F}} \langle \beta, \theta \rangle = \deg P_{\beta, \theta}$.

A linear transformation $\theta \in \mathscr{E}(\mathscr{V})$ is said to be *cyclic* on $\mathscr{V}$ provided there is an $\alpha \in \mathscr{V}$ such that $\langle \alpha, \theta \rangle = \mathscr{V}$. If $\mathscr{V}$ is of finite dimension and θ is cyclic on $\mathscr{V}$, say $\langle \alpha, \theta \rangle = \mathscr{V}$, then

$$\alpha, \alpha\theta, \dots, \alpha\theta^{n-1}$$

is a basis for $\mathscr{V}$, and hence θ has a matrix ring representation

$$\mathbf{M} = \begin{pmatrix} 0 & 1 & 0 & \cdots & & 0 \\ 0 & 0 & 1 & \cdots & & 0 \\ \vdots & & & & & \vdots \\ 0 & \cdots & & & 0 & 1 \\ -p_0 & -p_1 & & \cdots & & -p_{n-1} \end{pmatrix},$$

where $x^n + p_{n-1}x^{n-1} + \cdots + p_0 = P_{\alpha,\theta} = P_\theta$. A matrix of the type $\mathbf{M}$ is called a *companion matrix* to the polynomial $x^n + \cdots + p_0$. We have shown

LEMMA *If θ is a cyclic transformation on $\mathscr{V}$, then θ has the companion matrix to its minimal polynomial as one of its matrix ring representations.*

Now the determinant of a triangular matrix is the product of the diagonal terms. The minors of the elements in the last row of $\mathbf{I}x - \mathbf{M}$ are all lower triangular, and it is easily verified that

$$\det(\mathbf{I}x - \mathbf{M}(\theta)) = \Gamma_\theta = P_\theta.$$

Conversely, suppose $\Gamma_\theta = P_\theta$. By Proposition 89 there is an $\alpha \in \mathscr{V}$ such that $P_{\alpha,\theta} = P_\theta = \Gamma_\theta$. By Proposition 93, $\langle \alpha, \theta \rangle$ is of dimension n over $\mathscr{F}$, and hence $\mathscr{V} = \langle \alpha, \theta \rangle$. We have proved

OPOSITION 94 *θ is cyclic on $\mathscr{V}$ if and only if the minimal polynomial of θ and the characteristic polynomial of θ are identical.*

In the general situation we have

OPOSITION 95 *If $\mathscr{V}$ is of finite dimension and $\theta \in \mathscr{E}(\mathscr{V})$, then the minimal polynomial of θ is a factor of the characteristic polynomial of θ.*

PROOF. By Proposition 89 there is an $\alpha \in \mathscr{V}$ such that $P_{\alpha,\theta} = P_\theta$. If $P_\theta = p_0 + \cdots + p_{m-1}x^{m-1} + x^m$, then $\{\alpha, \alpha\theta, \dots, \alpha\theta^{m-1}\}$ is a basis of $\langle \alpha, \theta \rangle$. Let $\mathscr{W}$ be a subspace of $\mathscr{V}$ complimentary to $\langle \alpha, \theta \rangle$, and let

$\{\beta_1, \ldots, \beta_{n-m}\}$ be a basis of $\mathscr{W}$. Then $\{\alpha, \ldots, \alpha\theta^{m-1}, \beta_1, \ldots, \beta_{n-m}\}$ is a basis of $\mathscr{V}$. Relative to this basis, θ has the matrix representation

$$\mathbf{M} = \begin{pmatrix} \mathbf{A} & \mathbf{O} \\ \mathbf{B} & \mathbf{C} \end{pmatrix}, \qquad \text{where} \qquad \mathbf{A} = \begin{pmatrix} 0 & 1 & 0 & \cdots & 0 \\ 0 & 0 & 1 & \cdots & 0 \\ & & & & \\ -p_0 & & -p_1 & \cdots & -p_{m-1} \end{pmatrix}.$$

Then $\Gamma_\theta = P_\theta \det(x\mathbf{I}_{n-m} - \mathbf{C})$.

PROPOSITION 96 *If θ is a primary transformation that is cyclic on $\mathscr{V}$ and $P_\theta = Q^m$, where Q is irreducible, then θ has a matrix ring representation*

$$\mathbf{M} = \begin{pmatrix} \mathbf{C}_1 & \mathbf{D} & \mathbf{O} & \cdots & & \mathbf{O} \\ \mathbf{O} & \mathbf{C}_2 & \mathbf{D} & \cdots & & \mathbf{O} \\ & & & & & \\ & & & & \mathbf{C}_{m-1} & \mathbf{D} \\ \mathbf{O} & \cdots & \cdots & \cdots & \mathbf{O} & \mathbf{C}_m \end{pmatrix}, \tag{13}$$

where each $\mathbf{C}_i$ is the companion matrix for Q, and $\mathbf{D}$ is a square matrix with 1 in the lower left-hand corner and zero elsewhere.

PROOF. Let $\mathscr{V} = \langle \alpha, \theta \rangle$. Suppose $\deg Q = q$, then $\{\alpha, \alpha\theta, \ldots, \alpha\theta^{mq-1}\}$ is a basis of $\mathscr{V}$. If we replace

$$\alpha\theta^{qt+r} \text{ by } \alpha Q^t(\theta)\theta^r, \qquad t = 0, 1, \ldots, m-1,\ r = 0, 1, \ldots, q-1,$$

we still have a basis. With this new basis we obtain the desired matrix representation.

PROPOSITION 97 *If θ is cyclic on $\mathscr{V}$ and $\theta \simeq \varphi$, then φ is cyclic on $\mathscr{V}$.*

The proof is left to the reader.
We next prove

PROPOSITION 98 *If θ is a primary linear transformation on a finitely dimensional space $\mathscr{V}$, then*

$$\mathscr{V} = \mathscr{W}_1 + \cdots + \mathscr{W}_s \text{ (direct)},$$

where θ is cyclic on each of the $\mathscr{W}_j$.

Our proof will be indirect. We shall need some new notation and several lemmas. Let $\dim \mathscr{V} = n$. We may suppose $P_\theta = Q^m$, where Q is an irreducible polynomial over $\mathscr{F}$ of degree $q \geq 1$. Let

$$\mathscr{Z} = \{\mathscr{W} \in \mathscr{V} \mid \mathscr{W} = \langle \alpha_1, \theta \rangle + \cdots + \langle \alpha_t, \theta \rangle \text{ (direct)},\ t \in \mathbf{Z}^+\};$$

i.e., $\mathscr{Z}$ is the set of all subspaces of $\mathscr{V}$ that are direct sums of subspaces on which θ is cyclic. $\mathscr{Z}$ is not empty, since it contains all the spaces $\langle \beta, \theta \rangle$, $\beta \in \mathscr{V}$. The spaces $\langle \alpha_i, \theta \rangle$ are invariant under θ, and hence each $\mathscr{W} \in \mathscr{Z}$ is invariant relative to θ. Since the $\langle \alpha_i, \theta \rangle$ are subspaces of $\mathscr{V}$, we see from Proposition 93 that $P_{\langle \alpha_i, \theta \rangle, \theta} = P_{\alpha_i, \theta} = Q^{e_i}$, for some

$e_i \le m$. If $\langle \alpha_i, \theta \rangle \ne \mathcal{O}$, then $1 \le e_i \le m$ and $\dim \langle \alpha_i, \theta \rangle \ge q$. Consequently no subspace of $\mathscr{V}$ can be the direct sum of more than n/q proper cyclic spaces. If $\mathscr{W} \subset \mathscr{Z}$, we can arrange the α_i so that $\mathscr{W}$ is the direct sum of exactly u cyclic spaces, where $u \le n/q < u + 1$, some of these spaces may be zero, and

$$e_1 \ge e_2 \ge \cdots \ge e_u \ge 0.$$

If $\mathscr{W}$, $\mathscr{W}' \in \mathscr{Z}$, we say $\mathscr{W} > \mathscr{W}'$ provided there is a k, $(1 \le k \le u)$, such that $e_v = e'_v$, $(v = 1, 2, \ldots, k-1)$, and $e_k > e'_k$.

LEMMA 1 A. *The relation > is a transitive relation on* $\mathscr{Z}$.
B. *If* $\mathscr{W} \subset \mathscr{Z}$ *and there are* $\mathscr{W}_v \in \mathscr{Z}$ *such that*

$$\mathscr{W} < \mathscr{W}_1 < \cdots < \mathscr{W}_p,$$

then $p \le (m+1)^u$.

PROOF. The reader can readily verify the first statement. As for the second, we observe that, since $0 \le e_i \le m$, there are only $(m+1)^u$ possible sequences $\{e_1, \ldots, e_u\}$. Hence given any $\mathscr{W} \in \mathscr{Z}$, we cannot find as many as $p = (m+1)^u + 1$ spaces $\mathscr{W}_v \in \mathscr{Z}$ such that

$$\mathscr{W} = \mathscr{W}_0 < \mathscr{W}_1 < \cdots < \mathscr{W}_p.$$

LEMMA 2 *Assume the hypothesis of Proposition* 98. *If* $\mathscr{W} \in \mathscr{Z}$ and $\mathscr{W} \ne \mathscr{V}$, *then there is a* $\mathscr{W}' \in \mathscr{Z}$ *such that* $\mathscr{W}' > \mathscr{W}$.

PROOF. Let $\mathscr{W} = \langle \alpha_1, \theta \rangle + \cdots + \langle \alpha_h, \theta \rangle$ (direct) where $\alpha_1, \ldots, \alpha_h$ are not $\mathbf{0}$. If $\mathscr{W} \ne \mathscr{V}$, then there is an $\alpha \in \mathscr{V}$ such that $\alpha \notin \mathscr{W}$. Let

$$\mathscr{I} = \{A \in \mathscr{F}[x] \mid \alpha A(\theta) \in \mathscr{W}\}.$$

If $A, B \in \mathscr{I}$, then clearly $A + B \in \mathscr{I}$. $\mathscr{W}$ is invariant relative to θ; therefore, if $B \in \mathscr{F}[x]$, then $\mathscr{W}B(\theta) \subset \mathscr{W}$. Hence if $A \in \mathscr{I}$ and $B \in \mathscr{F}[x]$, then $\alpha A(\theta) \in \mathscr{W}$, and so $\alpha A(\theta)B(\theta) \in \mathscr{W}$; i.e., $AB \in \mathscr{I}$. We have shown that $\mathscr{I}$ is an ideal in $\mathscr{F}[x]$. Let R be the monic polynomial that generates $\mathscr{I}$. Since $\alpha \notin \mathscr{W}$, $R \ne 1$. Now $\alpha P_\theta(\theta) = \mathbf{0}$, and hence $P_\theta \in \mathscr{I}$, and so $R \mid P_\theta$; i.e., $R = Q^e$, where $1 \le e \le m$.

Since $\alpha R(\theta) \in \mathscr{W}$, we have

$$\alpha R(\theta) = \alpha Q^e(\theta) = \alpha_1 G_1(\theta) + \cdots + \alpha_h G_h(\theta), \qquad G_v \in \mathscr{F}[x].$$

We distinguish two cases: (A) R is a factor of each G_v; (B) there is a j such that R is not a factor of G_j.

CASE A. We are given that $G_v = RH_v$, where $H_v \in \mathscr{F}[x]$, $v = 1, \ldots, h$. Let

$$\beta = \alpha_1 H_1(\theta) + \cdots + \alpha_h H_h(\theta).$$

Then $\beta \in \mathscr{W}$ and $\beta R(\theta) = \alpha R(\theta)$. Let $\gamma = \beta - \alpha$; then $\gamma \ne \mathbf{0}$, since $\gamma = \mathbf{0}$ implies that $\alpha = \beta \in \mathscr{W}$. Clearly $\gamma R(\theta) = \mathbf{0}$, and therefore $P_{\gamma,\theta}$ is a factor of R, say $P_{\gamma,\theta} = Q^s$. Then $(\beta - \alpha)Q^s(\theta) = \mathbf{0}$ or $\alpha Q^s(\theta) = \beta Q^s(\theta) \in \mathscr{W}$, and hence $Q^s \in \mathscr{I}$. But R is the generator of $\mathscr{I}$ and so must divide Q^s. It follows that $P_{\gamma,\theta} = R = Q^e$.

If $\delta \in \langle \gamma, \theta \rangle \cap \mathscr{W}$, then $\delta = \gamma K(\theta)$ for some $K \in \mathscr{F}[x]$. But then $\alpha K(\theta) = -\delta + \beta K(\theta) \in \mathscr{W}$, and hence $K \in \mathscr{I}$. It follows that $K = RT$, and therefore $\delta = \gamma K(\theta) = \gamma R(\theta)T(\theta) = \mathbf{0}T(\theta) = \mathbf{0}$. Set $\mathscr{W}' = \langle \alpha_1, \theta \rangle + \cdots + \langle \alpha_h, \theta \rangle + \langle \gamma, \theta \rangle$. We have just shown that this sum is a direct sum; hence $\mathscr{W}' \in \mathscr{L}$. Associated with $\mathscr{W}$ is the sequence $e_1, \ldots, e_h$, $0, \ldots, 0$, while associated with $\mathscr{W}'$ is a sequence containing $e_1, \ldots, e_h, e$, and $u-h-1$ zeros. Thus $\mathscr{W}' > \mathscr{W}$, and we have proved the lemma for this case.

CASE B. We are given that there is a j such that $R \nmid G_j$. Let $k+1 = \min\{j \in \mathbf{Z}^+ \mid R \text{ does not divide } G_j\}$. Put $G_v = RH_v$ for $v = 1, 2, \cdots, k$. (In case $k = 0$, no such expressions occur.) Let

$$\beta = \begin{cases} \mathbf{0}, & \text{if } k = 0, \\ \alpha_1 H_1(\theta) + \cdots + \alpha_k H_k(\theta), & \text{if } k \geq 1. \end{cases}$$

Then $\beta \in \mathscr{W}$, $\gamma = \alpha - \beta \notin \mathscr{W}$, and

$$\gamma R(\theta) = \alpha_{k+1} G_{k+1}(\theta) + \cdots + \alpha_h G_h(\theta);$$

i.e., $$\gamma R(\theta) \in \mathscr{U}_2 = \langle \alpha_{k+1}, \theta \rangle + \cdots + \langle \alpha_h, \theta \rangle \text{ (direct)}.$$

If $k \geq 1$, let $\mathscr{U}_1 = \langle \alpha_1, \theta \rangle + \cdots + \langle \alpha_k, \theta \rangle$. Then $\mathscr{W} = \mathscr{U}_1 + \mathscr{U}_2$ (direct). If $\delta \in \langle \gamma, \theta \rangle \cap \mathscr{U}_1$ then $\delta = \gamma K(\theta) \in \mathscr{U}_1$, for some $K \in \mathscr{F}[x]$. We have

$$\alpha K(\theta) = \gamma K(\theta) + \beta K(\theta) \in \mathscr{U}_1 \subset \mathscr{W}.$$

Hence $K \in \mathscr{I}$ and $K = RT$. Consequently

$$\delta = \gamma K(\theta) = \gamma R(\theta) T(\theta) \subset \mathscr{U}_2 T(\theta).$$

Now $\mathscr{U}_2$ is the direct sum of spaces invariant under θ, and hence $\mathscr{U}_2$ is itself invariant under θ. Hence $\mathscr{U}_2 T(\theta) \subset \mathscr{U}_2$. But then we would have $\delta \in \mathscr{U}_1 \cap \mathscr{U}_2$, and it follows that $\delta = 0$. We have shown that $\mathscr{U}_1 + \langle \gamma, \theta \rangle$ is a direct sum of cyclic spaces and hence lies in $\mathscr{L}$.

We now put

$$\mathscr{W}' = \begin{cases} \langle \gamma, \theta \rangle, & \text{if } k = 0, \\ \langle \alpha_1, \theta \rangle + \cdots + \langle \alpha_k, \theta \rangle + \langle \gamma, \theta \rangle \text{(direct)}, & \text{if } k \geq 1. \end{cases}$$

In either case $\mathscr{W}' \in \mathscr{L}$. By hypothesis θ is a primary transformation on $\mathscr{V}$; i.e., $P_\theta = Q^m$, where Q is a monic irreducible polynomial of positive degree and $m \geq 1$. Since $\gamma \neq 0$, we have $P_{\gamma,\theta} = Q^s$ for some $s \geq 1$. Now

$$e = \min\{t \in \mathbf{Z}^+ \mid \gamma Q^t(\theta) \in \mathscr{W}\} = \min\{t \in \mathbf{Z}^+ \mid \alpha Q^t(\theta) \in \mathscr{W}\}.$$

It follows that $e \leq s$. Let $G_{k+1} = Q^f J$, where $(Q, J) = 1$. By the hypothesis of Case B, $f < e$. Then

$$\mathbf{0} = \gamma Q^s(\theta) = \gamma Q^e(\theta)Q^{s-e}(\theta) = \gamma R(\theta)Q^{s-e}(\theta)$$

$$= (\alpha_{k+1}G_{k+1}(\theta) + \cdots + \alpha_h G_h(\theta))Q^{s-e}(\theta) \subset \mathscr{U}_2 Q^{s-e}(\theta) \subset \mathscr{U}_2.$$

Since $\mathscr{U}_2 = > \alpha_{k+1}, \theta\rangle + \cdots + \langle\alpha_h, \theta\rangle$ (direct), we must have

$$\alpha_{k+1}G_{k+1}(\theta)Q^{s-e}(\theta) = \mathbf{0}.$$

Hence $P_{\alpha_{k+1}, \theta} = Q^{e_{k+1}}$ is a factor of $G_{k+1}Q^{s-e} = Q^{s-e+f}J$. Thus

$$e_{k+1} \leq s - e + f \qquad \text{or} \qquad s \geq e_{k+1} + e - f > e_{k+1}.$$

Associated with $\mathscr{W}$ we have the sequence $e_1, \ldots, e_k, e_{k+1}, \ldots, e_h, 0, \ldots, 0$, while associated with $\mathscr{W}'$ we have either the sequence $s, 0, \ldots, 0$ or a sequence containing $e_1, \ldots, e_k, s$ and $u - k - 1$ zeros. Since $s > e_{k+1}$, we have in either case $\mathscr{W}' > \mathscr{W}$. This completes the proof of Lemma 2.

Proof of Proposition 98. We need to prove that $\mathscr{V} \in \mathscr{Z}$. Suppose that $\mathscr{V} \notin \mathscr{Z}$. Since $\mathscr{Z}$ is not empty, there is a $\mathscr{W} \in \mathscr{Z}$. By Lemma 2 there is a $\mathscr{W}' \in \mathscr{Z}$ so that $\mathscr{W}' > \mathscr{W}$. Since $\mathscr{V} \notin \mathscr{Z}$, we can apply Lemma 2 again to obtain $\mathscr{W}'' \in \mathscr{Z}$ such that $\mathscr{W}'' > \mathscr{W}'$. We can continue in this way to find an arbitrarily long sequence

$$\mathscr{W} < \mathscr{W}' < \mathscr{W}'' < \cdots$$

contrary to Lemma 1. It follows therefore that the assumption that $\mathscr{V} \notin \mathscr{Z}$ is false. This completes the proof of the Proposition.

Our propositions lead to

THEOREM 2 *If $\theta \in \mathscr{E}(\mathscr{V})$ and $\mathscr{V}$ is of finite dimension, then*

$$\mathscr{V} = \mathscr{W}_{1,1} + \cdots + \mathscr{W}_{1,s(1)} + \mathscr{W}_{2,1} + \cdots + \mathscr{W}_{r,s(r)} \text{ (direct)},$$

where θ is cyclic on each $\mathscr{W}_{ij}$ and is primary on each $\mathscr{W}_i = \mathscr{W}_{i,1} + \cdots + \mathscr{W}_{i,s(i)}$ (direct). *Furthermore*

$$\mathbf{M}(\theta) = \begin{pmatrix} \mathbf{M}_{11} & \mathbf{O} & \cdots & \mathbf{O} \\ \vdots & & \ddots & \vdots \\ \mathbf{O} & \cdots & & \mathbf{M}_{r,s(r)} \end{pmatrix}, \tag{14}$$

where the $\mathbf{M}_{ij}$ are as in (13) *or are companion matrices to $P_{\mathscr{W}_{ij},\theta}$.*

Proof. By Proposition 90, $\mathscr{V} = \mathscr{W}_1 + \cdots + \mathscr{W}_r$ (direct), where θ is primary on each of the $\mathscr{W}_j$. By Proposition 98, $\mathscr{W}_i = \mathscr{W}_{i,1} + \cdots + \mathscr{W}_{i,s(i)}$(direct), $(i = 1, 2, \ldots, r)$, where θ is cyclic on $\mathscr{W}_i$. The matrix ring representation (14) follows from applications of Proposition 96.

Eventually we shall show that each similarity class contains only one matrix of the type specified in Theorem 2.

10 INVARIANT FACTORS

Let $\mathbf{M}$ be a matrix ring representation for $\theta \in \mathscr{E}(\mathscr{V})$. By Exercise 23, Sec. 5, the matrix $x\mathbf{I} - \mathbf{M}$ is equivalent[†] over $\mathscr{F}[x]$ to a unique diagonal matrix

$$\begin{pmatrix} E_1 & 0 & \cdots & 0 \\ 0 & \ddots & & \vdots \\ \vdots & & \ddots & \\ 0 & & \cdots & E_n \end{pmatrix}, \tag{15}$$

where the E_ν are either 0 or monic polynomials over $\mathscr{F}$ and $E_j \mid E_{j+1}$, $(j = 1, \ldots, n-1)$. The determinants of two matrices equivalent over a ring differ by a multiple of a unit of the ring. Since $\det(x\mathbf{I} - \mathbf{M})$ is a monic polynomial of degree n and

$$\det\begin{pmatrix} E_1 & & \\ & \ddots & \\ & & E_n \end{pmatrix} = E_1 \cdots E_n,$$

we see that each E_i is a nonzero divisor of Γ_θ. Also each irreducible factor of Γ_θ must be a factor of ΠE_ν, but each $E_\nu \mid E_n$, and therefore each irreducible factor of Γ_θ is a factor of E_n. Since the E_ν and Γ_θ are monic, we have $\Gamma_\theta = \Pi E_\nu$.

If $\mathbf{M}$ and $\mathbf{M}'$ are each matrix ring representations of θ, say $\mathbf{M} = \mathbf{U}\mathbf{M}'\mathbf{U}^{-1}$, where $\mathbf{U}$ is nonsingular, then

$$x\mathbf{I} - \mathbf{M} = \mathbf{U}(x\mathbf{I} - \mathbf{M}')\mathbf{U}^{-1},$$

and consequently $x\mathbf{I} - \mathbf{M}$ and $x\mathbf{I} - \mathbf{M}'$ are equivalent over $\mathscr{F}[x]$. It follows that these two matrices are equivalent over $\mathscr{F}[x]$ to the same diagonal matrix (15). Thus the polynomials $E_1, \ldots, E_n$ do not depend on the matrix ring representation and are uniquely determined by θ. We call $E_1, \ldots, E_n$, the *invariant factors* associated with θ. As we have already noted

PROPOSITION 99 *Similar transformations have the same invariant factors.*

Invariant factors are further invariants of a similarity class. We shall show that there is a bijective map of the collection of all possible sets of invariant factors onto the collection of all matrices of the type specified in Theorem 2. We shall further show that there is exactly one such matrix in each similarity class. Thus this set of matrices is a collection of canonical matrices for similarity classes, and the invariant factors are a complete set of invariants of a similarity class.

† Here $x\mathbf{I} - \mathbf{M}$ equivalent to $\mathbf{E}$ means $x\mathbf{I} - \mathbf{M} = \mathbf{U}\mathbf{E}\mathbf{V}$, where $\mathbf{U}, \mathbf{V}$ are unimodular matrices over $\mathscr{F}[x]$.

LEMMA *Let* $\mathbf{N}$ *be the companion matrix of a monic polynomial* $G(x) = x^n + a_{n-1}x^{n-1} + \cdots + a_0$; *then* $G(x)$ *is the only nonconstant invariant factor of* $\mathbf{N}$.

PROOF.

$$x\mathbf{I} - \mathbf{N} = \begin{pmatrix} x & -1 & 0 & \cdots & 0 \\ 0 & x & -1 & & 0 \\ \vdots & & & & \vdots \\ 0 & 0 & & & -1 \\ a_0 & a_1 & \cdots & & a_{n-1} + x \end{pmatrix},$$

which is equivalent over $\mathscr{F}[x]$ to

$$\begin{pmatrix} -1 & 0 & \cdots & 0 & x \\ x & -1 & & 0 & 0 \\ \vdots & & & & \vdots \\ a_1 & a_2 & \cdots & a_{n-1} + x & a_0 \end{pmatrix},$$

which is equivalent over $\mathscr{F}[x]$ to

$$\begin{pmatrix} -1 & 0 & 0 & \cdots & 0 & 0 \\ x & -1 & 0 & & 0 & x^2 \\ 0 & x & -1 & \cdots & 0 & 0 \\ \vdots & & & & & \vdots \\ a_1 & a_2 & a_3 & \cdots & a_{n-1} + x & a_0 + a_1 x \end{pmatrix},$$

which is equivalent over $\mathscr{F}[x]$ to

$$\begin{pmatrix} -1 & 0 & \cdots & 0 \\ 0 & -1 & & x^2 \\ \vdots & & & \vdots \\ 0 & a_2 & \cdots & a_0 + a_1 x \end{pmatrix}.$$

Continuing this process, we find that $x\mathbf{I} - \mathbf{N}$ is equivalent over $\mathscr{F}[x]$ to

$$\begin{pmatrix} 1 & 0 & \cdots & 0 \\ 0 & 1 & & 0 \\ \vdots & & & \vdots \\ 0 & 0 & \cdots & G(x) \end{pmatrix}.$$

This completes the proof of the lemma.

Combining this lemma with the lemma to Proposition 94, we obtain

POSITION 100 *If* θ *is cyclic on* $\mathscr{V}$, *then the only nonconstant invariant factor of* θ *is* $\Gamma_\theta = P_\theta$.

Suppose $\mathscr{V} = \langle \alpha_1, \theta \rangle + \cdots + \langle \alpha_n, \theta \rangle$(direct), where $P_{\alpha_j,\theta} = Q^{e_j}$, Q is monic irreducible and $0 < e_1 \leq \cdots \leq e_r$. By Proposition 98 and the lemma to Proposition 94, it follows that θ has a matrix ring representation

$$\mathbf{M} = \begin{pmatrix} \mathbf{N}_1 & & & \mathbf{O} \\ & \mathbf{N}_2 & & \\ & & \ddots & \\ \mathbf{O} & & & \mathbf{N}_n \end{pmatrix},$$

where $\mathbf{N}_j$ is the companion matrix to Q^{e_j}, $(j = 1, \ldots, r)$. Hence $x\mathbf{I} - \mathbf{M}$ is equivalent over $\mathscr{F}[x]$ to

$$\begin{pmatrix} 1 & 0 & & \cdots & & & 0 \\ 0 & 1 & & & & & \\ & & \ddots & & & & \\ \vdots & & & 1 & & & \vdots \\ & & & & Q^{e_1} & & \\ & & & & & \ddots & \\ 0 & & & \cdots & & & Q^{e_r} \end{pmatrix}.$$

Thus θ has as its nonconstant invariant factors the polynomials $Q^{e_1}, \ldots, Q^{e_r}$. If we could also write $\mathscr{V} = \langle \beta_1, \theta \rangle + \cdots + \langle \beta_s, \theta \rangle$(direct), then $P_{\beta_j,\theta} = Q^{f_j}$. Suppose we have labeled the subscripts so that $0 < f_1 \leq \cdots \leq f_s$; then θ would have $Q^{f_1}, \ldots, Q^{f_s}$ as its nonconstant invariant factors. Since the invariant factors of a linear transformation θ are uniquely determined by θ, we must have $r = s$ and $e_j = f_j$, $(j = 1, \ldots, r)$. Consequently, although the cyclic spaces $\mathscr{W}_1, \ldots, \mathscr{W}_r$ in Proposition 98 are not uniquely determined, we have proved

PROPOSITION 101 *If θ is a primary transformation on $\mathscr{V}$ and if $\mathscr{V} = \mathscr{W}_1 + \cdots + \mathscr{W}_r$(direct) $= \mathscr{U}_1 + \cdots + \mathscr{U}_s$(direct) are decompositions of $\mathscr{V}$ such that θ is cyclic on each $\mathscr{W}_i$ and on each $\mathscr{U}_j$, then $r = s$; and after a rearrangement we have $P_{\mathscr{W}_j,\theta} = P_{\mathscr{U}_j,\theta}$, $(j = 1, \ldots, r)$.*

PROPOSITION 102 *A primary transformation θ on $\mathscr{V}$ with nonconstant invariant factors $Q^{e_1}, \ldots, Q^{e_r}$ with $0 < e_1 \leq \cdots \leq e_r$ has a unique matrix ring representation in the form*

$$\begin{pmatrix} \mathbf{B}_1 & \mathbf{O} & & \mathbf{O} \\ \mathbf{O} & \mathbf{B}_2 & & \\ & & \ddots & \\ \mathbf{O} & & & \mathbf{B}_r \end{pmatrix}, \tag{16}$$

where $\mathbf{B}_j$ is the companion matrix of Q^{e_j}.

PROOF. In the proof of Proposition 101 we have shown that each primary transformation θ has a representation of the type (16). As for uniqueness, we note that two different matrices of type (16) have different invariant factors and so could not represent the same linear transformation.

Thus we have shown that every primary matrix is similar to a unique matrix of type (16). In particular, each similarity class of primary matrices contains one and only one matrix of type (16). Hence such matrices can serve as our canonical matrices for the similarity classes of primary matrices.

POSITION 103 *Let P and Q be monic polynomials over $\mathscr{F}$. The matrices* $\begin{pmatrix} P & 0 \\ 0 & Q \end{pmatrix}$ *and* $\begin{pmatrix} 1 & 0 \\ 0 & PQ \end{pmatrix}$ *are equivalent over $\mathscr{F}[x]$ if and only if P and Q are relatively prime.*

The proof is left to the reader. It will be useful in the proof to recall that, if $(P, Q) = 1$, then there exist $A, B \in \mathscr{F}[x]$ such that $\begin{pmatrix} A & B \\ Q & P \end{pmatrix}$ is a unimodular matrix in $\mathfrak{M}_{22}(\mathscr{F}[x])$.

If the linear transformation θ is not a primary transformation, then, by Proposition 91, θ decomposes uniquely into a direct sum of primary transformations; i.e., $\theta = \theta_1 + \cdots + \theta_r$(direct) where $\mathscr{V} = \mathscr{W}_1 + \cdots + \mathscr{W}_r$(direct) and the θ_j are primary on $\mathscr{W}_j$. Furthermore $\mathscr{W}_j = \mathscr{W}_{j,1} + \cdots + \mathscr{W}_{j,s(j)}$(direct), where $\theta_j = \theta_{j,1} + \cdots + \theta_{j,s(j)}$ (direct) and $\theta_{j,h} = \operatorname{res}_{\mathscr{W}_{j,h}} \theta_j$ is primary cyclic on $\mathscr{W}_{j,h}$. Say $P_{\theta_{j,h}} = Q_j^{f_{j,h}}$ with $1 \le f_{j,1} \le \cdots \le f_{j,s(j)}$. As we saw in Theorem 2, θ has a matrix ring representation

$$\mathbf{M} = \begin{pmatrix} \mathbf{M}_{1,1} & & \mathbf{O} \\ & \ddots & \\ \mathbf{O} & & \mathbf{M}_{r,s(r)} \end{pmatrix}, \tag{17}$$

where the $\mathbf{M}_{j,h}$ are companion matrices to $Q_j^{f_{j,h}} = P_{j,h}$. By the lemma to Proposition 100, we see that $x\mathbf{I} - \mathbf{M}$ is equivalent over $\mathscr{F}[x]$ to

$$\begin{pmatrix} 1 & 0 & \cdots & & 0 \\ 0 & 1 & & & \\ & & \ddots & & \\ \vdots & & P_{1,1} & & \vdots \\ & & & \ddots & \\ 0 & & \cdots & & P_{r,s(r)} \end{pmatrix}.$$

Let $s = \max\{s(1), \ldots, s(r)\}$, and put $e_{j1} = \cdots = e_{j,s-s(j)} = 1, e_{j,s-s(j)+1} = f_{j,1}, \ldots e_{j,s} = f_{j,s(j)}$. After repeated use of Proposition 100, we see that $x\mathbf{I} - \mathbf{M}$ is equivalent over $\mathscr{F}[x]$ to

$$\begin{pmatrix} 1 & & \cdots & & 0 \\ & \ddots & & & \\ \vdots & & 1 & & \vdots \\ \vdots & & & E_1 & \vdots \\ & & & & \ddots \\ 0 & & \cdots & & E_s \end{pmatrix},$$

where $E_j = Q_1^{e_{1,j}} \ldots Q_r^{e_{r,j}}$. Note that $Q_j^{f_{j,1}}, \ldots, Q_j^{f_{j,s(j)}}$ are the nonconstant invariant factors of θ_j. Thus we see that we can construct the invariant factors of θ provided we know the invariant factors of the primary components of θ_j. Conversely, since the invariant factors of θ are independent of the representation, we see that the invariant factors of θ_j can be determined from the invariant factors of θ. Specifically if $E_h = Q_1^{e_{1,h}} \cdots Q_r^{e_{r,h}}$, then all the nonconstant invariant factors of θ_j appear in the set $Q_j^{e_{j,1}}, \ldots, Q_j^{e_{j,s}}$.

As we saw in Proposition 102, the invariant factors determine a unique matrix representation of a primary transformation. Since the θ_j are uniquely determined by θ, we see that the invariant factors of θ determine a unique (to within order of arrangement of the primary components) matrix of type (17). We have proved

THEOREM 3 *The invariant factors of θ determine a matrix ring representation of θ of type* (17) *that is unique to within the order of the primary components.*

Two matrices of type (17) have the same invariant factors if and only if they are equal. Since invariant factors are invariants of a similarity class, i.e., similar transformations have the same invariant factors, we have proved

THEOREM 4 *Each similarity class of n by n matrices contains exactly one matrix of type* (17). *Hence these matrices are a set of canonical matrices for the set of similarity classes of matrices.*

The set of all matrices of type (17) is called the set of *rational canonical matrices*. The submatrices in (17), i.e., the companion matrices to the primary invariant factors, can always be replaced by matrices of type (13). As long as we are consistent as to the type of representation we are using, we have a set of canonical matrices.

PROPOSITION 104 *The largest invariant factor of θ is the minimal polynomial of θ.*

PROOF. Let E_n be the largest invariant factor of θ, and say $E_n = Q_1^{m_1} \cdots Q_r^{m_r}$. In the proof of Theorem 3 we have seen that there are subspaces $\mathscr{W}_j$ of $\mathscr{V}$ such that $\mathscr{V} = \mathscr{W}_1 + \cdots + \mathscr{W}_r$(direct),

$\theta = \theta_1 + \cdots + \theta_r$(direct), θ_j primary on $\mathscr{W}_j$, and the largest invariant factor of θ_j is $Q_j^{m_j}$. But then

$$P_{\mathscr{W}_{j},\theta_j} = Q_j^{m_j} = P_{\mathscr{W}_j,\theta}.$$

By Proposition 88 there is a subspace $\mathscr{W}$ such that $P_{\mathscr{W},\theta} = E_n$. Hence the minimal polynomial P_θ is divisible by E_n. On the other hand

$$\mathscr{V} = \mathscr{W}_{1,1} + \cdots + \mathscr{W}_{1,s(1)} + \cdots + \mathscr{W}_{r,s(r)} \text{ (direct)},$$

where θ is cyclic on $\mathscr{W}_{j,h}$ and $P_{\mathscr{W}_{j,h},\theta}$ is a divisor of E_n. As P_θ is the least common multiple of the $P_{\mathscr{W}_{j,h},\theta}$ we see that P_θ is a divisor of E_n. It follows that $P_\theta = E_n$.

POSITION 105 *Let θ be a linear transformation on a space of finite dimension. An irreducible polynomial Q is a factor of P_θ if and only if Q is a factor of Γ_θ.*

PROOF. The proof follows trivially from the following facts:

$$\Gamma_\theta = E_1, \ldots, E_n, \qquad E_i \mid E_n (i = 1, \ldots, n), \qquad E_n = P_\theta.$$

If $c \in \mathrm{Sp}(\theta)$, then $x - c$ is a factor of Γ_θ, and hence $x - c$ is a factor of P_θ. Suppose $\Gamma_\theta = (x - c)^m J$ and $P_\theta = (x - c)^q K$, where $m \geq q \geq 1$, $(x - c, J) = (x - c, K) = 1$. Then θ has a matrix representation

$$\begin{pmatrix} \mathbf{M}_1 & \cdots & \mathbf{O} \\ \vdots & \ddots & \vdots \\ \mathbf{O} & \cdots & \mathbf{M}_r \end{pmatrix},$$

where $\mathbf{M}_1$ is the primary matrix associated with the irreducible polynomial $x - c$. We can express $\mathbf{M}_1$ as the direct sum of matrices of type (13) and so have

$$\mathbf{M}_1 = \begin{pmatrix} \mathbf{M}_{11} & & \mathbf{O} \\ & \ddots & \\ \mathbf{O} & & \mathbf{M}_{1s} \end{pmatrix},$$

where $\mathbf{M}_{ij}$ is a q_j by q_j matrix of the type

$$\begin{pmatrix} c & 1 & 0 & \cdots & 0 \\ 0 & c & 1 & & \\ & & & \ddots & \\ & & & c & 1 \\ 0 & & & & c \end{pmatrix}, \tag{18}$$

and where $q_1 \leq q_2 \leq \cdots \leq q_s = q$, and $q_1 + \cdots + q_s = m$.

We next observe that $\iota c - \theta$ has the matrix ring representation

$$\begin{pmatrix} \mathbf{T} & \mathbf{O} & & \mathbf{O} \\ \mathbf{O} & c\mathbf{I}_2 - \mathbf{M}_2 & & \\ & & \ddots & \\ \mathbf{O} & \cdots & & c\mathbf{I}_r - \mathbf{M}_r \end{pmatrix},$$

where $\mathbf{T}$ is a m by m strictly upper triangular matrix and

$$\det(c\mathbf{I}_2 - \mathbf{M}_2) \cdots \det(c\mathbf{I}_r - \mathbf{M}_r) = J(c) \neq 0.$$

It follows that $\mathbf{T}$ is nilpotent, since some power of $\mathbf{T}$ is the $\mathbf{O}$ matrix, and the other blocks are nonsingular matrices. Thus there is a decomposition

$$\mathscr{V} = \mathscr{W}_c + \mathscr{W}_c' \text{ (direct)}, \qquad \dim \mathscr{W}_c = m,$$

such that $\iota c - \theta$ is nilpotent on $\mathscr{W}_c$ and is nonsingular on $\mathscr{W}_c'$.

If $\varphi \in \mathscr{E}(\mathscr{V})$, then $\mathscr{V}_\varphi \subset \mathscr{V}_{\varphi^2} \subset \cdots$. Put $\mathscr{N}(\varphi) = \bigcup_{\nu=1}^{\infty} \mathscr{V}_{\varphi^\nu}$. Then $\mathscr{N}(\varphi)$ is a subspace of $\mathscr{V}$ invariant under φ. We call $\mathscr{N}(\varphi)$ the radical of φ. If $\mathscr{V}$ is of finite dimension, then there is an integer k such that $\mathscr{N}(\varphi) = \mathscr{V}_{\varphi^k} =$ the kernel of φ^k. In that case, put $\mathscr{M}(\varphi) = \mathscr{V}\varphi^k$. Clearly $\mathscr{M}(\varphi) \cap \mathscr{N}(\varphi) = \mathscr{O}$. Since

$$\dim \mathscr{M}(\varphi) = \dim \mathscr{V} - \text{nullity } \varphi^k = \dim \mathscr{V} - \dim \mathscr{N}(\varphi),$$

we see that

$$\mathscr{V} = \mathscr{M}(\varphi) + \mathscr{N}(\varphi) \text{ (direct)}.$$

If $\alpha \in \mathscr{M}(\varphi)$ and $\alpha\varphi = 0$, then $\alpha = \beta\varphi^k$ and $\beta \in \mathscr{V}_{\varphi^{k+1}} = \mathscr{V}_{\varphi^k}$, whence $\alpha = \beta\varphi^k = \mathbf{0}$. Thus $\mathscr{M}(\varphi) \cap \mathscr{V}_\varphi = \mathscr{O}$. Also $\mathscr{M}(\varphi)$ is invariant under φ; otherwise some nonzero element of $\mathscr{M}(\varphi)$ would lie in $\mathscr{V}_{\varphi^{2k+1}} \subset \mathscr{N}(\varphi)$. If $\alpha \in N(\varphi)$, then $\alpha\varphi^k = \mathbf{0}$, and hence φ is nilpotent on $N(\varphi)$. Since $\mathscr{V}_{\varphi^k} = \mathscr{V}_{\varphi^{k+1}}$, we have $M(\varphi) = \mathscr{V}\varphi^k = \mathscr{V}\varphi^{k+1} = M(\varphi)\varphi$, and hence φ is an automorphism on $M(\varphi)$. We have

PROPOSITION 106 *If φ is a linear transformation on a finitely dimensional space, then $\mathscr{V} = \mathscr{M}(\varphi) + \mathscr{N}(\varphi)$*(direct) *such that φ is nilpotent on $\mathscr{N}(\varphi)$ and is an automorphism on $\mathscr{M}(\varphi)$.*

We then have

PROPOSITION 107 *If $\mathscr{V}$ is of finite dimension and $\theta \in \mathscr{E}(\mathscr{V})$ and $c \in \text{Sp}(\theta)$, then the radical of $\iota c - \theta$ is the primary space $\mathscr{W}_c$ associated with the irreducible factor $x - c$ of the characteristic polynomial Γ_θ.*

If $c \neq d \in \text{Sp}(\theta)$, then $\mathscr{W}_c \cap \mathscr{W}_d = \mathscr{O}$, and we have

PROPOSITION 108 *If θ is a linear transformation on a finite dimensional space $\mathscr{V}$, then*

$$\sum_{c \in \text{Sp}(\theta)} \mathscr{N}(\iota c - \theta) = \sum_{c \in \text{Sp}(\theta)} \mathscr{W}_c$$

is a direct sum.

Since $\mathscr{W}(c, \theta) = \mathscr{V}_{\iota c - \theta} \subset \mathscr{N}(\iota c - \theta)$, Proposition 108 is an extension of Proposition 84. More specially we have

POSITION 109 *If θ is a linear transformation on a finitely dimensional space $\mathscr{V}$ and the characteristic polynomial Γ_θ splits into a product of linear polynomials, then*

$$\mathscr{V} = \sum_{c \in \mathrm{Sp}(\theta)} \mathscr{N}(\iota c - \theta) \text{ (direct)}$$

and θ has a matrix ring representation of the type

$$\begin{pmatrix} \mathbf{M}_{c_1} & & \\ & \ddots & \\ & & \mathbf{M}_{c_r} \end{pmatrix}, \qquad c_\nu \in \mathrm{Sp}(\theta), \tag{19}$$

where
$$\mathbf{M}_{c_\nu} = \begin{pmatrix} \mathbf{N}_{c_\nu 1} & & \\ & \ddots & \\ & & \mathbf{N}_{c_\nu s_\nu} \end{pmatrix},$$

the dimension of $\mathbf{M}_{c_\nu}$ is the multiplicity of $x - c_\nu$ in Γ_θ, and

$$\mathbf{N}_{c_\nu \mu} = \begin{pmatrix} c_\nu & 1 & 0 & \cdots & & 0 \\ 0 & c_\nu & 1 & & & \\ 0 & 0 & c_\nu & \ddots & & \vdots \\ \vdots & & & \ddots & & \\ 0 & & \cdots & & c_\nu & 1 \\ 0 & & \cdots & & 0 & c_\nu \end{pmatrix}.$$

Matrices of type (19) are called *jordan matrices*. As a consequence of Theorem 3, we have

THEOREM 5 *If $\mathscr{V}$ is a finitely dimensional vector space over an algebraic closed field, then every $\theta \in \mathscr{E}(\mathscr{V})$ has exactly one matrix ring representation that is a jordan matrix.*

EXERCISES 1 A. Exhibit all jordan canonical matrices having $(x - c)^5(x - d)^3$ as their characteristic polynomial.

B. Exhibit all rational canonical matrices over **Q** having $P = (x^2 - 2)^2 (x^2 + 1)(x^2 - 1)$ as their characteristic polynomial.

C. Exhibit all rational canonical matrices over **R** having P as their characteristic polynomial.

D. Exhibit all rational canonical matrices over **C** having P as their characteristic polynomial.

2 Prove: A matrix is always similar to its transpose.

3 Prove:

A. If $P \in \mathscr{F}[x]$ and $P(x) \mid P(x^2)$, then $P(x) = x^q(x - 1)^m$. (Hint: Examine the zeros of P.)

B. An idempotent transformation has a matrix ring representation that is diagonal with 0's and 1's on the diagonal.

C. If θ, φ are idempotent transformations on a finitely dimensional space $\mathscr{V}$, then $\theta \simeq \varphi$ if and only if rank $\theta =$ rank φ.

4 Prove: Let θ be a linear transformation on a finitely dimensional space. θ has a matrix ring representation that is a diagonal matrix if and only if the minimal polynomial of θ is a product of distinct linear factors.

5 Prove: If θ is a linear transformation on a finitely dimensional space $\mathscr{V}$ over **C** such that $\theta^m = 1$, then θ has a matrix ring representation that is diagonal.

6 Prove: A linear transformation θ on a finitely dimensional space is nonsingular if and only if its minimal polynomial has a nonzero constant term. If θ is nonsingular, then there is a polynomial A such that $\theta^{-1} = A(\theta)$.

7 Prove: The element $c \in \mathrm{Sp}\,(\theta)$ if and only if c is a zero of the minimal polynomial of θ.

8 A. Determine the eigenvalues of θ if $\theta^2 = \iota$.

B. Discuss the relationship between the eigenvalues of a matrix A and the matrix $-A$.

11 COMMUTING ALGEBRAS

We now show one instance where canonical matrices are useful. Let $\mathscr{V}$ be a finitely dimensional vector space over an algebraically closed field $\mathscr{F}$. If $\theta \in \mathscr{E}(\mathscr{V})$, let

$$\mathscr{C}(\theta) = \{\varphi \in \mathscr{E}(\mathscr{V}) \mid \theta\varphi = \varphi\theta\}.$$

The reader can easily verify

PROPOSITION 110 *$\mathscr{C}(\theta)$ is a subalgebra of $\mathscr{E}(\mathscr{V})$.*

$\mathscr{C}(\theta)$ is called the *commuting algebra of* θ. We now seek to determine what elements lie in $\mathscr{C}(\theta)$. We observe that, if $\theta = \chi\theta_1\chi^{-1}$, then

$$\mathscr{C}(\theta_1) = \chi^{-1}\mathscr{C}(\theta)\chi.$$

Hence, if we know the commuting algebra of an element θ, we can easily find the commuting algebra of any transformation similar to θ.

Also, an isomorphism of $\mathscr{E}(\mathscr{V})$ into $\mathfrak{M}_{n,n}(\mathscr{F})$ taking θ onto **M** induces an isomorphism of $\mathscr{C}(\theta)$ onto $\mathscr{C}(\mathbf{M})$. Hence we can restrict our attention to finding the commuting algebra of a matrix in rational canonical form.

$$\text{If}\quad \mathbf{A} = \begin{pmatrix} \mathbf{A}_{11} & \mathbf{A}_{12} & \cdots & \mathbf{A}_{1r} \\ \mathbf{A}_{21} & & & \\ \vdots & & & \\ \mathbf{A}_{r1} & & & \mathbf{A}_{rr} \end{pmatrix}, \qquad \mathbf{B} = \begin{pmatrix} \mathbf{B}_{11} & \mathbf{B}_{12} & \cdots & \mathbf{B}_{1r} \\ \mathbf{B}_{21} & & & \\ \vdots & & & \\ \mathbf{B}_{r1} & & & \mathbf{B}_{rr} \end{pmatrix},$$

where $\mathbf{A}_{ij}$ and $\mathbf{B}_{ij}$ are n_i by n_j matrices with $\sum n_i = n$, then

$$\mathbf{AB} = \begin{pmatrix} \mathbf{C}_{11} & \cdots & \mathbf{C}_{1r} \\ \vdots & & \vdots \\ \mathbf{C}_{r1} & & \mathbf{C}_{rr} \end{pmatrix},$$

with $\mathbf{C}_{ij} = \sum_{m=1}^{r} \mathbf{A}_{im}\mathbf{B}_{mj}$.

Suppose further that $\mathbf{A}$ is a jordan matrix. We can then partition $\mathbf{A}$ in such a way that

$$\mathbf{A}_{ij} = 0 \text{ whenever } i \neq j,$$

and

$$\mathbf{A}_{ii} = \begin{pmatrix} c_i & 1 & 0 & 0 \\ & \cdot & & \\ & & \cdot & \\ & & c_i & 1 \\ 0 & & & c_i \end{pmatrix} = \mathbf{I}_i c_i + \mathbf{T}_i, \tag{20}$$

where $\mathbf{T}_i$ is a matrix such that $t_{i,i+1} = 1$ and all other entries are 0. If $\mathbf{AB} = \mathbf{BA}$, then

$$\mathbf{A}_{ii}\mathbf{B}_{ij} = \mathbf{B}_{ij}\mathbf{A}_{jj}, \qquad i, j = 1, 2, \ldots, r. \tag{21}$$

Two cases occur:

CASE A. $c_i \neq c_j$. Equation 21 becomes

$$(c_i - c_j)\mathbf{B}_{ij} = \mathbf{B}_{ij}\mathbf{T}_j - \mathbf{T}_i\mathbf{B}_{ij}.$$

Let $a = c_i - c_j$, then

$$\mathbf{B}_{ij} = a^{-1}(\mathbf{B}_{ij}\mathbf{T}_j - \mathbf{T}_i\mathbf{B}_{ij}). \tag{22}$$

We now substitute the expression on the right-hand side of (22) for the $\mathbf{B}_{ij}$'s occurring in the right-hand side of (22) to get

$$\begin{aligned} \mathbf{B}_{ij} &= a^{-1}[a^{-1}(\mathbf{B}_{ij}\mathbf{T}_j - \mathbf{T}_i\mathbf{B}_{ij})\mathbf{T}_j - a^{-1}\mathbf{T}_i(\mathbf{B}_{ij}\mathbf{T}_j - \mathbf{T}_i\mathbf{B}_{ij})] \\ &= a^{-2}[\mathbf{B}_{ij}\mathbf{T}_j^2 - 2\mathbf{T}_i\mathbf{B}_{ij}\mathbf{T}_j + \mathbf{T}_i^2\mathbf{B}_{ij}]. \end{aligned}$$

Repeating the process, we obtain

$$\mathbf{B}_{ij} = a^{-3}[\mathbf{B}_{ij}\mathbf{T}_j^3 - 3\mathbf{T}_i\mathbf{B}_{ij}\mathbf{T}_j^2 + 3\mathbf{T}_i^2\mathbf{B}_{ij}\mathbf{T}_j - \mathbf{T}_i^3\mathbf{B}_{ij}].$$

We can now proceed inductively, to obtain

$$\mathbf{B}_{ij} = a^{-m}\left[\sum_{s=0}^{m} (-1)^s \binom{m}{s} \mathbf{T}_i^{m-s}\mathbf{B}_{ij}\mathbf{T}_j^{s}\right].$$

Now choose $m > n_i + n_j$; then at least one of $\mathbf{T}_i^{m-s}$ and $\mathbf{T}_j^{m}$ is $\mathbf{O}$, and hence $\mathbf{B}_{ij} = \mathbf{O}$.

CASE B. $c_i = c_j$. Equation (21) becomes

$$\mathbf{T}_i\mathbf{B}_{ij} = \mathbf{B}_{ij}\mathbf{T}_j. \tag{23}$$

To simplify notation, suppose $\mathbf{B}_{ij}$ is a u by v matrix (b_{st}). Let $q = \min(u, v)$. Then Eq. (23) becomes

$$\begin{pmatrix} b_{21} & \cdots & b_{2v} \\ \vdots & & \\ b_{u1} & & b_{uv} \\ 0 & \cdots & 0 \end{pmatrix} = \begin{pmatrix} 0 & b_{11} & \cdots & b_{1,v-1} \\ & & & \\ & & & \\ 0 & b_{u1} & & b_{u,v-1} \end{pmatrix},$$

and it follows that

$$\begin{aligned} & b_{q,v} = b_{q-1,v-1} = \cdots = b_{1,v-q+1}, \\ & b_{q-1,v} = b_{q-2,v-1} = \cdots = b_{1,v-q+2}, \\ & \vdots \\ & b_{2v} = b_{1,v-1}, \\ & b_{st} = 0 \text{ whenever } s < t,\ t \le v-q, \text{ or } s > q. \end{aligned} \tag{24}$$

A square matrix satisfying Eq. (24) is called a *strip matrix*. We have shown that

$$\mathbf{B}_{ij} = \begin{pmatrix} \mathbf{C} \\ \mathbf{O} \end{pmatrix} \qquad \text{or} \qquad (\mathbf{O}, \mathbf{C}),$$

where $\mathbf{C}$ is a strip matrix.

It would perhaps clarify matters if we gave an example. If

$$\mathbf{A} = \left(\begin{array}{ccc|cc|c|cc} 2 & 1 & 0 & & & & & \\ 0 & 2 & 1 & & \mathbf{O} & & \mathbf{O} & \\ 0 & 0 & 2 & & & & & \\ & & & 2 & 1 & & & \\ & \mathbf{O} & & 0 & 2 & & \mathbf{O} & \\ & & & 0 & 0 & 2 & 0 & 0 \\ & & & & & & 3 & 1 \\ & \mathbf{O} & & & \mathbf{O} & & 0 & 3 \end{array}\right),$$

and $\mathbf{AB} = \mathbf{BA}$, then

$$\mathbf{B} = \left(\begin{array}{ccc|cc|c|cc} a & b & c & s & t & u & & \\ 0 & a & b & 0 & s & 0 & \mathbf{O} & \\ 0 & 0 & a & 0 & 0 & 0 & & \\ 0 & u & v & c & d & p & & \\ 0 & 0 & u & 0 & c & 0 & \mathbf{O} & \\ 0 & 0 & z & 0 & q & e & 0 & 0 \\ & \mathbf{O} & & & \mathbf{O} & 0 & f & g \\ & & & & & 0 & 0 & f \end{array}\right).$$

The reader can prove

PROPOSITION 111 *Let θ be a primary linear transformation on $\mathscr{V}$. Let $(x-c)^{e_1}, \ldots, (x-c)^{e_h}$,* *with* $e_1 \le e_2 \cdots \le e_h$, *be the nonconstant invariant factors of* θ. *Then*

$$\dim \mathscr{C}(\theta) = e_h + 3e_{h-1} + 5e_{h-2} + \cdots + (2h-1)e_1.$$

COROLLARY $\dim \mathscr{C}(\theta) \ge e_1 + e_2 + \cdots + e_h = \dim \mathscr{V}$.

EXERCISES 1 Prove: If the vector space is over an algebraically closed field and if $\theta = \theta_1 + \cdots + \theta_r$ (direct), where θ_i are primary transformations with relatively prime minimal polynomials, then

$$\mathscr{C}(\theta) = \mathscr{C}(\theta_1) + \cdots + \mathscr{C}(\theta_r) \text{ (direct).}$$

2 Assuming the vector space is over an algebraically closed field, determine necessary and sufficient conditions that $\dim \mathscr{C}(\theta) = \dim \mathscr{V}$.

3 Let $\mathscr{V}$ be a vector space over an algebraically closed field $\mathscr{F}$. Prove:
A. If A is a polynomial over $\mathscr{F}$ and $\theta \in \mathscr{E}(\mathscr{V})$, then $A(\theta) \in \mathscr{C}(\theta)$.
B. If every $\varphi \in \mathscr{C}(\theta)$ is expressible as a polynomial in θ, then the characteristic polynomial of θ is the minimal polynomial for θ.

4 If $\mathbf{A}$ is a square matrix, let D_p be the greatest common divisor of the determinants of the p by p minors of the matrix $x\mathbf{I} - \mathbf{A}$. Prove:
A. $D_p \mid D_{p+1}$, $(p = 1, 2, \ldots, n-1)$.
B. If $E_1, \ldots, E_n$ are the invariant factors of A, then $E_1 = D_1$, $E_2 = D_2/D_1, \ldots, E_n = D_n/D_{n-1}$.

5 Prove:
A. If $a_2 \ne 0$, the strip matrix

$$\mathbf{A} = \begin{pmatrix} a_1 & a_2 & \cdots & a_n \\ 0 & a_1 & & a_{n-1} \\ \vdots & & & \\ 0 & & & a_1 \end{pmatrix}$$

has $D_{n-1} = 1$. Hence $\Gamma_{\mathbf{A}}$ is the minimal polynomial for $\mathbf{A}$.
B. If $a_2 = \cdots = a_q = 0$, $a_{q+1} \ne 0$, and $n = tq + r$, $0 \le r < q$, then the invariant factors of $\mathbf{A}$ are $E_1 = \cdots = E_{n-q} = 1$, $E_{n-q+1} = \cdots = E_{n-q+r} = (x - a_1)^{t+1}$, and $E_{n-q+r+1} = \cdots = E_n = (x - a_1)^t$.

6 Let

$$\mathbf{A} = \begin{pmatrix} a & 1 & & & \\ & a & 1 & & \\ & & \ddots & & \\ & & & a & 1 \\ & & & & a \end{pmatrix}$$

be a m by m matrix over a field of characteristic 0. Prove:
A. $\mathbf{A}^h$ is a strip matrix whose first row is $a^h, \binom{h}{1} a^{h-1}, \ldots, \binom{h}{m} a^{h-m}$.
B. If P is a polynomial and $P^{(j)}$ is its jth derivative, then $P(\mathbf{A})$ is a strip matrix whose first row is $P(a), P'(a), P''(a)/2!, \ldots, P^m(a)/m!$.

C. $P(\mathbf{A})$ has but one nonconstant invariant factor, namely, $(x - P(a))^m$.

D. If $\mathbf{A}_1$, $\mathbf{A}_2$ are strip matrices with first row a_i, 1, 0, ..., 0 and

$$\mathbf{A} = \begin{pmatrix} \mathbf{A}_1 & \mathbf{O} \\ \mathbf{O} & \mathbf{A}_2 \end{pmatrix}, \text{ then } P(\mathbf{A}) = \begin{pmatrix} P(\mathbf{A}_1) & \mathbf{O} \\ \mathbf{O} & P(\mathbf{A}_2) \end{pmatrix}.$$

7 Prove:

A. If $\mathbf{A}$ is a jordan matrix with invariant factors $E_j = (x - c_1)^{m_{j1}}, \ldots, (x - c_r)^{m_{jr}}$, $(j = 1, 2, \ldots, n)$, and if P is a polynomial, then the invariant factors of $P(\mathbf{A})$ are

$$E_j^* = (x - P(c_1))^{m_{j1}} \cdots (x - P(c_r))^{m_{jr}}.$$

B. If $\mathbf{B}$ is a square matrix over an algebraically closed field determine the invariant factors of $P(\mathbf{B})$.

8 A. Let $\mathbf{A}_0, \ldots, \mathbf{A}_m$ be n by n matrices. Let $P(t) = \mathbf{A}_m t^m + \cdots + \mathbf{A}_0$. If $\mathbf{X}$ is a n by n matrix then $P(\mathbf{X}) = \mathbf{A}_m\mathbf{X}^m + \cdots + \mathbf{A}_1\mathbf{X} + \mathbf{A}_0$ and $\hat{P}(\mathbf{X}) = \mathbf{X}^m\mathbf{A}_m + \cdots + \mathbf{X}\mathbf{A}_1 + \mathbf{A}_0$ are possibly different matrices. We divide $P(t)$ by $\mathbf{I}t - \mathbf{B}$ on the left and on the right; i.e.,

$$P(t) = (\mathbf{I}t - \mathbf{B})Q(t) + \mathbf{L},$$

$$P(t) = S(t)(\mathbf{I}t - \mathbf{B}) + \mathbf{R}.$$

Prove: $L = \hat{P}(\mathbf{B})$, $\mathbf{R} = P(B)$.

B. Let $g(t) = \det P(t)$. Prove: If $P(\mathbf{B}) = \mathbf{O}$, then $g(\mathbf{B}) = \mathbf{O}$. If $\hat{P}(\mathbf{B}) = \mathbf{O}$, then $g(\mathbf{B}) = \mathbf{O}$.

C. Show that Proposition 95 is a special case of (B).

9 Let $\mathbf{A} = \begin{pmatrix} 1 & 1 & 0 \\ 0 & 1 & 0 \\ 0 & 0 & 1 \end{pmatrix}$:

A. Prove that, if $\mathbf{X}$ is a 3 by 3 matrix such that $\mathbf{X}^2 = \mathbf{A}$, then the minimal polynomial of $\mathbf{X}$ is a divisor of $x^2 - 1$.

B. Determine all $\mathbf{X}$ with entries from $\mathbf{C}$ such that $\mathbf{X}^2 = \mathbf{A}$.

C. Determine all $\mathbf{X}$ with entries from $\mathbf{C}$ such that $\mathbf{X}^3 = \mathbf{A}$.

INDEX

A GLOSSARY OF SPECIAL SYMBOLS

$\underline{|a|}$: the equivalence class containing a, 81, 157

$a|b$: a divides b, 18

(a, b): the greatest common divisor of a and b, 19, 153

$[a, b]$: l.c.m$[a, b]$, the least common multiple of a and b, 25

$\mathscr{A}(\mathscr{G})$: automorphism group of $\mathscr{G}$, 102

$\mathfrak{A}(M)$: the alternating group on M, 68

$\mathfrak{A}_m$: the alternating group on $\{1, \ldots, m\}$, 68

$\mathfrak{A}^*(X)$: the annihilating set of X, 248

$\mathbf{C}$: the field of complex numbers, 228

$\mathfrak{C}(\theta)$: the algebra of transformations commuting with θ, 306

$\mathfrak{c}(X)$: the conjugate class containing X, 103

$d(A)$: degree of the polynomial A, 161

$\Delta(\theta)$: determinant of the linear transformation θ, 259

det $\mathbf{A}$: determinant of the matrix $\mathbf{A}$, 263

$\mathscr{E}(\mathscr{G})$: ring of endomorphisms of $\mathscr{G}$, 140

$\mathscr{F}(M)$: the group of transformations on M oving finitely many elements, 59

$\mathscr{G}/\mathscr{H}$: the quotient group of $\mathscr{G}$ by $\mathscr{H}$, 93

$[\mathscr{G}:\mathscr{H}]$: index of $\mathscr{H}$ in $\mathscr{G}$, 89

$\mathscr{G} \times \mathscr{H}$: cartesian product of $\mathscr{G}$ by $\mathscr{H}$, 111

$\mathscr{H} \lhd \mathscr{G}$: $\mathscr{H}$ is a normal subgroup of $\mathscr{G}$, 92

$\mathscr{I}(\mathscr{G})$: group of inner automorphisms of $\mathscr{G}$, 102

$I(\varphi)$: the set of elements left fixed by φ, 56

$\mathfrak{M}_{n,m}(\mathscr{R})$: the space of n by m matrices over $\mathscr{R}$, 259

$\mathbf{M}(\theta, \mathfrak{A}, \mathfrak{B})$: matrix representation of θ, 260

$N(X)$: normalizer of X, 104

$o(\alpha)$: order of α, 60, 85

P_θ: minimal polynomial of θ, 290

$\mathscr{P}(\mathscr{R})$ or $\mathscr{R}^+$: the positive cone of $\mathscr{R}$, 198

$\Pi(M)$: the group of transformations on M, 33, 57

Π_m: the group of transformations on $\{1, \ldots, m\}$, 57
$\mathbf{Q}$: the field of rational numbers, 517
$\mathbf{Q}^+$: the positive rational numbers, 199
$\mathscr{Q}(\mathscr{D})$: the quotient field of the domain $\mathscr{D}$, 158
$\mathbf{R}$: the field of real numbers, 205
$\mathbf{R}^+$: the positive real numbers, 206
$\mathscr{R}[x]$: the ring of polynomials in x over $\mathscr{R}$, 159
$\mathrm{res}_L\varphi$: the restriction of the map φ to L, 31
$<S>$: the group (or ring or space) generated by S, 85
$\mathrm{Sp}(\theta)$: the spectrum of θ, 285
ST: subset multiplication, 12, 90
$S + T$: set addition, 12
$\mathscr{G} + \mathscr{H}$: the cartesian sum, 111
$T - S$: the complement of S in T, 3
$\mathscr{V}|\mathscr{F}$: vector space $\mathscr{V}$ over a field $\mathscr{F}$, 233
$\mathscr{V}_\theta$: the kernel of θ, 254
$X(\varphi)$: the set of elements moved by φ, 59
$\mathbf{Z}$: the ring of integers, 5
$\mathbf{Z}^+$: the positive integers, 9
$\mathbf{Z}_m$: the residue class group (ring) of $\mathbf{Z}$ modulo m, 82
$\mathbf{Z}_m'$: the multiplicative group of residue classes, 82
$\mathfrak{Z}(\varphi)$: the centralizer of φ, 66, 104
$\mathbf{Z}|m|$: a quadratic extension of $\mathbf{Z}$, 148
$\mathbf{0}$: the zero of a vector space, 234
$\mathscr{O}$: the zero space, 235
$\in$: is an element of, 2
$\subset$: is a subset of, 3
$\varnothing$: the empty set, 3
$x \xrightarrow{\varphi} x^\varphi = y$: φ is the map taking x into y, 28
$\times\mathscr{G}_\lambda$: the cartesian product, 114
$r\times\mathscr{G}_\lambda$: the restricted cartesian product, 114
$\Sigma\mathscr{G}_\lambda$: the cartesian sum, 111
$|X|$: the order of the set X, 35
$\| \ \|$: valuation, 213
$\cong$: is isomorphic to, 97
$\simeq$: is similar to, 282
$\{x \in X|*\}$: the subset of X satisfying condition *, 3

Format by Susan Bishop
Set in Monotype Times Roman
Composed by Santype Limited
Printed by The Murray Printing Company
Bound by The Haddon Craftsmen, Inc.
HARPER & ROW, PUBLISHERS, INCORPORATED